Fundamentals of Ornithology

Fundamentals

JOSSELYN VAN TYNE

Late Curator of Birds
University of Michigan Museum of Zoology

ANDREW J. BERGER

Professor of Zoology
University of Hawaii

of Ornithology

SCIENCE EDITIONS®

JOHN WILEY & SONS, INC., NEW YORK

First Science Editions printing 1966
Science Editions Trademark Reg. U.S. Pat. Off.

Library of Congress Catalog Card Number: 59-9355

Printed in the United States of America

TO THOSE WHO HAVE GONE BEFORE

TO THOSE WHO ARE YET TO COME

Preface

On may 9, 1956, a cold and rainy wednesday, Josselyn Van Tyne and Gerald L. Brody left Ann Arbor for Mio, Michigan, in order to determine the arrival date of the Kirtland's Warbler on its breeding grounds. During their 4-day sojourn on the Jack-Pine plains, Van Tyne experienced pain in his chest. Never one to thrust his problems on others, he remained silent, and the field trip was continued as planned.

A physical examination, made after their return to Ann Arbor, indicated that it would be necessary for Van Tyne to undergo surgery. Late in May, before his operation, he asked me if I would promise to finish his textbook of ornithology in the event that he was unable to do so. I promised. Ever mindful of his responsibilities to others, Van wrote, on June 1, 1956, to John Wiley & Sons informing them of his impending operation and of his agreement with me regarding the book.

Van's recovery from surgery was so rapid that he decided to return to Mio in order to continue his observations at a new study area, where Harold Mayfield and I had worked in June. Van and I left for the Jack-Pine plains on July 1. He established our working schedule, at least 10 hours in the field each day. His apparent recovery was most encouraging. The Kirtland's Warbler, with its loud, persistent song and its relative unconcern over the presence of man, is a fascinating bird. The bird, the fragrance of the sweet fern, the cold, clear mornings, and the hot, dry afternoons are not soon forgotten. Van was rarely more content and relaxed than during his annual trips to the warbler's habitat. He visited the area again later in the summer.

I had read drafts of chapters written by Van, but, although it may appear inexplicable except to those who knew him well, we did not discuss the text in any detail after his operation. I am sure that during the summer of 1956 neither of us would admit that he might not live to see the book completed. During the autumn months he became too weak to do original work, and, perhaps for entirely different reasons, we rarely mentioned the book. It was not until mid-January that we made plans to meet at his office the following Tuesday in order to discuss the book again. The discussion did not take place, for Van did not return to the museum. He died on January 30, 1957. The text materials were turned over to me in March.

Van Tyne had written the chapters on Plumage and Molt, Migration, Bird Distribution, Ornithological Sources, and the long chapter on The Classification of World Birds by Families, which, in a sense (and for good reason), he considered *the book.* In addition, he had prepared manuscript pages for about one-half of two other chapters (Anatomy, Food and Feeding Habits) and he had written five pages on territory and eggs for the chapter on Breeding Behavior. I completed these and wrote the remaining chapters. For certain chapters (Paleontology, Voice and Sound Production, Food and Feeding Habits, Taxonomy and Nomenclature), there were either chapter outlines or lecture notes in the files, but for other chapters (Senses and Behavior, Flight, Social Relations) I found nothing in the files turned over to me except bibliography cards. Van Tyne had prepared on 3 by 5 cards about one-half of the definitions in the Glossary and had indicated many other terms that he intended to include. The Table of Contents (i.e., chapter topics and sequence) was planned by Van Tyne.

Van Tyne felt strongly that a student should become well grounded in the several basic branches of biology before specializing in ornithology. Birds of the World, as he taught it, was a graduate course intended for those who had at least an undergraduate degree in zoology. Van wrote that this book "should provide the background" for his graduate course. He anticipated that the book would fill many other needs: as a quick reference for information on all the families of birds; as a dictionary of ornithological terms; as a general reference for those interested in life history, taxonomy, and anatomy; as a summary of anatomical characters used in the classification of birds; and as a guide to ornithological literature.

The increase in knowledge during the past 50 years has been so great, both in ornithology and in biology in general, that most of the chapters included here might easily be expanded to book length, and a half dozen other subjects pertaining to birds might well receive the same treatment. When Van Tyne first conceived the outline for the book in 1946, he envisioned 21 chapters plus a glossary. It soon became evident, however, that the cost of publishing such a book would be prohibitive. Thus, instead of receiving full chapter treatment, some important subjects (e.g., physiology, genetics, ecology, study methods) had to be mentioned very briefly where pertinent in several chapters, and still other subjects (conservation, game management, population dynamics, museum techniques) not at all. Despite these necessary and intentional omissions, I believe that the book covers the fundamentals of bird study. Any graduate student worth his salt must gain a familiarity with the research literature and must acquire the habit of referring to it for additional information. Consequently, considerable emphasis has been placed on the list of references at the end of each chapter. Included in these lists are early "classic" works and a sampling of later papers that present different points of view. To be only partly facetious I may say that the Glossary should enable the student to translate the first paragraph of any of Robert Ridgway's "technical diagnoses."

A typical example of Van Tyne's attention to detail is seen in a folder labeled "Text: acknowledgement of assistance," which contained the names of those whom he planned to thank for assistance in various ways (reading manuscript, checking or loaning specimens, granting permission to use published illustrations, sending information on the habits of foreign birds, etc.): Dean Amadon, Paul H. Baldwin, William Beebe, Biswamoy Biswas, James P. Chapin, W. Powell Cottrille, Lee S. Crandall, David E. Harrower, Robert M. Mengel, Alden H. Miller, William H. Partridge, Frank A. Pitelka, Austin L. Rand, Robert W. Storer, Frederick H. Test, Alexander Wetmore. Had he been able to complete the book, Van Tyne would have expressed his deep appreciation to G. Reeves Butchart, a gifted editor who served as his highly valued editorial assistant for many years and until the very day of his death.

I wish to express my gratitude to the following, each of whom read one or more of the chapters that I wrote in part or entirely: John T. Emlen, Jr., Herbert Friedmann, Claude W. Hibbard, Hans P. Liepman, Alfred M. Lucas, William A. Lunk, Harold Mayfield, Margaret M. Nice, George M. Sutton, Harrison B. Tordoff, Alexander Wetmore. In thanking these generous people, I do not in any way wish to imply that they agree with what I have said or with my method of presentation. One may always welcome suggestions, but, after study, decide not to follow them. In some instances I did just that. I wish to thank the several people who granted permission to use photographs or published illustrations; their names appear with their illustrations in the text. Special thanks are due George M. Sutton for his inimitable pen and ink drawings of world birds, and William L. Brudon and William A. Lunk for the remaining original illustrations. For many weeks of indispensable proofreading I am indebted to my wife and to Harriet Bergtold Woolfenden. To the McGregor Fund of Detroit, Michigan, I am grateful for a grant which enabled me to devote full time to indexing and publication details during the summer of 1958.

Josselyn Van Tyne had few peers among ornithologists. He was both a great ornithologist—in the modern sense—and a true scholar—in the oldest and best sense. For any ways in which I may have failed him, I offer my profound apologies to the spirit of Josselyn Van Tyne.

ANDREW J. BERGER

Ann Arbor, Mich.
March, 1958

Contents

1 PALEONTOLOGY 1

2 ANATOMY 21

3 PLUMAGE AND MOLT 70

4 SENSES AND BEHAVIOR 108

5 VOICE AND SOUND PRODUCTION 131

6 BIRD DISTRIBUTION 155

7 MIGRATION 182

8 FLIGHT 218

9 FOOD AND FEEDING HABITS 237

10 BREEDING BEHAVIOR 265

11 SOCIAL RELATIONS 327

12 TAXONOMY AND NOMENCLATURE 349

13 THE CLASSIFICATION OF WORLD BIRDS BY FAMILIES 376

ORNITHOLOGICAL SOURCES 553

GLOSSARY 559

INDEX 587

1. Paleontology

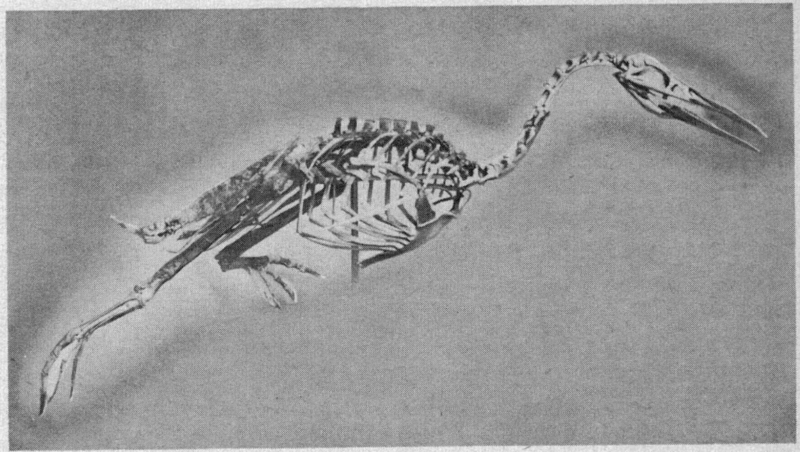

Fig. 1. Skeleton of *Hesperornis regalis* from the Upper Cretaceous of Kansas. (Courtesy of Alexander Wetmore and the Smithsonian Institution.)

THE STUDY of comparative anatomy and of the fossil evidence of ancient life has convinced zoologists that birds are unquestionably descended from reptiles. The bird skeleton shows so many reptilian characters that T. H. Huxley said that birds are "glorified reptiles," and many zoologists have preferred to combine birds with reptiles in a single class, the Sauropsida. Some of the skeletal characters which birds share with reptiles are these:

1. The skull has a single occipital condyle.
2. The lower jaw is composed of several elements (usually five) and is hinged on a movable quadrate bone (as in snakes and some extinct reptiles).
3. Both groups have a single ear ossicle, the columella.
4. Most birds have uncinate (epipleural) processes on the ribs—a character found elsewhere only in the Reptilia (e.g., *Sphenodon, Euparkeria*).

5. The ankle joint is between two rows of tarsal bones (intertarsal), instead of being between the tibia and the tarsal bones.
6. The backward slant of the pubis is similar to that found in certain dinosaurs.

Some other characters shared by the two groups are the ambiens muscle, nucleated red blood corpuscles, an egg-tooth on the upper jaw at hatching, and the same general type of egg and embryological development.

The most obvious feature which distinguishes birds from reptiles is the presence of feathers. Birds also are warm-blooded (homoiothermic), and have only a right aortic arch (in contrast to the left aortic arch of mammals). The four-chambered heart of birds is approached among the reptiles only in the heart of the Crocodilia.

The Origin of Birds

Many of the predentate dinosaurs (Ornithischia) had a pelvis superficially similar to that found in birds, and a few early writers believed that birds were descended from the "birdlike" dinosaurs. Yet these forms lacked a clavicle and they differed widely from birds in other skeletal features. Furthermore, the dinosaurs occurred too late (mostly in the Cretaceous) to fit into the ancestral line of birds, which are first known from the Jurassic.

It is generally agreed now that both birds and dinosaurs are descended from primitive, unspecialized thecodont reptiles belonging to the suborder Pseudosuchia. These were small carnivorous animals possessing many teeth set in sockets (i.e., thecodont) in the jaws. Their hind limbs were longer than their front limbs, and in some forms, at least, the fifth hind toe was reduced in length. However, no pseudosuchian yet described could well be *the* ancestor of birds. In his monograph on the origin of birds, Gerhard Heilmann (1927) reconstructed a hypothetical "Proavian" form intermediate between certain pseudosuchians (*Ornithosuchus* and *Euparkeria*) and the most primitive bird known.

The Origin of Flight

One of the main points in the analysis of the immediate bird ancestor is the question of the origin of flight. Two main theories have been proposed.

A cursorial origin of flight was postulated by Nopcsa (1907), who envisioned the development of flight in long-tailed, bipedal reptiles which flapped their forelimbs as they ran rapidly along the ground. The scales on the forelimb became elongated, and their posterior margins frayed-out, in time evolving into feathers. Nopcsa imagined three stages in the evolution of flight: (1) parachute or *passive flight,* (2) flight by flapping the wings or *flight by force,* and (3) soaring or *flight by skill. Archaeopteryx* "was yet in the first stage of active flight."

Marsh (1880: 113), Osborn (1900), Heilmann, and many others, however, believed that the first birds were arboreal in habit. Their terrestrial ancestors became tree climbers before there was a great disparity in the relative length of the front and back limbs, although the bipedal gait had already resulted in some elongation of the metatarsals. Jumping from branch to branch favored the further elongation of the metatarsals and the development of a backward-directed hallux, which enabled the animals to secure a good grasp of branches. Now used for climbing, the forelimbs "preserved claws on their digits, remained large, and were not reduced as is commonly the case in cursorial animals which adopt the bipedal mode of progression" (De Beer, 1954: 51). Each limb, therefore, became adapted to specialized and different functions. Heilmann (1927: 198) emphasized this independence of the two limbs in contrast to the situation found in Pterosaurs (flying reptiles, in no way directly related to the avian stem) and flying mammals, in which both the forelimbs and hind limbs are connected by a patagial skin fold. Heilmann further believed that the development of feathers (from scales) preceded homoiothermism. (Some authors think that the Pterosaurs also may have been partially warm-blooded.) Böker (1927: 318–319) suggested that the original birds flapped their forelimbs when jumping from branch to branch, but De Beer (1954: 51) thought it "probable that simple gliding preceded flapping because *Archaeopteryx* had no carina and its pectoral muscles must have been feeble."

Beebe (1915) also believed that flight in *Archaeopteryx* and its predecessors was limited to gliding and scaling, but he advocated a "Tetrapteryx" stage in the evolution of flapping flight. Beebe's hypothetical pre-Jurassic Tetrapteryx bird possessed not only an alar feather tract but also a "pelvic wing," both of which served merely as "passive parachutes." Beebe thought that he found evidence in the embryo and nestling of some modern birds of a recapitulation of such a four-winged stage. Heilmann (1927: 195–

199) and De Beer (1954: 52) felt that Beebe placed too much emphasis on his "pelvic wing," that the "tibial quills" of *Archaeopteryx* actually were contour feathers, and that the feathers in question represent no more than the femoral feather tract in modern birds.

The Fossil Record of Birds

The massive bones and dense plates, horn-cores, teeth, and spines of many vertebrates were admirably suited for preservation through the ages, assuming, of course, the requisite conditions for fossilization. By contrast, bird bones are fragile and many are hollow, and thus easily broken and fragmented. One may assume also that many ancient birds, like those of today, served as prey for carnivorous animals, whose digestive processes left little for preservation. Howbeit, relatively few complete fossilized skeletons of birds have been discovered. Numerous fragments of bones have been found, usually the larger and denser ends of wing and leg bones or parts of the pectoral girdle. Many genera have been established on the basis of such fragments or on single bones. Several authors have discussed the problems involved in past attempts to relate inadequate fossil material to modern forms. Howard (1950: 5), for example, pointed out that "taxonomy among fossil birds cannot be entirely coordinated with that of modern forms," and that the assignment of single or dissociated bones "to modern genera is to some extent a matter of convenience." Darlington (1957: 276) has expressed clearly the skepticism with which most workers now view the conclusions reached by some early avian paleontologists. In speaking of the presumed occurrence of modern passerine families and genera during the Eocene and Oligocene of Europe, Darlington commented:

> This seems to prove at least the existence of modern families and genera of Oscines fairly early in the Tertiary. But it may be doubted whether the fossils are what they are supposed to be. Some of them are skeletal impressions (which are not the same as complete skeletons), and some are fragments, but all seem to have been identified only by superficial comparison with existing birds. Their phylogenetic characters and real relationships have not been determined, so they are not very good evidence of the age of songbirds.

There are two noteworthy examples that illustrate a careful, rather than a "superficial," comparison of fossil passerine material from the Tertiary period with modern birds. In both cases the fossil bird was represented by a nearly complete skeleton. It is perhaps significant that, after careful analysis, the authors concluded that their specimens represented a now-extinct family of passerine birds. Wetmore (1925) examined the specimen of *Palaeospiza bella,* which had been described in 1878, and concluded that it belonged to a distinct family (Palaeospizidae), whose characters suggested that it "occupies a somewhat connecting position between the Mesomyodi and the acutiplantar Oscines"; the fossil appears to be of Oligocene age. Howard (1957b) described a new bird, from the Miocene of California, which "does not fit clearly into any one family of living oscine birds as now defined." She named the specimen *Palaeoscinis turdirostris,* "an ancient oscine bird with a thrushlike beak" (family Palaeoscinidae). Dr. Howard would tentatively place the newly erected family near the Pycnonotidae or the Bombycillidae.

Because paleontology is largely a study of bones, it is obvious that the proper allocation of fossil material to family or genus is dependent on the availability of an adequate skeletal collection of modern birds with which the fossils may be compared (see Howard's pertinent discussion, 1946: 143, 147). The modern approach to the study of fossils is well illustrated by Storer's (1956) analysis of *Colymboides minutus,* and Howard's (1957a) description of *Osteodontornis.*

Although Osborn (1900) and others believed that the avian ancestors lived during the Permian period of the Palaeozoic era or in the Triassic period of the Mesozoic era, the actual fossil record of birds begins millions of years later, in the Jurassic period. (See Table 1.) Some 787 fossil birds had been described by the end of 1949 (Wetmore, 1951b). We have selected for discussion a few of the best known forms and several American sites which have been unusually productive in yielding bird fossils.

The Mesozoic Era

1. Jurassic period. Evidences of the oldest known bird were found in the Solnhofen or lithographic stone of Upper Jurassic age, and are estimated to be 130,000,000 years old. In all, an isolated feather and two nearly complete skeletons were discovered in the slate of a quarry located near Pappenheim, Bavaria. The first skeleton (now in the British Museum of Natural History) was found in 1861, and was named *Archaeopteryx lithographica.* The second skeleton (now in Berlin) was found in 1877 about 10 miles

TABLE 1

The Geologic Time Scale*

Abridged to emphasize the eras and periods concerned in the evolution of birds

ERAS	PERIODS	EPOCHS	Approximate Age at Beginning
CENOZOIC	Quaternary	Recent	15,000 years
		Pleistocene	1,000,000 years
	Tertiary	Pliocene	10,000,000 years
		Miocene	30,000,000 years
		Oligocene	40,000,000 years
		Eocene	60,000,000 years
MESOZOIC	Cretaceous		120,000,000 years
	Jurassic		150,000,000 years
	Triassic		180,000,000 years
PALAEOZOIC			540,000,000 years at beginning of first period (Cambrian)
	Pre-Cambrian time		2,000,000,000 years

* Reproduced by permission from Hildegarde Howard, *Ibis,* 1950.

distant from the site of the discovery of the British Museum specimen. The Berlin specimen has been called *Archaeopteryx "siemensi"* and *"Archaeornis siemensi,"* but after a careful analysis of the two specimens, De Beer (1954: 57) concluded that the two were conspecific, partly because age and sex could "easily account for the so-called generic differences" between the two specimens.

The skeleton of *Archaeopteryx* is more reptilian than avian, and, in fact, Lowe (1944) denied that *Archaeopteryx* was a bird. It was, Lowe suggested, an arboreal, climbing dinosaur which "takes its place not at the bottom of the avian phylum but at the top of the reptilian." Despite Lowe's assertions, however, the avian affinities of *Archaeopteryx* are now generally accepted.

De Beer, in his recent monograph, presented additional information on the British Museum specimen of *Archaeopteryx,* made possible by further exposure of the fossil elements and by the use of newer methods (e.g., ultraviolet light and special photographic techniques). The Berlin specimen is more complete in some respects and data from the two fossils are complementary. The chief anatomical features of *Archaeopteryx* may be summarized as follows:

The orbit is large, and a sclerotic ring of plates is present, as in modern birds and in certain early reptiles (e.g., *Euparkeria, Saurolophus,* Pterosaurs). The prefrontal and lacrimal (adlacrimal) bones appear to be similar to those in *Euparkeria.* Both jaws possess teeth, which are set in sockets, and the mandible has a retroarticular process. The palate seems to be of the schizognathous type.

The vertebral column is composed of 49 or 50 vertebrae. There are 10 cervical vertebrae, 6 of which bear cervical ribs, but it is the 2nd to 7th (and not the posterior 6) vertebrae which possess the ribs. Of the 19 or 20 "trunk" vertebrae (dorsal, lumbar, and sacral), the caudal 6 are regarded as sacral and the posterior 5 are fused together to form a primitive synsacrum. Eleven pairs of ribs have been associated with the dorsal and lumbar vertebrae. These "nonavian" ribs are unjointed, lack uncinate processes, and do not articulate with the sternum. In addition to these ribs a series of bilateral, bony, dermal ribs (gastralia) have been preserved; such ribs were a common feature in the ventral abdominal wall of early reptiles. There are 20 free caudal vertebrae; a pygostyle is not present. The vertebrae of *Archaeopteryx* have disklike or biconcave (*amphicoelous*) articular facets, as did those of many primitive reptiles. In modern birds the articular surfaces of the vertebral bodies (*centra*) are primarily saddle-shaped (*heterocoelous*); the atlas, however, typically is of the *procoelous* type (see Glossary), and *opisthocoelous* vertebrae are found in certain regions of the vertebral column in some birds (e.g., penguins, cormorants, anhingas, gulls, auks, some parrots, and oilbirds).

The wing and leg are about equal in length. There is no evidence that any of the bones were pneumatic (pneumatic bones were characteristic of the Pterosaurs). The ulna is stouter and a little longer than the radius. The hand contains three separate metacarpals. De Beer reported that there is a "fusion of the 3rd metacarpal with the carpal ossification" to form a 3rd carpometacarpal bone, but not a carpometacarpus, so that "*Archaeopteryx* presents an intermediate condition between the reptiles and the other birds." The two clavicles are fused to form a furcula. No trace of a carina has been found on the sternum.

The bones of the pelvic girdle (ilium, ischium, pubis) are separate elements, rather than fused into a single pelvic bone. The two pubic bones are directed caudad, and they fuse to form a pubic symphysis (as in the pseudosuchians and the ostrich). The fibula is as long as the tibia, and the metatarsals are not fused to form a tarsometatarsus (i.e., there is a true heel joint). The hallux is directed backwards.

There seems to be little doubt but that *Archaeopteryx* had a reptilelike brain, with some birdlike features. The cerebellum did not extend anteriorly to overlie the posterior part of the cerebral hemispheres, and the optic lobes were located dorsally (see p. 28; Edinger, 1926; De Beer, 1954: 12–13).

The most important avian feature of the anatomy of *Archaeopteryx,* however, is the presence of feathers. Their structure is typical of that of the feathers of modern flying birds. De Beer concluded that *Archaeopteryx* probably had six primaries and ten secondaries, and that the wing was eutaxic (see p. 81), contrary to Steiner's (1918) theory that the wing was diastataxic. There are conflicting statements in the literature concerning the number of tail feathers (rectrices), but according to De Beer there were 15 pairs of rectrices which were "attached by ligaments to the lateral surface of their vertebrae." The first pair of rectrices was attached to the sixth free caudal vertebra. Contour feathers on the body were well developed.

In systems of classification, *Archaeopteryx* is placed in the subclass Archaeornithes, meaning the ancestral birds; all other birds, in the subclass Neornithes, or true birds (Wetmore, 1951a). Most of the anatomical differences between *Archaeopteryx* and the true birds are associated with centralization of body weight and improvement of the basic structure for flight. Despite the many differences between *Archaeopteryx* and all other birds, however, it is difficult to find many anatomical characters which hold without exception for the Neornithes. This is true largely because of the extreme specialization of the ratite assemblage (see p. 47). The true birds, however, have the tail much shortened, and the rectrices are arranged fanlike around the terminal caudal vertebrae, which typically, but not invariably, are fused to form a pygostyle. Uncinate processes are found on the ribs of all true birds except the Anhimidae. The bones of the wrist and hand (when present) are fused to form a carpometacarpus, the bones of the pelvic girdle are at least partially fused anteriorly, and a fused tarsometatarsus is present.

2. Cretaceous period. Nearly complete bird skeletons have been found in the marine Niobrara Cretaceous chalk beds of Kansas (Fig. 1). First described by Marsh (1880 and earlier), these birds have long been spoken of as the Cretaceous "toothed birds" (Odontornithes; superorder Odontognathae in current systems of classification). Two orders (Hesperornithiformes and Ichthyornithiformes) and five families have been recognized.[1] J. T. Gregory (1952) recently studied the toothed jaw ascribed to *Ichthyornis* and concluded that it belonged to a small mosasaur[2] (an aquatic lizard) and not to *Ichthyornis;* only fragments of an upper jaw had been described by Marsh and these are "quite indeterminate as to what bone was represented as well as what animal." Hence it is not known whether the presence of teeth was a universal character of these Cretaceous birds; except for *Hesperornis,* complete jaws have not been found for the other genera placed in the superorder Odontognathae.

Hesperornis was a large (nearly 5 feet long), flightless, loonlike bird, highly specialized for swimming; *Ichthyornis,* a small, gull-like bird, specialized for flying. The striking divergence in the osteology of these two early birds reveals the wide radiation of birds during the interval (of unknown length) between the Jurassic and the Cretaceous periods, and also suggests a long history of development for these Cretaceous birds. Some differences between the two genera are given in Table 2.

TABLE 2

Some Osteological Differences Between *Hesperornis* and *Ichthyornis*

Hesperornis	*Ichthyornis*
1. Clavicles are not fused.	1. Typical furcula is present.
2. Carina sterni is absent.	2. Carina is well developed.
3. Wing is composed of a vestigial humerus only.	3. Wing is well developed, including a carpometacarpus.
4. Vertebrae are heterocoelous.	4. Vertebrae are amphicoelous.
5. Teeth are present in both jaws.	5. Jaws are unknown.
6. The mandibular rami are united by ligament, rather than by a bony symphysis.	6. Jaws are unknown.

[1] Marsh erected the superorder Odontolcae for *Hesperornis,* in which the teeth were set in grooves in the jaws (the premaxillary bone of the upper jaw, however, was edentulous); in the superorder Odontotormae, established for *Ichthyornis,* the teeth were set in separate sockets.

[2] Gregory pointed out that no mosasaur small enough to fit the jaws in question has as yet been found. On the other hand, many workers, including Marsh, have been impressed by the discrepancy in size and proportion between the typical avian skull of *Ichthyornis* and the jaws that Marsh associated with it.

Many of the differences in structure between *Hesperornis* and *Ichthyornis* are obviously correlated with their locomotor patterns, whereas other differences (e.g., type of vertebrae) cannot be explained adequately with information now available.

The following characters are shared by the two genera: a typical avian tarsometatarsus, a single-headed quadrate, and a small skull whose bones were fused nearly as well as in modern birds. Edinger (1951) reported that all evidence indicates that *Hesperornis* and *Ichthyornis* had typical avian brains, contrary to the conclusions reached by Marsh.

Information on other genera (e.g., *Baptornis, Apatornis*) classified as "toothed birds" may be found in the works of Marsh (1880), Lambrecht (1933), Romer (1945), and Wetmore (1956). There are very few records of other birds from the Cretaceous, but bones of this age found in Europe have been allocated to the orders Pelecaniformes, Ciconiiformes, and Anseriformes, and a "toothless lower mandible of avian character" (but also of reptilian character) was found in Canada (see Howard, 1950: 3).

The Cenozoic Era

This era of geological history began some 60,000,000 years ago. Most modern orders of birds were well differentiated by the Eocene epoch. Many of the most completely preserved fossils from Eocene to Recent times have been much publicized, largely because of their great size. A bird with a head as big as that of a horse justifiably stimulates man's imagination. Such gigantic birds, however, represent the ends of evolutionary series. This, coupled with the great hiatuses in the fossil record, means that the structure of these, and many other, fossil birds reveals little concerning their relationships to modern orders. By and large, most of the early Cenozoic fossil forms serve to emphasize the early radiation of birds and the paucity of information about that early evolutionary history.

Members of the order Diatrymiformes (Fig. 2) were giant terrestrial birds, whose bones have been found in the United States (Wyoming, New Mexico, and New Jersey) and, possibly, in France and Britain. *Diatryma steini* from the Lower Eocene of Wyoming was almost 7 feet tall. It had a massive head, holorhinal nostrils, greatly reduced wings and uncinate processes, a small hallux, and a very large pelvis. Taxonomists place the Diatrymiformes near the Gruiformes, a heterogeneous order to which several other large

Fig. 2. Skeleton of *Diatryma giganteum* from the Lower Eocene of New Mexico. (Courtesy of Dean Amadon and the American Museum of Natural History.)

extinct birds have been assigned (e.g., *Phororhacos, Brontornis, Bathornis*).

Among the several diurnal raptores (Falconiformes) recorded from Eocene time in Europe and America (see Howard, 1950: 11–12), one of the most interesting is *Neocathartes grallator,* a terrestrial vulture from Wyoming, which had long legs, well-developed toes, and reduced wings; see Fig. 3. It was able to fly, but "evidently was mainly terrestrial," and "apparently stood in the same relation to the species of the Cathartidae that the Secretary-bird, *Sagittarius serpentarius,* does to the true hawks and eagles" (Wetmore, 1955: 50).

It is of interest as a possible indication of the great age of some modern genera to note that specimens from the Oligocene have

Fig. 3. Restoration by Walter A. Weber of the terrestrial vulture *Neocathartes grallator* (Wetmore), "shown against a background of landscape designed to represent the ecological conditions of the late Eocene of Wyoming." (Reproduced by courtesy of Alexander Wetmore and the Carnegie Museum.)

been assigned to the modern genera *Pelecanus, Phalacrocorax, Aythya, Anas, Vanellus, Strix, Bubo, Lanius, Motacilla, Passer,* etc. That the fossils assigned to certain of these genera have been properly identified is, as mentioned above, open to question. Other orders of birds (e.g., Cuculiformes, Trogoniformes) make their first appearance in the fossil record of the Oligocene.

The relationship of the penguins (Sphenisciformes) to other birds has puzzled ornithologists for a long time (Fig. 4). Penguins are "the most specialized of our living birds in the sense that they have departed far from the standard form adapted for flight that has controlled the development of other groups" (Wetmore, 1955: 46). As long ago as 1883, Watson postulated that the ancestral penguins were flying birds, a view held by many later ornithologists. Lowe (1933; 1939), however, denied that penguins were derived from flying ancestors. He asserted that the evidence indicated that the penguins and the "Struthiones" represent two natural groups whose common ancestor "left the main avian stem before flight had been attained." From that ancient, nonflying ancestor, the ratite birds specialized directly for a cursorial mode of existence, and the penguins "specialized from the same ancestor for an aquatic life" (1933: 533). Simpson's study, however, leaves little doubt that penguins are derived from flying ancestors, even though the earliest known fossil penguins (from the Miocene; fragments from the Eocene of New Zealand) were already flightless and specialized for an aquatic existence. It is pertinent to note that all of the fossil penguins have been found within the present range of the group (Simpson, 1946: 71; 1957). Mayr and Amadon (1951: 3) believe that the penguins "are clearly related" to the Procellariiformes.

A most significant recent discovery in avian paleontology is a giant oceanic bird from the Miocene of California (Howard, 1957a). *Osteodontornis orri,* as the fossil has been named, is exceptional, not so much for its extraordinary wingspread (estimated between 14 and 16 feet), but because both jaws contain toothlike bony projections. These "bone teeth" are highly specialized elaborations of the jawbones, and, hence, exhibit a similar histological pattern; they are in no way homologous with the teeth of *Hesperornis.* It is assumed that the "teeth" and the jaws were sheathed with a

Fig. 4. Upper—Great Auk (*Pinguinus impennis*); middle—Common Loon (*Gavia immer*); lower—Emperor Penguin (*Aptenodytes forsteri*). (Courtesy of Dean Amadon and the American Museum of Natural History.)

horny covering, as in other birds. *Osteodontornis* further provides "clarifying evidence of the validity of an extinct order, whose existence had been previously postulated but questioned." Dr. Howard presents a technical diagnosis of the order Odontopterygiformes and the family Pseudodontornithidae, to which she assigns *Osteodontornis,* and she suggests that this order be inserted between the Procellariiformes and the Pelecaniformes in taxonomic lists.

Fossil evidence of prehistoric life is recorded in many ways. The Miocene "Lompoc Diatomitic Shales" of California are noteworthy because in bird fossils (Miller and DeMay, 1942: 49–50):

> The bone has turned dark brown and completely fallen to powder. This material is dusted out with a camel's-hair brush and there is left an imprint of the skeleton etched in sepia on a white background. Most of the specimens show several of the bones in their proper anatomical relation, and many show nearly the complete skeleton.

A brief reference to certain Tertiary beds of the High Plains is desirable, not only for the fauna already described, but because several investigators are now studying extensive collections from some of the localities. Many interesting papers on these faunas can be expected in the future. A. H. Miller (1944) reported a collection from the Lower Miocene of South Dakota. He found with the typical North American genera "an Old World element and a Neotropical element, each consisting of two forms." Tordoff and MacDonald (1957) described a new cracid from the Oligocene, also from South Dakota. Wetmore (1944) and Tordoff (1951) presented data on specimens taken from Pliocene beds in Kansas; many additional fossils belonging to the Rexroad fauna have been collected. Wetmore, in a series of papers, has also described birds from the Miocene and Pliocene of Nebraska.

The birds discussed below lived during the Pleistocene, when the avian fauna was richer than that of today. Among the most remarkable fossil beds yet discovered are the "asphalt traps" of California. Miller and DeMay (1942: 64) wrote that at the Rancho La Brea in Los Angeles "the fauna of 105 species of birds is represented by over 100,000 determinable bones." *Teratornis,* a large vulture, is represented by more than 1000 bones. Mammals that are now extinct (saber-toothed tiger, wolf, horse, antelope), as well as birds, were entrapped in the asphalt pools.

> The bone, still clothed in its activating tissues, was plunged into liquid asphalt which soon penetrated its most minute structure and sealed it away from most of the destructive agencies, so that now after a thousand centuries it may be exposed to the air without traceable deterioration.

Another western site which has contributed much to our knowledge of Pleistocene bird life is Fossil Lake, Oregon. Discovered in 1876, this desert fossil bed has yielded some 2500 bones, representing 66 forms. Grebes, swans, geese, and ducks account for about four-fifths of the specimens. Howard (1946) re-examined this material, and, after correcting earlier errors in identification, concluded that "the number of individuals of extinct species in the Fossil Lake avifauna is but 15 per cent of the total number of individuals estimated for that assemblage," so that the avifauna in general was "like that to be found living today about inland lakes of Oregon and California" (see also Wetmore's 1955 account of Fossil Lake).

The known fossil beds, however, are not limited to the western part of the United States. Wetmore (1931) reported on several widely separated areas in Florida where fossil birds had been discovered, and Brodkorb (1957) stated that 4000 specimens of birds' bones have been collected near Reddick, Florida, during the last few years.

The much-debated causes of extinction are multiple: e.g., overspecialization, climatic and environmental changes, competition with more adaptable forms, the ascendancy of higher groups, etc. Be that as it may, some of the largest birds for which there is a fossil record lived during the Pleistocene (and until Recent times) on Madagascar and New Zealand, large, isolated islands with a meager mammalian fauna and no large endemic carnivores. The elephantbirds, *Aepyornis* and *Mullerornis* (order Aepyornithiformes), of Madagascar and the moas, *Dinornis* and related genera,[3] of New Zealand (Fig. 5) became extinct after man reached these islands. The largest species of *Dinornis* stood about 10 feet tall. The elephantbirds were smaller in stature (about ostrich size) but had a massive build. Both orders are related to the ratite assemblage of flightless birds, and may be characterized, in part, as follows: the quadrate has a single articular condyle; the sternum is short and broad and lacks a keel; the wing is rudimentary (elephantbirds) or absent (moas); the ilium and ischium are not fused posteriorly; a pygostyle is wanting; most of the species have four toes (the hallux elevated), but some have only three. The feathers of the moas (e.g., *Megalapteryx*) lack barbicels and are soft and loose-webbed, as in living ratites; the aftershaft is well developed. Relatively

---

[3] Archey (1941) has grouped the moas (order Dinornithiformes) into two families: the Dinornithidae, containing 6 species of the genus *Dinornis;* and the Anomalopterygidae, containing 5 genera and 14 species. Oliver (1955), however, recognized 8 species of *Dinornis* and 6 genera in the Anomalopterygidae (*Pachyornis, Emeus, Euryapteryx, Zelornis, Anomalopteryx, Megalapteryx*).

Fig. 5. Skeleton of a small moa (*Euryapteryx*) from New Zealand. (Courtesy of Dean Amadon and the American Museum of Natural History.)

thin-shelled, cream-colored eggs have been attributed to three different genera, and pale green fragments have been described.

Aepyornis is noted for having laid the largest birds' eggs known. Those of the largest species measure approximately 9½ by 13 inches, and have a capacity of over 2 gallons. It has been estimated that such an egg would hold the contents of 7 ostrich eggs or over 12,000 hummingbird's eggs. The wealth of clinical and experimental data on the role of the pituitary gland in growth regulation in man and laboratory animals led Edinger (1942) to examine brain endocasts of four species of elephantbirds, with special reference to the relative size of this gland ("PB") to forebrain volume and to body height. In this series, she found that "while body-height was about doubled, the volume of the forebrain increased by four fifths, but PB-volume became eightfold." She concluded that "the extraordinary size of the aepyornithid eggs and the loose luxuriant plumage of the large ratites now appear as signs of hyperpituitarism."

In closing this brief survey of the fossil record, it seems desirable to mention the Dodos (*Raphus*) and the Solitaires (*Pezophaps*) even though they have become extinct within the last 300 years. These peculiar, flightless birds, related to the Columbidae, inhabited the Mascarene Islands (Mauritius, Rodriguez, and Réunion). The ornithological history of these islands and their distinctive avifauna have been described by Hachisuka (1953).

References

Andrews, Charles W. 1896. Remarks on the Stereornithes, a Group of Extinct Birds from Patagonia. *Ibis,* 1896: 1–12. (See also pp. 586–587.)

———— 1899. On the Extinct Birds of Patagonia—1. The Skull and Skeleton of *Phororhacos inflatus* Ameghino. *Trans. Zool. Soc. London,* 15 (1901): 55–86.

Archey, Gilbert. 1941. The Moa, a Study of the Dinornithiformes. *Bull. Auckland Inst. & Mus.,* No. 1.

Beebe, C. William. 1915. A Tetrapteryx Stage in the Ancestry of Birds. *Zoologica,* 2: 39–52.

Böker, Hans. 1927. Die biologische Anatomie der Flugarten der Vögel und ihre Phylogenie. *Jour. f. Ornith.,* 75: 304–371.

Bradbury, Wm. C. 1919. Some Notes on the Egg of *Aepyornis maximus. Condor,* 21: 97–101.

Brodkorb, Pierce. 1957. New Passerine Birds from the Pleistocene of Reddick, Florida. *Jour. Paleo.,* 31: 129–138.

Broman, Ivar. 1948. Über die Relation zwischen Steuerfederzahl und Wirbelzahl im Embryonalen "Archaeopteryxschwanz" der Vögel. *Acta Anat.,* 6: 55–79.

Cauderay, Henry. 1931. Étude sur l'Aepyornis. *L'Ois. et Rev. Franç. d'Ornith.,* 1 (Nou. Ser.): 624–644.

Darlington, Philip J., Jr. 1957. *Zoogeography: The Geographical Distribution of Animals.* John Wiley & Sons, New York.

De Beer, Sir Gavin. 1954. *Archaeopteryx lithographica.* British Museum (Nat. Hist.), London.

———— 1956. The Evolution of Ratites. *Bull. Brit. Mus. (Nat. Hist.) Zool.,* 4: 57–70.

Edinger, Tilly. 1926. The Brain of *Archaeopteryx*. *Ann. & Mag. Nat. Hist., London* (9), 18: 151–156.

——— 1942. The Pituitary Body in Giant Animals Fossil and Living: a Survey and a Suggestion. *Quart. Rev. Biol.,* 17: 31–45.

——— 1951. The Brains of the Odontognathae. *Evolution,* 5: 6–24.

Enlow, Donald H., and Sidney O. Brown. 1957. A Comparative Histological Study of Fossil and Recent Bone Tissues. Part II. *Texas Jour. Sci.,* 9: 186–214.

Fisher, Harvey I. 1947. The Skeletons of Recent and Fossil *Gymnogyps*. *Pacif. Sci.,* 1: 227–236.

Gregory, Joseph T. 1952. The Jaws of the Cretaceous Toothed Birds, *Ichthyornis* and *Hesperornis*. *Condor,* 54: 73–88.

Gregory, William K. 1916. Theories of the Origin of Birds. *Ann. N. Y. Acad. Sci.,* 27: 31–38.

——— 1946. Some Critical Phylogenetic Stages Leading to the Flight of Birds. *Proc. Linn. Soc. N. Y.,* Nos. 54–57: 1–15.

——— 1949. The Humerus from Fish to Man. *Amer. Mus. Novitates, No. 1400.*

Hachisuka, Masauji. 1953. *The Dodo and Kindred Birds.* H. F. & G. Witherby, London.

Hay, Oliver P. 1910. On the Manner of Locomotion of the Dinosaurs Especially Diplodocus, with Remarks on the Origin of the Birds. *Proc. Wash. Acad. Sci.,* 12: 1–25.

Heilmann, Gerhard. 1927. *The Origin of Birds.* D. Appleton & Co., New York.

Howard, Hildegarde. 1929. The Avifauna of Emeryville Shellmound. *Univ. Calif. Publ. Zool.,* 32: 301–394.

——— 1946. A Review of the Pleistocene Birds of Fossil Lake, Oregon. *Carnegie Inst. Wash., Publ. 551:* 141–195.

——— 1950. Fossil Evidence of Avian Evolution. *Ibis,* 92: 1–21.

——— 1957a. A Gigantic "Toothed" Marine Bird from the Miocene of California. *Santa Barbara Mus. Nat. Hist. Bull. 1* (Geology).

——— 1957b. A New Species of Passerine Bird from the Miocene of California. *Contr. in Science,* No. 9 (Los Angeles County Mus.).

Lambrecht, Kálmán. 1933. *Handbuch der Palaeornithologie.* Gebrüder Borntraeger, Berlin.

Lowe, Percy R. 1930. On the Relationships of the Aepyornithes to other Struthiones as revealed by a Study of the Pelvis of *Mullerornis*. *Ibis,* 1930: 470–490.

——— 1933. On the Primitive Characters of the Penguins, and their Bearing on the Phylogeny of Birds. *Proc. Zool. Soc. London,* 1933, pt. 2: 483–538.

——— 1935. On the Relationship of the Struthiones to the Dinosaurs and to the rest of the Avian Class, with special reference to the position of Archaeopteryx. *Ibis,* 1935: 398–432.

——— 1939. Some Additional Notes on Miocene Penguins in relation to their Origin and Systematics. *Ibis,* 1939: 281–296.

——— 1944. An Analysis of the Characters of Archaeopteryx and Archaeornis. Were they Reptiles or Birds? *Ibis,* 86: 517–543.

Lucas, Frederic A. 1890. The Expedition to Funk Island, with Observations Upon the History and Anatomy of the Great Auk. *Rept. U. S. Natl. Mus.,* 1887–1888: 493–529.

——— 1902. Aves. In Karl A. von Zittel, *Text-book of Palaeontology.* Macmillan and Co., London.

Lydekker, Richard. 1896. Fossil birds. In A. Newton and H. Gadow, *A Dictionary of Birds.* Adam and Charles Black, London, pp. 277–289.

"ring" is actually a tubelike or conelike structure. A freely movable quadrate bone (usually articulating with the squamosal bone) suspends the mandible from the cranium. Lowe (1925, 1926) described the morphology of the "quadrato-tympanic joint" in a number of nonpasserine birds as an aid in determining relationships. (The nares, nasal bones, and the palate are discussed on pp. 40–45; for details of skull development and structure, see Gadow, 1896: 870; Pycraft, 1903; De Beer, 1937; Hofer, 1945; Barnikol, 1952; Frank, 1954; Starck, 1955; Lang, 1956.)

The several regions of the vertebral column are designated as cervical, dorsal, synsacral, caudal, and the pygostyle (urostyle). The pygostyle is formed by the fusion of 4 to 7 embryonic vertebrae; a true pygostyle (or ploughshare bone) is absent in most ratites and in the Tinamidae. The number of vertebrae anterior to the pygostyle varies from about 33 to 58 in the several orders and families of birds. The dorsal (or back) vertebrae (commonly 4 to 6 in number) are those that are connected by ribs with the sternum and that do not fuse with the synsacrum. In certain families (e.g., Podicipedidae, some Falconidae, Cracidae, Gruidae, Pteroclidae, Columbidae, etc.), 2 or more (commonly 3 to 5) of the dorsal vertebrae fuse to form an *os dorsale* (*notarium*); 1 or more free dorsal vertebrae are interposed between the notarium and the synsacrum. The synsacrum is formed by the fusion of a series (10 to 23 bones) of thoracic, lumbar, sacral, and urosacral vertebrae; usually these vertebrae also fuse with the ilium. Most authors consider that there are 2 true sacral vertebrae in birds, but *Struthio, Apteryx,* and the Pelecanidae are said to have 3. Huxley (1867: 422) defined the urosacral vertebrae as "those caudal vertebrae which unite with one another and with antecedent vertebrae to form the 'sacrum' of a bird." There are 4 to 9 *free caudal vertebrae,* 6 or 7 being most common. The numbers of cervical and dorsal vertebrae are relatively constant within a species, whereas the numbers of synsacral and free caudal vertebrae exhibit considerable individual variation.

The *true ribs* consist of a dorsal segment that has two articulations (*capitulum* and *tuberculum*) with a dorsal vertebra, and a ventral segment (*sternal rib*) which articulates with the sternocostal process of the sternum. Thoracic ribs (when present) articulate dorsally with the anterior synsacral vertebrae; a sternal segment may be present or absent. Thoracic ribs may articulate with the sternum, fuse with the sternal part of the last true rib (or the preceding thoracic rib), or end freely in the abdominal musculature.

There is much individual variation in the number of ribs that articulate with the sternum.

The *clavicles, coracoids,* and *scapulae* form the pectoral girdle. Superiorly, the three bones bound the *foramen triosseum,* through which the tendon of M.[1] supracoracoideus passes to its insertion on the humerus. The coracoid and scapula form the *glenoid fossa* in which the head of the humerus articulates. In most birds (exceptions: some parrots, barbets, toucans), the clavicles fuse inferiorly to form the furcula (wishbone); the area of fusion may be expanded into a *hypocleidium.* The clavicles are absent or rudimentary in ratites, the mesites, in some parrots, pigeons, and barbets, and in *Atrichornis* (see Gadow, 1896: 858; Glenny and Friedmann, 1954; Glenny and Amadon, 1955). In *Opisthocomus* the furcula is ankylosed with the coracoids and the sternum. The coracoids and scapulae are fused in ratites and in *Fregata.*

The pelvic girdle is formed by the fusion of three paired bones (*ilium, ischium,* and *pubis*) and the synsacrum. A *pubic symphysis* is found only in *Struthio;* an *ischiadic symphysis,* only in *Rhea.* Lebedinsky (1913: 721), in an excellent study of the pelvis, summarized data on the presence or absence of M. ambiens and the *pectineal process* (spina pubica, iliopectineal process) throughout the orders of birds.

A *sesamoid bone* (or cartilage) is one that develops in the tendon of a muscle and improves the angle of pull of that muscle. Such sesamoids occur in the tendons of Mm. triceps brachii, extensor metacarpi radialis, flexor carpi ulnaris, femorotibialis, extensor proprius digiti III, etc. The *os humeroscapulare* (scapula accessoria) is a sesamoid found in the capsule of the shoulder joint in many families. (The appendicular bones and certain special osteological characters are discussed in Chapters 1 and 8.)

The Muscular System

The muscles are those organs of the body that produce motion. They are composed of greatly lengthened cells (called fibers), which contract—become shorter and thicker—when stimulated by nerves. In birds and other vertebrates, most of the "fleshy" structure of the body consists of *striated* or *voluntary muscles* whose action is more or less consciously controlled. Typically, these are

[1] "Musculus" before names of muscles is commonly abbreviated M.; plural, Mm.

bundles of multinucleate, fleshy fibers enclosed in a fascial sheath and tapering at the ends into dense, connective tissue sheets or tough, cordlike tendons which attach the muscles to bones. The respiratory, circulatory, digestive, and urogenital systems contain layers of mononucleate, *smooth* (*nonstriated*) muscles whose action is automatic (involuntary). Typically, these muscles are sheets of more or less parallel fibers which contract in unison; bundles, mesh, and network arrangements of the fibers also occur. *Cardiac* or *heart muscle,* a third type, is intermediate in character between striated and smooth muscle.

Two different color types of striated muscles are distinguished in birds (and some mammals): "red" muscle and "white" muscle. "Red" muscle fibers have a richer blood supply, contain more myoglobin and less water, are smaller in diameter, and have their more abundant nuclei located more peripherally than do "white" fibers. M. pectoralis is a "white" muscle in certain galliform and tinamiform birds, but it is a "red" muscle in *Perdix, Falco, Larus, Corvus,* and *Passer;* both types of fibers are said to occur in this muscle in *Columba* (see Stresemann, 1934: 95; Watzka, 1939).

The long Latin names of muscles frequently discourage the beginning student, but a familiarity with these and a general picture of the muscular system can be quickly acquired if the names of certain classes of muscles are first learned separately. A few muscle names are arbitrary or fanciful, e.g., *sartorius* for a long muscle extending from the pelvis across the thigh to the inner surface of the tibia (so called because *sartor* is the Latin name for tailor, and in man this muscle helps rotate the leg for sitting in tailor fashion). But the longer muscle names are actually compact descriptions of the muscles themselves, one word often defining the muscle's type of motion (extensor), a second the part of the body which it moves (digitorum), and a third its relative position or size (longus, brevis). Thus Mm. extensor digitorum longus and extensor digitorum brevis are two muscles (one long and one short) that extend the toes. Pairs of muscles whose functions and positions are similar are distinguished by being called "major" and "minor," "magnus" and "minimus." Other pairs of muscles are distinguished by naming their relative positions: superior, inferior; medialis, lateralis; profundus, superficialis. Some names simply tell where the muscle arises and inserts: coracobrachialis (origin: coracoid; insertion: brachium = arm). The name may also describe its shape (rhomboideus), its structure (semimembranosus), or its location (brachialis).

An *extensor* extends the arm, thigh, or other part (stretches it out or increases the angle between the bones); a *flexor* flexes it (bends it or reduces the angle). An *adductor* pulls the part inward (usually toward the axis of the body or a specified digit); an *abductor* pulls it away from that axis. A *pronator* "pronates"—turns the hand palm downward—and is accomplished by the rotation of the radius around the ulna; a *supinator* turns the palm upward. A *levator* raises the part; a *depressor* lowers it.

Flexor and extensor muscles are antagonistic and complementary to each other in their actions; it is the contraction, not the relaxation, of a muscle that produces movement. Hence, the contraction of a flexor muscle reduces the angle between two bones; contraction of the appropriate extensor muscle, accompanied by the relaxation of the flexor, increases the angle. The two muscles work in harmony to produce a regulated, steady movement both in flexion and extension.

When considering the actions and innervation of muscles of the appendages, it is convenient and meaningful to think in terms of two major groups of muscle masses: preaxial and postaxial. Postaxial (or extensor) muscles develop dorsal to the developing limb bones (the axis of the appendage), whereas preaxial (or flexor) muscles form ventral to the axis. Furthermore, the nerves which innervate the extensor muscles arise from the dorsal side of the great plexuses of the spinal cord (the brachial and lumbosacral plexuses). Nerves to the flexor muscles arise from the ventral side of the plexuses. Familiarity with the simple concept of preaxial and postaxial muscle groups enables one to systematize information on a large number (about 94 in the wing and the leg) of muscles and their nerves so that less rote memory is required to remember and understand nerve-muscle relationships.

Many of the appendicular muscles of birds are characterized by having very long tendons of insertion. The fleshy bellies, therefore, occupy a proximal position near the center of gravity. The long tendons of some muscles cross two or more joints and act on each joint crossed. M. flexor hallucis longus, for example, arises from the distal end of the femur; its tendon inserts on the distal (ungual) phalanx of the hallux. This muscle, therefore, aids in flexing the tibiotarsus at the knee, aids in extending the tarsometatarsus, and flexes the tarsometatarsal-phalangeal joint and the interphalangeal joint of the first toe.

In gross pattern and appearance, the muscular system in birds is remarkably uniform. Little has been written about the microscopic structure of avian striated muscles, but Nel (1940) found a quantitative difference in the distribution of "fibrillar" and "columellar" fibers of certain thigh muscles, correlated with differences in locomotor habits.

The approximately 175 different muscles (most of which are paired) which have been described in birds may be grouped as follows: muscles of the skull and jaws; tongue, trachea, and syrinx; orbit and ear; vertebral column; tail; body wall; pectoral appendage; pelvic appendage; and striated "dermal" muscles (mostly specialized slips of other muscles). (For detailed descriptions of muscles, see Buri, 1900; Fürbringer, 1902; Hudson, 1937, 1948; Hofer, 1950; Beecher, 1951a; Starck and Barnikol, 1954; Hudson and Lanzillotti, 1955; Fisher and Goodman, 1955; Berger, 1957.)

The Nervous System

The nervous system perceives stimuli from the environment and integrates the activities of the body. It is composed of conducting elements (*neurons*) and supporting elements (*neuroglia* and *ependyma*). A neuron is a nerve cell. It is composed of a cell body, its processes (nerve fibers), which conduct an impulse either toward (*dendrite*) or away from (*axon*) the cell body, and its endings. Typically, each neuron has multiple dendrites but a single axon. A "nerve" is a collection of many nerve fibers (both dendrites and axons) held together and surrounded by a connective tissue sheath. The brain and spinal cord constitute the *central nervous system.* Cranial and spinal nerves, with their associated *ganglia* (groups of nerve cell bodies located outside the central nervous system), compose the *peripheral nervous system.*

The Central Nervous System

The *cerebral hemispheres* of birds are characterized by having a well-developed *hyperstriatum* (a "vicarious cortex," which replaces the function of a true cortex). The hyperstriatum (also found in reptiles) develops inward into the lateral ventricles, whereas in mammals the expansion of the cortical area is on the surface of the hemisphere. This inward massing of the gray matter is self-limiting and favors the development of a very efficient, but highly stereotyped, pattern of behavior; there is a capacity for infinite detail but little variability. The higher birds appear to have greater intelligence than the lower mammals, but they do not possess the potentiality for higher development phylogenetically.

The greatly enlarged *optic lobes* (small in *Apteryx*) are situated at the sides of the brain rather than forming the roof (*tectum*) of the midbrain, as in reptiles and mammals. The optic lobes occupy a lower position on the brain in the more advanced groups (e.g., Passeriformes); this is presumed to be an example of *neurobiotaxis* (the phylogenetic movement of nerve cell bodies towards the stimuli). (See Fig. 1.)

Associated with the importance of *vestibular* (equilibrium) and *coordination* centers for flight, the *cerebellum* is highly developed (with a small ventricle) in most birds, but it is relatively small (with a large ventricle) in *Apteryx*, a flightless bird. The relative size of the several subdivisions of the cerebellum in various birds is correlated generally with locomotor pattern (Larsell, 1948). *Cerebellar hemispheres* (the neocerebellum of authors) make their appearance phylogenetically in mammals.

The *medulla oblongata* is essentially reptilian in form but it exhibits certain elaborations associated with hearing, equilibrium, and the development of the syrinx. A *pons* is absent both in reptiles and in birds.

The *spinal cord* extends the entire length of the vertebral column; a *cauda equina* and a *filum terminale* are absent. Either the *cervical* or the *lumbosacral enlargement* may be larger, depending on the relative development of the wing or leg, or they may be about the same size. A distinctive feature of the avian spinal cord is the presence of a *rhomboid sinus* in the lumbosacral region. This sinus (a cavity) results from the lateral deflection of the dorsal funiculus due to an increase in numbers of incoming (afferent) sensory fibers from the leg and is thought to exhibit its best development in birds with powerful legs. The cavity is filled with a gelatinous substance and with crossing myelinated nerve fibers; the cells of the roof (called the "glycogenic body") contain glycogen.

The Peripheral Nervous System

Birds have 11 (not 12) cranial nerves: the spinal accessory nerve (cranial nerve XI), which innervates Mm. trapezius and sternocleidomastoideus in mammals, is absent. Bulbar (from the medulla) XI in birds, as in mammals, is simply a caudal extension of the vagal (cranial nerve X) nuclear group.[2] The fibers of von Lenhossék, arising from upper cervical segments of the spinal cord and running with the dorsal roots of cervical nerves (and not through the foramen magnum), are thought to be homologous with the spinal portion of the mammalian accessory nerve. Table 1 lists the cranial nerves and their primary functions.

The number of spinal nerves varies in different birds (e.g., 39 pairs in *Columba,* 51 pairs in *Struthio*). Each nerve has a single dorsal root but several ventral rootlets. The *ventral rami* (branches) of several (usually 4 to 6) of the lower cervical nerves, and sometimes the first thoracic, form a brachial plexus whose branches distribute primarily to the wing. A variable number of lumbosacral nerves take part in the formation of three plexuses (lumbar, sacral, pudendal) which supply the lower extremity, the pelvis, and the caudal region (see Huber, 1936; Fisher and Goodman, 1955).

American neuroanatomists consider the *autonomic nervous system* to be entirely a *general visceral efferent* system, which is to say that it is composed of motor fibers which distribute to glands and to the smooth muscle of the viscera and blood vessels. (It should be understood that *general visceral afferent* (sensory) fibers accompany the motor fibers; both are essential for a reflex arc.) Two anatomical or physiological parts of the autonomic system are recognized: (1) craniosacral or parasympathetic, associated with certain cranial nerves (III, VII, IX, X) and the sacral spinal cord (see Yntema and Hammond, 1955), and (2) thoracolumbar or sympathetic, which has its origin in thoracic and lumbar segments (also cervical in birds) of the spinal cord. The system is further characterized by having both a preganglionic and a postganglionic neuron (i.e., there is a two-neuron chain), and generally (except to the appendages) there is a double innervation of organs (e.g., stimulation of parasympathetic vagal fibers inhibits heart beat, whereas cardiac sympathetic stimulation accelerates heart rate). The *synapse*[3] between the preganglionic and the postganglionic neuron is located in a *chain* (paravertebral), *collateral,* or *terminal ganglion.*

---

[2] A "nucleus" is a group or column of nerve cell bodies located within the central nervous system.

[3] A synapse is the region where an impulse is transmitted from the axon of one neuron to the dendrite of another neuron. The actual method by which the impulse is transmitted is still in debate, but the synapse controls the direction in which the impulse is directed, i.e., it is polarized.

TABLE 1

Cranial Nerves in Birds

Number and Name	Function
I. Olfactory	Smell; small in most birds.
II. Optic*	Vision; large in most birds.
III. Oculomotor	Motor to medial, superior, and inferior rectus, and the inferior oblique ocular muscles, and to the levator of the upper eyelid; parasympathetic to eye (via ciliary ganglion), and (?) to Harder's gland (Stresemann, 1934: 102).
IV. Trochlear	Motor to superior oblique muscle.
V. Trigeminal	Sensory to eye, oral cavity, bill, etc.; motor to certain jaw muscles and to Mm. tensor periorbita and depressor palpebrae.
VI. Abducens	Motor to lateral rectus muscle and to muscles of the nictitating membrane.
VII. Facial	Motor to muscles associated with the hyoid arch (e.g., depressor mandibulae, mylohyoideus posterior, sphincter colli); sensory (including taste) from palate, also part of nasal cavity, orbit, etc.; parasympathetic to salivary glands.
VIII. Acoustic	Hearing and equilibration.
IX. Glossopharyngeal	Sensory (including taste) from oral cavity, pharynx, larynx, etc.; motor to M. kerato-mandibularis (geniohyoideus); parasympathetic to salivary glands.
X. Vagus	Sensory (including taste) and motor (parasympathetic) for viscera of pharynx, neck, and thoraco-abdominal cavity; motor to M. cucullaris. Recurrent laryngeal branch (? bulbar XI = "spinal accessory") is the motor supply to muscles of the larynx.
XII. Hypoglossal	Motor to muscles of tongue and syrinx.

* This is not a true nerve but a fiber tract of the brain.

The Digestive System

The digestive system begins with the oral cavity and ends at the vent, the *bill* being the usual food-gathering organ of birds. Based on relative lengths and relationships of the two mandibles, different types of bills have been named *epignathous, hypognathous, fissirostral, conirostral,* etc. (see the Glossary; Coues, 1903: 105–106). Sexual dimorphism in shape (see *Neomorpha,* p. 536) or color and seasonal changes in color (e.g., *Sturnus vulgaris)* of the bill occur.

The *tongue,* adapted to feeding habits, exhibits great diversity in form and structure. Among different birds it serves, as pointed out by Gardner, as a probe, a sieve, a capillary tube, a brush, a rasp, etc. Consequently, in shape the tongue may be rectangular, cylindrical, lanceolate, spoon-shaped, flat, cupped, grooved, tubular, or bifid; it may be fleshy, horny, spined, "feathery," brush-tipped, or rudimentary (for details, see Gardner, 1925; Scharnke, 1931, 1932). In the wryneck *Jynx ruficollis* the tongue is nearly two-thirds the length (exclusive of tail) of the bird (Roberts, 1939). In such birds, the posterior elements of the hyoid (the support for the tongue) curve upward to follow the contour of the skull (see Coues, 1903: 174).

A horny sheath (*rhamphotheca*) covers the bony components which form the upper and lower jaws (both sometimes referred to as "mandibles"). The oral cavity is bounded by the horny coverings of the upper (*rhinotheca*) and lower (*gnathotheca*) mandibles. A median ridge and a pair of lateral ridges on the palatal surface of the rhinotheca form the "horny palate" of Sushkin (1927) and Beecher (1951b). Caudal to the horny palate, palatal folds, separated by a palatal fissure (or fossa), are found in the roof of the pharynx. The two *choanae* (internal nares) open into the roof of the pharynx anteriorly, and caudal to them the two *eustachian* (pharyngotympanic) tubes open, usually into a single, median fossa. The *glottis* (entrance to the larynx and trachea) lies in the floor of the pharynx. Dorsal to the glottis, the pharynx leads into the esophagus, a musculomembranous tube, which conveys food from the pharynx to the stomach. In some birds (e.g., Galliformes, Thinocoridae, Pteroclidae, Columbidae, Psittacidae, and in some members of the Drepaniidae, Icteridae, Zosteropidae, and Fringillidae) there is a permanent dilatation (*crop*) in the lower part of the esophagus; in other birds the lower portion of the esophagus may be dilated to form a temporary crop. In *Opisthocomus* the crop is unusually large and muscular, forming a double loop which impinges on the pectoral muscles and the carina of the sternum.

The *stomach* of most birds is divided into a glandular *proventriculus* and a muscular *ventriculus* (gizzard) (Fig. 2). In certain tanagers (*Chlorophonia* and *Tanagra*) the gizzard is reduced to a

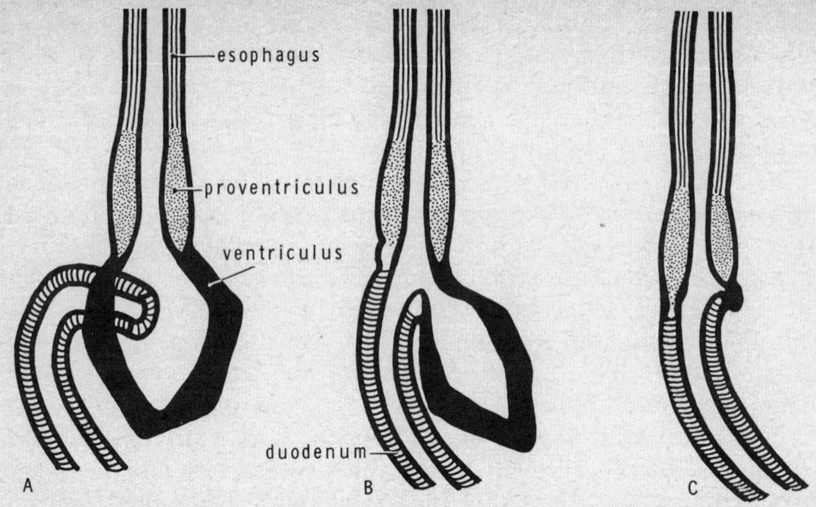

Fig. 2. Schematic representation to show progressive reduction in the ventriculus of fruit-eating birds. A. Ventriculus of a primitive insect-eating flowerpecker (Dicaeidae). B. Ventriculus of a specialized flowerpecker that eats both fruit and animal food. C. The rudimentary ventriculus of a euphonia (Thraupidae). (After Desselberger, 1931.)

thin, membranous area lying between the proventriculus and the duodenum. In nectar-eating hummingbirds, honey-eaters, and sunbirds (Trochilidae, Meliphagidae, Nectariniidae) the openings to esophagus and duodenum are adjacent to each other rather than being at the opposite ends of the stomach. This specialization is carried further in certain fruit-eating flowerpeckers (Dicaeidae), in which the gizzard is a blind diverticulum from the lowermost end of the proventriculus so that the proventriculus leads directly into the duodenum (Desselberger, 1931, 1932).

A short, U-shaped *duodenum* and a long, coiled *ileum* form the small intestine. A *pyloric sphincter* separates the terminal end of the stomach from the duodenum. The duodenum receives the *bile* and *pancreatic ducts,* and the *pancreas* lies between its two limbs. An ileocecal "valve" marks the separation between ileum and "rectum" (the large intestine in birds). A pair[1] of caeca (see p. 62) is found in most birds at the beginning of the rectum. The rectum is usually a short, straight tube, but in *Opisthocomus, Chauna,* and

[1] One in herons, in *Chrysococcyx,* and as a variable feature in those birds (e.g., *Anhinga*) with vestigial caeca (see Forbes, 1882a; Wetmore, 1920).

in struthious birds it is long and coiled. The rectum empties into the *coprodeum* (innermost compartment of the *cloaca*), from which the feces pass through the *proctodeum* to the vent. The *bursa Fabricii* opens into the roof of the proctodeum and a *copulatory organ* may be associated with its floor.

The *liver, pancreas,* and *salivary glands* are accessory organs derived embryologically from the digestive tube (the liver and pancreas from entoderm, the salivary glands from stomodeal ectoderm). Most birds possess several groups of salivary glands (angular, palatine, lingual, sphenopterygoid, crico-arytenoid, esophageal, maxillary, and mandibular); they are said to be absent in the Pelecaniformes. The number, especially in aquatic birds, varies with food habits. The very large *glandula picorum* (a special subgroup of the mandibular glands) is characteristic of the Picidae and the Jyngidae (see Antony, 1920). The salivary glands of most birds contain mucus-secreting cells, but serous cells (which presumably secrete a diastatic enzyme) have been reported in a few seed-eating birds (especially fringillids). In swifts and crested-swifts (Apodidae and Hemiprocnidae), salivary secretions are used in nest construction and in the genus *Collocalia* the entire nest is composed of saliva.

Indicative of its many functions, the liver is the largest of the viscera. Its relative size varies both with diet and with age. Of the two major lobes, the right is larger than the left in most birds, but there is much individual variation not only in relative size of the two lobes but also in their shape (Lucas and Denington, 1956). A series of *peritoneal ligaments* (falciform, coronary, gastrohepatic, etc.) connect the liver with adjacent structures.

The gall bladder is attached by peritoneum to the inferior surface of the right lobe of the liver and usually is oval or saccular in form. In the Capitonidae, Indicatoridae, Ramphastidae, and some Picidae, however, it is very long and tubular ("intestiniform"). The gall bladder is said to be absent in the Trochilidae; it is present in some genera of the Columbidae, Psittacidae, Cuculidae, and Picidae, but absent in others. In certain instances (e.g., *Rhea, Mergus, Grus, Cuculus*) absence of the gall bladder seems to be a matter of individual variation.

A two-layered fold *(mesoduodenum)* of peritoneum extending between the two limbs of the duodenum contains the pancreas, an important endocrine and exocrine gland. It is formed from three pancreatic buds but in the adult bird it is a single or bilobed organ exhibiting considerable individual variation in configuration. Two or three pancreatic ducts drain into the duodenum. (For a discussion of pancreatic structure and function, see Nagelschmidt, 1939; Benoit, 1950: 310.)

The Respiratory System

The avian respiratory system is composed of a series of channels leading from the external nares to the lungs and air sacs. In sequence these channels are: nasal cavities, nasopharynx, larynx, trachea, and bronchi. Certain specializations of this system in birds are associated with the high body temperature (104 to 112°F., or even higher), the high metabolic rate, and the absence of sweat glands. Body temperature and metabolic rate vary (as in mammals) with degree of activity; there is a daily, and probably a seasonal, fluctuation in temperature within certain normal limits (see Baldwin and Kendeigh, 1932). Body feathers serve as an excellent mechanism for heat conservation. In the absence of sweat glands, an increase in respiratory rate effectively increases heat loss because of the relationship of the lungs to the pulmonary air sacs—a bird opens the bill and increases its respiratory rate during periods of high temperature or when taking a sun bath. The same relationship of lungs to air sacs meets the respiratory demands of flight.

The trachea is a long tube, located ventral to the esophagus, supported by a series of cartilaginous or bony rings. The entrance (glottis) to the trachea is surrounded by a series of cartilages (*cricoid, procricoid, arytenoid*) which form the larynx. Usually elliptical or round in cross section, the trachea may be compressed dorsoventrally, as in parrots. In some birds the trachea is greatly elongated and forms coils or loops within the thorax (male of *Ibis ibis*), between ventral musculature and the skin (male of *Ortalis*), or within the sternum (*Olor columbianus*). In different species of a given genus, or in male and female of the same species, the trachea may be either coiled or straight. Subcutaneous tracheal loops occur in the cervical, thoracic, or abdominal regions (e.g., *Anseranas, Tetrao,* some curassows, *Rostratula, Manucodia, Phonygammus*). In the guineafowl *Guttera plumifera* the trachea of both sexes is looped into the furcula (see figure in Chapin, 1932: 667). The most extensive excavation of bone, however, occurs in certain swans and cranes in which the trachea may extend through the entire length of the carina sterni. The trachea may contain one (screamers, males of some ducks, some cotingas) or two (some ducks) dilatations between the larynx and the bronchi, in addition to the tracheal bulla (*bulla ossea*), an enlargement at its inferior end in ducks. (See also "Syrinx" p. 58; Chapter 5; Forbes, 1882b; Rüppell, 1933: 433; Berndt, 1938.)

Inferiorly the trachea divides to form two bronchi. In most birds (some exceptions: *Ciconia*, etc.; and swallows) at least the first few bronchial rings are incomplete, with only a membrane completing the ring (a semiring) on the inner side. The bronchi lead to the lungs, which lie in serous-lined, right and left pleural sacs. The ventral part of each pleural sac is sometimes called the *pulmonary aponeurosis;* costopulmonary muscles extend from it to the true ribs. The *oblique septum* extends caudad from the pericardium to the lateral body wall as a membranous partition (sometimes partly covered by smooth or striated muscle bundles) between the peritoneal cavity and the posterior intermediate (= anterior abdominal) air sac; the latter is often described as being enclosed between two layers of the oblique septum.

The thin-walled air sacs, which are derived from the primary or secondary bronchi, usually consist of three or four paired sacs (frequently asymmetrical in shape) and an unpaired interclavicular sac; from these sacs diverticulae may extend around the viscera or into bones. Although there is disagreement as to the method by which the air flow is regulated, it is agreed that air passes through the lungs and into the air sacs during inspiration, and that during expiration the same air passes out through the lungs again. Terminal alveoli are absent, being replaced by a bronchial capillary network. Thus there is little or no residual air trapped in the lungs, and the oxygen and carbon dioxide exchange of external respiration may take place during both inspiration and expiration. In the absence of a thoraco-abdominal diaphragm, the intercostal and abdominal muscles effect quiet respiratory movements, whereas the pectoral musculature produces the more rapid respiratory rate required in flight.

One of the peculiar features of the air sacs is that they may send diverticulae into nearly any part of the skeleton. The bones most frequently pneumatized are the humerus, femur, ribs, and vertebrae, but in screamers and hornbills (Anhimidae and Bucerotidae), even the pygostyle and the phalanges of the fingers and toes are pneumatic. In some birds (e.g., swifts, many passerines) the cranial bones are pneumatized by extensions from the nasopharyngeal chambers. Subcutaneous air cells are well developed in tropicbirds, pelicans, boobies, and screamers (see DeMay, 1940).

The Circulatory System

The circulatory system transports food materials and oxygen to the cells and the waste products of metabolism away from the cells; it also carries hormones, antibodies, and leucocytes. Thus it aids the nervous system in integrative processes and it is important in protecting the animal against disease and infection, in repairing injuries, and in controlling body temperature. It is composed of the blood-vascular system (heart, arteries, veins, and capillaries) and the lymphatic system. Avian erythrocytes (red blood cells) and thrombocytes are nucleated and generally oval in shape.

The heart lies in the median plane of the thoraco-abdominal cavity, enclosed in a protective fibrous sac, the *pericardium.* Covering the inner surface of the pericardium and the outer surface of the heart (*epicardium*) are serous membranes, which secrete a watery, lubricating fluid. The avian heart is divided into a right and a left half, the interatrial and interventricular septa being complete in adult birds, as in mammals. Venous blood enters the "right heart," passing from atrium to ventricle to pulmonary artery and thence to the lungs; this is the *pulmonary circuit.* Oxygenated pulmonary blood is returned to the "left heart," entering the left atrium and then passing through the left ventricle to the right aortic arch, whose branches supply blood to the rest of the body; this is the *systemic circuit.* A single, musculomembranous atrioventricular valve prevents the backflow of blood from the right ventricle into the right atrium. The left atrioventricular valve consists of three flaplike cusps (two in some birds). Three papillary muscles of the left ventricular wall give rise to tendinous strands (*chordae tendineae*), which insert on the inferior surface of the cusps. The muscular wall (*myocardium*) of the left ventricle is much thicker than the wall of the right ventricle. At the beginning of the aorta and the pulmonary artery, three semilunar valves prevent the blood from flowing back into the left or right ventricles, respectively.

Heart size varies, in part, with degree of activity and concomitant metabolic rate. Hartman (1955: 237) observed that "larger hearts may be associated with permanent residence at high altitude." He reported that the heart was 2.4 per cent of the total body weight in certain hummingbirds but only 0.2 per cent in tinamous. Odum (1945) showed that heart rate, also, is much higher in small birds; he gave basal heart rates varying from 135 beats per minute in the Mourning Dove (*Zenaidura macroura*) to 615 in the Ruby-throated Hummingbird (*Archilochus colubris*); even higher maximum rates were recorded.

Birds and other vertebrates have a hepatic portal[5] circulation that carries venous blood from the abdominal and pelvic portions of the digestive tract to the liver. Hepatic veins then carry the blood to the postcaval (inferior caval) vein, a large trunk that conducts venous blood from the lower extremity and the abdominopelvic regions to the right atrium. Paired right and left precaval (superior caval) veins conduct blood from the head, neck, wing, and chest wall to the right atrium. A renal portal circulation is important during development but in the adult bird the so-called renal portal vein (a portion of the iliac vein) does not terminate in a capillary network in the kidneys, though branches are sent to those organs. (Space does not permit further discussion of the numerous branches and tributaries of the arterial and venous systems. The carotid and thigh arteries are treated on p. 60; for details of the vascular system, consult Gadow and Selenka, 1891: 756; Slonaker, 1918: 372; Kern, 1926; Craigie, 1940; Lechner, 1942; Witschi, 1956.)

Lymph is a chemically complex plasmalike fluid. The tissue fluid that fills the interstices between the cells of the body is called lymph after it is absorbed by lymphatic capillaries. These carry the lymph to a series of progressively larger channels which eventually drain into the venous system (usually into the jugular, precaval, and hypogastric veins). Paired *thoracic ducts* conduct much of the lymph from the abdominopelvic region. Pulsating *lymph hearts,* associated with coccygeal segmental veins, have been found in the embryos of all birds studied but generally atrophy after hatching; they persist throughout life in *Struthio, Casuarius,* the Anatidae, Laridae, Ciconiidae, and in the Passeriformes. Few lymph nodes are found in birds and these (cervicothoracic and lumbar nodes) have been demonstrated only in *Fulica, Larus,* and the Anatidae (Fürther, 1913; but see Biggs, 1957). Lymphatic

[5] A "portal" system is one that begins and ends in a capillary network. Thus the hepatic portal vein has its beginning in the capillaries of the gut wall; the vein again breaks up into capillaries in the substance of the liver.

tissue, however, is present in the thymus gland, the spleen, and in the wall of the intestine, including the caeca and the bursa Fabricii.

The Urogenital System

Because of their intimate embryological relationship, the excretory and reproductive organs and their accessory parts are grouped together as the urogenital system. The nitrogenous wastes of metabolism are synthesized to the relatively insoluble uric acid in the liver. The urine excreted by the kidneys is concentrated during its passage through the renal tubules and additional water absorption takes place in the coprodeum, where the urine is mixed with the feces.

The elongate avian kidneys are usually distinctly divided into three major lobes (two in some hornbills), each of which contains numerous lobules. The kidneys lie in a retroperitoneal position in the dorsal part of the pelvis, and the lobes fill the spaces between the transverse processes of certain of the synsacral vertebrae; the entire irregular-shaped area so occupied is sometimes referred to as the "renal depression." Tubular ureters lead from the kidneys to the urodeum, the middle of the three compartments forming the cloaca. There is no urinary bladder. In the male, the ureters pass caudad parallel to the ductus deferentia, but in the female the ureters lie dorsal to the oviducts.

The adult female reproductive system is characterized in most birds by the presence of a single (left) functional ovary. A rudimentary right gonad may persist as a potential ovary, testis, or ambisexual organ; destruction of the left ovary by disease (or surgery) may thus result in sex reversal in an individual which possesses a testicular rudiment (for summaries of experimental work on sex differentiation, see Domm, 1955; Witschi, 1956). In certain hawks (especially the genera *Accipiter, Circus,* and *Falco*), 50 per cent or more of the females have paired ovaries (Gunn, 1912; Fitzpatrick, 1934; Wood, 1932). Rand (1935) reported that paired ovaries were "not unusual" in some parrots and lories collected in Madagascar.

The proximal end (*infundibulum*) of the left oviduct is held in position near the inferior pole of the left ovary by a ligament (the *mesotubarium*). The enlarged caudal end of the oviduct is called the *uterus;* it leads through a constricted portion (*vagina*) to the urodeum. The several parts of the oviduct secrete albumen, membranes, shell, pigment, and mucus during formation of the egg (for details, see Romanoff and Romanoff, 1949: 182). The right oviduct is a functionless tube, usually of small size and associated with the cloaca. Paired rudimentary deferent ducts may extend from kidney levels to the cloaca. (Paired oviducts in the male atrophy before hatching.)

Male birds possess two functional testes that vary in shape from round to vermiform. Either the right or left testis may be larger; asymmetry in size and shape has been reported by several writers (Friedmann, 1927; Rand, 1933; Test, 1945).

Deferent ducts (*ductus deferentia*) lead from the gonads to the urodeum. The caudal end of each duct expands into a thick-walled ampullary duct, which passes through the wall of the urodeum as an ejaculatory duct. During the breeding season the highly coiled deferent ducts develop to form seminal vesicles (*seminal glomera*). In all passerine families thus far investigated (e.g., Alaudidae, Turdidae, Prunellidae, Parulidae, Icteridae, Ploceidae, Fringillidae), the seminal vesicles hypertrophy to such an extent that they cause an enlargement and protrusion of the cloacal region. The *cloacal protuberance* thus formed aids in identifying male birds and in determining the stage of the reproductive cycle (Salt, 1954; Wolfson, 1954).

A *copulatory organ* (cloacal penis in male; clitoris in female) in ratites and some carinate birds develops from the ventral wall of the proctodeum as paired right and left halves that remain separated dorsally by a longitudinal groove. This type of organ is well developed in the Struthionidae, Casuariidae, Dromiceiidae, and Apterygidae, and can be protruded and retracted by special muscles. In the Rheidae and the Anatidae, the two halves are specialized by "being spirally twisted and being reversible like the finger of a glove" (Gadow, 1896: 91). A smaller, less elaborate penis has been found in the Tinamidae, the Galliformes (especially the Cracidae), many Ciconiiformes, and the Burhinidae. A "phalloid organ" has also been described and illustrated for *Bubalornis* (Ploceidae) by Sushkin (1927: 30–32).

Although not a part of the urogenital system, the adrenal glands have a close positional relationship to the kidneys and gonads. The adrenals lie near the anterior poles of the kidneys and between them and the gonads. Although typically paired glands, the two adrenals may, as a matter of individual variation, be fused into a single mass. Variation in color (cream, yellow, orange, pink, gray, reddish brown) probably is partly the result of diet (Hartman and Albertin, 1951).

Anatomy of Parts Used in Classification of Birds[6]

Nostrils (or Nares)

The condition of the external openings (nostrils) of the nasal cavities is often cited by taxonomists. Usually the nostrils are open (*pervious*), but in adult cormorants, gannets, etc., they are completely closed (*impervious*). In many birds the two nostrils are separated by a complete internasal septum (a condition called *imperforate*), but in others (cranes, American vultures, rails) there is a central opening in the partition (*perforate*). Commonly the nostrils are placed laterally on the bill and are posterior to the mid-point, but the position ranges from very near the bill tip (uniquely in *Apteryx*) to the posterior rim of the bill (*Ramphastos* toucans, in which the nostrils open to the rear). In outline, nostrils range from round through various oval shapes to linear slits. In albatrosses and other "tubinares" the nostrils are horny tubes; in many nightjars (Caprimulgidae) they are rather long, soft, flexible tubes. A further modification is a protective *operculum* (cover) over the nostril, as in Galliformes and some passerines. In wrynecks (Jyngidae) the flap is attached to the lower side of the nostril, with the nostril opening above it. There are other special conditions; e.g., in falcons (*Falco, Polihiërax*) and some cuckoos (*Chrysococcyx*), the nostril is circular but has a conspicuous central tubercle. The nostrils are usually exposed, but in some birds, such as grouse and crows, the feathers from the forehead extend over the nostrils and may completely conceal them from view.

Nasal Bones

Garrod (1873a) described the two principal arrangements of the bony structure forming the nasal openings in the skulls of birds (see Fig. 3) and proposed the following terms:

Holorhinal: the posterior outline of the opening is fairly rounded. A line drawn over the culmen connecting the posterior ends of the

---

[6] For feather structures so used, see Chapter 3.

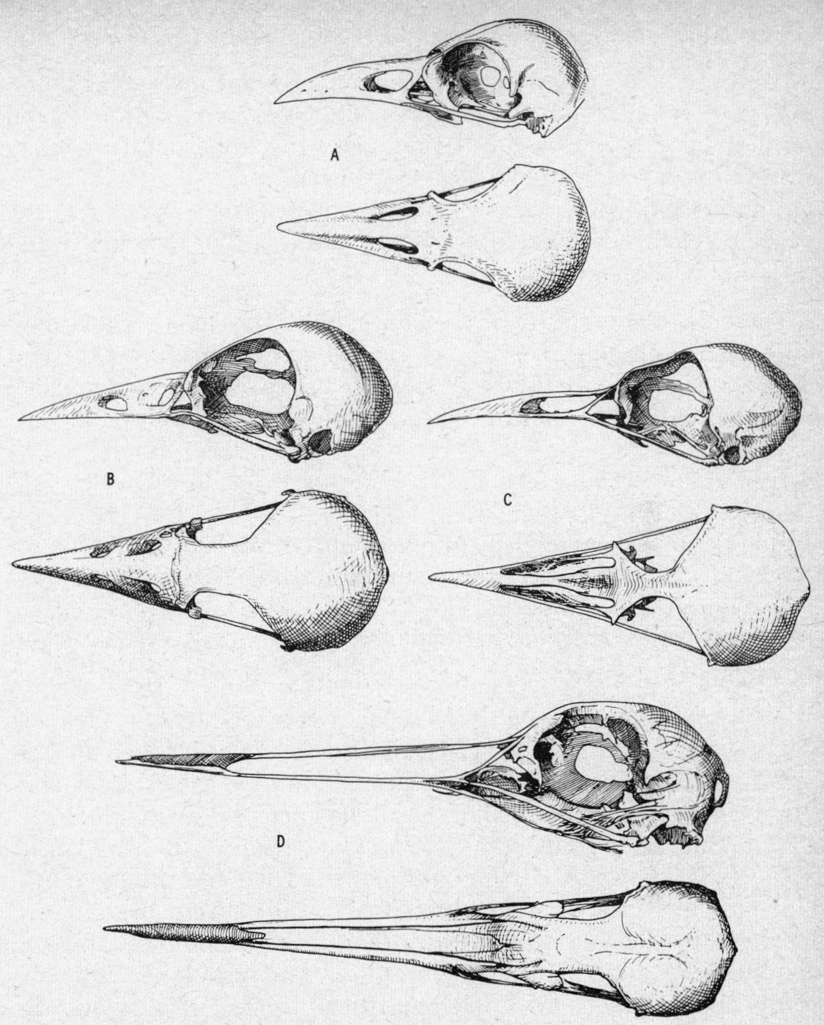

Fig. 3. Dorsal and lateral views of skulls to show the four main types of bony nostrils. A. Holorhinal—*Corvus brachyrhynchos* (Corvidae). B. Amphirhinal—*Gymnopithys leucaspis* (Formicariidae). C. Pseudoschizorhinal—*Cinclodes antarcticus* (Furnariidae). D. Schizorhinal—*Grus canadensis* (Gruidae).

two nasal openings will pass across the nasal processes of the premaxilla. Examples: rails, grouse, pheasants.

Schizorhinal: the posterior outline of the nasal opening forms a deep slit. In most cases a line drawn between the openings as noted above will pass behind the nasal processes of the premaxilla. Examples: gulls, cranes.

Two additional categories, proposed later, are:

Pseudoschizorhinal: a modification of the holorhinal type; found in many ovenbirds (Furnariidae). The posterior outline of the nasal opening is rounded, but the openings extend far back—even posterior to the nasal processes of the premaxilla.

Amphirhinal: with two bony nostril openings (one anterior to the other) on each side. Examples: some antbirds (Formicariidae) and antpipits (Conopophagidae).

These characters of the nasal bones, like many another anatomical basis for classification, have proved to be less important and less dependable than originally supposed, but they do have a value and are still used in the characterization of higher categories.

Palate

In an effort to arrange the major groups of birds in their true relationships, T. H. Huxley (1867) turned to the palate and proposed four major groups in the "carinate" birds. [He placed "Dromaeus" (the Emu) and the other "struthious" birds in a separate division, the Ratitae.]

1. Dromaeognathous (Fig. 4). The prevomers[7] extend far back and articulate with the posterior ends of the palatines and the anterior ends of the pterygoids, separating both from the parasphenoid ("basisphenoid" of some authors). Huxley placed only the tinamous (Tinamidae) in his suborder "Dromaeognathae." Later Pycraft (1900, 1901) showed that the palate of the Rhea fits the same fundamental description and must likewise be called dromaeognathous. He went further and brought all other struthious birds (emu and cassowaries, ostrich, apteryx, the moas, and aepyornis) into one group and called them "paleognathous" birds. However, McDowell (1948) has now demonstrated that this group cannot in fact be covered by a single, inclusive palate definition; he finds at least four types of palates among these birds and calls them: tinamiform, casuariiform, struthioniform, and apterygiform.

2. Schizognathous. Prevomers completely fused and fairly large or small. Maxillopalatines do not meet along the central line. Palatines and pterygoids articulate with the parasphenoid rostrum. Characteristic of the Galliformes, Gruiformes, Charadriiformes, Piciformes, etc.

---

[7] Formerly called "vomers" but not homologous with the mammalian vomer.

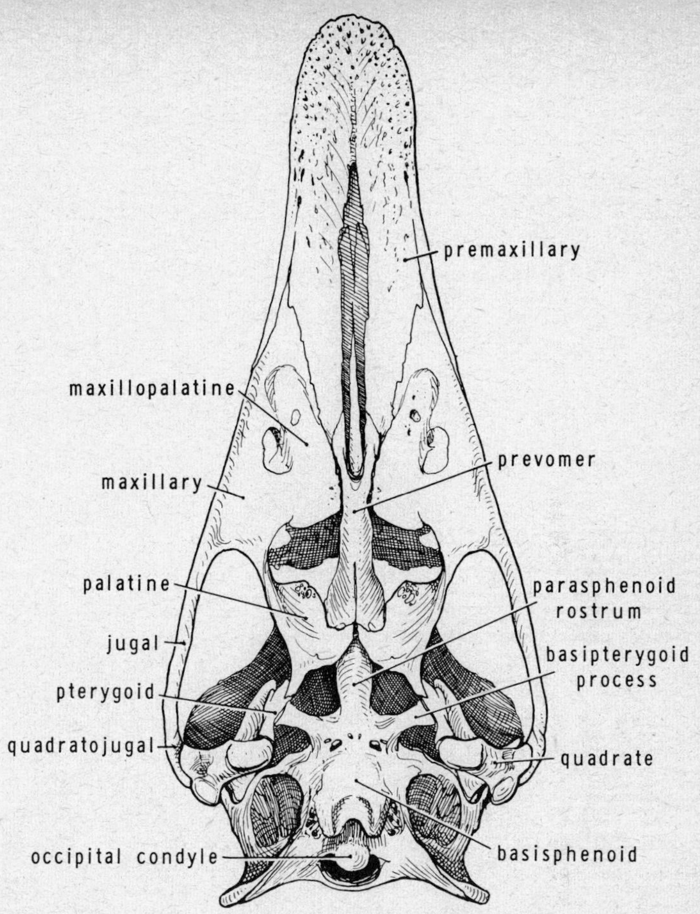

Fig. 4. Ventral view of skull of *Rhea americana* to illustrate the dromaeognathous palate.

3. Desmognathous. Prevomers fused or absent. Maxillopalatines meet in the mid-line (and, in many cases, fuse). Palatines and pterygoids articulate with the parasphenoid rostrum. Characteristic of Anseriformes, Ciconiiformes, Pelecaniformes, Falconiformes, and many others.

4. Aegithognathous. Prevomers large, completely fused and truncated in front, separating the maxillopalatines. Characteristic of passerine birds and swifts.

These last three palate types are shown in Fig. 5.

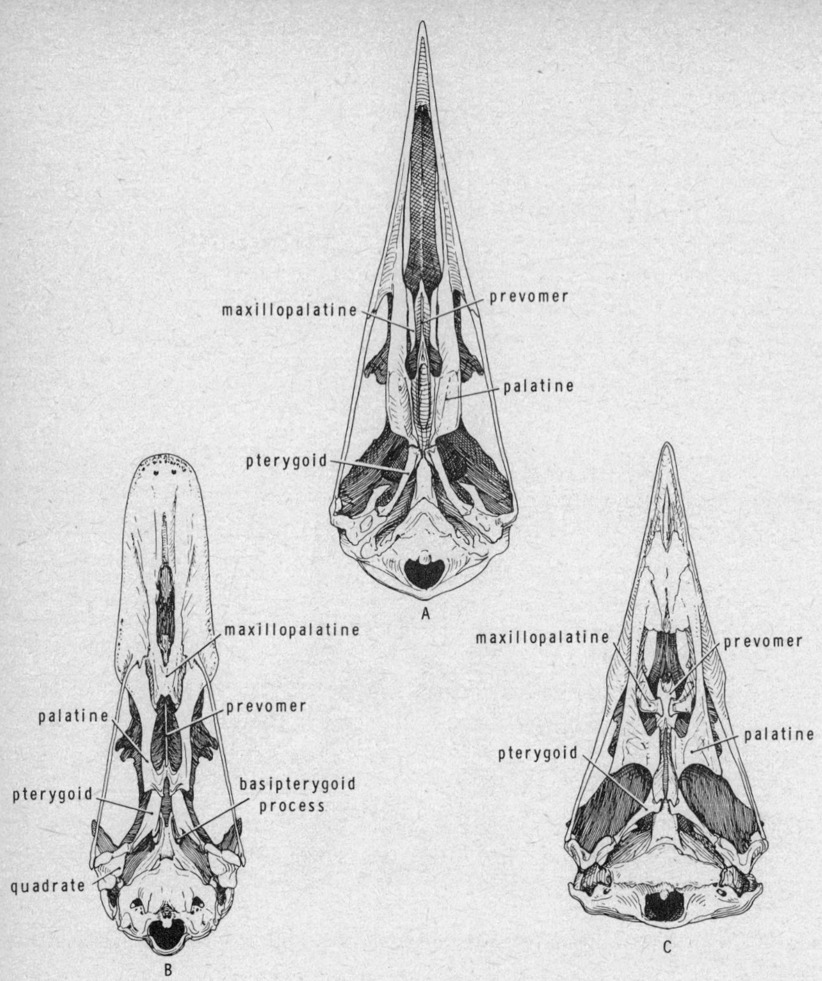

Fig. 5. The three other "classic" types of palate. A. Schizognathous—*Larus atricilla.* B. Desmognathous—*Branta canadensis.* C. Aegithognathous—*Corvus corax.*

W. K. Parker (1875) proposed adding a fifth category, "saurognathous," to describe the woodpeckers, but it has since been demonstrated that this distinction may not be maintained.

Further study has shown that the second, third, and fourth palate types merge into each other, and even the dromaeognathous type is not always sharply demarked. (The young of many birds actually develop a dromaeognathous palate first and later acquire a palate of type 2, 3, or 4.)

Although Huxley's suborders "Schizognathae," "Desmognathae," etc., prove not to be natural taxonomic units, nevertheless the terms "schizognathous," "desmognathous," etc., continue to be of value when used as part of the diagnosis of larger taxonomic categories.

Cervical Vertebrae

Unlike mammals, which regularly have 7 cervical vertebrae, birds of different groups have numbers that range from 13 (e.g., certain passerines, some cuckoos) to 25 (certain swans). The most frequent number is 14 or 15.

The cervical vertebrae (singular: vertebra) are defined as those between the head and the trunk. One or more of the posteriormost cervical vertebrae commonly bear short, incomplete ribs (cervical or cervicodorsal ribs), and these vertebrae are designated as "cervicodorsal" but are always included in the counts of cervical vertebrae for taxonomic diagnoses. [Adolphi (1922) in his excellent monograph, however, considered some of the cervicodorsal ribs as belonging to cervical vertebrae, others to dorsal vertebrae.]

As in all higher vertebrates, the first (anteriormost) vertebra of birds is called the "atlas" (since it supports the globe of the head); the second vertebra is called the "axis" because of its importance in the pivoting of the head. The odontoid process of the axis may articulate in an open notch ("notched" atlas) or it may fit into a bony canal in the atlas ("perforated" atlas).

Sternum (Fig. 6)

The characters of the breastbone have been much employed in taxonomy. Its unkeeled or keeled condition was long used to define two major groups, the "ratite" and "carinate" birds (Merrem, 1812–1813).[8]

In the carinates, the main central portion of the sternum bears a keel (carina sterni) which serves as an extensive area of attachment for the great breast (pectoral) muscles used in flight; at the anterior end (where the coracoids are attached) are two median projections, the *spina interna* (dorsal; toward the inside of the bird)

[8] After it was realized that the tinamous (Tinamidae), a strongly keeled group, were more closely related to the "ratite" (flat-sternumed) birds than to other "carinate" (keel-sternumed) birds, these terms were no longer used for taxonomic units, but they remain as important ornithological adjectives.

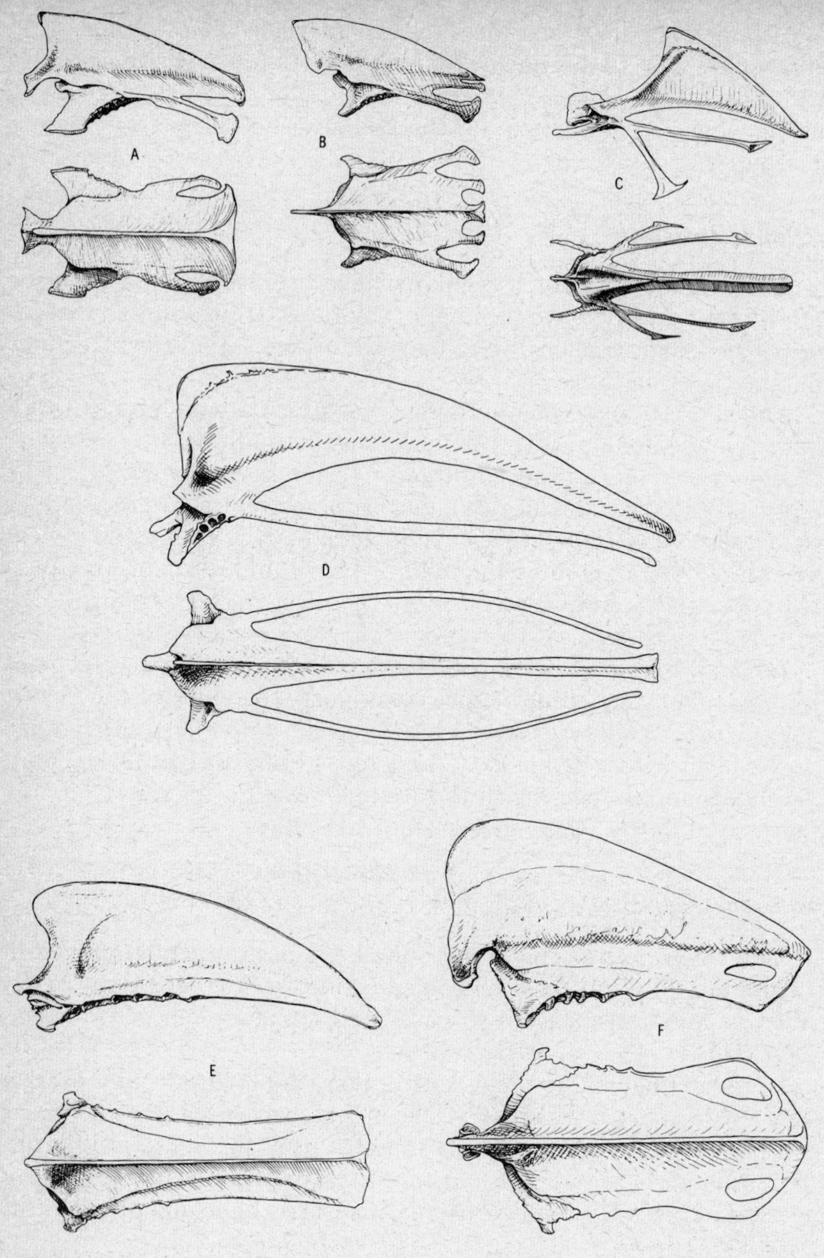

Fig. 6. Selected examples of the avian sternum. A. *Ostinops alfredi* (Icteridae). B. *Megaceryle alcyon* (Alcedinidae). C. *Callipepla squamata* (Phasianidae). D. *Tinamus major* (Tinamidae). E. *Aramus guarauna* (Aramidae). F. *Ara macao* (Psittacidae).

and the *spina externa* (ventral); in some birds, such as pheasants, these two fuse to form a *spina communis.* Anterior to the costal facets for the sternal ribs there is a single anterolateral projection (sternocoracoidal process or *processus lateralis anterior*), which affords origin for the sternocoracoideus muscle. On each side of the sternum, caudal to the rib facets, there is usually a posterolateral projection (*processus lateralis posterior*). In many galliform birds there is also an oblique process (*processus obliquus*), which extends upward and backward from the base of the posterolateral process. In some groups, a pair of intermediate processes (*processus intermedius* or internal lateral "xiphoid" process) is present between the posterolateral process (external lateral "xiphoid" process) and the median metasternum, producing a "double-notched" posterior border of the sternum (for details of the embryological formation of these processes, see Lindsay, 1885). In other birds, especially those of strong flight (e.g., hawks), the spaces between the posterior processes are largely filled in, leaving only small openings (fenestra); in some the spaces are completely filled in, producing a continuous bony plate. These types of sternum are called *notched, fenestrate,* and *entire.*

In "ratite" birds (families 2 to 6 of our classification; see p. 379) and in some flightless "carinate" birds, such as the New Zealand parrot *Strigops* and the rail *Notornis,* there is virtually no keel on the sternum. The flightless parrot and rail are obviously degenerate members of well-known families of carinate, flying birds, and it now appears that the "ratite" birds also are descended from flying (and therefore "keeled") birds and are not closely related, but are thrown together in our classification largely because they are all flightless and keelless (McDowell, 1948).

Tarsometatarsus ("Tarsus")

The tarsometatarsus shows a variety of characters much used in taxonomy. In some species, such as grouse, sandgrouse, and many owls, it is partly or wholly feathered, but in most other birds it is unfeathered. The unfeathered sheath (*podotheca*) of the tarsometatarsus may be:

scutellate (with large scalelike segments)
reticulate (with a network of small scalelike segments)
scutellate-reticulate (scaled in front and reticulate behind)
booted, or "ocreate" (with a smooth sheath, lacking segmentation—except, in some cases, at the lower end)

scaleless (the sheath soft, undivided, bare skin), e.g., the American green kingfishers, *Chloroceryle*

In passerines, in which the character of the tarsus has proved especially useful in classification, the horny sheath of the tarsometatarsus is obviously divisible into an anterior segment called the *acrotarsium* (*akron,* top) and a posterior segment or *planta* ("the sole").

The shape of the cross section of the tarsus is of two sorts in the higher songbirds (Oscines). Most species have the hinder part of the tarsus sharp-angled and are called "acutiplantar oscines"; the larks, family Alaudidae, have the hinder part of the tarsus rounded, and they are called "latiplantar oscines."

Several types of passerine tarsal scutellation have been described (Sundevall, 1872–1873; Reichenow, 1871, 1914; von Boetticher, 1929), and they have been rather extensively used in taxonomy, especially by Ridgway in his great work on the birds of North and Middle America (1901–1911. For a discussion of these terms see pt. 1, p. 18; pt. 4, p. 328.).

Seven categories are commonly distinguished (Figs. 7, 8). Most of the primitive passerine birds fit readily into one of these classes, but some are intermediate in various respects.

Pycnaspidean (*pycnos,* dense): With rear (plantar) surface of the tarsus densely covered with small scales or granules.

Exaspidean: With anterior, scutellated segment of tarsal sheath extending across the external side of tarsus.

Endaspidean: The reverse of the preceding. Anterior, scutellated segment of tarsal sheath extends across the inner side of the tarsus.

Holaspidean: With rear surface of tarsus covered by a single series of broad, rectangular scales.

Taxaspidean: With rear surface of tarsus covered by two (or, sometimes three) series of small, rectangular (or hexagonal) scales.

Booted ("ocreate"): Scutella fused into a single smooth sheath or "boot," except, in some cases, at the very lower end.[9]

Laminiplantar: With a smooth, undivided plantar (posterior) tarsal surface, but a scutellate acrotarsal (anterior) surface.

[9] Unfortunately, German and French authors have not only used other names (i.e., "knemidophorer" or "cnémidophore") for this type of tarsal sheath, but they have transferred Sundevall's term "ocreate" to the type of tarsus (laminiplantar) characteristic of most higher passerine birds. The term "booted" is used in poultry literature to designate feathered shanks; the preferred term is *ptilopody.*

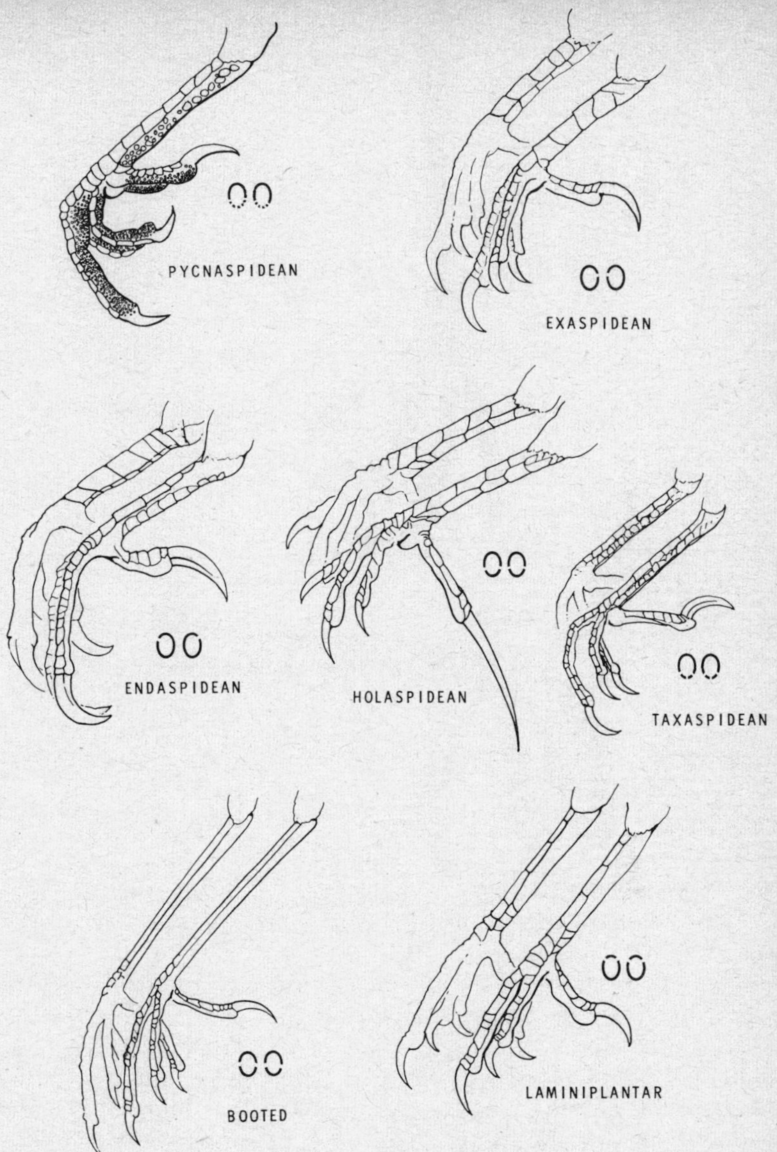

Fig. 7. Examples of tarsal scutellation in passerine birds. Pycnaspidean—*Phytotoma rara* (Phytotomidae; after Küchler, 1936). Exaspidean—*Muscivora forficata* (Tyrannidae). Endaspidean—*Dendrocolaptes platyrostris* (Dendrocolaptidae). Holaspidean—*Alauda arvensis* (Alaudidae). Taxaspidean—*Acropternis orthonyx* (Rhinocryptidae). Booted—*Turdus migratorius* (Turdidae). Laminiplantar—*Richmondena cardinalis* (Fringillidae).

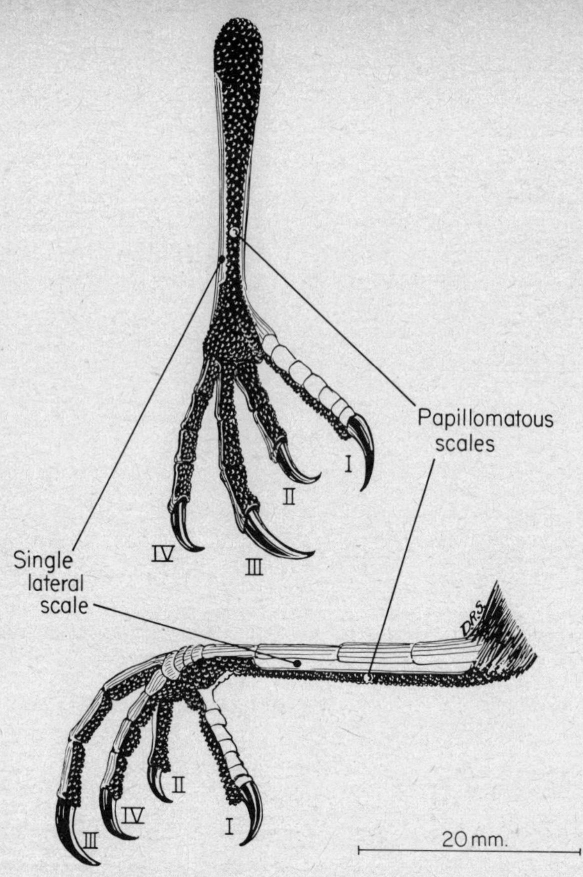

Fig. 8. Posterior and lateral views of tarsal scutellation of *Artamella viridis* (Vangidae). (Courtesy of the American Museum of Natural History.)

Toes

The foot of the bird has, typically, four toes—a hind toe (hallux) and three front toes. The toes are numbered as follows: I, hallux; II, inner front toe; III, central front toe; IV, outer front toe.

The number of bones (phalanges) in the toes of birds is extraordinarily constant: toe no. I typically has two bones, no. II has three, no. III has four, and no. IV has five. (Note that each toe has one more phalanx than its ordinal number.) This invariance helps us to ascertain the homology of bird toes even when in the course of evolution toes have been lost or turned to different positions. A few swifts, nightjars, and some other birds have a reduced number of phalanges in some toes (Forbes, 1882c).

The hallux in most birds is functional and is at the same level as the other toes (a condition called *incumbent*), but in some species the hallux is *elevated* and may not touch the ground at all (e.g., in cranes and many rails).

In a few birds, specialization of several sorts has been accompanied by a reduction in the number of toes—usually to three. For example, we find this condition in some running birds (rhea, emu, cassowaries, bustards, Golden Plover, and Sanderling), in tree-climbing birds (several species of woodpeckers), and certain birds which swim under water primarily with their wings (diving petrels and the Auk family). In a single passerine species, the timaliid *Paradoxornis paradoxa* of western China, there are only three functional toes, no. IV having been reduced to a vestigial stub, the possible significance of the reduction being unknown. In most three-toed birds it is the hallux (no. I) that has been lost, but in certain kingfishers, toe no. II is lacking. In the ostrich alone, two toes (nos. I and II) have been lost.

There are several variations from the usual toe arrangement, the most frequent being the zygodactyl or yoke-toed foot characteristic of woodpeckers, toucans, cuckoos, and parrots. Owls, touracos, and *Pandion* are zygodactyl but can move the outer toe freely from back to front. The zygodactyl foot, adapted to climbing and grasping, is found mainly in arboreal groups, such as the cuckoos. (The cuckoo known as the Roadrunner, *Geococcyx,* has become cursorial but has retained the zygodactyl grouping of the toes.)

A less common arrangement is called *syndactyl:* two toes are fused for a part of their length, as, for example, in kingfishers and hornbills.

Pamprodactyl feet—having all toes turned forward (or capable of being turned forward)—are characteristic of colies (Coliidae) and swifts.

Heterodactyl feet—in which toes nos. I and II are turned backward—are peculiar to trogons.

Swimming birds (or birds whose ancestors swam) commonly have adaptive modifications of the feet. The best-known example is a duck, with its front toes fully webbed. Gulls and terns have similarly webbed feet, but some, like the Fairy Tern (*Gygis*)—less aquatic in habit—have the webs much "incised" and reduced in area. Many wading birds (e.g., herons, shorebirds) have only a small web between two of the toes. Other birds, such as cormo-

Anatidae, many Galliformes, Gruidae, Rallidae, Charadriidae, Laridae, Alcidae, Columbidae (in which the biceps slip is very large), Caprimulgidae, and some other nonpasserine genera (e.g., *Phaëthon, Anhinga, Phoenicopterus,* etc.).

The Expansor Secundariorum Muscle (Fig. 10)

Garrod (1876a: 193) first described this peculiar wing muscle and Fürbringer (1886: 124) later stated that it was composed of nonstriated fibers. The muscle is present both in passerine and nonpasserine birds (Berger, 1956). In passerine birds and in certain unrelated nonpasserine genera, the muscle arises by a tendon from the distal end of the humerus and/or the humero-ulnar pulley. In other nonpasserines there are two tendons of origin: one from the humerus, the other from the pectoral girdle (scapula, coracoid, or sternum) and/or one or more of the following muscles: dorsalis scapulae, subcoracoideus, coracobrachialis posterior, sternocoracoideus, pectoralis. The fleshy belly, located at the elbow, inserts on the calami of two (rarely) or more (six in *Grus canadensis* and *Aceros undulatus*) of the proximal secondaries (occasionally on some of the distal tertials). Widely used in technical diagnoses, the value of this muscle for such purposes cannot be known until further information is available on its presence or absence throughout the orders of birds.

Thigh Muscles (Fig. 11)

Garrod (1873–1874) studied the muscles of the thigh in birds and decided that five were so variable in their occurrence among different groups of birds that a concise statement of their occurrence might be useful in taxonomy.

Garrod arbitrarily assigned the letters A, B, X, and Y to these variable muscles and indicated the presence or absence of the ambiens muscle[10] by placing a plus or minus sign at the end of the series of letters. Hudson (1937: 59) proposed that two other muscles, designated C and D, should be added to the muscle formula,

---

[10] Garrod thought that the ambiens (a slender muscle near the surface on the inner side of the thigh) was one of such critical importance that he proposed a division of birds into two subclasses, the Homalogonatae ("with typical knees") and the Anomalogonatae ("with aberrant knees"), largely according to the presence or absence of this muscle. It soon became apparent that these categories were unnatural ones, and the terms are now obsolete.

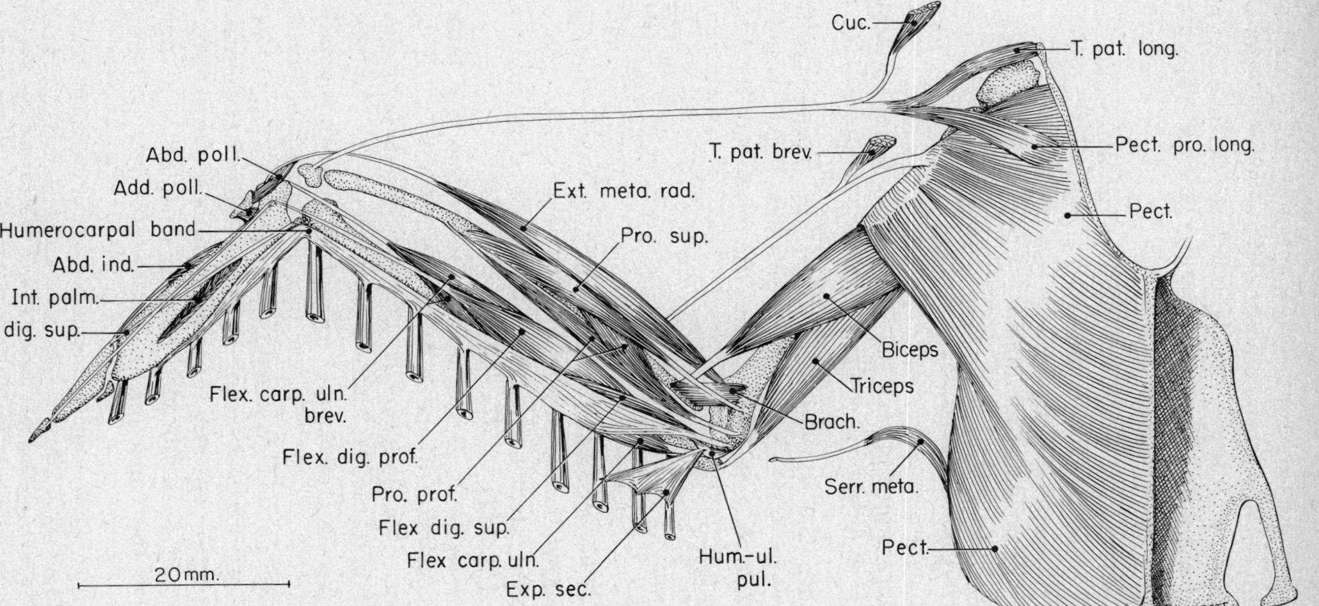

Fig. 10. Ventral view of wing muscles of *Fregilupus varius.* Abd. ind., abductor indicis; Abd. poll., abductor pollicis; Add. poll., adductor pollicis; Brach., brachialis; Exp. sec., expansor secundariorum; Flex. carp. uln., flexor carpi ulnaris; Flex. carp. uln. brev., flexor carpi ulnaris brevis; Flex. dig. prof., flexor digitorum profundus; Flex. dig. sup., flexor digitorum superficialis; Hum.-ul. pul., humero-ulnar pulley; Pect., pectoralis, pars thoracicus; Pro. prof., pronator profundus; Pro. sup., pronator superficialis; Serr. meta., serratus metapatagialis. (Courtesy of the American Museum of Natural History.)

that the ambiens muscle should be represented by the symbol Am, and that the *vinculum* (a fibrous band) often connecting the tendons of Mm. flexor perforatus digiti III and flexor perforans et perforatus digiti III should be represented by the letter V. The list of symbols thus stands:

A—M. piriformis, pars caudofemoralis[11]
B—M. piriformis, pars iliofemoralis
C—M. iliotrochantericus medius
D—M. gluteus medius et minimus
X—M. semitendinosus
Y—M. accessorius semitendinosi
AM—M. ambiens
V—Vinculum connecting the tendons of Mm. flexor perforatus digiti III and flexor perforans et perforatus digiti III

We then write the muscle formula of the Turkey Vulture (*Cathartes aura*) as ACDXYAmV; the formula of the Great Blue Heron (*Ardea herodias*) as ADXY; and the formula of the Chimney Swift (*Chaetura pelagica*) as A.

The Deep Plantar Tendons

The value to the bird taxonomist of the variation in these tendons was first shown by the Swedish ornithologist, Sundevall, and the idea was then further developed by the English anatomist, Garrod (1875).

All birds have two deep flexor muscles of the toes (i.e., muscles which close the digits of the foot): flexor hallucis longus and flexor digitorum longus. The fleshy bellies of these muscles lie in the leg (above the tarsometatarsus) and are connected with the toes by long tendons (the *plantar tendons*) which extend down the back of the tarsometatarsus. These tendons may be distinguished because the flexor hallucis longus is external to the flexor digitorum longus.

In all passerines studied except the broadbills (Eurylaimidae), these two tendons are entirely separate;[12] in most other birds the two are connected by a fibrous band (a vinculum, but not to be confused with the vinculum in muscle formulae). There are

[11] Fisher and Goodman (1955) use different names for some of the formulae muscles: A, B—caudofemoralis; D—piriformis; X, Y—flexor cruris lateralis.

[12] Forbes (1880: 390–391) proposed that passerine birds be separated into two major divisions: the Desmodactyli, those in which the plantar vinculum is present (the Eurylaimidae), and the Eleutherodactyli, those in which this vinculum is absent.

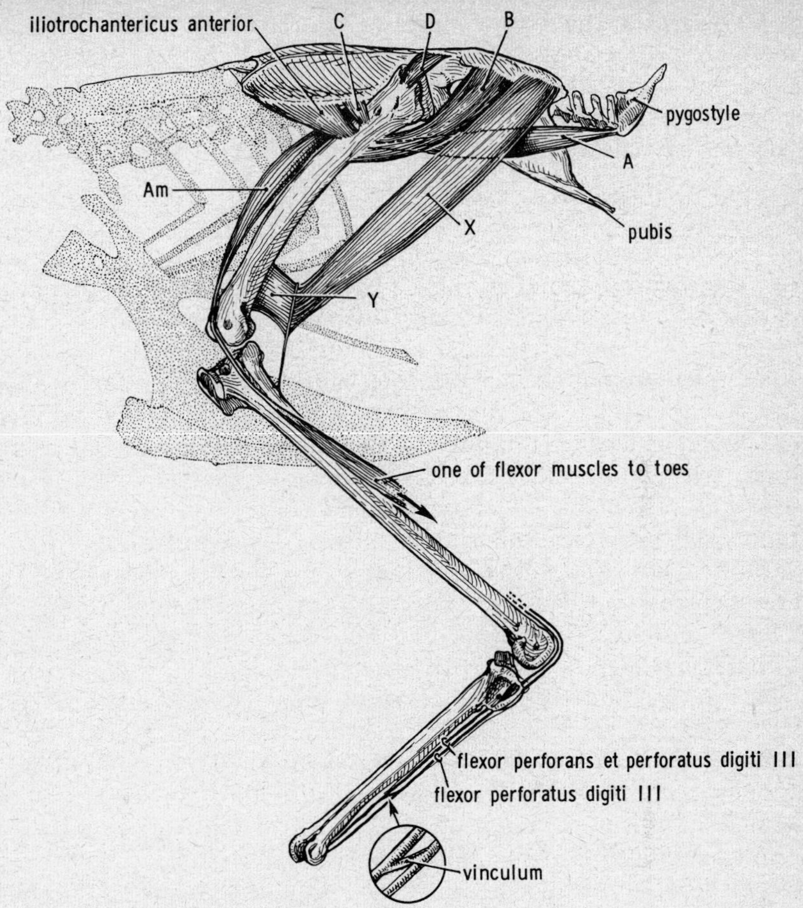

Fig. 11. A generalized illustration of the formulae muscles of the hind limb as proposed by Garrod and Hudson.

also differences in the insertion of these tendons. In one common type, the flexor digitorum inserts on digits II, III, and IV, flexor hallucis inserts only on digit I (hallux). In another type, flexor digitorum inserts only on digits III and IV, and flexor hallucis on digits I and II. In a few birds (e.g., *Gavia, Podiceps, Hydrophasianus, Larus*), the tendon of the flexor hallucis does not insert on the hallux at all, but fuses with the tendon of flexor digitorum. In tridactyl birds (hallux absent), also, the hallucis tendon fuses with the tendon of M. flexor digitorum longus. Twelve major types of arrangement of the plantar tendons have been described, and a good many intermediate conditions are recorded. These arrangements are sometimes referred to as "type III," "type VIII," etc., following the designations of Gadow (1896: 615–618). The terms antiopelmous, desmopelmous, schizopelmous, and synpelmous (see Glossary) are also sometimes used to designate types of arrangement.

Syrinx (Fig. 12)

The functioning sound box of birds "with voice" is not the larynx but the syrinx, which may be (1) bronchial—simply a modification of the first few bronchial rings (in part membranous and called "semirings"); or (2) tracheal—a modification of the lower end of the trachea (windpipe); or (3), as in most birds, tracheobronchial—involving both the trachea and the bronchi. Bronchial syringes are found in cuckoos, nightjars and allied families, and in some owls; tracheal syringes are characteristic of certain New World passerines (ovenbirds, woodcreepers, antbirds, antpipits, and tapaculos), which are sometimes called "tracheophones."

Much more important to the taxonomist than the location of the syrinx is the number, and especially the arrangement, of its "intrinsic" muscles. That is, leaving out of consideration the muscles which connect the syrinx with other parts of the bird ("extrinsic" muscles), we find from one to eight pairs (Köditz, 1925; Mayr, 1931) of syringeal muscles, the greater numbers, in general, being found in birds with elaborate song and their relatives. Functional syringeal muscles are lacking in some ratite birds, in storks, and in American vultures. Such birds "grunt," "boom," and make mechanical noises but in general are called "voiceless."

The different arrangements of these muscles have proved to be a good basis for dividing the great order—more than 5000 species—of passerine birds (Passeriformes) into natural groups (see Gadow, 1896: 937–942). Exclusive of the peculiar broadbills (Eurylaimidae), the passerines are commonly divided into:

Mesomyodian passerines ("Clamatores"), which have the syringeal muscles attached to the middle of the bronchial semirings ("myodian" referring to "myos," meaning muscle; "meso" meaning middle).

Acromyodian passerines ("Passeres" or Oscines; Lyrebirds; Scrub-birds), which have the syringeal muscles attached to the extremities of the bronchial semirings ("acro" meaning extremity or end).

There are also the following terms (defined in the Glossary) which are in more or less regular use to describe various distinctive

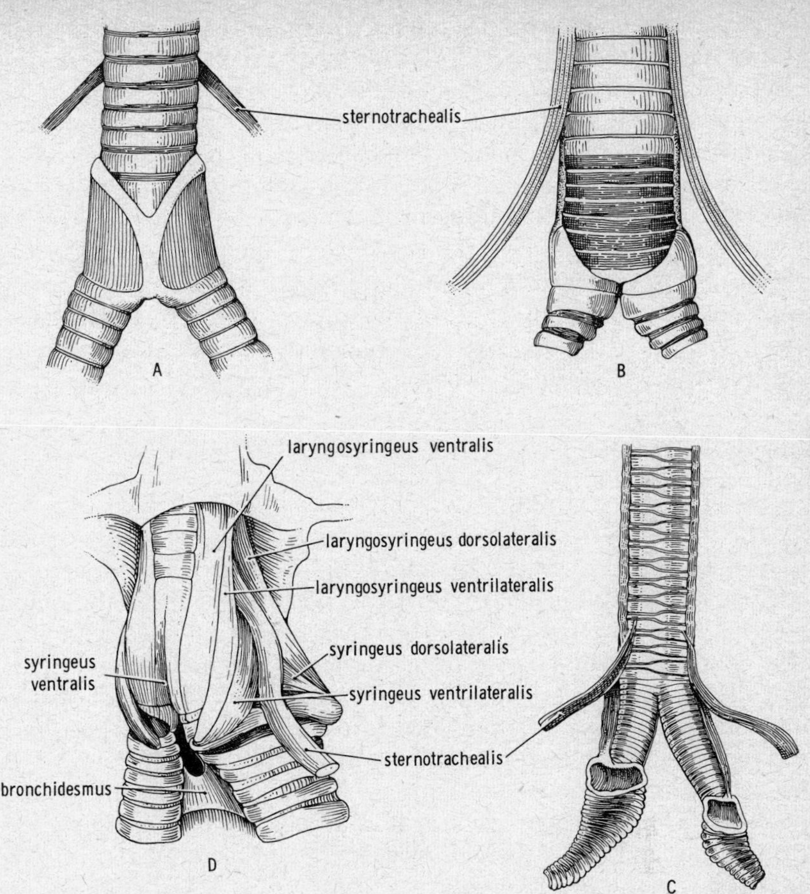

Fig. 12. Types of syringes. A. Tracheobronchial syrinx of *Neodrepanis coruscans* (after Amadon, 1951). B. Tracheal syrinx of *Conopophaga aurita* (after Müller, 1878). C. Bronchial syrinx of *Steatornis caripensis* (after Garrod, 1873c). D. Tracheobronchial syrinx of the sunbird *Arachnothera longirostris* (after Köditz, 1925).

characteristics of the syringeal muscles in passerine birds: anisomyodian, diacromyodian, catacromyodian, and anachromyodian. (Two other terms, oligomyodian and polymyodian, appear in the nineteenth century literature, but are now obsolete.)

Carotid Arteries

The chief artery, or (primitively) pair of arteries, which supplies the head shows in various birds a number of modifications which Garrod (1873b) and Forbes (1881) found useful in taxonomy. In all passerines, for example, only the left dorsal carotid persists ("aves laevocarotidinae"). In other birds the two dorsal carotids have fused in various ways; in still others, one (or even both) has become vestigial and been replaced by an artery nearer the surface. Beddard (1898: 52–54) recorded eight major patterns of the carotid arteries (see also Gadow, 1896: 76–77). Glenny (1955: 544–548), however, described 20 different patterns of the dorsal carotid arteries in birds, based on the presence of one (*unicarotid*) or two (*bicarotid*) dorsal carotid arteries and on the persistence of various embryological remnants. Probably many of these ligamentous vestiges represent individual variation and are of doubtful value in classification (see Fisher, 1955a).

Arteries of the Thigh

The chief blood supply to the pelvic appendage of birds is carried by the ischiadic (ischiatic, sciatic) artery. This artery leaves the pelvis, by passing out the ischiadic (ilio-ischiatic) fenestra, to accompany the sciatic nerve down the posterior side of the thigh. Garrod (1876b: 516–517) reported that in certain passerine birds (Pipridae and Cotingidae—except *Rupicola*) the main artery of the thigh is the femoral artery. He proposed, therefore, that the Mesomyodian passerines be subdivided into the *Heteromeri* (those with the femoral artery predominant) and the *Homoeomeri* (those with the ischiadic artery predominant). Among nonpasserine genera, however, *Dacelo,* some genera of touracos, and *Centropus phasianus* (but not other species of that genus) are said to have the enlarged femoral artery.

Intestinal Convolutions (Fig. 13)

The pattern of arrangement of the much coiled and looped intestine in the bird has been studied and the data used with some success as one more item in the diagnosis of genera and families. Gadow (1889) gave the classic account, describing seven general types, which he called *isocoelous, anticoelous,* etc., but in practice these are commonly designated as type I, type II, etc. Gadow also provided two general descriptive terms, *orthocoelous* (straight-gutted, i.e., with long loops parallel to the long axis of the body) and *cyclocoelous* (with coils in some of the loops).

The use of the pattern of the intestinal convolutions for taxonomic purposes has been much criticized, but the fact remains that

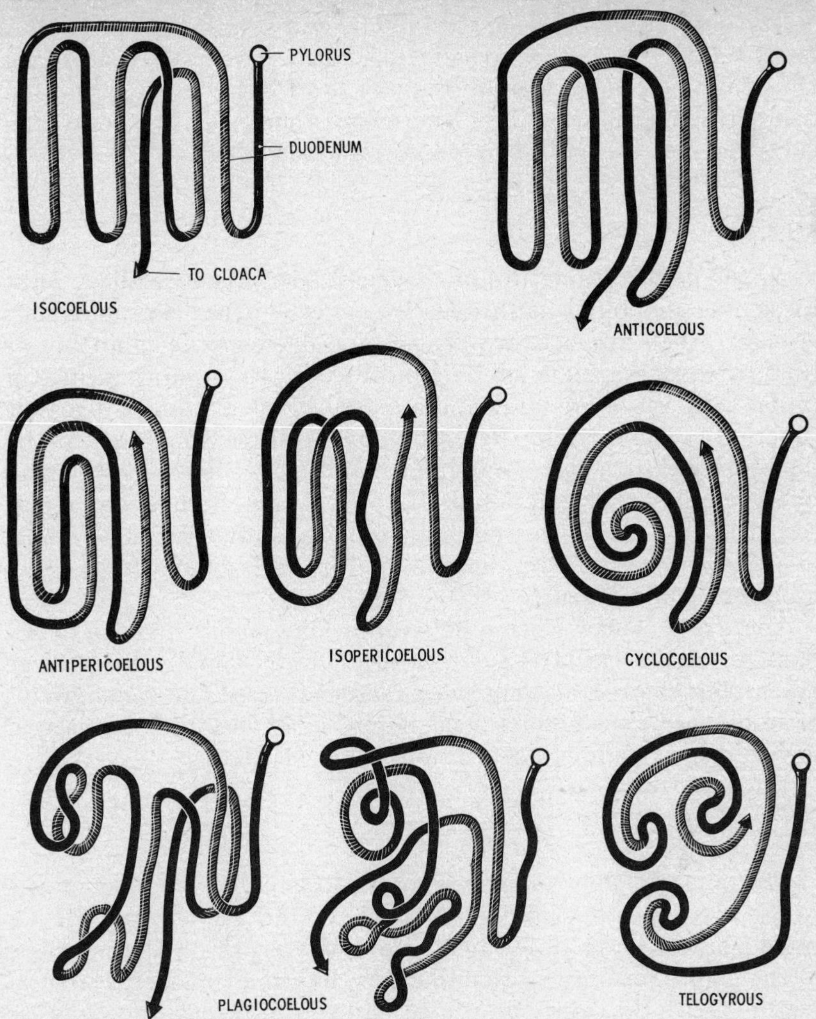

Fig. 13. Patterns of the intestinal loops (after Gadow, 1889). The ascending limb of each loop is shaded; the descending limb, black.

if we arrange the groups of birds according to their intestinal pattern the resulting series does parallel arrangements based on other anatomical criteria, and in many groups the type is quite consistent throughout. Such birds as the screamer (*Chauna chavaria*) have an arrangement of the intestines only slightly advanced from that of the Crocodilia (Beddard, 1898: 26).

The correlation between food habits and length of the intestine has not been adequately investigated, but it is well established that fruit-eating birds tend to have a very short but wide intestine and fish-eating birds a very long and narrow one. Phylogenetic relations may be obscured by extreme diet specialization.

Caeca

At the point of juncture of the small and large intestines, most birds have two blind sacs (diverticulae) called the caeca (singular: caecum); their absence, or presence and degree of development, is used by taxonomists in the technical diagnosis of major groups of birds. The caeca are large and apparently have a major digestive function in the ostrich, rhea, tinamous, gallinaceous birds, many ducks, shorebirds, etc. In a great many birds the caeca are small but seemingly still functional. In others (e.g., herons, gulls, passerines), the caeca are vestigial and probably nonfunctional. Finally, in pigeons, woodpeckers, hummingbirds, and a number of other groups they are absent.

There is some correlation between feeding habits and the development of the caeca (e.g., vegetarian birds usually have large caeca), but there is also a genetic factor involved and some groups of birds with very similar food habits have very different caecal development (Gadow, 1896: 68–70).

Oil Gland (Uropygial Gland)

The oil gland shows some variations which have led taxonomists to use its condition as a diagnostic character. In the majority of birds a circlet of small feathers immediately surrounds the orifice of the gland, forming a brushlike tuft, but in a considerable number of species the orifice is "nude." In the latter case, however, as Gadow (1896: 653–654) pointed out, the area about the orifice is covered with down interspersed with a few stiff feathers. W. deW. Miller (1924: 321–324) showed that although many bird families may be characterized by the invariable presence or absence of a tuft of feathers on the oil gland, others, such as the Rallidae, the Ardeidae, and the Strigidae, show much variation among the species.

The oil gland is absent in the ostrich, emu, cassowaries, bustards (Otididae), frogmouths (Podargidae), the mesite (*Mesoenas*), some parrots, some pigeons, and some woodpeckers.

"Wing Formula"

Regardless of how total wing length may vary among individuals of a species, the lengths of the remiges (especially the primaries) *relative to each other* are usually constant. Description of the relative lengths is called the "wing formula" of that species. In certain groups, such as harriers (*Circus*), Old-world warblers (Sylviidae) (see Fig. 14), tyrant-flycatchers (Tyrannidae), and vireos (Vireonidae), the comparison of wing formulae is often one of the best ways of identifying specimens of closely similar species.

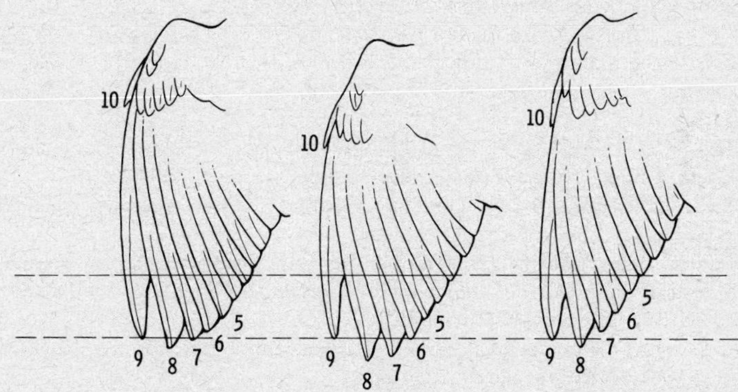

Fig. 14. The wing formulae of three species of Old-world warblers (Sylviidae). Left: Reed Warbler (*Acrocephalus scirpaceus).* Center: Blyth's Reed Warbler (*A. dumetorum*). Right: Marsh Warbler (*A. palustris*). (Reproduced by courtesy of Roger Tory Peterson and the Houghton Mifflin Company from *A Field Guide to the Birds of Britain and Europe.*)

References

Adolphi, Hermann. 1922. Über den Brustkorb und die Wirbelsäule der Vögel. *Zeitschr. f. Anat. u. Entwicklungs.,* 65: 1–149; 328–481.

Amadon, Dean. 1951. Le Pseudo-Souimanga de Madagascar. *L'Ois. et Rev. Franç. d'Ornith.,* 21: 59–63.

Antony, Mathilde. 1920. Über die Speicheldrüsen der Vögel. *Zool. Jahrb.,* 41: 547–660.

Baldwin, S. Prentiss, and S. Charles Kendeigh. 1932. Physiology of the Temperature of Birds. *Sci. Publ. Cleveland Mus. Nat. Hist.,* 3: x + 196 pp.

Barnikol, A. 1952. Korrelationen in der Ausgestaltung der Schädelform bei Vögeln. *Morph. Jahrb.,* 92: 373–414.

———— 1953a. Zur Morphologie des Nervus trigeminus der Vögel unter besonderer Berücksichtigung der Accipitres, Cathartidae, Striges und Anseriformes. *Zeitschr. f. wiss. Zool.,* 157: 285–332.

Barnikol, A. 1953b. Vergleichend anatomische und taxonomisch phylogenetische Studien am Kopf der Opisthocomiformes, Musophagidae, Galli, Columbae und Cuculi. *Zool. Jahrb.,* 81: 487–526.

Bartsch, Paul, W. H. Ball, W. Rosenzweig, and S. Salman. 1937. Size of Red Blood Corpuscles and their Nucleus in Fifty North American Birds. *Auk,* 54: 516–519.

Beddard, Frank E. 1898. *The Structure and Classification of Birds.* Longmans, Green, and Co., London.

Beecher, William J. 1951a. Adaptations for Food-getting in the American Blackbirds. *Auk,* 68: 411–440.

——— 1951b. Convergence in the Coerebidae. *Wils. Bull.,* 63: 274–287.

Benoit, Jacques. 1950. Les glandes endocrines. In Grassé's *Traité de Zoologie,* Vol. 15, Oiseaux, Masson et Cie, Paris, pp. 290–334.

Berger, Andrew J. 1956. The Expansor Secundariorum Muscle, with Special Reference to Passerine Birds. *Jour. Morph.,* 99: 137–168.

——— 1957. On the Anatomy and Relationships of *Fregilupus varius,* an Extinct Starling from the Mascarene Islands. *Bull. Amer. Mus. Nat. Hist.,* 113: 225–272.

Berndt, Rudolf. 1938. Intrasternale Trachealschlingen bei Vögeln. *Morph. Jahrb.,* 82: 27–118.

Biggs, P. M. 1957. The Association of Lymphoid Tissue with the Lymph Vessels in the Domestic Chicken (*Gallus domesticus*). *Acta Anat.,* 29: 36–47.

Blanchard, Émile. 1859. Recherches sur les Caractères Ostéologiques des Oiseaux. *Ann. des Sci. Nat.* (*Zool.*), Paris, 11: 11–145.

Blaszyk, Paul. 1935. Untersuchungen über die Stammesgeschichte der Vogelschuppen und Federn und über die Abhängigkeit ihrer Ausbildung am Vogelfuss von der Funktion. I, II. *Morph. Jahrb.,* 75: 483–567.

Boas, J. E. V. 1933. Kreuzbein, Becken und Plexus Lumbosacralis der Vögel. *Mém. Acad. Roy. Sci. Danemark,* Ser. 9, 5, 74 pp.

Boetticher, Hans von. 1929. Morphologische und phylogenetische Studien über die hornige Fussbekleidung der Vögel. *Jena. Zeitschr. f. Naturwiss.,* 64: 377–448.

——— 1951. Etwas über Zehenreduktion bei Vögeln. *Zool. Anz.,* 146: 113–118.

Buri, R. O. 1900. Zur Anatomie des Flügels von *Micropus melba* und einigen anderen Coracornithes . . . . *Jena. Zeitschr. f. Naturwiss.,* 33: 361–610.

Chapin, James P. 1932. The Birds of the Belgian Congo. Part I. *Bull. Amer. Mus. Nat. Hist.,* 65: x + 756 pp.

Clark, Eliot R., and Eleanor Linton Clark. 1920. On the Origin and Early Development of the Lymphatic System of the Chick. *Contrib. Embryology, No. 45,* Carnegie Inst., Washington, 9: 447–482.

Cole, Leon J. 1945. Effect of Roentgen Rays on Bone Growth in Pigeons. *Jour. Exper. Zool.,* 100: 487–495.

Condon, H. T. 1939. The Cranial Osteology of Certain Tubinares. *Trans. Roy. Soc. South Australia,* 63: 311–330.

Coues, Elliott. 1903. *Key to North American Birds.* 5th ed. Dana Estes & Co., Boston.

Craigie, E. Horne. 1940. The Area of Distribution of the Middle Cerebral Artery in Certain Birds. *Trans. Roy. Soc. Canada,* 34: 25–37.

Curtis, Elizabeth L., and Robert C. Miller. 1938. The Sclerotic Ring in North American Birds. *Auk,* 55: 225–243.

Davis, David E. 1947. Size of Bursa of Fabricius Compared with Ossification of Skull and Maturity of Gonads. *Jour. Wildl. Manag.,* 11: 244–251.

De Beer, G. R. 1937. *The Development of the Vertebrate Skull.* Oxford Univ. Press, Oxford.

DeMay, Ida S. 1940. A Study of the Pterylosis and Pneumaticity of the Screamer. *Condor,* 42: 112–118.

Desselberger, Hermann. 1931. Der Verdauungskanal der Dicaeiden nach Gestalt und Funktion. *Jour. f. Ornith.,* 79: 353–370.

———— 1932. Ueber den Verdauungskanal nektarfressender Vögel. *Jour. f. Ornith.,* 80: 309–318.

Domm, L. V. 1939. Modifications in Sex and Secondary Sexual Characters in Birds. In *Sex and Internal Secretions,* ed. by E. Allen *et al.* 2nd ed. Williams & Wilkins Co., Baltimore, pp. 227–327.

———— 1955. Recent Advances in Knowledge Concerning the Role of Hormones in the Sex Differentiation of Birds. In *Recent Studies in Avian Biology.* Univ. Illinois Press, Urbana, pp. 309–325.

Elder, William H. 1954. The Oil Gland of Birds. *Wils. Bull.,* 66: 6–31.

Eyton, Thomas C. 1867–1875. *Osteologia Avium.* R. Hobson, Wellington, Salop.

Ferris, H. B. 1933. Triple Testes in a Snowy Plover. *Condor,* 35: 124.

Fisher, Harvey I. 1955a. Major Arteries near the Heart in the Whooping Crane. *Condor,* 57: 286–289.

———— 1955b. Avian Anatomy, 1925–1950, and Some Suggested Problems. In *Recent Studies in Avian Biology.* Univ. Illinois Press, Urbana, pp. 57–104.

———— and Donald C. Goodman. 1955. The Myology of the Whooping Crane, *Grus americana. Illinois Biol. Monogr.,* 24, 127 pp.

Fitzpatrick, F. L. 1934. Unilateral and Bilateral Ovaries in Raptorial Birds. *Wils. Bull.,* 46: 19–22.

Forbes, W. A. 1880. Contributions to the Anatomy of Passerine Birds—Part III. *Proc. Zool. Soc. London,* 1880: 387–391.

———— 1881. On the Contributions to the Anatomy and Classification of Birds made by the late Prof. Garrod, F.R.S. *Ibis,* 1881: 1–32.

———— 1882a. Note on the Gall-bladder, and some other points in the Anatomy of the Toucans and Barbets (Capitonidae). *Proc. Zool. Soc. London,* 1882: 94–96.

———— 1882b. On the Convoluted Trachea of two Species of Manucode (*Manucodia atra* and *Phonygama gouldi*); with Remarks on Similar Structures in other Birds. *Proc. Zool. Soc. London,* 1882: 347–353.

———— 1882c. On the Variations from the Normal Structure of the Foot in Birds. *Ibis,* 1882: 386–390.

Frank, G. H. 1954. The Development of the Chondrocranium of the Ostrich. *Annals Univ. Stellenbosch, Ser. A.,* no. 4: 179–248.

Friedmann, Herbert. 1927. Testicular Asymmetry and Sex Ratio in Birds. *Biol. Bull.,* 52: 197–207.

Fürbringer, Max. 1886. Über Deutung und Nomenklatur der Muskulatur des Vogelflügels. *Morph. Jahrb.,* 11: 121–125.

———— 1888. *Untersuchungen zur Morphologie und Systematik der Vögel.* Van Holkema, Amsterdam. 2 vols.

———— 1902. Zur Vergleichenden Anatomie des Brustschulterapparates und Schultermuskeln. *Jena. Zeitschr. f. Naturwiss.,* 36: 289–736.

Fürther, Hubert. 1913. Beiträge zur Kenntnis der Vogellymphknoten. *Jena. Zeitschr. f. Naturwiss.,* 50: 359–410.

Gadow, Hans. 1887. Remarks on the Cloaca and on the Copulatory Organs of the Amniota. *Phil. Trans. Royal Soc. London, Ser. B,* 178: 5–37.

Gadow, Hans. 1889. On the Taxonomic Value of the Intestinal Convolutions in Birds. *Proc. Zool. Soc. London,* 1889: 303–316. (See also: Newton and Gadow, *A Dictionary of Birds,* 1896: 141–148.)

——— 1896. *In A Dictionary of Birds,* A. Newton and H. Gadow. Adam and Charles Black, London. Caeca, pp. 68–70; cloaca, pp. 90–91; muscular system, pp. 602–620; oil gland, pp. 653–654; syrinx, pp. 937–942.

——— and Emil Selenka. 1891. Vögel. In Bronn's *Klassen und Ordnungen des Thier-Reichs.* C. F. Winter'sche Verlagshandlung, Leipzig.

Gardner, Leon L. 1925. The Adaptive Modifications and the Taxonomic Value of the Tongue in Birds. *Proc. U. S. Natl. Mus.,* 67: 1–49.

Garrod, A. H. 1873a. On the Value in Classification of a Peculiarity in the Anterior Margin of the Nasal Bones in Certain Birds. *Proc. Zool. Soc. London,* 1873: 33–38.

——— 1873b. On the Carotid Arteries of Birds. *Proc. Zool. Soc. London,* 1873: 457–472.

——— 1873c. On Some Points in the Anatomy of *Steatornis. Proc. Zool. Soc. London,* 1873: 526–533.

——— 1873–1874. On Certain Muscles of the Thigh of Birds, and on Their Value in Classification. *Proc. Zool. Soc. London,* 1873: 626–644; 1874: 111–123.

——— 1875. On the Disposition of the Deep Plantar Tendons in Different Birds. *Proc. Zool. Soc. London,* 1875: 339–348.

——— 1876a. On the Anatomy of *Chauna derbiana,* and on the Systematic Position of the Screamers (Palamedeidae). *Proc. Zool. Soc. London,* 1876: 189–200.

——— 1876b. On some Anatomical Characters which bear upon the Major Divisions of the Passerine Birds—Part I. *Proc. Zool. Soc. London,* 1876: 506–519.

Gier, H. T. 1952. The Air Sacs of the Loon. *Auk,* 69: 40–49.

Glenny, Fred H. 1955. Modifications of Pattern in the Aortic Arch System of Birds and Their Phylogenetic Significance. *Proc. U. S. Natl. Mus.,* 104: 525–621.

——— and Dean Amadon. 1955. Remarks on the Pigeon, *Otidiphaps nobilis* Gould. *Auk,* 72: 199–203.

Glenny, Fred H., and Herbert Friedmann. 1954. Reduction of the Clavicles in the Mesoenatidae, with some Remarks Concerning the Relationship of the Clavicle to Flight-function in Birds. *Ohio Jour. Sci.,* 54: 111–113.

Greschik, Eugen. 1915. Über den Bau der Milz einiger Vögel mit besonderer Berücksichtigung der *Schweigger-Seidelschen* Kapillarhülsen. *Aquila,* 22: 133–159.

Gunn, T. E. 1912. On the Presence of two Ovaries in certain British Birds, more especially the Falconidae. *Proc. Zool. Soc. London,* 1912: 63–79.

Hartman, Frank A. 1955. Heart Weight in Birds. *Condor,* 57: 221–238.

——— and Robert H. Albertin. 1951. A Preliminary Study of the Avian Adrenal. *Auk,* 68: 202–209.

Hickey, Joseph J., and Hans Elias. 1954. The Structure of the Liver in Birds. *Auk,* 71: 458–462.

Hofer, Helmut. 1945. Untersuchungen über den Bau des Vogelschädels, besonders über den der Spechte und Steisshühner. *Zool. Jahrb.,* 69: 1–158.

——— 1949. Die Gaumenlücken der Vogel. *Acta Zool.,* 30: 209–248.

——— 1950. Zur Morphologie der Kiefermuskulatur der Vögel. *Zool. Jahrb.,* 70: 427–556.

Huber, John Franklin. 1936. Nerve Roots and Nuclear Groups in the Spinal Cord of the Pigeon. *Jour. Comp. Neur.,* 65: 43–91.

Hudson, George Elford. 1937. Studies on the Muscles of the Pelvic Appendage in Birds. *Amer. Midl. Nat.,* 18: 1–108.

Hudson, George Elford. 1948. Studies on the Muscles of the Pelvic Appendage of Birds II: The Heterogeneous Order Falconiformes. *Amer. Midl. Nat.,* 39: 102–127.

——— and Patricia J. Lanzillotti. 1955. Gross Anatomy of the Wing Muscles in the Family Corvidae. *Amer. Midl. Nat.,* 53: 1–44.

Huxley, Thomas H. 1867. On the Classification of Birds; and on the Taxonomic Value of the Modifications of Certain of the Cranial Bones observable in that Class. *Proc. Zool. Soc. London,* 1867: 415–472.

Kattinger, Emil. 1929. Sexual- und Subspecies-Unterschiede im Skelettbau der Vögel. *Jour. f. Ornith.,* 77: 41–149.

Kern, Albert. 1926. Das Vogelherz. *Morph. Jahrb.,* 56: 264–315.

Köditz, Walter. 1925. Über die Syrinx einiger Clamatores und ausländischer Oscines. *Zeitschr. f. wiss. Zool.,* 126: 70–144.

Küchler, Werner. 1936. Anatomische Untersuchungen an *Phytotoma rara* Mol. *Jour. f. Ornith.,* 84: 352–362.

Kummerlöwe, Hans. 1930–1931. Vergleichende Untersuchungen über das Gonadensystem weiblicher Vögel. *Jahrb. f. Morph. u. Mikros. Anat.,* 21: 1–156; 22: 259–413; 24: 455–631; 25: 311–319.

Lang, Charlotte. 1956. Das Cranium der Ratiten mit besonderer Berücksichtigung von *Struthio camelus.* *Zeitschr. f. wiss. Zool.,* 159: 165–224.

Larsell, O. 1948. The Development and Subdivisions of the Cerebellum of Birds. *Jour. Comp. Neur.,* 89: 123–189.

Lebedinsky, N. G. 1913. Beiträge zur Morphologie und Entwicklungsgeschichte des Vogelbeckens. *Jena. Zeitschr. f. Naturwiss.,* 50: 647–774.

Lechner, Wilhelm. 1942. Herzspitze und Herzwirbel. Vergleichende Untersuchungen am Vogel- und Säugerherz. *Anat. Anz.,* 92: 249–283.

Lemmrich, Werner. 1931. Der Skleralring der Vögel. *Jena. Zeitschr. f. Naturwiss.,* 65: 513–586.

Lindsay, Beatrice. 1885. On the Avian Sternum. *Proc. Zool. Soc. London,* 1885: 684–716.

Lowe, Percy R. 1924. On the Anatomy and Systematic Position of the Madagascan Bird *Mesites* (*Mesoenas*), with a Preliminary Note on the Osteology of *Monias.* *Proc. Zool. Soc. London,* 1924: 1131–1152.

——— 1925. On the Classification of the Tubinares or Petrels. *Proc. Zool. Soc. London,* 1925: 1433–1443.

——— 1926. More Notes on the Quadrate as a factor in Avian Classification. *Ibis,* 1926: 152–188.

Lucas, A. M., and E. M. Denington. 1956. Morphology of the Chicken Liver. *Poultry Sci.,* 35: 793–806.

Lucas, Frederic A. 1882. Notes on the Os Prominens. *Bull. Nuttall Ornith. Club,* 7: 86–89.

McDowell, Sam. 1948. The Bony Palate of Birds. Part I. The Palaeognathae. *Auk,* 65: 520–549.

Mayr, Ernst. 1931. Die Syrinx einiger Singvögel aus Neu-Guinea. *Jour. f. Ornith.,* 79: 333–337.

Merrem, Blasius. 1812–1813. Tentamen Systematis naturalis Avium. *Abhandl. Kgl. Akad. Wiss., Berlin,* 1812–1813: 237–259.

Miller, Adam M. 1913. Histogenesis and Morphogenesis of the Thoracic Duct in the Chick . . . . *Amer. Jour. Anat.,* 15: 131–197.

Miller, W. DeW. 1924. Further Notes on Ptilosis. *Bull. Amer. Mus. Nat. Hist.,* 50: 305–331.

Müller, Johannes. 1878. *On Certain Variations in the Vocal Organs of the Passeres That Have Hitherto Escaped Notice.* Clarendon Press, Oxford, 74 pp.

Nagelschmidt, Lotte. 1939. Untersuchungen über die *Langerhans*schen Inseln der Bauchspeicheldrüse bei den Vögeln. *Jahrb. f. Morph. u. Mikros. Anat.*, 45: 200-232.

Nel, Jeffrey Theophilus. 1940. Histologische und anatomische Untersuchungen an der Hinterextremität einiger Vögel. *Verhandl. Naturhist.-Med. Vereins,* Heidelberg, 18: 223-244.

Odum, Eugene P. 1945. The Heart Rate of Small Birds. *Science,* 101: 153-154.

Parker, W. K. 1875. On the Morphology of the Skull in the Woodpeckers (*Picidae*) and Wrynecks (*Yungidae*). *Trans. Linn. Soc. London, Zool.*, 1, pt. 1: 1-22.

Peterson, Roger Tory, Guy Mountfort, and P. A. D. Hollom. 1954. *A Field Guide to the Birds of Britain and Europe.* Houghton Mifflin Co., Boston, xxxiv + 318 pp.

Petrén, T. 1926. Die Coronararterien des Vogelherzens. *Morph. Jahrb.*, 56: 239-249.

Piiper, Johannes. 1928. On the Evolution of the Vertebral Column in Birds, illustrated by its Development in *Larus* and *Struthio.* *Phil. Trans. Roy. Soc. London, Ser. B,* 216: 285-351.

Portmann, Adolphe. 1946. Études sur la Cérébralisation chez les Oiseaux. *Alauda,* 14: 2-20.

——— 1955. Die postembryonale Entwicklung der Vögel als Evolutionsproblem. *Acta XI Congr. Internatl. Ornith., 1954:* 138-151.

Price, John Basye. 1938. The Embryology of the Cormorant (Phalacrocorax penicillatus) During the Period of Somite Formation. . . . *Amer. Jour. Anat.*, 63: 409-455.

Pycraft, W. P. 1900. On the Morphology and Phylogeny of the *Palaeognathae* (*Ratitae* and *Crypturi*) and *Neognathae* (*Carinatae*). *Trans. Zool. Soc. London,* 15: 149-290.

——— 1901. Some Points in the Morphology of the Palate of the *Neognathae.* *Jour. Linn. Soc. London, Zool.*, 28: 343-357.

——— 1903. A Contribution Towards Our Knowledge of the Morphology of the Owls. Part II. Osteology. *Trans. Linn. Soc. London,* 9: 1-46.

Rand, A. L. 1933. Testicular Asymmetry in the Madagascar Coucal. *Auk,* 50: 219-220.

——— 1935. On Paired Ovaries. *Auk,* 52: 329-330.

Reichenow, Anton. 1871. Die Fussbildung der Vögel. *Jour. f. Ornith.*, 19: 403-458.

——— 1914. *Die Vögel: Handbuch der Systematischen Ornithologie.* Vol. 2. Ferdinand Enke, Stuttgart.

Ridgway, Robert. 1901-1911. The Birds of North and Middle America. *U. S. Natl. Mus. Bull.*, 50, pts. 1-5.

Roberts, W. W. 1939. Bird with the Longest Tongue in the World. *Ostrich,* 10: 133-136.

Romanoff, A. L., and A. J. Romanoff. 1949. *The Avian Egg.* John Wiley & Sons, New York.

Rüppell, Werner. 1933. Physiologie und Akustik der Vogelstimme. *Jour. f. Ornith.*, 81: 433-542.

Salt, W. Ray. 1954. The Structure of the Cloacal Protuberance of the Vesper Sparrow (*Pooecetes gramineus*) and Certain Other Passerine Birds. *Auk,* 71: 64-73.

Scharnke, Hans. 1931. Beiträge zur Morphologie und Entwicklungsgeschichte der Zunge der Trochilidae, Meliphagidae und Picidae. *Jour. f. Ornith.*, 79: 425-491.

——— 1932. Ueber den Bau der Zunge der Nectariniidae, Promeropidae and Drepanididae nebst Bemerkungen zur Systematik der blütenbesuchenden Passeres. *Jour. f. Ornith.*, 80: 114-123.

Schinz, Hans R., and Rainer Zangerl. 1937. Beiträge zur Osteogenese des Knochensystems beim Haushuhn, bei der Haustaube und beim Haubensteissfuss. *Denkschr. Schweizer. Naturforsch. Ges.*, 72: 117–165.

Sims, R. W. 1955. The Morphology of the Head of the Hawfinch (*Coccothraustes coccothraustes*). *Bull. Brit. Mus.* (*Nat. Hist.*), *Zool.*, 2: 371–393.

Slonaker, James Rollin. 1918. A Physiological Study of the Anatomy of the Eye and its Accessory Parts of the English Sparrow (Passer domesticus). *Jour. Morph.*, 31: 351–459.

Stallcup, William B. 1954. Myology and Serology of the Avian Family Fringillidae, A Taxonomic Study. *Univ. Kans. Publ. Mus. Nat. Hist.*, 8: 157–211.

Starck, Dietrich. 1955. Die endokraniale Morphologie der Ratiten, besonders der Apterygidae und Dinornithidae. *Morph. Jahrb.*, 96: 14–72.

——— and Albert Barnikol. 1954. Beiträge zur Morphologie der Trigeminusmuskulatur der Vögel. *Morph. Jahrb.*, 94: 1–64.

Stejneger, Leonhard. 1888. Passeres. In *The Riverside Natural History,* Vol. 4, ed. by J. S. Kingsley. Houghton, Mifflin and Co., Cambridge, Mass.

Stingelin, Werner. 1956. Studien am Vorderhirn von Waldkauz (*Strix aluco* L.) und Turmfalk (*Falco tinnunculus* L.). *Rev. Suisse de Zool.*, 63: 551–660.

Stresemann, Erwin. 1927–1934. Aves. Vol. 7, part 2, of *Handbuch der Zoologie,* W. Kükenthal and T. Krumbach. Walter de Gruyter, Berlin.

Sundevall, Carl Jacob. 1872–1873. *Methodi naturalis avium disponendarum tentamen.* Samson & Wallin, Stockholm. 4to.

Sushkin, Peter P. 1927. On the Anatomy and Classification of the Weaver-birds. *Bull. Amer. Mus. Nat. Hist.*, 57: 1–32.

Test, Frederick, H. 1945. Testicular Asymmetry in the Woodpecker *Colaptes. Pap. Mich. Acad. Sci., Arts, Letters,* 30, 1944: 347–353.

Tiemeier, Otto W. 1950. The Os Opticus of Birds. *Jour. Morph.*, 86: 25–46.

Tordoff, Harrison B. 1954. A Systematic Study of the Avian Family Fringillidae Based on the Structure of the Skull. *Misc. Publ. Univ. Mich. Mus. Zool.*, no. 81.

Watzka, Max. 1939. "Weisse" und "rote" Muskeln. *Jahrb. f. Morph. u. Mikros. Anat.*, 45: 668–678.

Wedin, Bertil. 1953. The Development of the Eye Muscles in Ardea cinerea L. *Acta Anat.*, 18: 30–48.

Wetmore, Alexander. 1914. The Development of the Stomach in the Euphonias. *Auk,* 31: 458–461.

——— 1920. Intestinal Caeca in the Anhinga. *Auk,* 37: 286–287.

Williams, John Lecoq. 1942. The Development of Cervical Vertebrae in the Chick under Normal and Experimental Conditions. *Amer. Jour. Anat.*, 71: 153–179.

Wingstrand, Karl Georg. 1951. *The Structure and Development of the Avian Pituitary.* C. W. K. Gleerup, Lund, 316 pp.

Witschi, Emil. 1956. *Development of Vertebrates.* W. B. Saunders, Philadelphia.

Wolfson, Albert. 1954. Notes on the Cloacal Protuberance, Seminal Vesicles, and a Possible Copulatory Organ in Male Passerine Birds. *Bull. Chicago Acad. Sci.*, 10: 1–23.

Wood, Merrill. 1932. Paired Ovaries in Hawks. *Auk,* 49: 463.

Wortham, Ruby A. 1948. The Development of the Muscles and Tendons in the Lower Leg and Foot of Chick Embryos. *Jour. Morph.*, 83: 105–148.

Yntema, Chester L., and Warner S. Hammond. 1955. Experiments on the Origin and Development of the Sacral Autonomic Nerves in the Chick Embryo. *Jour. Exper. Zool.*, 129: 375–413.

3. Plumage and molt

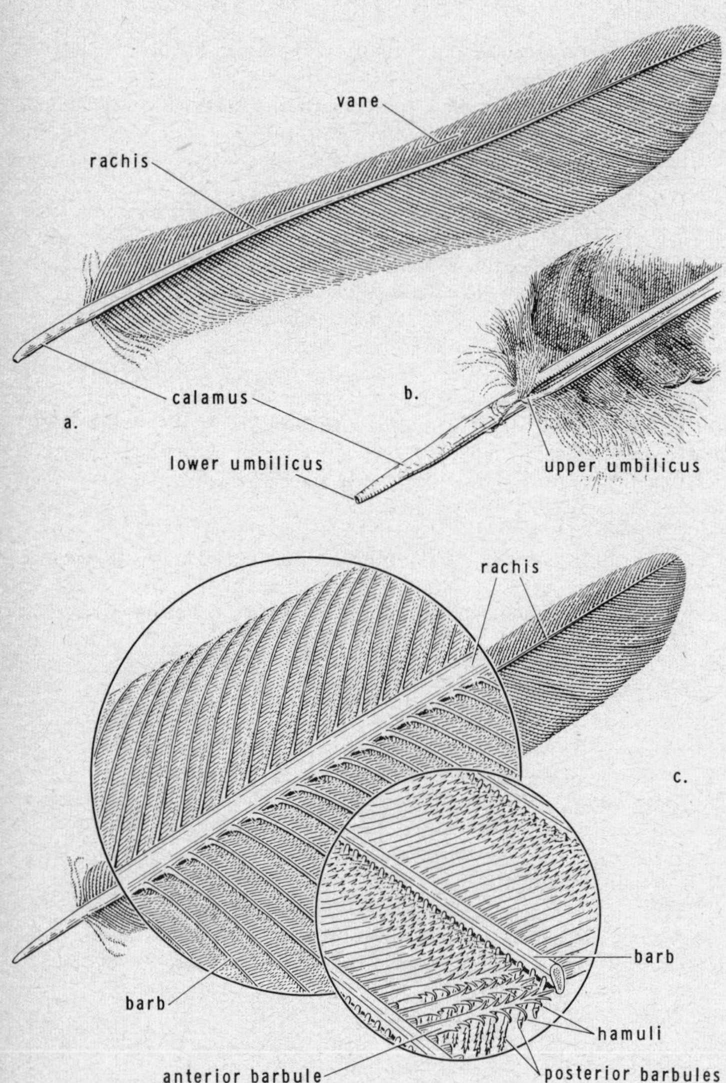

Fig. 1. A typical flight feather and the nomenclature of its parts: (a) General view. (b) Detail of the base of the feather. (c) Detail of the vane.

FEATHERS, unlike the skin structures of cold-blooded vertebrates or mammals, have become highly diversified and specialized in form, color, and arrangement, so that the space of this single chapter will suffice for only a very brief outline of the subject.

Feathers are peculiar to birds, and all adult birds are largely covered by them; this characteristic alone distinguishes birds from all other animals.

It is probable that in their evolutionary history birds began with a covering of scales and a few feather filaments (cryptoptiles) scattered between them. As birds became homoiothermous ("warm-blooded") the filaments became of survival value as an insulating layer and in the course of evolution became more abundant and longer. The sequence of these ancestral stages, as now generally accepted, may be outlined thus:

1. Cryptoptiles: Theoretical simple filaments which formed the covering of the primitive birds of earlier geological ages.
2. Neossoptiles (nestling feathers).
   a. Protoptiles.
   b. Mesoptiles.
3. Teleoptiles (adult feathers).

The occurrence of two successive coats of nestling down was first noted by Clarke (1906), in penguins, and later recorded in most owls and in certain other groups. Most birds of the higher groups have but one coat of nestling down, and it is generally accepted that in them the first, or protoptile, coat has persisted and that the second, or mesoptile,[1] coat has been suppressed (see Ingram, 1920). According to Ewart (1921), some ducks and geese exhibit an intermediate stage (i.e., mesoptiles occur in the development of wing and tail). Ewart also found indications that in the King Penguin the protoptile coat is "disappearing." It was Pycraft's theory

[1] These terms were coined by Pycraft (1907: 11); his spelling: "protoptyle" and "mesoptyle."

(1907) that the protoptile, not the mesoptile, coat is suppressed in most birds.

The Feather

The typical feather (see Fig. 1) has a long, tapering central axis, supporting on each side a row of small branches, or barbs (*rami*), set at an angle inclined toward the tip of the feather. These branches form the web or vane (*vexillum*) of the feather. The central shaft is divisible into two main parts: (1) a hollow, cylindrical basal section called the *calamus;* (2) a solid, angular shaft called the *rachis* (or *rhachis*).

At the lower end of the calamus is a small hole, the *lower umbilicus;* at the upper end another hole, the *upper umbilicus.*

Branching from each barb, but in the same plane, are two rows (one on each side) of still smaller branches, or *barbules,* set at an angle inclining toward the tip of the barb. The barbules on the two sides of the barb are very unlike; the *anterior barbules* (which point toward the tip of the feather) are flat basally and have a series of small projections (*barbicels*); the barbicels along the middle portion of the underside are hooked (then called *hamuli*). The *posterior barbules* (on the opposite side of the barb) are also flat basally but have no hamuli; they form ridges on which the opposite anterior barbules hook, thus making the vane with its extraordinary lightness and strength (Wray, 1887a; Pycraft, 1911; Sick, 1937).

Feathers are horny (keratin) structures, produced by papillae in the skin. The early development of the feather is quite similar to that of a scale. Strongly vascular dermal tissue, covered with a thin layer of epidermis, first forms a cone-shaped structure. Then (unlike a developing scale) the epidermal layer sinks inward and forms a follicle out of which the papilla continues to grow and develop into a feather. At least once a year the feather is molted and a new feather grows from the same papilla.

Contour feathers are those which form the contour or outline of the body. Typically they have a large, firm vane, but the base of the feather is commonly plumulaceous (downy). A few of the contour feathers on the wing (remiges) and tail (rectrices) have become highly specialized for flight (or display); these include the largest and most highly developed of all feathers. Contour feathers grow only in the feather tracts (pterylae).

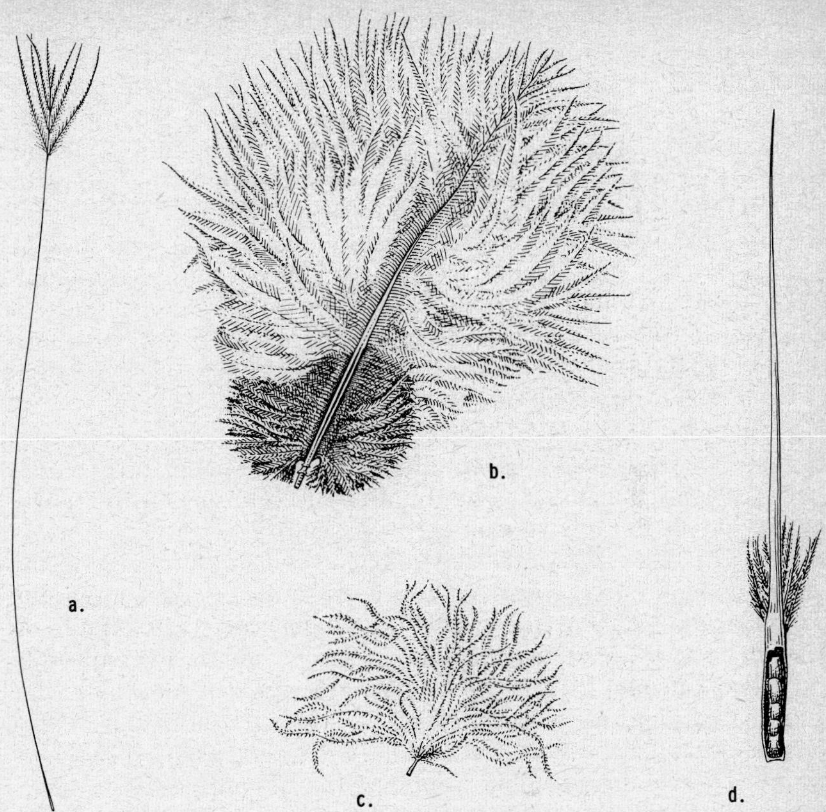

Fig. 2. (a) Filoplume, *Lophura edwardsi* (×2). (b) Semiplume, Curassow (×3/4). (c) Down, *Grus* sp. (×1). (d) Bristle: an eyelash; *Circus c. hudsonius* (after Chandler, 1914). (×16.)

Semiplumes (Fig. 2b) are a type of loose-webbed (plumulaceous) contour feather, with a definite rachis but no hamuli and therefore no firm vane. These feathers occur especially at the margins of the feathered areas (tracts) and are usually overlain by the general mass of typical contour feathers. There is a complete intergradation between semiplumes and firm-webbed (pennaceous) feathers, but the fully developed "semiplume" type of feather is such a well-marked entity that it deserves a special name. Semiplumes apparently serve to insulate, to provide flexibility at constricted points about the base of moving parts, and—in the case of waterbirds—to increase buoyancy.

Filoplumes (Fig. 2a) are very specialized, hairlike feathers, always associated with contour feathers. There seem to be two distinct kinds of feathers included at present under this name. One kind nearly always has a minute vane (or vestige of one) at the tip; filoplumes of this kind occur in groups of two to eight about the base of a contour feather and appear to grow from the same papilla. They are usually completely covered by the surrounding feathers. The second type of filoplume lacks any vane whatever and often extends like a long hair beyond the contour feathers. This type occurs most frequently on the nape and upper back and may be readily seen on close examination, for example, of any fresh-plumaged American Robin (*Turdus migratorius*). Notable instances of this second type of filoplume occur among the bulbuls (Pycnonotidae), the extreme condition being found in the Hairy-backed Bulbul (*Microscelis criniger*) of Malaysia (Fig. 3).

Filoplumes of at least the first type occur among the contour feathers of most birds (except the ostrich and other ratites, and perhaps some pelicans). The function of filoplumes is unknown, but it may be decorative and, perhaps, sensory.

Nitzsch (1867: 15) tentatively applied the term filoplume to the white filamentous feathers on the head and neck of cormorants (some later authors even included the ornamental white plumes on the flanks of the same bird in this category), but these feathers do not seem to come within the modern definition of filoplumes, for on close examination a rather extensive, though vestigial, web may be seen along the whole shaft. There are certain other feathers which superficially resemble filoplumes but actually differ in structure. The "bristles" of the Bristle-thighed Curlew (*Numenius tahitiensis*) and the long, frontal plumes of the Spangled Drongo (*Dicrurus h. hottentottus*), for example, are true contour feathers (with a webbed base) whose outer portions have become bare and hairlike.

Bristles, which occur about the mouth, nostrils, and eyes (Fig. 2d)

Fig. 3. Filoplumes on the nape and back of the Hairy-backed Bulbul (*Microscelis criniger*). (After Delacour, 1943.)

of many birds, are modified (vaneless and nearly vaneless) feathers. Chandler (1914: 360) has shown that in the Marsh Hawk (*Circus cyaneus*) these range, with all intergrades, from loosely woven feathers with some vane basally and a prolonged naked shaft to a simple, bare shaft. Therefore, we conclude that they are not filoplumes, as some authors have thought, but specialized contour feathers.

The bristles about the nostrils seem to sift the air drawn in there; the long bristles (rictal bristles) about the mouth of many birds probably enlarge the effective gape of the mouth and thus help in the capture of flying insects. Chandler commented that the various bristles about the face of the Marsh Hawk are less easily ruffled, worn, and soiled than ordinary contour feathers; they may also have some sensory functions.

Bristles that form definite mammalian-like eyelashes occur in some birds of widely scattered groups: hornbills (Bucerotidae), many cuckoos (Cuculidae), hoatzins (Opisthocomidae), and the ostrich (Struthionidae).

Down feathers (plumules) (Fig. 2c) of adult birds are usually concealed beneath the contour feathers. They are small and soft (without a vane), with rachis very short or even vestigial. Down feathers are not confined to the pterylae (except in the tinamous); they are usually rather widely distributed on the bird, but they may be confined to the apteria or even be absent entirely. Their principal function seems to be insulation. Down feathers are especially well developed in waterbirds. Research on comparative structure in down feathers has been scattered, fragmentary, and much obscured by contradictory statements, noncomparable techniques, and confused terminology. No generalizations can safely be made in advance of a critical and sweeping review. Judging from the published data, it appears that in the adult down feather the shaft is always present, at least residually; that in neossoptile down a shaft is sometimes detectable; that in all groups of birds except penguins the neossoptile down differs in structure, at least microscopically, from adult down (the barbs may be long or short; smoothly threadlike, ribbonlike, nodular, pronged, or ciliated; flat-tipped; etc.); that type of down structure may have some value as a taxonomic character, but that groups of birds may have similar nestling down though widely different adult down.

Powder downs are much-modified body feathers which retain little of the definite structure of the normal feather. Apparently most bird feathers produce at least minute particles of powder.

One can find among birds every intermediate condition between the typical contour feather and the true powder down. A typical powder down from an American Bittern (*Botaurus lentiginosus*), for example, may have a calamus several centimeters long. In other species the calamus of the powder down may barely protrude from the skin. From the calamus there extend a number of long, silky filaments, among which the powder occurs. The most strongly developed powder downs, such as are found in herons, grow continuously from the base and disintegrate at the tip. Part of the keratin of the growing powder-down feather, instead of forming barbs, is given off as a very finely divided powder made up of minute scalelike particles. This fine, waxy, powdery substance produces a characteristic bloom on the plumage of the bird.

Powder downs are usually massed in solid, paired tracts on the ventral and sometimes the dorsal parts of the body, but they may be scattered throughout the plumage, as in parrots.

Pycraft (1908), Wetmore (1920), and Hindwood (1933) have shown that powder-down tracts are used at least by herons in dressing plumage; Schüz (1927) concludes a monographic study of powder downs with the opinion that they serve to protect the feathers from moisture and, in some species, affect the apparent color of the bird.

According to Schüz (1927), powder downs are lacking, or nearly so, in ratite birds, but are present in some degree in most other birds. The extreme development of powder downs occurs only in the tinamous, herons, mesites (Mesoenatidae), and cuckoo-rollers (Leptosomatidae).

The complete primitive feather consists of two shafts, an outer one (the feather we ordinarily see) and an inner one, the *aftershaft* (also called hyporachis or hypoptilum). In the Emu (Fig. 4) the two are nearly equal, but in most other birds the aftershaft is much reduced in size or may even be entirely lost. The presence of an aftershaft is a primitive condition, but its reduction or loss has not occurred uniformly during the evolution of higher types of birds. W. DeW. Miller (1924a; 1924b: 325–327) thus summarized the different degrees of loss of the aftershaft which he found in a survey of a very large number of bird genera:

1. Only two families, the cassowaries (Casuariidae) and emus (Dromiceiidae), have aftershafts nearly equal to the main feather in size.

2. Many tinamous (Tinamidae) and most of the higher galli-

naceous birds (Tetraonidae, Phasianidae) have a large aftershaft, often nearly as long as the main feather but considerably narrower and more plumaceous. The aftershaft in these groups is unquestionably still of real importance in insulation.

3. Many herons, hawks, parrots, and others have aftershafts that are nearly or quite as long as those in Group 2, but the aftershaft is still less like the main feather and usually has a very feeble rachis. In this group also the aftershaft surely has real insulating effect.

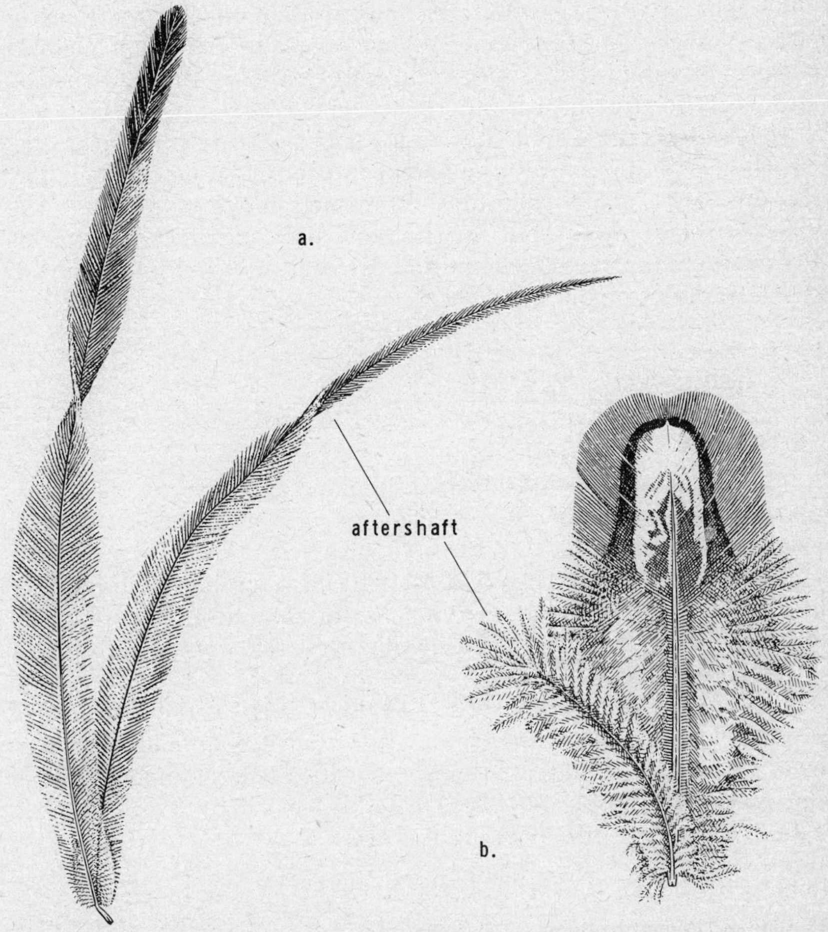

Fig. 4. Feathers with well-developed aftershaft. (a) Emu; the aftershaft is nearly equal to the main feather (×3/4). (b) Pheasant (*Phasianus*) back feather (×1).

4. The toucans, woodpeckers, and most songbirds (Oscines) have still less aftershaft, and the aftershaft itself has very little rachis.

5. The curassows (Cracidae) and hoatzins (Opisthocomidae) have the aftershaft represented only by a tuft of barbs that lack a central shaft.

6. The ducks, American vultures, and most owls have only a vestigial fringe of tiny filaments to represent the aftershaft.

7. The aftershaft has been entirely lost by pigeons, hornbills, and most of the primitive passerine birds (Dendrocolaptidae, Formicariidae, etc.).

In general, the aftershaft is never found on the rectrices or larger remiges but commonly occurs on all of the other contour feathers of any bird that has the structure at all. In a few species, however, the aftershaft is found only on certain body feathers.

It has been suggested that there may be some correlation between low temperatures and the occurrence of a large aftershaft (presumably of value as insulation) in such northern groups as the grouse (Tetraonidae), but for the most part the aftershaft seems to be a nonadaptive character and for that very reason of considerable value in taxonomy.

Remiges

Primaries

The flight feathers attached to the hand (manus) are called primaries. Their number is very constant within most bird groups. Flying birds have 12, 11, 10, or 9 primaries. Among primitive flightless birds some (rhea and ostrich) have an increased number of remiges on the hand (serving as purely decorative plumes), whereas others (together with the flightless rail *Porzanula*) have a reduced number.

The outermost primary (12th, 11th, or 10th) is reduced in size in many species, sometimes so much so that it is difficult to recognize. This small outer primary is called the "remicle" (little remex) (Wray, 1887b: 344; W. DeW. Miller, 1924b: 316).

Some recorded primary numbers are:

FLYING BIRDS

12, grebes (Podicipedidae)
storks (most) (Ciconiidae)
flamingos (Phoenicopteridae)

11, many families, including
 herons (Ardeidae)
 ducks (Anatidae)
 gulls (Laridae)

10, the majority of birds

9, honeyguides (Indicatoridae)
 some Old World passerines
 some New World passerines, viz:
 swallows (Hirundinidae)
 larks, in part (Alaudidae)
 pipits (Motacillidae)
 vireos, in part (Vireonidae)
 Hawaiian honeycreepers (Drepaniidae)
 American wood-warblers (Parulidae)
 troupials (Icteridae)
 swallow-tanager (Tersinidae)
 tanagers (Thraupidae)
 plush-capped finch (Catamblyrhynchidae)
 finches (Fringillidae)

FLIGHTLESS BIRDS

3, Cassowary (*Casuarius*)
4, Kiwi (*Apteryx*)
7, Emu (*Dromiceius*)
8, the flightless rail *Porzanula*
12, Rhea (*Rhea*)
16, Ostrich (*Struthio*)

Primaries are referred to individually by number, and the count should always be made from the inner (proximal) primary to the outer (distal) one. The reason is that when primaries are lost in the course of evolution they are always lost from the outer end of the series. Thus, homologous primaries in various families and genera will have the same number only if the count is made from the inner end of the series. Unfortunately, some ornithologists, especially in the Old World, ignore this fundamental reason for numbering the primaries outward and call the outermost (and most easily found) primary "number 1." The student must watch for this pitfall when reading papers that refer to primaries by number.

The several primaries are typically of different relative lengths, and these relationships are extraordinarily consistent in any given kind of bird, as discussed elsewhere (Chapter 2, p. 63).

The proximal primaries are attached to the fused metacarpal bones and are referred to as "metacarpal primaries"; the remainder, attached to the fingers or digits, are called "digital primaries." The number of metacarpal primaries is apparently a rather fundamental taxonomic character (rheas, grebes, storks, and flamingos have 7; most other birds have 6).

Secondaries ("Cubitals")

The flight feathers attached to the forearm (ulna) are called secondaries. They have a much greater range in number (6 to 32) than the primaries; the number seems to be related to the length of the forearm. The smallest number (6 to 7) is found in hummingbirds, which combine very small body size and short forearm with great development of the manus of the wing. Most passerine birds have 9 secondaries (except the Oriolidae, Corvidae, Paradisaeidae, Vangidae, and Laniidae, which have 10 or 11—Reichling, 1915: 250). Other recorded numbers are:

10, Bobwhite (*Colinus*)
    Blue Coua (*Coua*)
11, woodpeckers
    Hoatzin (*Opisthocomus*)
12, Cuban Trogon (*Priotelus*)
    the kingfisher *Alcedo*
13, bee-eaters (*Merops*)
    rollers (*Coracias*)
14, Great Horned Owl (*Bubo*)
    Passenger Pigeon (*Ectopistes*)
15, Cooper's Hawk (*Accipiter cooperii*)
16, Wild Turkey (*Meleagris*)
    Prairie Falcon (*Falco mexicanus*)
17, Red-tailed Hawk (*Buteo jamaicensis*)
18, Turkey Vulture (*Cathartes*)
19, Black Vulture (*Coragyps*)
    Mallard (*Anas platyrhynchos*)
20, Osprey (*Pandion*)
21, King Vulture (*Sarcoramphus*)
22, California Condor (*Gymnogyps*)
25, Andean Condor (*Vultur*)
32, Wandering Albatross (*Diomedea*)

Secondaries are numbered from the outermost (next to the primaries) inward to the elbow. As explained under "Diastataxy and Eutaxy," many species have a gap in the row of secondaries just proximal to the fourth, but this gap should be ignored in numbering the secondaries, for we now believe that "diastataxic" and "eutaxic" species differ only in the presence or absence of a gap, not of a feather.

Carpal Remex

On the dorsal surface of the wing, in the gap between the primaries and secondaries, many birds have an additional remex, the "carpal remex," with a major upper covert ("carpal covert"). The carpal remex seems to be disappearing in the course of evolution. It appears in some gallinaceous birds and in some gulls as a strong pennaceous feather half as long as the adjacent secondaries—to which series it seems to belong. Some groups, such as the woodpeckers (Burt, 1929: 439), retain it only as a small feather without a covert. Frequently we find the covert without the remex (in the shrike *Lanius,* and in passerine birds generally—A. H. Miller, 1928: 398), or a small covert with an even smaller carpal remex (Fig. 5). Boulton (1927: 392) and others have identified a feather on the ventral surface of the wing as the carpal remex under covert, but the homology seems uncertain at best.

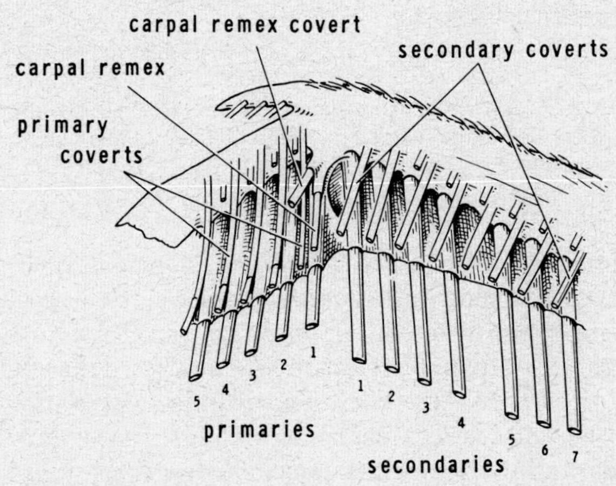

Fig. 5. The carpal remex and the diastataxic condition of the secondaries in the Painted Snipe (*Rostratula*). (Adapted from Lowe, 1931; drawn by W. A. Lunk.)

Diastataxy and Eutaxy[2]

There is a remarkable peculiarity in the arrangement of the secondary remiges. In a great many species the fifth secondary (counting inward from the end of the primary series) seems to be missing, but its usual position is clearly marked by a gap and a major covert above it (Fig. 6). Steiner, who made an intensive study (1918) of "diastataxy" (literally, "arranged with a gap"), decided that the secondaries are derived from two embryonic series: the four outer secondaries belong to the same embryonic series as the greater under coverts, which extend inward along the wing; the remaining (inner) secondaries belong to the embryonic row of

[2] The old terms "aquincubital" (for diastataxic) and "quincubital" (for eutaxic) are to be avoided, since it is now agreed that it is a *gap* which is present or absent, not a feather.

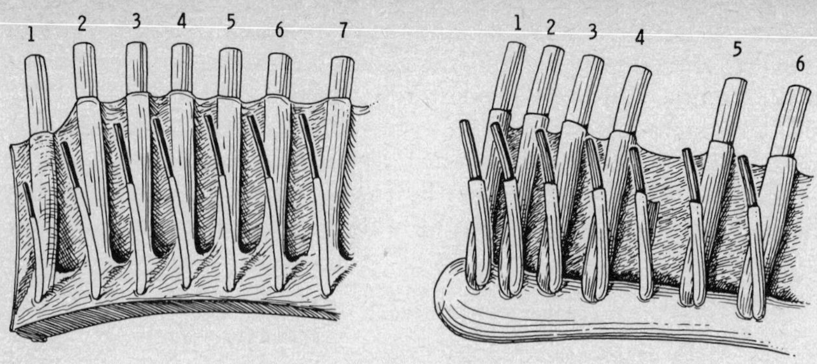

Fig. 6. Eutaxic and diastataxic arrangements of the major coverts and secondaries (dorsal view). Left: Pheasant (eutaxic). Right: Golden Eagle (diastataxic). (After Wray, 1887b.)

feathers that includes the greater *upper* coverts of the outer part of the forearm. During embryonic development these two rows of feathers shift around the ulna, moving dorsally and coming to form a single continuous series of secondaries. At the point of junction of the two series (between secondaries 4 and 5) an extra greater upper covert is retained (but without a secondary to match it). It appears that the diastataxic condition is the more primitive one; in some species, or groups of species, evolution has proceeded a step further and the gap has been closed. The arrangement without a gap is termed "eutaxic." Many of the more primitive groups of birds are diastataxic; all passerine birds and some other families, such as bee-eaters, motmots, and trogons, are eutaxic. In a number of other orders and families both conditions are found. For example, in the hummingbirds one subfamily (Phaethornithinae) is eutaxic and the others diastataxic; the American Woodcock (*Philohela*) is eutaxic but, as far as known, all other members of the Charadriiformes (shorebirds, gulls, etc.) are diastataxic (W. DeW. Miller, 1924b). No bird has ever been recorded which showed an intermediate condition.

Alula

The group of feathers borne by the "thumb" or "pollex" is called the alula (see Glossary for other terms). There may be only 2 quills (in hummingbirds), but as many as 5 or 6 are recorded in certain cuckoos, the peafowl (*Pavo*), trumpeter (*Psophia*), and a touraco (*Tauraco*). In most passerines the number is 3 or 4, but 6 are recorded in the Lyrebird (*Menura*) and 5 in two other large Australian passerines (*Gymnorhina* and *Struthidea*).

The relative lengths of alula quills are significant in taxonomy: in all passerines and in most other birds the distal one is the longest, but in the cuckoo *Tapera,* for example, the next-to-distal one is the longest. *Tapera* is called "four-winged" because of the very large and conspicuously displayed alula, and a strongly developed alula is, in fact, characteristic of a number of cuckoos.

Alula quills should be numbered from the innermost to the outermost, since in the known cases of reduction in number within a taxonomic group, it is the outermost quills that are lost (see, e.g., Compton, 1938: 202–204); also, this order agrees with the order of molt (Mayaud, 1950: 59). Unfortunately, the practice has not been standardized, and such an eminent student of ptilosis as W. DeW. Miller (1924b: 318) numbered alula quills in the opposite order.

Tertiaries (or "Tertials")

Long ago, Wray (1887b: 344), after considering the matter with Flower and Sclater, proposed that the name "tertial" or "tertiary" be abandoned. Unfortunately, Stone (1896) and Dwight (1900) revived this term and applied it to the proximal three secondaries of passerine birds. (Since Stone and Dwight did not recognize any vestigial innermost secondary, they listed 6 secondaries and 3 "tertials" for all the passerine birds whose molt they described.) Because these inner secondaries are often sharply differentiated in ducks, Kortright (1942: 10, 11, 16) yielded to the temptation and labeled them "tertials" in his figures of the wing, but admitted in the accompanying text that they merely "pass under the name of tertials"! It is true that a group of inner secondaries are often differently colored and shaped and behave differently in molt; but if we attempt to count them separately from the other secondaries, we are completely lost when making comparisons with species in which these feathers do not differ morphologically. Modern students of pterylosis have usually followed the practice advocated here and have termed "secondaries" all feathers attached to the ulna. (Fig. 7.)

Some birds, especially large, long-winged forms, have well-developed flight feathers attached to the humerus; these may be called tertiaries, but they seem to be continuous with upper wing

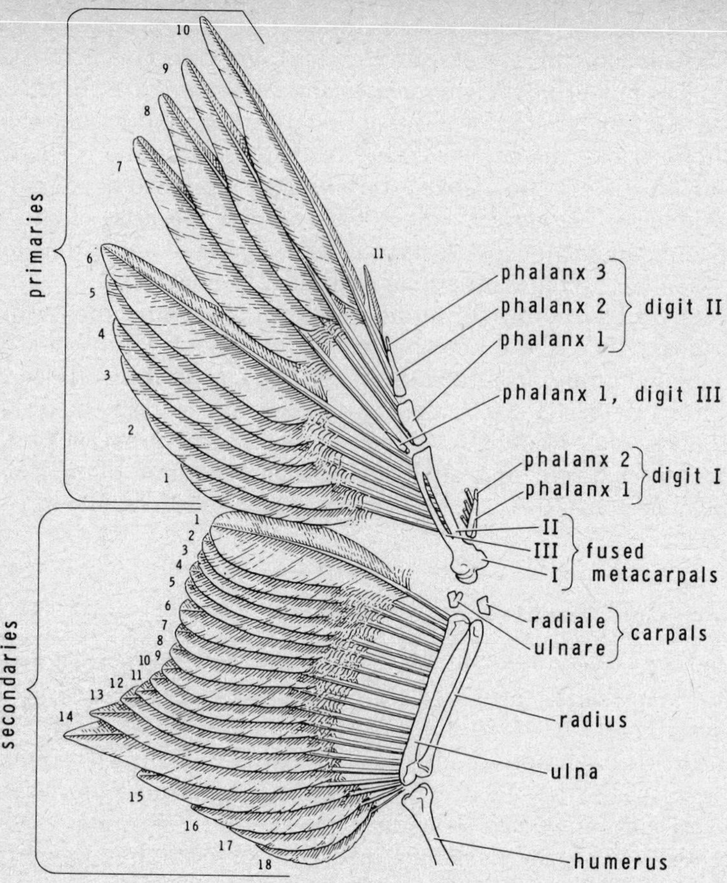

Fig. 7. The wing bones and flight feathers as seen from below. (After Wray, 1887b; drawn by W. A. Lunk.) (Montagna, 1945, maintains that the fingers represented in the birds' wing are nos. II, III, and IV, but this does not seem to be demonstrated beyond doubt and therefore we retain the "I, II, III" numbering.)

coverts rather than with secondaries. Fisher (1942: 32) recorded 13 tertiaries in the Andean Condor (*Vultur*).

Reduction in Remiges

The general trend in the evolution of birds seems to have been toward a reduction in the number of remiges (both primaries and secondaries). Among flying birds the greatest number of remiges is found among certain rather primitive long-winged birds, such as the Wandering Albatross, *Diomedea exulans* (10 primaries + 32 secondaries) and the Andean Condor, *Vultur gryphus* (11 + 25). The minimum number of primaries in a flying bird is 9, and that is found in certain families such as the Fringillidae and Icteridae, which on the basis of other evidence are commonly considered the highest point in avian evolution. (The only birds which have fewer than 9 primaries are certain flightless rails and ratite birds with obviously very degenerate wings.)

Wing Coverts ("Tectrices")

Typically, each wing quill (remex) is covered at its base on the upper side of the wing by a greater ("major") covert. Passing from the greater coverts toward the leading edge of the spread wing, we find successive rows of smaller and smaller feathers: one row of middle ("median") coverts, several rows of lesser ("minor") coverts, and an indefinite number of marginal coverts. The rows of coverts above the primaries are all referred to as "primary coverts"; those above the secondaries are called "secondary coverts."

The coverts on the under side of the wing are arranged similarly, but the feathers are less fully developed and some rows, especially among the lesser coverts, are incomplete. In passerine birds and woodpeckers, greater secondary under coverts are lacking or are rudimentary.

All of the remiges overlap laterally in a uniform way: the inner vane of each feather is overlapped (as considered from above) by the next proximal feather. All greater coverts, above and below, overlap the same way as the remiges and therefore, following Bates (1918: 532–533), we say that these coverts have a "conforming" overlap (i.e., are like the remiges); the opposite type is called "contrary" overlap.[3] Many of the rows, or parts of rows, of smaller coverts have, in various combinations in different species and genera, partly a contrary and partly a conforming overlap. Bates (1918: 578–583) showed that in birds of strong flight the method of overlap is clearly adaptive—a contrary overlap (which seals the interstices between the remiges more effectively) appearing regularly in such birds, especially in the areas of greatest strain.

[3] In the early literature, overlap is described as "distal" or "proximal," but Goodchild (1886) called one type of overlap "distal," whereas Gadow (1893: 949–952) and others used the term "distal" to denote the opposite type of overlap. Bates pointed out this conflicting usage and the added problem which arises when we wish to discuss both upper and under coverts; he therefore proposed the terms "conforming" and "contrary."

In 1843 the Swedish ornithologist Sundevall (1886) pointed out that some or all of the greater and median coverts on the under surface of the wing are "reversed," i.e., their concave surface faces outward. Wray (1887b: 353–354) was the first to see that this was to be explained by their origin. These coverts, now on the under surface of the wing, were originally on the upper surface and have retained their primitive orientation. A study of their embryological history shows that they begin to develop on the dorsal side of the wing and then are carried to the ventral side as the remiges of the adjoining row become larger and larger. The dorsal origin of these under coverts is most strikingly demonstrated in such a bird as the great Military Macaw (*Ara militaris*), which has on the upper side of the wing bicolored coverts (blue-green on the exposed surface and dull olive beneath). By turning over the "reversed" under coverts one finds that they too are a bright blue-green dorsally, but in their position under the wing the bright surface is concealed and the dull olive surface exposed—contrary to the otherwise invariable rule of feather coloration.

Feathers of the Tail

Rectrices

The flight feathers (quills) of the tail are called rectrices. Normally they are even in number. Ornithologists identify them numerically, counting from the center outward.

Most birds have 12 rectrices (6 pairs); a few have 10 (hummingbirds, swifts, most cuckoos, most of the motmots, the toucans, etc.); some have but 8 (the cuckoo genus *Crotophaga,* some rails, some grebes); and at least three species, all very small birds, have but 6 (a timaliid, *Pnoepyga,* of southeastern Asia; a sylviid, *Stipiturus,* of Australia; and a furnariid, *Sylviorthorhynchus,* of southern South America). Many examples of an increase over the usual 12 rectrices can be cited:

14, guinea fowl (*Numida*)
Scaled Quail (*Callipepla*)
16, ptarmigan (*Lagopus*)
Silver Pheasant (*Lophura*)
18, ♀ Peafowl (*Pavo*)
Prairie Chicken (*Tympanuchus*)
Ring-necked Pheasant (*Phasianus*)
20, ♂ Peafowl (*Pavo*)
Blue Grouse (*Dendragapus*)
24, White Pelican (*Pelecanus erythrorhynchos*)
26, Pintail Snipe (*Capella stenura*)
32, White-tailed Wattled Pheasant (*Lobophasis bulweri*)

The ostrich is said to have 50 to 60 tail feathers (e.g., Blake, 1956: 27) but most of these feathers occur in layers above the 14 or so true rectrices and we judge that they are not homologous with the rectrices of other birds.

Tail feathers vary in number within bird groups more than wing feathers do. For example, the Rhinocryptidae as a family have 12 (but one genus, *Pteroptochos,* has 14); the Cuculidae characteristically have 10 (but the genus *Crotophaga* has 8); the Dicruridae as a family have 10 (but the genus *Chaetorhynchus* has 12). The female peafowl (*Pavo*) has 2 tail feathers less than the male (which has a tremendous "train" of tail coverts, supported by 20 rectrices). There is also some individual variation.

Tail Coverts

The rectrices are overlain by the greater upper coverts, with lesser upper coverts above them. Clark (1918) investigated the numbers and arrangement of the greater coverts. In many birds he found that each rectrix had a greater upper covert; however, in a few groups (especially swimming birds) there were more coverts than rectrices, and in the majority of bird *species,* including all of the passerine birds that he examined, the greater upper coverts were fewer in number than the rectrices. Usually it was the central pair of rectrices which lacked greater upper coverts. More recently, A. H. Miller (1931: 128) and others have found a few passerine birds which have an equal number of rectrices and major upper coverts. The greater under tail coverts are often less clearly defined than the greater upper coverts; their number has been recorded in but few species; it may be the same as the number of rectrices, or several more or less than that.

Number of Contour Feathers

Since the flight feathers and their coverts have been found to be regularly arranged and definite in number according to the kinds of birds, it should not surprise us that the whole covering of the bird is made up of a rather definite number of feathers according to kind. In 1882, Ernest Thompson Seton (1940: 197) counted 4915 feathers on a Brewer's Blackbird (*Euphagus cyanocephalus*), and a few years later Dwight (1900: 119) recorded 3235 feathers on a Bobolink (*Dolichonyx oryzivorus*), but only recently have feather counts been made on significant numbers of birds (Wetmore, 1936; Trainer, 1947; Brodkorb, 1951).

The smallest number of feathers (940) was recorded from a Ruby-throated Hummingbird (*Archilochus colubris*) and the largest (25,216) from a Whistling Swan (*Olor columbianus*). Passerine birds (omitting the most diminutive species) range between about 1500 and 3000 (in one case, 4600). Wetmore showed that the more hardy species, which winter in regions that are cold for at least short periods, show an adaptation to these conditions by acquiring only part of their winter feathers at the annual molt in late summer but adding more as winter approaches. On the other hand, birds such as vireos and wood-warblers, which retire to warm regions for the winter, have "a speedy, complete renewal" of the body plumage before they migrate.

Wetmore (1936) found no sexual variation in feather number (he did not study any species with marked size difference between the sexes). Counts for individuals of the same species were surprisingly close, often varying by only a fraction of 1 per cent.

Pterylosis

The feathers of the ostrich, of penguins, and of the South American screamers (Anhimidae) are distributed over the body in an almost continuous fashion, but all other birds have their feathers restricted to definite tracts (pterylae), leaving bare spaces (apteria) between. In life, the apteria are entirely covered by the overlapping feathers from adjoining pterylae. To study the elaborate patterns formed by pterylae (which have proved of value in tracing the relationships of birds), ornithologists clip the feathers from a bird's body, leaving only short feather stubs, or they remove the skin from the specimen and reverse it, tracing the patterns formed by the feather papillae on the inside of the skin.

As can be seen in Fig. 8, these tracts may be readily classified according to their anatomical location. The major tract names used in discussing these pterylae are:

Capital tract. Comprises the upper half of the head, from the base of the bill posteriorly to the base of the skull, where it blends with the spinal tract. The capital tract is commonly subdivided into a number of "regions" (Fig. 8).

Spinal tract. The spinal pteryla extends along the back from the base of the skull to the base of the tail, ending at the oil gland

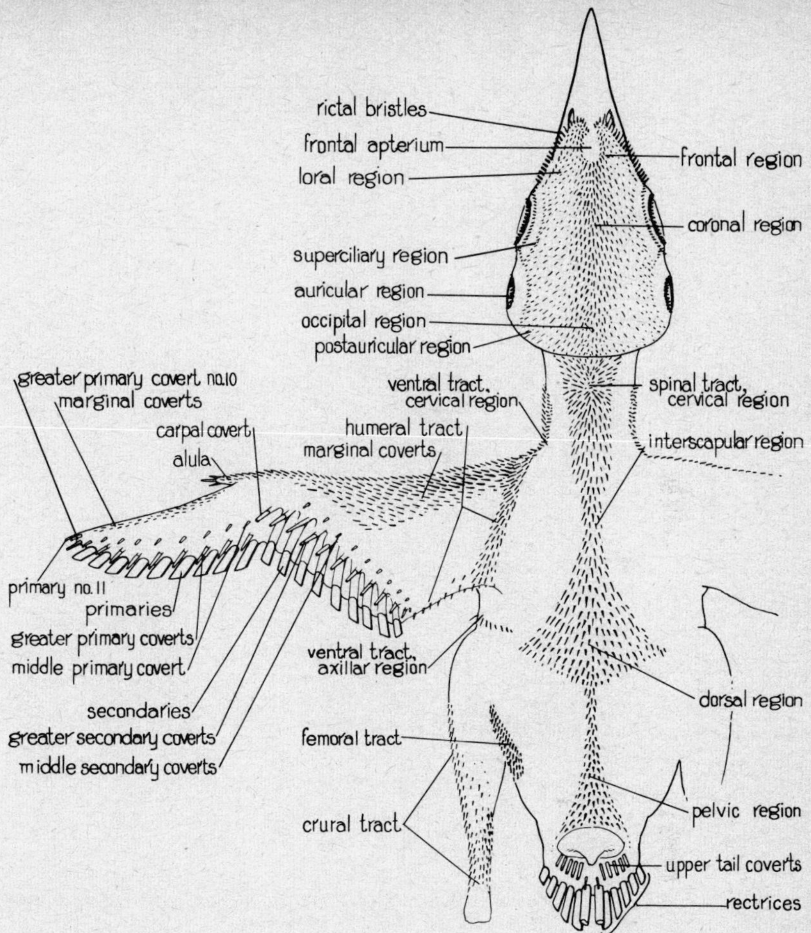

Fig. 8. Pterylography of the shrike *Lanius ludovicianus* (dorsal view). (Courtesy of A. H. Miller.)

and upper tail coverts. This tract is divided into cervical, interscapular, dorsal, and pelvic regions; it is a tract which varies greatly among the families and genera of birds. Compare Fig. 8 (shrike) with Fig. 9 (cuckoo).

Humeral tract. This narrow tract, beginning at the shoulder, extends down across the dorsal surface of the base of the wing to the region of the elbow; it includes the scapular feathers. This tract shows little variation in form.

Femoral tract. A narrow, rather uniform tract, extending from

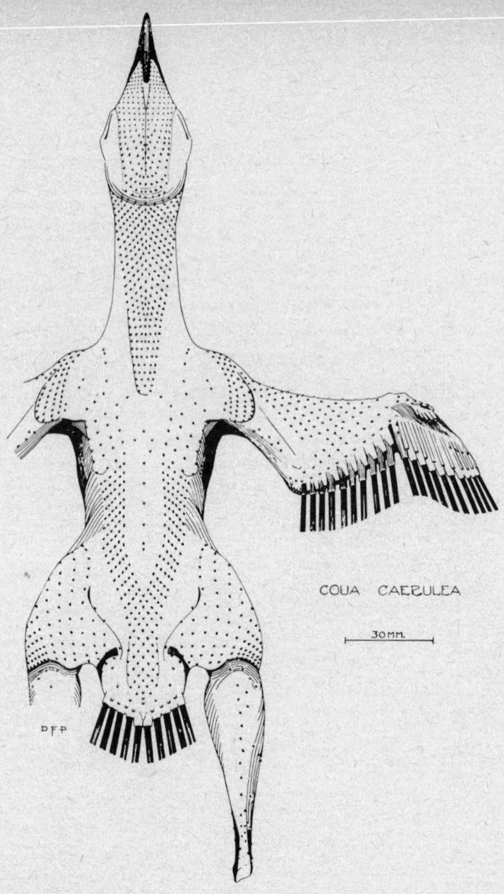

Fig. 9. Dorsal view of the feather tracts of a cuckoo (*Coua caerulea*). (From Berger, 1953.)

the region of the femur along the flank toward the tail (but always ending short of that).

Crural tract. The tract (inner and outer) covering the leg.

Alar tract. The feathers of the wing exclusive of the humeral tract.

Caudal tract. The rectrices, their coverts, the anal circlet, and the feathers on the oil gland (these last are lacking in passerines and many other birds).

Ventral tract. The feathers of the under parts (beginning at base of bill) exclusive of the humeral and femoral tracts. This tract is usually forked. It is divided into interramal, submalar, cervical, sternal, axillar, and abdominal regions (Fig. 10).

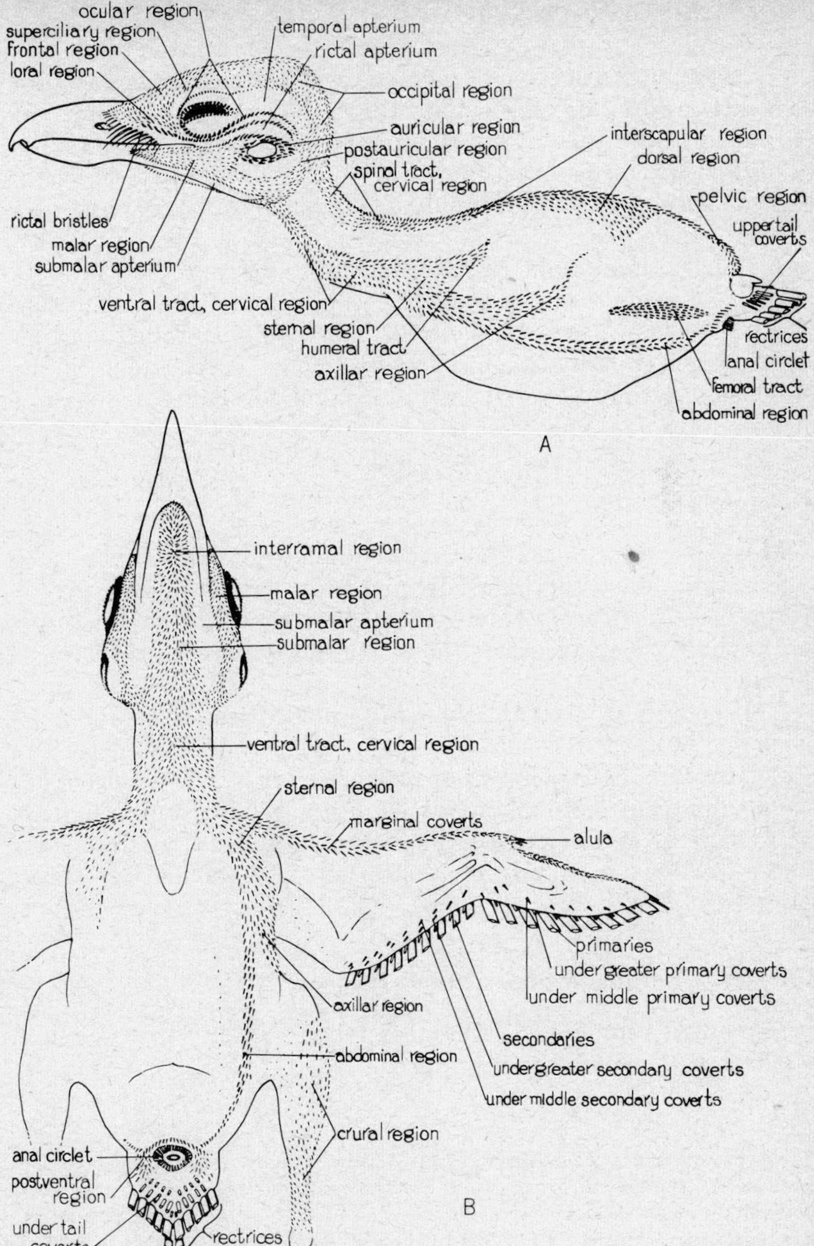

Fig. 10. Pterylography of the shrike *Lanius ludovicianus* (A, lateral view; B, ventral view). (Courtesy of A. H. Miller.)

Plumage succession

Beginning with the first plumage, worn at hatching or acquired soon after hatching, birds pass through a series of molts[4] and plumages before they attain the fully adult plumage. Thereafter, in all healthy birds all feathers are replaced at least once a year; in some species much of the plumage is replaced two or even three times during a year.

A single annual molt (the postnuptial) appears to be characteristic of most species; a few have a second molt (the prenuptial), which is in some cases complete (e.g., in the Sharp-tailed Sparrow, *Ammospiza caudacuta*), but in most cases partial (e.g., in the crowned sparrows *Zonotrichia*); ptarmigan (*Lagopus*) have three, or even four, molts per year (Höst, 1942).

Time of Molt

Most species of migratory birds complete the postnuptial molt before they start on their fall migration, but swallows, tyrant-flycatchers, bee-eaters (Meropidae), and shearwaters (*Puffinus*), and perhaps others postpone the molt until they reach their winter quarters.

Molt periods are very closely synchronized with the reproductive cycle and with the seasons of the year. Experiments to determine the controlling factors have been going on for nearly 50 years, and the results point more and more definitely to light, and in particular to increase and decrease of daylight, as the chief environmental factor involved in timing molt (see, e.g., Lesher and Kendeigh, 1941; Höst, 1942).

Time Required for Attaining Adult Plumage

There are very great differences among species in the age at which the adult plumage is acquired.

---

[4] Obviously, change of plumage by "molt" involves two processes: the loss of the old feathers and the growth of new ones. Ornithologists formerly discriminated clearly between the two processes in their terminology, calling them "ecdysis" ("putting off") and "endysis" ("putting on"). Unfortunately, these terms are now little used and when ornithologists use the term "molt" they sometimes are referring to the loss of feathers only; at other times they are referring to the double process of loss and replacement of feathers.

3 months. Some species of birds, like the Horned Lark (*Eremophila alpestris*), acquire the fully adult plumage at the time of the postjuvenal molt—in late summer or early fall—at about 3 months of age.

8 months. In other species, e.g., the Bobolink (*Dolichonyx oryzivorus*), the adult plumage is acquired by an extensive (or complete) prenuptial molt during the late winter and early spring of the bird's first year, i.e., at an age of about 8 months.

14 months. Many passerine birds acquire the adult plumage by the first postnuptial molt. For example, the Rose-breasted Grosbeak (*Pheucticus ludovicianus*) molts into the adult plumage in August of its second year, at the age of about 14 months.

3 years, 7 months. The Herring Gull (*Larus argentatus*) attains adult plumage with its fourth winter plumage, acquired by a postnuptial molt from August to midwinter. A few individuals of this species apparently do not come into the adult plumage until the fourth nuptial plumage, at more than 3 years, 7 months.

5 to 10 years. A Bald Eagle (*Haliaeetus leucocephalus*) studied in captivity assumed adult plumage at the end of its fifth year; however, it did not acquire the completely white tail until the end of its tenth year (Crandall, 1941).

7 years. At least 7 years are required for the male of the Twelve-wired Bird-of-Paradise (*Seleucides melanoleucus*) to acquire the fully adult plumage, according to Crandall (1937).

Variation in Extent or Occurrence of Molt

Whistler (1941) has shown that there may be marked differences, apparently of adaptive significance, between the molts of two otherwise very similar subspecies. The European form of Short-toed Lark (*Calandrella cinerea*), for example, has no spring (prenuptial) molt, but an Asiatic subspecies, *dukhunensis,* which lives under very windy desert conditions causing excessive abrasion of the plumage, has a very extensive body molt in spring. In the Phainopepla (*Phainopepla nitens lepida*), A. H. Miller (1933) found marked differences in the postjuvenal molt between different geographical components of a single subspecies. The nonmigratory population of the Colorado Desert of California molted more completely than the population of the cooler coastal belt, which began nesting later and thus had less time to complete a molt before beginning its fall migration.

Order of Molt in the Individual

Except in penguins (in which great patches of feathers are shed in a seemingly irregular pattern), molt in birds is a surprisingly orderly process. A complete molt commonly begins with the loss of the innermost primaries on both sides. Then, usually in regular succession, the other primaries drop out as their predecessors are being replaced, so that there is only a small gap at any one time, and the bird thus retains the power of flight. When the molt of the primaries is about half completed, the secondaries usually begin to molt, starting with the outermost and progressing inward. Soon after the molt of the wing feathers is under way, molt begins in the tracts of body feathers. The tail feathers, like the wing feathers, are usually molted serially (by pairs), so that here, too, a continuously useful organ of flight is maintained. In most cases the molt begins at the center (or next to center) and progresses outward—an order of molt which Beebe (1916: 74) termed centrifugal; but the molt is centripetal (progresses from outer feathers inward) in colies and in certain toucans and woodpeckers (Friedmann, 1930). Some pheasants have a centrifugal, some a centripetal, tail molt; in others the molt starts at an intermediate point and progresses both outward and inward (Beebe, 1914).

Simultaneous Molt of Flight Feathers

Striking exceptions to the rule that remiges are molted gradually and serially are to be found in some quite unrelated birds which have one thing in common: a habitat (usually aquatic) where they can elude their enemies for a few weeks without resorting to flight. These birds drop all their remiges at once. Examples of birds molting thus are (Grant, 1914): waterfowl (Anatidae), most rails (Fig. 11), many alcids (Alcidae), and probably loons (Gaviidae).

The Mayrs (1954) found that small owls usually lose all of their tail feathers at once, whereas large owls (e.g., *Tyto, Bubo, Strix*), which pursue larger and more speedy prey and probably cannot secure adequate food without strong powers of flight, molt their tail feathers gradually. Woodpeckers (Picidae) and creepers (Certhiidae) maintain a supporting tail without interruption by molting the long central feathers only after the other rectrices have been replaced.

The most remarkable of all simultaneous molts occurs in females

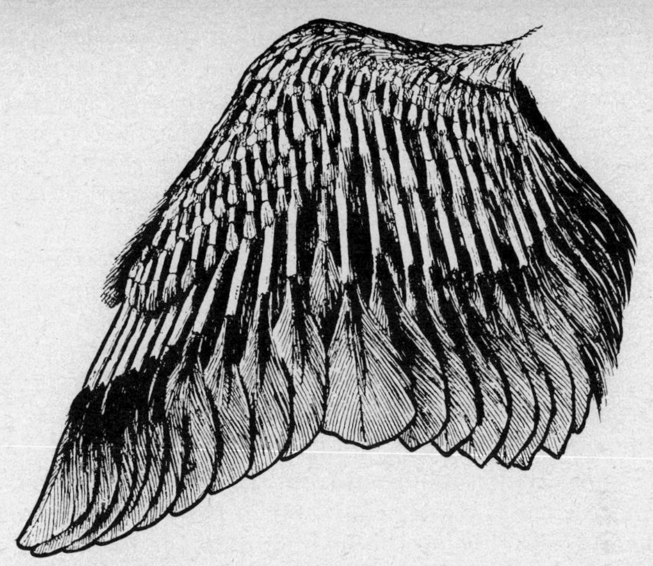

Fig. 11. Under side of the wing of a rail (*Gallinula chloropus*) in full molt. The incoming feathers are all of about the same age. (After Grant, 1914: 302.)

of a number of hornbills (Bucerotidae) which molt *all* their wing and tail feathers at once (and in some species the body feathers also) while they are walled up in the nest with their eggs and are being fed entirely by the male (Moreau, 1937).

Plumages and Molts of Immature Birds

The series of plumages of the typical bird may be outlined as follows:

Natal (or nestling) down. This plumage is found on the majority of birds at hatching. In some groups (e.g., the pelicans and their relatives) the young are hatched naked, but after some days they develop a downy covering to the whole body. Other groups (e.g., woodpeckers, kingfishers, and a very few passerine birds) have completely naked young; their first plumage, when it finally grows out, is of feathers very much like those of adults. In still other groups (penguins, most owls, and a few other birds), the first coat of down (protoptile) is succeeded by a second (mesoptile) nestling down coat. (See discussion on p. 71.)

Downy newly hatched birds are classified under two main types: (1) Many of the primitive groups, such as ducks and gallinaceous birds, are completely covered at hatching time with a dense and often elaborately patterned coat of down; they are called *ptilopaedic* young. (2) Higher types of birds, especially the passerines, have only scant wisps of long fragile down, which is confined to the future feather tracts (pterylae), leaving much of the young bird bare; these are called *psilopaedic* young. (As mentioned above, a few species completely lack down.)

Juvenal plumage. The first plumage of typical contour feathers was named the "juvenal" plumage by Dwight (1900). It is worn for only a short time. In fact, it may not even exist as a complete plumage on a given individual bird. Sutton (1935), for example, has shown that many young sparrows begin to molt into the next plumage before the juvenal rectrices have completed their growth. Although composed of the adult type of feather, the juvenal plumage is easily distinguished from true adult plumages by the softer, more loose-textured character of the feathers. Passerine (nidicolous) birds develop the juvenal plumage before they leave the nest. As the juvenal plumage grows in, it carries out on the feather tips remnants of natal down. (A few species, e.g., the Blue Jay, *Cyanocitta cristata,* apparently pass through a *postjuvenal* plumage before acquiring the winter plumage.)

First winter plumage. This plumage is much like the adult winter plumage, but is frequently distinguishable by duller colors or immature types of pattern; it is acquired by a partial or complete postjuvenal molt. A number of species retain at least the flight feathers of the juvenal stage through the first winter plumage. This plumage may be acquired very early. For example, Sutton (1948) described a young Warbling Vireo (*Vireo gilvus*) which had acquired an apparently complete first winter plumage by July 28.

The winter plumage is sometimes called the "internuptial" plumage.

First nuptial plumage. In many species this plumage is like, or nearly like, the adult nuptial plumage; it is acquired by the wearing off of contrasting tips and edges of the body feathers or by a (usually incomplete) prenuptial molt. The name of this plumage is somewhat misleading, for birds of many species (especially large birds) are not yet ready to breed when they assume the first nuptial plumage. The nuptial plumage of the common Starling (*Sturnus vulgaris*) is a familiar example of the effects of wear.

Second winter plumage. This plumage in most species of birds is indistinguishable from that of adults of any age; in that case it may be called simply "adult winter plumage." It is acquired by a complete postnuptial molt—the complete annual molt of all birds.

Eclipse plumage. It has long been known that the males of most Northern Hemisphere ducks assume an "eclipse" plumage in midsummer. Brooks (1938) called attention to eclipse plumages in the males of some Southern Hemisphere ducks and in some female ducks in both hemispheres.

When the females begin incubating their eggs the males flock by themselves, usually in secluded marshes, and molt rapidly into a very inconspicuous, female type of plumage[5] which they retain, in most species, for only about a month, after which they assume the full winter plumage—which is also the nuptial plumage. The Blue-winged Teal and Shoveller retain the eclipse plumage for several months; the Ruddy Duck until the following March or April. In molting into the eclipse plumage the male ducks suddenly (actually in a matter of hours) lose all their flight feathers and are flightless for a few weeks until the new feathers have grown in. These new flight feathers are retained through the following year, whereas the body feathers are replaced at the end of the eclipse period.

According to one theory, the eclipse plumage represents a dull plumage once worn all winter but now lost after a few weeks and replaced by a much-hastened nuptial plumage (Snyder and Lumsden, 1951). An opposite theory maintains that the eclipse is a new, interpolated, plumage of a specialized nature which conceals and protects the male during his flightless period. In any case, it is known that the assumption of an eclipse plumage may be prevented by castration or by keeping experimental birds under abnormally low temperatures through the summer.

It was formerly supposed that eclipse plumages occurred only among ducks, but recently such plumages have been described among bee-eaters (Meropidae), cuckoo-shrikes (Campephagidae), sunbirds (Nectariniidae), and weaverbirds (Ploceidae).

Colors

Birds are perhaps the most colorful of all animals. Some of their colors ("biochromes") are due to true pigmentation; others ("schemochromes") are the effect of feather structure, either wholly

[5] The eclipse plumage and posteclipse molt are beautifully illustrated by T. M. Shortt (in Kortright, 1942, especially col. pls. 6, 11, 14, 17, 21 and 29).

(as in white feathers) or in part. As Fox (1944; 1953: 4), who suggested these two terms, pointed out, "the production of conspicuous schemochromic colors depends upon underlying light-absorbing deposits of biochromic material" (i.e., on natural pigments—usually one or more melanins).

***Biochromes* (Pigment Colors)**

Pigments are classified according to their chemical make-up. Three groups, respectively known as melanins, carotenoids, and porphyrins, include most of the pigments found in feathers.

1. Melanins.[6] The most common bird pigments are melanins, which range (unless modified by feather structure) from dull yellow through red-brown to dark brown and black. They are synthesized by birds and mammals, and occur in feathers and skin in granular form.

2. Carotenoids (lipochromes). Carotenoid pigments (named from the pigment in the root of the cultivated carrot, the first of the group to be discovered) may be divided into (a) hydrocarbon compounds called "carotenes" and (b) oxygen-containing carotene derivatives—xanthophylls of yellow and orange-yellow color, and carotenoid acids, which are red. These pigments usually produce yellow, orange, or red, and occur in diffused form (not in granules) in the feathers and skin of birds. Birds are known to be dependent (directly or indirectly) on plants for at least most of their carotenoid pigments. Some of these pigments are modified after ingestion, but many of the reds and yellows seen in birds (especially in the bill and legs) are the result of carotenoid pigment which has been taken up from the food and deposited in the bird with little or no chemical change.

The pigmentation of comparatively few species has been studied, but a surprising number of carotenoids have been identified in birds with some exactness (Völker, 1944, 1951; Fox, 1953):

Lutein (in the Old-world oriole *Oriolus,* the cotinga *Ampelion,* the wagtail *Motacilla,* and the weaverbird *Ploceus*)
Astaxanthin (in the shrike *Laniarius*)
Zeaxanthin (in the cotinga *Rupicola*)
Rhodoxanthin (in the cotinga *Phoenicircus*)
Picofulvin (in the woodpeckers *Picus* and *Piculus*)

[6] Melanins were formerly divided into "eumelanins" and "phaeomelanins" (Görnitz, 1923), but Frank (1939) showed that there is no qualitative difference between the two.

Canary-xanthophyll (in the carduelines *Serinus, Chloris,* and *Spinus*)

Alpha-carotene (in the woodpecker *Colaptes*)

3. Porphyrins (pyrrolic pigments). Porphyrins are nitrogenous compounds synthesized by all animals and they occur in diffused form. They are readily detected by their red fluorescence and are very common among birds. Some porphyrins reported from bird feathers are (Völker, 1944; Fox, 1953):

Turacoverdin, a green pigment found only in touracos (family Musophagidae).

Turacin, a red pigment found only in touracos.

Koproporphyrin, a pink pigment found in the bustards *Lophotis* and *Lissotis* (family Otididae).

Schemochromes (Structural Colors)

The simplest case of a schemochrome is whiteness. The color white in a bird is the result of the reflection of all elements (wave lengths) of the white light[7] striking the feather. "Chalky" and other nonlustrous whites are produced by a close-packed fibrous structure; lustrous whites by a porous, air-filled structure (in the latter case, immersion in balsam renders the feather transparent instead of white).

Erythrism, or the presence of an excessive amount of reddish-brown color, is uncommon. It does, however, occur with some regularity in the Prairie Chicken (*Tympanuchus cupido*); see Brewster (1895). The red-plumaged Least Bittern, once considered a distinct species (*"Ixobrychus neoxenus"*), is apparently only an erythristic phase (most recorded specimens were also partly albinistic). A reddish color in certain ducks, geese, and cranes is a ferric-oxide stain from iron-bearing water or mud and is not to be confused with erythrism (Bales, 1909; Kennard, 1918).

Schizochroism is a term applied to the condition which results from the absence of one of the pigments normally present in the plumage of a given species (Stresemann, 1927–1934: 47). Such birds commonly have the normal plumage pattern of the species but an abnormally pale, washed-out appearance. Storer (1952) figured Dovekies (*Plautus alle*) and Murres (*Uria lomvia*) of this sort. California Quail (*Lophortyx californicus*) and Mourning Doves (*Zenaidura macroura*), described by others under the terms

[7] Light that includes all the visible rays of the spectrum, as in pure sunlight.

"dilute" and "pale mutant" (Price and Danforth, 1941; Graefe and Hollander, 1945), are probably examples of schizochroism. The blue strain of the common green budgerigar (*Melopsittacus undulatus*) is a familiar instance.

Xanthochroism, an abnormally yellow coloration, is very rare in the wild, but it is sometimes seen in captive parrots. It apparently results from loss of the dark pigment which, with the physical structure of the feather and yellow pigment, produces the normal green. This is, of course, simply a special type of schizochroism.

Blue in feathers is apparently never the result of blue pigment. Noniridescent blues in feathers are caused by the structure of the barbs: a turbid, porous layer without pigment overlies a dark layer colored by granules of melanin. This colorless layer throws back (reflects) blue light, but other wave lengths pass through the layer and are absorbed by the dark pigment below. The cuticular sheath of the barb, above the reflecting layer, is transparent and without pigment.

Noniridescent green is in rare cases the result of green pigmentation, but in the great majority of noniridescent green-feathered birds the color results from the "blue structure" described above. In this case, however, the cuticular sheath of the barb is pigmented, either with yellow carotenoids (producing pure greens) or with melanins (producing olive greens).

Iridescent colors are the effect of interference of light by a thinly laminated structure in the barbules. Such colors are made more brilliant by underlying pigment, but are essentially independent of pigment. The metallic luster noted in some iridescent feathers is the result of dark pigment.

Color Changes

Birds show so many and such diverse changes in the colors of their coat of feathers that scientists often supposed new pigment must somehow spread at times into old feathers. Indeed, ornithologists even coined a word ("aptoso-chromatism") to apply to the supposed phenomenon, but after much study ornithologists now generally agree that the full-grown feather is not capable of further growth or repair, and its pigments are beyond any possible control by the bird's physiology (Allen, 1896; Dwight, 1900).

We may, then, accept it as a fact that any changes in the color of the full-grown feather are due to modified structure, to wear, or to fading. Much of our knowledge of this subject is the result of simple observation, but Test (1940), for example, made some experiments on feathers of the Flicker (*Colaptes*). He reported that melanic pigments were little affected except by wear; carotenoid colors (reds and yellows) were notably paled by 65 days of exposure to strong sunlight.

Functions of Color and Pattern in Birds

Our knowledge and theories of the uses that color may serve in birds are outlined below. (The biologist must, of course, bear in mind that in many instances color may be a "physiological accident" of little or no visual significance.)

1. Uses of color unrelated to the vision of other animals.
   a. Prevention of wear in feathers. Averill (1923) pointed out that melanin-bearing feathers (or parts of feathers) resist wear much better than white feathers (Fig. 12). The wing tips are especially subjected to wear, and strong-flying birds that are much on the wing usually have black wing tips.
   b. Insulation from injurious light and extremes of temperature. Meinertzhagen (1951: 161) suggests that the pinkish

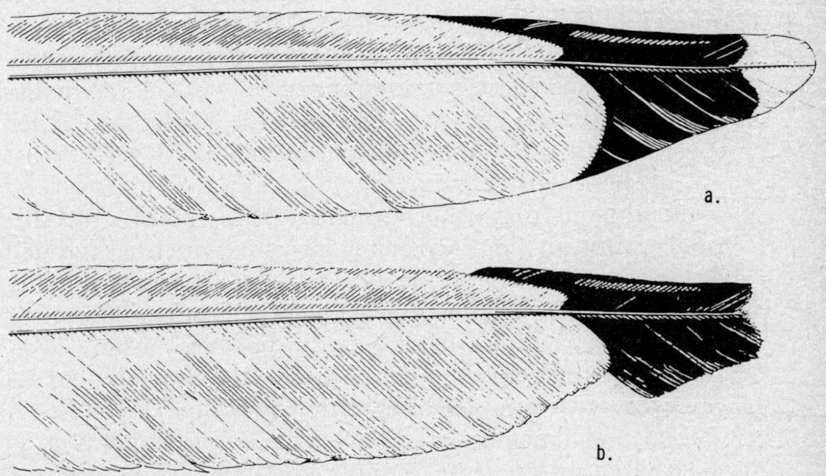

Fig. 12. The wear-resisting quality of melanin pigment in feathers is shown in a primary of a Ring-billed Gull (*Larus delawarensis*) in fresh, winter condition (a) and in worn, late-June condition (b). (Drawn by W. A. Lunk.)

buff so characteristic of desert birds is especially valuable in this connection.

c. Absorption of needed light and heat.

2. Related to the vision of other animals.

a. Advertisement

(1) A warning label on inedible prey species. Two African bustards (*Afrotis afra* and *Eupodotis rüppelli*) are, respectively, conspicuously and cryptically colored; the conspicuous one, Meinertzhagen (1951: 159) testifies, is (to man at least!) most inedible. ("Aposematic" colors or patterns.)

(2) A means (especially in gregarious birds) of attracting the attention of other individuals of the same species. Many flocking birds, such as crows, flamingos, etc., seem to be free of any need of cryptic coloration for protection from enemies, and we are probably justified in thinking that their conspicuous colors are useful in enabling individual birds to correlate their movements with those of the flock. In certain coots and other rails the downy young are brilliantly colored about the head, and this seems to assist the young in securing the attention of the parent bird bringing food (Boyd and Alley, 1948). ("Episematic" colors and patterns.)

(3) A means of attracting the attention of (and, perhaps, stimulating) members of the other sex. ("Gamosematic" and "Epigamic" colors and patterns.) Inextricably involved here is the "threat" use of color by males in territorial defense; Lack (1943: 37–45) concluded that this is the principal significance of the red breast of the English Robin.

b. Concealment from other animals. Many species of birds are "cryptically" marked, some matching their background so well that when motionless (as birds so marked commonly become in the presence of danger) they are difficult or impossible to detect from a little distance. Many owls, frogmouths (Podargidae), and nightjars (Caprimulgidae) are excellent examples of cryptic coloration (Fig. 13). A special and much-debated aspect of cryptic coloration is designated by the term "countershading." The essential point of this concept, presented by Abbott H. Thayer in the *Auk* in 1896 and elaborated by his son Gerald Thayer (1909), is that an animal with pale or white under parts is

Fig. 13. Protective coloration. Spotted Nightjar (*Eurostopodus guttatus*) of Australia on its nest. (Courtesy of *Australian Museum Magazine* and Norman Chaffer, photographer.)

less conspicuous than a uniformly shaded one because the white surface counteracts the revealing shadows cast by a solid object.

"Disruptive" patterns are a special category of cryptic marking. The pattern breaks the familiar bird outline and causes the eye of man or other predator to "pass over" the bird without recognizing its true nature. The White-headed Fruit Pigeon (*Leucotreron cincta*) of Malaysia, whose pure white head and neck are sharply demarked from a black and green body, is said to be very difficult to detect as it sits motionless in jungle trees (Cott, 1940: 197). Friedmann (1942: pl. 9) has pictured the Semipalmated Plover (*Charadrius semipalmatus*) as an example of this phenomenon (Fig. 14).

"Mimicry" in the restricted sense of advantageous resemblance to other birds has rarely been described by ornithologists. The young of some cuckoos (*Clamator* and *Eudynamis*) which are raised in the nests of crows and magpies have a blackish nestling plumage much like that of the

Fig. 14. The disruptive plumage pattern of the Semipalmated Plover is very conspicuous against a plain background (B), but actually makes the bird hard to discover in its normal habitat of stony shore (A). (W. A. Weber, artist; courtesy of the Smithsonian Institution.)

host young with which they are raised and unlike the gray or brown plumage of their parents or of related young cuckoos (Jourdain, 1925: 657). The adult Asiatic cuckoo *Surniculus lugubris* is so like a (highly belligerent) drongo of the same region that it is generally admitted to be a mimic.

References

Allen, J. A. 1896. Alleged Changes of Color in the Feathers of Birds without Molting. *Bull. Amer. Mus. Nat. Hist.,* 8: 13–44.

Averill, Charles K. 1923. Black Wing Tips. *Condor,* 25: 57–59.

Bales, B. R. 1909. The Brown Stain Occasionally Seen on the Feathers of Wild Ducks. *Wils. Bull.,* 21: 221–223.

Bates, George L. 1918. The Reversed Under Wing-Coverts of Birds and their Modifications, as exemplified in the Birds of West Africa. *Ibis,* 1918: 529–583.

Bean, Robert A. 1925. A Black Herring Gull. Yearbook Public Mus. of City of Milwaukee, vol. 3, for 1923, 1925: 177–181.

Beebe, C. William. 1914. Preliminary pheasant studies. *Zoologica,* 1: 261–285.

——— 1916. Notes on the Birds of Pará, Brazil. *Zoologica,* 2: 54–106.

Berger, Andrew J. 1953. The Pterylosis of *Coua caerulea. Wils. Bull.,* 65: 12–17.

Blake, Charles H. 1956. The Topography of a Bird. *Bird-Banding,* 27: 22–31.

Boulton, Rudyerd. 1927. Ptilosis of the House Wren (*Troglodytes aedon aedon*). *Auk,* 44: 387–414.

Boyd, H. J., and Ronald Alley. 1948. The Function of the Head-coloration of the Nestling Coot and other Nestling Rallidae. *Ibis,* 90: 582–593.

Brewster, William. 1895. A Remarkable Plumage of the Prairie Hen (*Tympanuchus americanus*). *Auk,* 12: 99–100.

Brodkorb, Pierce. 1951. The Number of Feathers in Some Birds. *Quart. Jour. Fla. Acad. Sci.,* 12, for 1949 (1951): 241–245.

Brooks, Allan. 1938. Eclipse in Ducks of the Southern Hemisphere. *Auk,* 55: 272–273.

Burt, William H. 1929. Pterylography of Certain North American Woodpeckers. *Univ. Calif. Publ. Zool.,* 30: 427–442.

Chandler, Asa C. 1914. Modifications and Adaptations to Function in the Feathers of *Circus hudsonius. Univ. Calif. Publ. Zool.,* 11: 329–376.

Clark, Hubert Lyman. 1918. Tail-feathers and their Major Upper Coverts. *Auk,* 35: 113–123.

Clarke, Wm. Eagle. 1906. Ornithological Results of the Scottish National Antarctic Expedition—II. On the Birds of the South Orkney Islands. *Ibis.* 1906: 145–187.

Compton, Lawrence V. 1938. The Pterylosis of the Falconiformes, with Special Attention to the Taxonomic Position of the Osprey. *Univ. Calif. Publ. Zool.,* 42: 173–211.

Cott, Hugh B. 1940. *Adaptive Coloration in Animals.* Methuen & Co., London.

Crandall, Lee S. 1937. Further Notes on Certain Birds of Paradise. *Zoologica,* 22: 193–195.

——— 1941. Notes on Plumage Changes in the Bald Eagle. *Zoologica,* 26: 7–8.

Delacour, Jean. 1943. A Revision of the Genera and Species of the Family Pycnonotidae (Bulbuls). *Zoologica,* 28: 17–28.

Dwight, Jonathan Jr. 1900. The Sequence of Plumages and Moults of the Passerine Birds of New York. *Annals N. Y. Acad. Sci.,* 13: 73–360.

Ewart, J. Cossar. 1921. The Nestling Feathers of the Mallard, with Observations on the Composition, Origin, and History of Feathers. *Proc. Zool. Soc. London,* 1921: 609–642.

Fisher, Harvey I. 1942. The Pterylosis of the Andean Condor. *Condor,* 44: 30–32.

Fox, Denis L. 1944. Biochromes. *Science,* 100: 470–471.

——— 1953. *Animal Biochromes and Structural Colours.* Cambridge Univ. Press, England.

Frank, Fritz. 1939. Die Färbung der Vogelfeder durch Pigment und Struktur. *Jour. f. Ornith.,* 87: 426–523.

Friedmann, Herbert. 1930. The Caudal Molt of Certain Coraciiform, Coliiform, and Piciform Birds. *Proc. U. S. Natl. Mus.,* 77, Art. 7: 1–6.

——— 1942. The Natural-history Background of Camouflage. *Smiths. Inst. War Background Studies,* No. 5: 1–17.

Gadow, Hans. 1893. Tectrices. In A. Newton and H. Gadow, *A Dictionary of Birds.* Adam and Charles Black, London, pp. 949–952.

Goodchild, J. G. 1886. Observations on the Disposition of the Cubital Coverts in Birds. *Proc. Zool. Soc. London,* 1886: 184–203.

Görnitz, Karl. 1923. Versuch einer Klassifikation der häufigsten Federfärbungen. *Jour. f. Ornith.,* 71: 127–131.

Graefe, C. F., and W. F. Hollander. 1945. A Pale Mutant Mourning Dove. *Auk,* 62: 300.

Grant, C. H. B. 1914. The Moults and Plumages of the Common Moorhen (*Gallinula chloropus* Linn.). *Ibis,* 1914: 298–304. (See also 528–532; 652–654.)

Hindwood, K. A. 1933. The Green-backed Mangrove-Heron. Part 2. Powder-down Feathers. *Emu,* 33: 97–102.

Hosker, Anne. 1936. Studies on the Epidermal Structures of Birds. *Phil. Trans. Roy. Soc. London, Ser. B.,* 226: 143–188.

Höst, Per. 1942. Effect of Light on the Moults and Sequences of Plumage in the Willow Ptarmigan. *Auk,* 59: 388–403.

Ingram, Collingwood. 1920. A Contribution to the Study of Nestling Birds. *Ibis,* 1920: 856–880; and (correction) 1921: 181.

Jourdain, F. C. R. 1925. A Study on Parasitism in the Cuckoos. *Proc. Zool. Soc. London,* 1925: 639–667.

Kennard, Frederic H. 1918. Ferruginous Stains on Waterfowl. *Auk,* 35: 123–132.

Kortright, Francis H. 1942. *The Ducks, Geese and Swans of North America.* American Wildlife Inst., Washington, D. C.

Lack, David. 1943. *The Life of the Robin.* H. F. & G. Witherby, London.

Lesher, S. W., and S. Charles Kendeigh. 1941. Effect of Photoperiod on Molting of Feathers. *Wils. Bull.,* 53: 169–180.

Lowe, Percy Roycroft. 1931. On the Relations of the Gruimorphae to the Charadriimorphae and Rallimorphae. . . . *Ibis,* 1931: 491–534.

Mayaud, Noël. 1950. Téguments et Phanères. In Grassé's *Traité de Zoologie,* Vol. 15, Oiseaux. Masson et Cie, Paris, pp. 4–77.

Mayr, Ernst, and Margaret Mayr. 1954. The Tail Molt of Small Owls. *Auk,* 71: 172–178.

Meinertzhagen, R. 1951. Desert Colouration. *Proc. 10th Internatl. Ornith. Congr., 1950*: 155–162.

Miller, Alden H. 1928. The Molts of the Loggerhead Shrike, *Lanius ludovicianus* Linnaeus. *Univ. Calif. Publ. Zool.,* 30: 393–417.

——— 1931. Systematic Revision and Natural History of the American Shrikes (Lanius). *Univ. Calif. Publ. Zool.,* 38: 11–242.

——— 1933. Postjuvenal Molt and the Appearance of Sexual Characters of Plumage in Phainopepla nitens. *Univ. Calif. Publ. Zool.,* 38: 425–446.

Miller, W. DeW. 1924a. Variations in the Structure of the Aftershaft and Their Taxonomic Value. *Amer. Mus. Novitates, No. 140.*

——— 1924b. Further Notes on Ptilosis. *Bull. Amer. Mus. Nat. Hist.,* 50: 305–331.

Montagna, William. 1945. A Re-investigation of the Development of the Wing of the Fowl. *Jour. Morph.,* 76: 87–113.

Moreau, R. E. 1937. The Comparative Breeding Biology of the African Hornbills (Bucerotidae). *Proc. Zool. Soc. London,* 107A: 331–346.

Nitzsch, Christian Ludwig. 1867. *Pterylography.* (Translated by W. S. Dallas; edited by P. L. Sclater.) Ray Society, London.

Price, John B., and C. H. Danforth. 1941. A Persistent Mutation in the California Quail. *Condor,* 43: 253–256.

Pycraft, W. P. 1907. On Some Points in the Anatomy of the Emperor and Adélie Penguins. *Natl. Antarct. Exped. 1901–1904, Zool.,* Vol. 2.

——— 1908. The 'Powder-Down' of the Heron. *Brit. Birds,* 1: 343–346.

——— 1911. Feather. *Encyclopaedia Britannica.* 11th ed. Vol. 10, pp. 224–228.

Reichling, Hermann. 1915. Die Flügelfedernkennzeichen der nordwestdeutschen Vögel. *Jour. f. Ornith.,* 63: 229–267, 305–340, 513–549.

Schüz, Ernst. 1927. Beitrag zur Kenntnis der Puderbildung bei den Vögeln. *Jour. f. Ornith.,* 75: 86–224.

Seton, Ernest Thompson. 1940. *Trail of an Artist-naturalist.* Charles Scribner's Sons, New York.

Sick, Helmut. 1937. Morphologisch-funktionelle Untersuchungen über die Feinstruktur der Vogelfeder. *Jour. f. Ornith.,* 85: 206–372.

Snyder, L. L., and H. G. Lumsden. 1951. Variation in *Anas cyanoptera. Occ. Papers, Roy. Ontario Mus. Zool., No. 10.*

Steiner, Hans. 1918. Das Problem der Diastataxie des Vogelflügels. *Jena. Zeitschr. f. Naturwiss.*, 55: 221–496.

Stone, Witmer. 1896. The Molting of Birds with Special Reference to the Plumages of the Smaller Land Birds of Eastern North America. *Proc. Acad. Nat. Sci. Phila.*, 1896: 108–167.

Storer, Robert W. 1952. A Comparison of Variation, Behavior, and Evolution in the Sea Bird Genera Uria and Cepphus. *Univ. Calif. Publ. Zool.*, 52: 121–222.

Stresemann, Erwin. 1927–1934. Aves. Vol. 7, pt. 2, of *Handbuch der Zoologie,* W. Kükenthal and T. Krumbach. Walter de Gruyter, Berlin.

Sundevall, C. J. 1886. On the Wings of Birds. *Ibis,* 1886: 389–457, pls. 10–11. (English translation by W. S. Dallas of article originally published in *Kongl. Vetensk.-Akad. Handl.*, 1843.)

Sutton, George Miksch. 1935. The Juvenal Plumage and Postjuvenal Molt in Several Species of Michigan Sparrows. *Cranbrook Inst. Sci., Bull. No. 3.*

——— 1948. The Juvenal Plumage of the Eastern Warbling Vireo (*Vireo gilvus gilvus*). *Univ. Mich. Mus. Zool. Occ. Papers, No. 511.*

Test, Frederick H. 1940. Effects of Natural Abrasion and Oxidation on the Coloration of Flickers. *Condor,* 42: 76–80.

Thayer, Gerald H. 1909. *Concealing-coloration in the Animal Kingdom.* Macmillan Co., New York.

Trainer, John E. 1947. The Pterylography of the Ruffed Grouse. In *The Ruffed Grouse,* Gardiner Bump *et al.* N. Y. State Conservation Dept., Albany.

Van Tyne, Josselyn. 1945. A Melanistic Specimen of Wilson's Snipe. *Wils. Bull.*, 57: 75–76.

Völker, Otto. 1944. Uebersicht der aus Vögeln isolierten und identifizierten Pigmente. *Jour. f. Ornith.*, 92: 133–139.

——— 1951. Die Isolierung eines gelben und eines roten Lipochroms aus Vogelfedern. *Jour. f. Ornith.*, 93: 20–26.

Wetmore, Alexander. 1920. The Function of Powder Downs in Herons. *Condor,* 22: 168–170.

——— 1936. The Number of Contour Feathers in Passeriform and Related Birds. *Auk,* 53: 159–169.

Whistler, Hugh. 1941. Differences of Moult in Closely Allied Forms. *Ibis,* 1941: 173–174.

Wray, Richard S. 1887a. On the Structure of the Barbs, Barbules, and Barbicels of a Typical Pennaceous Feather. *Ibis,* 1887: 420–423.

——— 1887b. On Some Points in the Morphology of the Wings of Birds. *Proc. Zool. Soc. London,* 1887: 343–357.

4. Senses and behavior

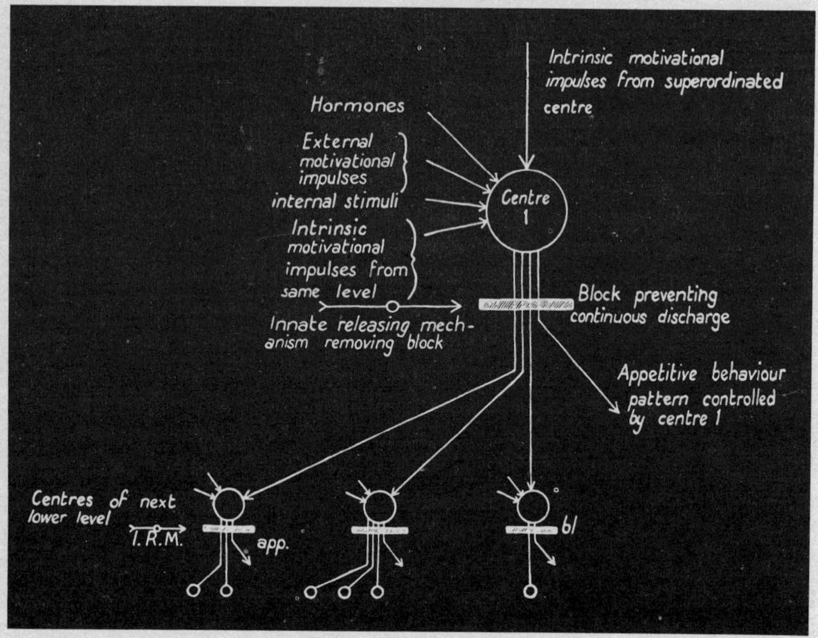

Fig. 1. Tinbergen's "tentative representation of an instinctive 'centre' of an intermediate level." (Reproduced by courtesy of N. Tinbergen and the Oxford University Press from *The Study Of Instinct,* 1951.)

IN THE simplest language, behavior is the way we act, and the way we act depends upon what we have to act with. If, for example, a fly alights on a man, he slaps the fly; a horse would "flick" its skin or switch its tail. To put this in a more scholarly form we might say that behavior is the "overt expression of the co-ordinated life processes" of an animal, including the means by which the animal "maintains its relation with the environment" (Emlen, 1955). If one is to deal with co-ordinated life processes and the environment, one must become familiar with the physical equipment which effects this co-ordination. The sense organs are an indispensable part of that equipment (see also Chapter 2).

The Sense Organs

Vision

Birds as a class have the best vision among animals. The bird eye is so large that the two eyeballs nearly touch each other in the median plane of the skull, and they may equal or exceed the weight of the brain. The eyes of most birds (exceptions: penguins, cormorants, pelicans, gulls, hornbills) have very limited mobility, and those of owls are immovably fixed in the orbits. The six oculomotor muscles are present but much reduced in size, and in a few birds they are functionless. What the bird lacks in eye mobility is compensated for by increased neck mobility (e.g., some owls are said to be able to rotate their heads through an arc of at least 270°). This set of circumstances may be significant in certain behavior studies because complex *reflex eye movements* tend to be replaced by *reflex neck movements.* Friedmann (1932) reported experiments that suggested that the movement of the nictitating membrane is correlated with the head movements made by pigeons when walking. It appears that "nictitation is primarily a type of reflex protection to the eye during jerky movements" of the head and "that its visual shutter function, if existent, is only a secondary coincidence."

Each of the three layers or tunics of the avian eyeball exhibits certain special features, some of which are found in lizards and other reptiles. The outer layer is composed of a posterior fibrous *sclera* and an anterior transparent *cornea.* Imbedded in the sclera are a sclerotic ring, a cup-shaped scleral cartilage, and, in some birds, an os opticus ("Gemminger's ossicle"). The middle or vascular tunic is composed of a thick *choroid,* a complex *ciliary body,* and a thin *iris.* In addition to blood vessels, the choroid may contain muscle fibers (either striated or smooth); the iris has striated sphincter and dilator fibers. The inner or nervous tunic is called the *retina;* its several parts line the vascular tunic. The retina is a complex laminated structure, whose light-perceptive cells are called rods and cones. The rods (containing rhodopsin) are highly sensitive to light (i.e., they are sensitive even to weak stimuli), and in nocturnal birds are present in greater numbers than cones; rods are greatly reduced in numbers in diurnal birds and may be absent in some. Cones are relatively insensitive visual cells; they are responsible both for sharp images (visual acuity) and for color vision. The cones of diurnal birds may contain red, orange, yellow, or colorless oil droplets; pale pigmented droplets are present in some nocturnal species. The light stimuli received by the rods and cones are first conducted to bipolar cells and then to ganglion cells, which carry the impulses to the brain. Typically, there is a one-to-one ratio between cones and ganglion cells, whereas a single ganglion cell receives stimuli from many rods. There is, however, a much higher ratio between numbers of optic-nerve fibers to visual cells in birds than in mammals, i.e., there is less "summation" of visual stimuli in birds. The *area centralis* is a modified region of the retina which provides the greatest visual acuity; in shape it may be round or a horizontal band, or there may be two round areae connected by a band; in some birds it is absent. The *fovea* is a depression within the area centralis which serves to magnify images; the fovea may be pitlike, troughlike, or absent; some birds have two foveae (see Walls, 1942: 187).

Many theories have been offered to explain the avian pecten, a pigmented and folded vascular structure projecting into the vitreous body from the head of the optic nerve, but Walls (p. 658) concluded that it fulfills the function of a retinal capillary network, which is characteristic of certain mammals. According to Walls, the pecten is a "supplemental nutritive device," and the need for a large or small pecten "seems to depend solely upon the rate-of-living of the sensory retina." Thus, a large pecten is needed by very active diurnal birds in which there is a high retinal temperature. Menner (see Crozier and Wolf, 1943; Pumphrey, 1948) found that the foldings or foliations of the pecten cast shadows on the retina and that the extent of the shadows is directly related to habit. The most elaborate foliations were found in the pectens of hawks and diurnal insectivorous birds, the simplest pattern in nocturnal birds. He suggested that the pecten might aid in the detection of movement since it is effective in creating contrast.

The intrinsic or intraocular eye muscles (Crampton's, Brücke's, Müller's, etc.) of birds and reptiles (especially lizards) differ from those of other vertebrates in being composed of striated rather than smooth fibers. The striated fibers presumably effect the rapid accommodation or focusing of images on the retina that is necessary in fast-flying birds. Accommodation is accomplished not only by adjustment of the lens but also by changes in the curvature of the cornea. Interesting modifications correlated with habits are seen in the eyes of certain amphibious birds (e.g., loons, cormorants, diving ducks, auks). In such birds, the transparent cornea is reduced in size; in some the nictitating membrane has a specialized central window which acts as a contact lens when it overlies the cornea; Crampton's muscle is reduced or absent; and Brücke's muscle is hypertrophied. The eyes of certain kingfishers (*Alcedo*) are so constructed that the birds apparently see clearly in air and water even though there is no elaborate accommodation mechanism to effect changes as the bird plunges from air into water. The lens and ciliary body are asymmetrical in shape, and each eye has two foveae, one of which is thought to function for aerial vision, the other for underwater vision.

Walls has discussed the correlation between food habits (predator and prey species) and the position of the eyes in the head: "The hunters tend toward frontality so as to have the best vision of the prey they are pursuing, while the hunted tend to retain laterality of eye position so as to be able to detect an enemy coming from any direction." Frontally placed eyes, usually accompanied by the presence of a temporal fovea (with or without a central fovea), result in increased binocularity, i.e., overlap in the visual fields of the two eyes. Such binocular vision is imperative for effective distance judgment, which is highly advantageous in the pursuit of prey. Thus, owls have a binocular field of 60 to 70°; hawks, up to 50° or more. Most granivorous birds, on the other hand, have binocular fields of considerably less than 25°. With the exception of the nocturnal *Strigops,* parrots have the smallest binocular fields (most often between 6 and 10°) yet found in birds. Only in certain penguins (*Spheniscus*) are the eyes so placed in the skull that there is no overlap in the visual fields of the two eyes, i.e., they have monocular vision in that each eye sees a different picture. Two interesting specializations in the location of the eyes are seen in bitterns and in the Woodcock (*Philohela minor*). When a bittern "freezes" with bill pointed skyward, the eyes can be turned ventrally so that the bird has a binocular field of vision parallel with the ground. The Woodcock's eyes are set so far back on the head that the "posterior binocular field probably is much wider than the anterior" (Walls, 1942: 295).

Hearing and Equilibrium

Hearing is keen and is next to sight in importance in birds. The three parts of the auditory system are: *external auditory meatus, middle ear cavity,* and the *internal ear.* An external ear flap (pinna) is absent; the external meatus ends internally at the eardrum (tympanic membrane). The middle ear extends from the tympanic membrane to the outer bony wall of the internal ear; it is connected with the pharynx by the pharyngotympanic tube. There is a single ear bone, the columella (partly cartilaginous), which transmits vibrations from the tympanic membrane to the oval window in the lateral wall of the internal ear. The auditory part of the inner ear is the *cochlea,* a complex structure responsible for transforming sound-wave stimuli to nerve impulses, which are conducted to the brain by the cochlear nerve. The *lagena* is a specialized portion of the cochlea that contains minute calcium carbonate "ear stones" (otoliths). It has been suggested that the lagena is responsive to low frequencies, the rest of the cochlea to high frequencies, and Beecher (1951) proposed that the lagena, along with the other otolith organs (portions of the utriculus and sacculus), form a "gravity system, capable of reporting changes in head position." The length and configuration of the cochlea vary among birds, and there is some evidence that there is a positive correlation between length of cochlea and complexity of song (Pumphrey, 1948). The very long cochlea of certain owls is correlated with asymmetry in position (and other specializations) of the two external meatuses. It has been shown that predatory birds in general have a keen sense of sound localization, and nocturnal predators, especially, are dependent on an accurate directional sensitivity to sound. The outer end of the meatus typically is located posterior to the orbit, but in the Common Snipe (*Capella*) and the Woodcock the opening lies ventral to the orbit.

There can be no doubt that birds hear the sounds produced by their own species and at least some of the sounds made by other species. That there is considerable difference in the range of hearing among various species has been shown by several investigators (e.g., Brand and Kellogg, 1939; Edwards, 1943; Schwartzkopff, 1955a, b). Conditioning experiments using sound stimuli have been conducted in the laboratory, but the role of hearing is infrequently mentioned in behavior studies, even though the sound-discriminatory abilities of birds must be taken for granted in all studies involving "voice." Loye Miller (1952) summarized interesting observations on the behavior of birds in response to human imitations of the calls of certain owls. He noted that imitations of large owls "invoke reactions in a species large enough to be endangered at one or another stage in its life history," but that small species do not react to large owls either by sight or by sound, and, further, that a "species resident in an area outside the native area of the owl seldom reacts to its note."

Also of importance is the sense of balance or equilibration. An animal must maintain both a static and a dynamic equilibrium with its environment. This involves the complex co-ordination between impulses arising in the semicircular canal systems of both the right and left inner ears with other sensory stimuli, and the subsequent association with motor neurons so that compensatory body movements (head, eyes, neck, etc.) can be effected as necessary. The importance of such compensatory motor movements for a flying animal are self-evident. It should be noted that the co-ordination of the sensory stimuli with the motor nerves is, even in man, essentially an unconscious adjustment, a reflex mechanism. As an example of the role of this mechanism, one can cite Beecher's (1951) comments on differences among various birds in the normal attitude of the head "which is the attitude in which the external semicircular canal is horizontal" and which is the position of the head in flight, though the body may twist and turn in banking maneuvers.

Olfaction

There is considerable variation in the development of the olfactory bulbs in birds. The bulbs are smaller, relatively, in passerine birds than in ducks. There is only one olfactory bulb in the House Sparrow, but there are two in the crow. *Apteryx* has large olfactory bulbs, which have a structure similar to that seen in mammals. In other birds that have well-developed olfactory bulbs, a typical lamination is seen.

The debate over the olfactory powers of birds has continued for over a century. Audubon thought that he had settled the question by experiments with vultures. He showed that vultures did not find carrion or freshy killed animals if they were covered, but that the vultures very quickly discovered a picture of a partly dissected sheep, and tried to eat the picture. Walter (1943) summarized the literature on the many experiments devised to test the sense of smell in birds. Bajandurow and Larin, for example, conducted a series of conditioned-reflex experiments on pigeons by using electrical stimuli and a series of different odorants. They were able to condition the pigeons so that leg movements were produced merely by exposing the birds to the odorants; after the cerebral hemispheres were removed, the reflexes were no longer elicited by olfactory stimuli. Walter undertook a long series of experiments with ducks, pigeons, parakeets, and siskins (*Carduelis*). He was unable to duplicate the results obtained by Bajandurow and Larin. Walter even removed the eyeballs of ducks in order to insure that sight played no part in food-finding by the experimental birds; these ducks were unable to find food by olfactory stimuli. In fact, all of Walter's experiments gave negative results: no evidence of a sense of smell was obtained for any of the birds. Hamrum (1953) carried out several much simpler experiments and concluded that the Bobwhite possesses an olfactory sense and that olfactory stimuli probably influence its choice of food.

Thus it is seen that data are too fragmentary and contradictory to warrant positive statements regarding the importance of the sense of smell in birds. Based on morphological evidence, however, one must assume that some birds have a sense of smell, but that, by and large, this sense is poorly developed in birds; its influence on behavior is little understood.

Taste

Taste, like smell, is a type of chemoreception. There is a great reduction in numbers of taste nerve fibers in birds, and most are said to have only 40 to 60 taste buds, although some parrots may have about 400. By comparison, the rabbit has some 17,000 taste buds. The taste buds in mammals are concentrated on the tongue; in birds they occur primarily in the palate, pharynx, and inferior surface of the epiglottis. Most of the tongue is devoid of taste receptors, but Moore and Elliott (1946) found from 27 to 59 taste buds in six pigeon tongues. Taste buds have been found on the edges of the mandibles in some birds.

Taste has not been studied much in birds. Hamrum's Bobwhites "responded" to certain gustatory stimuli (including a relatively high concentration of HCl) "in much the same manner as other animals." All that can be concluded at present (mostly from morphological evidence) is that birds possess a sense of taste, but we can only conjecture that certain insects are "distasteful" to birds.

Touch

Birds have an abundance of several types of tactile end organs: the corpuscles of Grandry, Herbst, and Key-Retzius. All have been found in the bills of aquatic birds. Herbst's corpuscles have been described for many unrelated birds, e.g., *Apteryx,* ducks, flamingos, parrots, woodpeckers, passerines, etc. They occur not only in the bill and oral cavity but also in the cloaca, crus, forearm, and skin, especially in the pterylae (but not in the apteria) at the bases of the rectrices, remiges, and other contour feathers, such as bristles, setae, and those of the oil gland (Schildmacher, 1931). Schwartzkopff has suggested a possible second function (reception of vibratory stimuli) for the Herbst corpuscles (see Portmann, 1950).

Other Senses

In addition to the debatable "direction sense" (Beecher, 1951, 1952), there are other sensory endings that enable an animal to respond to its total environment (both internal and external): neuromuscular, neurotendinous, pain, and temperature endings. These have been little studied in birds. In a comparative study of the domestic hen and the Herring Gull (*Larus argentatus*), Chatfield *et al.* (1953) found a species difference in the sensitivity of nerves to cold, and a temperature gradient in conductivity in different segments of the same nerve in the gull. The advantages to a species having such an adaptation to cold seem clear, and certainly have some bearing on behavior and distribution.

The Basis for Behavior

It should be clear that one discusses the special senses separately only because it is convenient to do so. The entire nervous system, the hormones, and the muscles are integral parts of the coordinating system mentioned on p. 108. Behavior, then, cannot be understood unless one considers the anatomy and physiology of the organism. Behavior is not a "thing" that exists apart from the organism. Tinbergen (1951: 5) has commented that behavior is "always the outcome of a highly complex integration of muscle contractions." We take the view in this chapter that all behavior is ultimately derived from the neurophysiology of the organism, and that our woefully inadequate knowledge of the mechanisms involved is not increased by postulating a "directive drive arising mainly outside the supposed system of channels in which it is 'flowing' " (Thorpe, 1956: 31). At the same time, there are, as Tinbergen has emphasized, several ways to approach the study of behavior in an attempt to understand the causative factors. Physiologists, ethologists, and many psychologists use an objective approach, and the combined efforts of these workers are necessary for a more complete understanding of this complex subject. There is a vast literature on behavior, but three recent monographs, with their extensive bibliographies, and the review by Emlen (1955) may form the nucleus of a library for a student of bird behavior: Armstrong, 1947; Tinbergen, 1951; Thorpe, 1956.

In the study of behavior one must inevitably consider the most profound question encountered by biologists: What is the nature of life? One cannot, therefore, escape becoming a philosophical zoologist, because one must deal with concepts that cannot be subjected to experimental analysis. Unfortunately, man himself possesses certain limitations for such philosophizing. It is man's ability to deal with abstract concepts and to use word symbols as language that sets him apart from lower animals. At the same time, man's tendency for rationalization and his remarkable ability to compartmentalize different aspects of his mental processes are well known and they may be considered a serious handicap when man attempts to analyze the world of which he is a part. And yet, one would agree with Dr. Thorpe when he comments that "subjective concepts derived from introspection are among the essential tools for the study of life, and the only hope for a complete biology is to combine subjective and objective in the right proportions, using each approach with due circumspection and adequate safeguards as it is required." The investigator must make every effort, both in his thinking and in his published reports, to separate the subjective from the objective.

It appears to be a natural tendency for man to assume that there must be "purpose" in life and specifically man's life. This "belief" falls within the realm of religion and philosophy; it cannot be proved nor disproved. One's personal belief in this matter, however, may lead one to conclude that the same or a similar purpose is characteristic of all living things. Such a concept is not compatible with an objective or scientific approach to the analysis of behavior, as Tinbergen has pointed out. It is desirable, therefore, to contrast the terms "directiveness" and "purposiveness" as delineated by Thorpe (1956: 3). He states: "All biologists agree that the behaviour of organisms as a whole is directive, in the sense that in the course of evolution some at least of it has been modified by selection so as to lead with greater or less certainty towards states which favour the survival and reproduction of the individual." Such a concept is a truism in the sense that life as we know it could not persist if the protoplasm were not so organized as to favor survival and reproduction. It must be borne in mind, however, that when the ethologist speaks of directive "forces" or "drives," he is referring to this directiveness which is inherent in the physiology of the organism itself.

Dr. Thorpe believes that such a concept is not sufficient to explain the phenomena of animal behavior. He proposes that perception is more than an automatic response to sensory stimuli. Perception is "an active organising process, itself possibly including an element of purpose, tending all the time to build up the primary perceptions into more and more complete and unitary systems." Perception "is a process in time" and involves conation, memory or comparison, and anticipation. If "a living organism is essentially something which perceives, . . . *some essential ability to deal with events in time or in space is, by definition, to be expected throughout the world of living things.*" In this sense, living organisms exhibit purposiveness, and "one of the chief criteria for the attribution of purpose to an active system is whether or not it employs variable means to an invariable end." But conation must, in our opinion, be defined as the power or act of striving without a conscious goal, and the term "anticipation" should not be thought of as having the same meaning when applied to lower animals as it does in describing human behavior since we have no basis for attributing consciousness to them. Where within the organism might the "center" for purposiveness be located? Thorpe concludes that the central nervous system "can have the necessary complexity of structure to enable it to originate or provide true purposiveness," although he does not, of course, suggest that there is a localized "center" in a physical sense. There is, in fact, no evidence for the existence of such a "center."

Instinct and Instinctive Behavior

Contemporary students of behavior recognize that the adult animal is the product of its genetic endowment and its environment. One can say that the environment begins to exert its influence as soon as the sperm enters the egg. However, the environment, both internal and external, can only modify—it cannot negate—the genetic constitution. At the same time, the genic pattern unfolds and finds expression through the medium of the total environment. These two factors are inextricably interrelated, and any attempt to interpret behavior that does not take both into consideration is doomed to failure. Emlen (1955: 120, 125) remarked that a "behavior pattern, like any structural character, is a phenotype, the result of interaction between heredity and environmental forces," and that the genetic and environmental contributions to the behavioral phenotype "are so intricately interdependent as to be almost inseparable even on theoretical grounds." Nevertheless, a familiarity with the theories of instinct and learning is prerequisite for interpreting the literature on bird behavior.

As interpreted by Lorenz, Tinbergen, and Thorpe, instinct is innate behavior, and innate behavior is that which has not been changed by learning processes. The behavior itself is the result of internal processes, conveniently referred to as "drives." Thus, one can say that instinctive or internal drive is the complex of internal states or processes that lead to a given unlearned behavior pattern. Thorpe listed four characteristics of instinctive behavior:

1. The instincts or drives are innate, which is to say that they are inherited.
2. All drives are essentially physiological in nature and they are "patterns of activity" within the central nervous system (C.N.S.). One of the key points in this concept is that these patterns of activity may or may not result from visceral or hormonal stimulation, i.e., they may be "truly endogenous in the sense of originating within" the C.N.S.
3. The instincts are expressed in complex and often highly rigid patterns of behavior.
4. The instinctive behavior is evoked by complex environmental situations, particularly through visual and auditory stimuli.

Thorpe further suggests that there are six basic, directive instincts "which at present seem an indispensable minimum in studies on birds and mammals": nutrition, fighting, reproduction, social relations, sleep, and care of the body surfaces.

Konrad Lorenz believed that true instinctive behavior is expressed by *fixed-action patterns.* These patterns are so rigid and specific that they are "in every way as constant as anatomical structures, and are potentially just as valuable for systematic phylogenetic studies" (Thorpe, 1956: 18). The final behavior resulting from this fixed-action pattern has been called the *consummatory act.* Now, it is important to note that Lorenz and Thorpe believe that the sequential development of the fixed-action pattern provides the source of the drive and that the consummatory act itself is "the effective goal" of the behavior. The drive does not exist in the absence of the pattern. Moreover, the fixed patterns "build up a kind of specific tension" (*specific action poten-*

tial) in the C.N.S. This potential becomes "dammed up" if the environmental situation is not appropriate for the normal release of the fixed-action pattern. The "tension" thus created in the C.N.S. "results in a lowering of the threshold to stimuli effective in releasing the particular activity concerned" and it "may accumulate to the point at which the instinct appears to go off" without any external stimulation, resulting in *overflow* or *vacuum activity.* In such a case, the consummatory act is performed in the absence of the normal stimuli so that the act or behavior does not fit into the environmental situation or the general behavior of the animal at the time. Thorpe and others now believe that the fixed-action patterns are not inflexible and that the energy of the internal drive probably is specific to *classes* of behavior patterns rather than to individual reactions. Consequently, "overflow tension" may also (through *sparking over*) express itself in *displacement activities,* in which the behavior is irrelevant to the initial fixed-action pattern. This assumes that the dammed-up energy finds release by setting off some unrelated behavior pattern.

Tinbergen then proposed a tentative hypothetical scheme to account for these innate behavioral phenomena. His *nervous hierarchy* consists of a series of functional centers of integration at different levels within the C.N.S. (Fig. 1). Each level for the innate pattern (a particular major instinct) is activated primarily by stimuli (motivational factors) descending from the next higher "center"; the discharge of the innate pattern is blocked until an *innate releasing mechanism* (I.R.M.) receives appropriate *sign stimuli* (*releasers*) and removes the block. Tinbergen considered all internal (and some external) stimuli to be motivational factors. In general, they do not "evoke the overt response; they merely determine the threshold of the response to the sensory stimuli." Motivational factors result in purposiveness, but "the end of purposive behavior is not the attainment of an object or a situation itself, but the performance of the consummatory action." In the absence of adequate specific releasers for the consummatory act, the motivational drive finds expression in *appetitive behavior.* Consummatory behavior is characterized by its stereotyped motor pattern; appetitive behavior, by its plasticity and purposiveness. Appetitive (or exploratory) behavior, then, is the "variable introductory phase" of an instinctive behavior pattern; it may be activated by centers of all the levels "above that of the consummatory act." Appetitive behavior continues until an appropriate releaser stimulates or trips off the I.R.M., i.e., releases its blocking or inhibitory effect. When studying bird behavior, it is important to keep in mind that it is the discharge of consummatory action and not the biological or survival value involved that is the real goal of appetitive behavior, as far as the individual bird is concerned. The behavior of the individual and the habits of the species to which it belongs are two quite different matters.

As the result of recent work by Hinde (1952) and others, some workers feel that "appetitive behaviour and consummatory act differ only in degree, and that no absolute distinction can be made between them." Thorpe (1956: 42) concludes: "Thus the classic examples of appetitive behaviour and consummatory act can be regarded as the two ends of a series ranging from extreme variability and plasticity on the one hand to almost complete fixity on the other."

Lehrman (1953) and others subscribing to the "Gestalt" school have criticized the Lorenz-Tinbergen theory of behavior. Lehrman denies that the problem facing the ethologist is one of distinguishing between the role of instinct and learning in understanding behavior. He believes that the "use of 'explanatory' categories such as 'innate' and 'genically fixed' obscures the necessity of investigating developmental *processes* in order to gain insight into the actual mechanisms of behavior and their interrelations. . . . The interaction out of which the organism develops is *not* one . . . between heredity and environment. It is between *organism* and environment! And the organism is different at each different stage of its development." Consequently, "to say a behavior pattern is 'inherited' throws no light on its development except for the purely negative implication that *certain types* of learning are not directly involved." The ethologist, therefore, is unrealistic when he attempts to distinguish between *instinctive behavior* and *learned behavior*. Lehrman also objects to this theory of instinct because "it involves preconceived and rigid ideas of innateness and the nature of maturation." Preconceived ideas, however, are not necessarily restricted to the instinct theorists.

Emlen (1955: 123) has pointed out that "differences between these various concepts of behavioral organization are partly real and partly in viewpoint. While the Lorenzian view tends to focus on the individual act or movement and look outward toward the complex pattern, the Gestalt view starts with the latter and searches inward. Neither would appear to be entirely true or false, for both schools admit that a behavior pattern exhibits emergent characteristics and is more than a simple summation of movements" (see also Thorpe, 1956, Chapter 7). Ewer (1957) has attempted to reconcile the opposing views of Lehrman and Tinbergen by suggesting that the term *innate* be replaced by the term *self-differentiating* (or *endogenous*). Ewer proposed that a particular behavior pattern may be considered to be self-differentiating if it (1) is shown at the appropriate stage, in the appropriate situation, by all members (or all members of one sex) of a species, and (2) if it has not required either "instruction" from another member of the species or previous conditioning by means of an externally provided reward or punishment which does not form an essential component of an environment that permits of normal physical development. A self-differentiating response comes "into being as part of the normal development of every individual." It includes "the phase during which it is in the process of differentiating; this makes it easier to understand that processes akin to learning can be an integral part of the differentiating process." For example, in "learning to walk" the locomotor pattern is self-differentiating but it involves increasingly improved co-ordination. Ewer believes that "by turning from *innate* to *endogenous,* we have shifted our emphasis from the time at which a piece of behavior occurs (which may not be very meaningful) and have focused it instead on how that behavior comes into being."

In addition to certain fundamental differences between the "Gestalt" school and the "Instinct" school, there seems also to be considerable playing with semantics. The basis for each theory lies ultimately in the neurophysiology of the C.N.S. and, so far as is now known, specifically in the functioning of the association neuron arcs in the brain. This is the *sine qua non* of behavior. This lies behind Emlen's statement about the "emergent characteristics" of behavior—it "is more than a simple summation of movements." Thorpe (1956: 6) was talking about the same thing when he said: "We are entitled to claim that when the words purpose, expectancy, and anticipation are used, we are, *as biologists,* for the time being speaking of a mechanism which acts in given circumstances *as if* it were purposive, expectant or anticipatory, as the case may be, *and reserving judgement on more fundamental issues"* (last italics ours). In other words, the C.N.S. does far more than co-ordinate sensory stimuli and effect a motor response. The association neuron arcs enable the animal to react to the environment in such a way that many biologists find it difficult to refrain from using teleological terms. The basic problem arises because so little is known about the ways (i.e., the mechanisms) in which the brain tissue produces the phenomena that we call memory, learning, insight, etc. The various theories attempt to "explain" the mechanisms by which an animal accomplishes both simple and complex acts. The fallacy lies not so much in the theories (a theory is offered as a "working hypothesis"), but in the uncritical acceptance of isolated parts of the theories out of context or without regard to all available facts. All too often scraps of "evidence" are cited to support a given theory, when in reality the evidence is entirely irrelevant. The followers of Lorenz and Tinbergen, for example, sometimes forget that Tinbergen (1951: 122) cautioned that "while such a graphic representation [of his nervous hierarchy] may help to organize our thoughts, it has grave dangers in that it tends to make us forget its provisional and hypothetical nature." Nevertheless, certain concepts and terms have been useful for describing behavioral activities, whether or not the actual mechanisms are understood. It must be remembered, however, that the mere use of "causal" adjectives, such as *intention* movement or *displacement* behavior, does not really explain the cause of the behavior concerned. It seems doubtful that anyone would assert that we are dealing with known facts rather than with theories.

Learning and Intelligence

The student must cope not only with the inherent complexity of behavior patterns but also with an extensive behavioral vocabulary. He must, in addition, learn the different meanings given to common words which are used without precise definition in everyday life. One such word is "intelligence." A pertinent example for the student of bird behavior is offered by Thorpe's comments on the following statement made by C. Judson Herrick in his book *Neurological Foundations of Animal Behavior:* "It is everywhere recognized that birds possess highly complex instinctive endowments *and that their intelligence is very limited.*" Thorpe (1956) states: "No present-day student familiar with recent work on bird behaviour would be willing to endorse to-day the words I have put in italics." The fact is that Herrick and Thorpe are not talking about the same thing. When Herrick spoke of intelligence, he was thinking of the assessment of situations in a creative way such as is exhibited by man. There appears to be not a particle of evidence to indicate that birds possess this ability. Herrick's statement is as true today as it was in 1924. Thorpe continues: "In some contexts it is doubtful whether the birds are exceeded in learning ability by any organisms other than the highest mammals, and in their powers of co-ordinating their sense impressions for purposes of orientation on homing and migratory flights, they appear supreme in the animal kingdom." Thorpe, therefore, is not speaking about intelligence in the same sense, but of learning ability, and he states (1956: 156) that the "three factors which are perhaps most important for the evolution of high learning ability are the necessity for precise orientation, for individual recognition and for manipulation of material." Few would deny that birds possess remarkable abilities, but few would agree that this complex of factors equals intelligence as that word is applied to the higher primates.

Thorpe defined learning as "that process which manifests itself by adaptive changes in individual behaviour as a result of experience." In rare cases it may be fairly evident where learning and experience are involved, but the problem is never simple. We may cite, as an example, the many investigations of the pecking behavior of chicks. Some of the early results suggested that experience has little effect on efficiency in pecking; the ability was "innate." Later experiments indicated that peck aim became "virtually perfect" during the first 30 hours after hatching and, apparently, was due not to learning but to the physical maturation of the neuromuscular system. When chicks were prevented from pecking for about 2 weeks, however, they had to be taught to peck. Thorpe (1956: 312) pointed out that "we have always to bear in mind that birds which have been artificially prevented from performing a natural act may be suffering not merely from lack of practice but also from the setting up of contrary habits."

Following is a brief discussion of the basic types of learning processes as they are thought by Thorpe to apply to bird behavior. It should be emphasized, however, that there is considerable disagreement among authorities on what are the "basic types" of learning, and some insist that there is only one type.

Habituation "is an activity of the central nervous system whereby innate responses to mild and relatively simple stimuli, especially those of potential value as warnings of danger, wane as the stimuli continue for a long period without unfavourable results." The animal learns *not* to respond to stimuli which are without significance in that they fail to release any consummatory act. Although Thorpe considers habituation to be the simplest and most elementary form of learning, most of the examples cited by him pertain to enemy recognition. Too great an efficiency in habituation would, as Thorpe has pointed out, be disastrous for a species. It does seem clear, however, that some birds do have to learn what not to be afraid of. A fledgling passerine bird, either hand-reared or wild, may have to learn that a cabbage butterfly is not a source of danger. Another example of habituation is seen in man's ability to "tune out" constant sounds in the environment. Failure of birds to respond to sounds which have become meaningless through repetition, such as pistol shots, may also be cited here.

Conditioning is the establishment of an additional or substitute stimulus in an existing stimulus-response association. Examples of conditioned-reflex experiments were given in the discussion on olfaction. Such experiments probably are of value primarily as tools for the investigation of the senses of the animals. The role of conditioning in wild populations is poorly known.

Trial-and-error learning is "essentially the procedure by which one response is selected from an array of possible responses in a problem situation." Among typical examples are those associated with feeding and drinking. There is evidence that the young of some species have to learn which food is edible, which is inedible, but this matter has not been studied intensively. Wallace Craig's work on doves is often cited to show that the dove's drinking movements are innate "but the bird has no concept of water as being the stuff to drink." Thorpe believes that trial-and-error learning probably plays an important part in the improvement of nest-building, especially in selecting the proper materials. (For a discussion of experiments with puzzle boxes and mazes, see Thorpe, 1956, Chapter 14.)

Insight learning functions in selecting an appropriate response for a problem situation but "it differs from trial-and-error learning in being sudden and in apparently eliminating the time-consuming procedure of alternately selecting and discarding the available response patterns" (Emlen, 1955: 131). Thorpe believes that perceptions of temporal and spatial relations are inborn faculties in all animals, that perception is "essentially a learning process," and that perception "could provide one of the bases of internal drive." He further assumes provisionally "that the essence of insight is the perception of relations." Now although Thorpe states that the examples he cites do not prove the existence of insight learning in birds, there is little doubt that the examples lie behind his belief that birds may exhibit "extraordinary" intelligence. We may quote one example that appears to have hig significance for those who hold that birds display a considerabl amount of insight learning (and intelligence).

> This is the ability to pull up food which is suspended by a thread, the pulled-in loop being held by the foot while the bird reaches with its beak for the next pull. Everyone who has seen this performance by an adept wild bird . . . will have been impressed by the smooth ease and certainty, and by the entire absence of fumbling, with which the complete act is accomplished. Seldom does one see anything suggestive of trial-and-error learning. The act appears at first sight to be a real and sudden solution of the problem from the start, and thus to qualify for inclusion under "insight learning" (Thorpe, 1956: 333).

The interpretation of such behavior, of course, depends on one's point of view. But it should be pointed out that to the comparative neuroanatomist and neurologist, raising food on the end of a string does not represent a high degree of intelligence—as compared with primates—but rather a low level of learning. One can recognize that birds may exhibit remarkable abilities in space- and time-perception without concluding that insight learning and intelligence are involved.

Imprinting is "a term applied to the rapid formation of stable primary stimulus-response associations or fixations during early infancy" (Emlen, 1955). In the classical example of imprinting, geese raised from artificially incubated eggs accepted their human keepers and followed them as they would have followed their own parents. Such imprinted birds typically direct sexual displays toward the human figure (although attachments to inanimate objects have also been reported). The interesting report by Räber (1948) of a hand-raised male turkey is a case in point. The turkey directed courtship displays toward any man, but reacted by fighting or retreating at the approach of a woman. Although the male turkey would not display to a female turkey, he would mount one when it was in the position for copulation. Imprinting has also been demonstrated for many ducks, gallinaceous birds, coots, doves, ravens, jackdaws, etc. Ramsay (1951) reported experiments in which incubator-hatched chicks and Canada Goose goslings became imprinted to and followed a small green box containing an alarm clock; the goslings and Muscovy ducklings similarly followed a football (see also Ramsay and Hess, 1954; and Chapter 11). The many ramifications of imprinting have been summarized by Thorpe (1956, Chapter 15). Contrary to early information on the subject, present data indicate that imprinting is not always irreversible, nor is it always dependent on the events occurring during the first few minutes after hatching (see Ramsay and Hess, 1954). Imprinting is considered an important phenomenon in support of the theory of instinctive behavior and of the concept of the innate releasing mechanism. Thorpe suggested that song learning is a special type of imprinting, and that the learning of territory may involve "something of the same nature."

On Behavioral Phenotypes

The objective study of behavior is a relatively new science. The current theories will be modified as more precise information becomes available on neurophysiological mechanisms. Perhaps the greatest weakness in overemphasizing the importance of either instinctive or learned behavior is the tendency to disregard the complex factors involved in the physical maturation of the whole organism. Thus there is a need for neuroembryological studies in order to determine the rate of maturation of the nervous system for various integrative mechanisms. It seems apparent that in certain cases the failure of a particular motor response to appear at a given time may be due to the state of development of neuromuscular relationships and not due to lack of experience or "practice." Differences between altricial and precocial species in maturation of the nervous system have been described by Sutter (1951). At the time of hatching, the brain of a precocial bird (e.g., *Megapodius*) may equal 40 per cent of the adult weight, whereas in an altricial species (*Turdus merula*) it amounts to only 10 per cent of the adult weight. Further, the relative proportions of the several parts of the brain approach the adult condition in *Megapodius;* the proportions in *Turdus* are embryonic in that the cerebral hemispheres are very small and the brain stem, the seat for the centers of certain vital processes, is more highly developed. Myelinization of nerve fibers also progresses more rapidly in precocial birds, which can see and move about shortly after hatching. Myelinization of the optic nerve, for example, is completed several days before hatching in precocial species; it is not completed until several days after hatching in a thrush or a starling, birds in which the eyes remain closed for some time after hatching. Such differences in physical development, of course, must be considered in the study and interpretation of the behavior of young birds.

Other types of information, both experimental and observational, are needed as well. The outstanding work of certain European ornithologists in raising birds from the egg in order to determine the role of learning in song acquisition offers a technique for other studies. But if behavior is what the bird does, there is a need for more detailed observations of both wild and aviary birds. The importance of such observations becomes evident when it is pointed out that parts of eight other chapters in this book are devoted to special types of behavioral phenomena. In addition to these major biological areas, a bird's activities may run the gamut from "anting" to "wing-quivering." Detailed descriptions of such acts provide the raw materials for analyzing behavioral phenotypes, but only through the intensive study of a bird's life cycle can these individual acts be seen in their proper perspective with respect to the total behavior pattern.

References

Armstrong, Edward A. 1947. *Bird Display and Behaviour.* Lindsay Drummond, London.

——— 1949. Diversionary Display. Parts 1 and 2. *Ibis,* 91: 88–97; 179–188.

——— 1954. The Ecology of Distraction Display. *Brit. Jour. Animal Behaviour,* 2: 121–135.

Beecher, William J. 1951. A Possible Navigation Sense in the Ear of Birds. *Amer. Midl. Nat.,* 46: 367–384.

——— 1952. The Unexplained Direction Sense of Vertebrates. *Sci. Monthly,* 75: 19–25.

Blair, H. M. S., H. R. Oliver, and A. H. Chisholm. 1950. "Rodent-run" Distraction-behaviour in Birds. *Ibis,* 92: 476–477.

Boss, Willis Robert. 1943. Hormonal Determination of Adult Characters and Sex Behavior in Herring Gulls (*Larus argentatus*). *Jour. Exper. Zool.,* 94: 181–203.

Brand, Albert R., and P. Paul Kellogg. 1939. Auditory Responses of Starlings, English Sparrows, and Domestic Pigeons. *Wils. Bull.,* 51: 38–41.

Bray, Charles W., and W. R. Thurlow. 1942. Temporary Deafness in Birds, *Auk,* 59: 379–387.

Chatfield, Paul O., Charles P. Lyman, and Laurence Irving. 1953. Physiological Adaptation to Cold of Peripheral Nerve in the Leg of the Herring Gull (*Larus argentatus*). *Amer. Jour. Physiol.,* 172: 639–644.

Cole, W. V. 1955. The Comparative Morphology of Sensory Endings in Striated Muscle. *Trans. Amer. Micro. Soc.,* 74: 302–311.

Craig, Wallace. 1912. Observations on Doves Learning to Drink. *Jour. Animal Behav.,* 2: 273–279.

Crozier, W. J., and E. Wolf. 1943. Theory and Measurement of Visual Mechanisms. X. *Jour. Gen. Physiol.,* 27: 287–313.

Daanje, A. 1950. On Locomotor Movements in Birds and the Intention Movements Derived from Them. *Behaviour,* 3: 48–98.

Detwiler, Samuel R. 1943. *Vertebrate Photoreceptors.* Exper. Biol. Monog., Macmillan Co., New York.

Dice, Lee R. 1945. Minimum Intensities of Illumination under which Owls Can Find Dead Prey by Sight. *Amer. Nat.,* 79: 385–416.

Edwards, Ernest P. 1943. Hearing Ranges of Four Species of Birds. *Auk,* 60: 239–241.

Emlen, John T., Jr. 1955. The Study of Behavior in Birds. In *Recent Studies in Avian Biology,* Univ. Illinois Press, Urbana, pp. 105–153.

Ewer, R. F. 1957. Ethological Concepts. *Science,* 126: 599–603.

Favaloro, Norman J. 1947. Birds Sheltering from Heat. *Emu,* 47: 61–62.

Fisher, Harvey I. 1957. Footedness in Domestic Pigeons. *Wils. Bull.,* 69: 170–177.

Friedmann, Herbert. 1930. The New Study of Bird Behavior. *Bird-Banding,* 1: 61–66.

——— 1932. On the Supposed Visual Function of the Nictitating Membrane in the Domestic Pigeon. *Jour. Comp. Psychol.,* 14: 55–61.

——— and Malcolm Davis. 1938. "Left-handedness" in Parrots. *Auk,* 55: 478–480.

Frings, Hubert, and William A. Boyd. 1952. Evidence for Olfactory Discrimination by the Bobwhite Quail. *Amer. Midl. Nat.,* 48: 181–184.

Gannon, G. R. 1945. The Nature of Bird Activities. *Emu,* 45: 153–169.

Goodwin, Derek. 1948. Some Abnormal Sexual Fixations in Birds. *Ibis,* 90: 45–48.

——— 1951. Some Aspects of the Behaviour of the Jay *Garrulus glandarius. Ibis,* 93: 414–442; 602–625.

Griffin, Donald R. 1953. Acoustic Orientation in the Oil Bird, Steatornis. *Proc. Natl. Acad. Sci.,* 39: 884–893.

Hamrum, Charles L. 1953. Experiments on the Senses of Taste and Smell in the Bob-white Quail (Colinus virginianus virginianus). *Amer. Midl. Nat.,* 49: 872–877.

Hauser, Doris C. 1957. Some Observations on Sun-bathing in Birds. *Wils. Bull.,* 69: 78–90.

Herrick, C. Judson. 1924. *Neurological Foundations of Animal Behavior.* Henry Holt & Co., New York.

Herrick, Francis H. 1939. Symposium on the Individual vs. the Species. 1. *Auk,* 56: 244–249.

Hinde, R. A. 1952. The Behaviour of the Great Tit (*Parus major*) and Some Other Related Species. *Behaviour, Suppl.* 2, 1952: (pp. x + 201).

——— 1953a. A Possible Explanation of Paper-tearing Behaviour in Birds. *Brit. Birds,* 46: 21–23.

——— 1953b. Appetitive Behaviour, Consummatory Act, and the Hierarchical Organisation of Behaviour—with Special Reference to the Great Tit (*Parus major*). *Behaviour,* 5: 189–224.

——— 1954. Factors Governing the Changes in Strength of a Partially Inborn Response, as Shown by the Mobbing Behaviour of the Chaffinch (*Fringilla coelebs*). I, II. *Proc. Roy. Soc. London,* 142B: 306–358.

——— and James Fisher. 1951. Further Observations on the Opening of Milk Bottles by Birds. *Brit. Birds,* 44: 393–396.

Huxley, J. S., Anthony Buxton, Collingwood Ingram, and Derek Goodwin. 1948. Tameness in Birds. *Ibis,* 90: 312–318.

Jones, Frederic Wood. 1937. The Olfactory Organ of the Tubinares. *Emu,* 36: 281–286; 37: 10–13; 128–131.

Lack, David. 1941. Some Aspects of Instinctive Behaviour and Display in Birds. *Ibis,* 1941: 407–441.

Lehrman, Daniel S. 1953. A Critique of Konrad Lorenz's Theory of Instinctive Behavior. *Quart. Rev. Biol.,* 28: 337–363.

Lorenz, Konrad Z. 1937. The Companion in the Bird's World. *Auk,* 54: 245–273.

——— 1952. *King Solomon's Ring.* Thomas Y. Crowell Co., New York.

McAtee, W. L. 1947. Torpidity in Birds. *Amer. Midl. Nat.,* 38: 191–206.

Miller, Alden H. 1951. The "Rodent-run" of the Green-tailed Towhee. *Ibis,* 93: 307–308.

Miller, Loye. 1952. Auditory Recognition of Predators. *Condor,* 54: 89–92.

Moore, A. D. 1946. Temperature Tolerance of Birds' Feet. *Auk,* 63: 127–128.

Moore, Charles Allan, and Rush Elliott. 1946. Numerical and Regional Distribution of Taste Buds on the Tongue of the Bird. *Jour. Comp. Neur.,* 84: 119–131.

Morrison-Scott, T. C. S. 1937. Experiments on Colour-Vision in the Satin Bower-Bird (*Ptilonorhynchus violaceus*), with other observations. *Proc. Zool. Soc. London,* 1937A: 41–49.

Moynihan, M. 1953. Some Displacement Activities of the Black-headed Gull. *Behaviour,* 5: 58–80.

Nice, Margaret Morse, and Joost Ter Pelkwyk. 1941. Enemy Recognition by the Song Sparrow. *Auk,* 58: 195–214.

Palmer, William. 1909. Instinctive Stillness in Birds. *Auk,* 26: 23–36.

Palmgren, Pontus. 1949. On the Diurnal Rhythm of Activity and Rest in Birds. *Ibis,* 91: 561–576.

Pettingill, Olin Sewall, Jr. 1938. Intelligent Behavior in the Clapper Rail. *Auk,* 55: 411–415.

Portmann, Adolphe. 1950. Les organes des sens. In Grassé's *Traité de Zoologie,* Vol. 15, Oiseaux. Masson et Cie, Paris, pp. 204–220.

Poulsen, Holger. 1953. A Study of Incubation Responses and Some Other Behaviour Patterns in Birds. *Vidensk. Meddel. Dansk Naturhist For. Köbenhavn,* 115: 1–139.

Pumphrey, R. J. 1948. The Sense Organs of Birds. *Ibis,* 90: 171–199.

Pycraft, W. P. 1908. On the Position of the Ear in the Woodcock (*Scolopax rusticula*). *Ibis,* 1908: 551–558.

Räber, Hans. 1948. Analyse des Balzverhaltens eines domestizierten Truthahns (*Meleagris*). *Behaviour,* 1: 237–266.

——— 1949. Das Verhalten Gefangener Waldohreulen (*Asio otus otus*) und Waldkäuze (*Strix aluco aluco*) zur Beute. *Behaviour,* 2: 1–95.

Ramsay, A. O. 1951. Familial Recognition in Domestic Birds. *Auk,* 68: 1–16.

——— and Eckhard H. Hess. 1954. A Laboratory Approach to the Study of Imprinting. *Wils. Bull.,* 66: 196–206.

Rand, A. L. 1941. Development and Enemy Recognition of the Curve-billed Thrasher *Toxostoma curvirostre. Bull. Amer. Mus. Nat. Hist.,* 78: 213–242.

——— 1943. Some Irrelevant Behavior in Birds. *Auk,* 60: 168–171.

Riddle, Oscar. 1947. *Endocrines and Constitution in Doves and Pigeons.* Carnegie Inst., Washington, D. C.

Schildmacher, Hans. 1931. Untersuchungen über die Funktion der Herbstschen Körperchen. *Jour. f. Ornith.,* 79: 374–415.

Schwartzkopff, Johann. 1952. Über den Gehörsinn der Vögel. *Jour. f. Ornith.,* 93: 91–103.

——— 1955a. On the Hearing of Birds. *Auk,* 72: 340–347.

——— 1955b. Schallsinnesorgane, ihre Funktion und biologische Bedeutung bei Vögeln. *Acta XI Congr. Internatl. Ornith. 1954:* 189–208.

Sibley, Charles G. 1955. Behavioral Mimicry in the Titmice (Paridae) and Certain Other Birds. *Wils. Bull.,* 67: 128–132.

Sperry, R. W. 1951. Mechanisms of Neural Maturation. In *Handbook of Experimental Psychology,* S. S. Stevens, ed. John Wiley & Sons, New York.
Strong, R. M. 1911. On the Olfactory Organs and the Sense of Smell in Birds. *Jour. Morph.,* 22: 619–661.
Sutter, Ernst. 1951. Growth and Differentiation of the Brain in Nidifugous and Nidicolous Birds. *Proc. 10th Internatl. Ornith. Congr., 1950:* 636–644.
Sutton, George Miksch. 1943. Notes on the Behavior of Certain Captive Young Fringillids. *Univ. Mich. Mus. Zool. Occ. Papers, No. 474:* 1–14.
———— 1947. A Female Cardinal and Her Reflection. *Bird-Banding,* 18: 151–154.
Tello, J. Francisco. 1922. Die Entstehung der motorischen und sensiblen Nervenendigungen. *Zeitschr. f. Anat. u. Entwicklungs.,* 64: 348–440.
Thomson, Arthur. 1929. The Pecten, considered from an Environmental Point of View. *Ibis,* 1929: 608–639.
Thorpe, W. H. 1951. The Learning Abilities of Birds. *Ibis,* 93: 1–52; 252–296.
———— 1956. *Learning and Instinct in Animals.* Harvard Univ. Press, Cambridge.
Tinbergen, N. 1948. Social Releasers and the Experimental Method Required for Their Study. *Wils. Bull.,* 60: 6–51.
———— 1951. *The Study of Instinct.* Oxford Univ. Press, London.
———— 1952. "Derived" Activities; Their Causation, Biological Significance, Origin, and Emancipation during Evolution. *Quart. Rev. Biol.,* 27: 1–32.
Vanderplank, F. L. 1934. The Effect of Infra-red Waves on Tawny Owls (*Strix aluco*). *Proc. Zool. Soc. London,* 1934: 505–507.
Walls, Gordon Lynn. 1942. The Vertebrate Eye and Its Adaptive Radiation. *Cranbrook Inst. Sci., Bull. No. 19.*
Walter, W. G. 1943. Some Experiments on the Sense of Smell in Birds. *Arch. Néerland. Physiol.,* 27: 1–72.
Watson, Frank G. 1940. A Behavior Study of the White-tailed Kite. *Condor,* 42: 295–304.
Weston, Francis M. 1913. Swimming of Young Herons. *Auk,* 30: 111.
Whitaker, Lovie M. 1957. A Résumé of Anting, with Particular Reference to a Captive Orchard Oriole. *Wils. Bull.,* 69: 195–262.
Williamson, Kenneth. 1948. Eider Duck Plucking Down during Distraction-display. *Ibis,* 90: 142–143.
———— 1952. Regional Variation in the Distraction Displays of the Oyster-catcher. *Ibis,* 94: 85–96.
Wood, Casey Albert. 1917. *The Fundus Oculi of Birds, Especially as Viewed by the Ophthalmoscope.* The Lakeside Press, Chicago.
Wynne-Edwards, V. C. 1947. Sun-bathing by Birds. *Brit. Birds,* 40: 256.

5. Voice and sound production

THROUGHOUT THE animal kingdom birds are outstanding for the variety of sounds they make and for the versatility of their songs. Other vertebrate animals are, by comparison, primarily a quiet lot. A few fish "grunt"; frogs and toads "sing" during certain periods of the year, but the calls of any one species are of a limited variety. Few are the sounds made by reptiles: alligators bellow, some snakes hiss, rattlesnakes produce a mechanical sound, and the blue racer may vibrate its tail against vegetation. Except for man and some apes (especially gibbons), most mammals have a small repertory, although some (e.g., Howler monkeys, wapiti, hyenas) do make remarkable sounds. Among invertebrate animals some insects are instrumentalists, producing sounds by rubbing together modified areas of the body. The monotonous or stridulant tones made by cicadas, grasshoppers, and crickets are well known, and the males of certain tropical American butterflies make a mechanical clicking noise in flight.

Mechanical Sounds

Nonvocal sounds are produced by birds too. The flightless and secretive *Apteryx* of New Zealand stamps its feet when annoyed. Boat-billed Herons (*Cochlearius*), Whale-billed Storks (*Balaeniceps*), and other storks rattle or clap their mandibles. The Roadrunner (*Geococcyx*) also rattles or clatters its mandibles. Woodpeckers produce a drumming sound by pounding trees or metal roofs with their bills. "Drumming" is also accomplished with the wings, as is the case with the Ruffed Grouse (*Bonasa umbellus*). The wings of the Common Goldeneye (*Bucephala clangula*) make such a noticeable noise in flight that the bird has been called the "Whistler." One may first become aware of the presence of Mourning Doves (*Zenaidura macroura*) by hearing the whistling sound of the wings as the birds fly by. The wings of the Woodcock (*Philohela minor*) are responsible for a melodious sound during springtime courtship flights. During the breeding season the male nighthawk (*Chordeiles*) frequently interrupts its lazy and somewhat erratic flight high above ground to dive earthward. When close to the ground, the bird pulls out of its dive, and the air rushing through its wing feathers produces a characteristic booming noise.

Collingwood Ingram (1956: 673) has described the "eccentric nuptial flight" of the Little Bustard (*Otis tetrax*) in which a structural modification of the seventh (fourth according to British numbering) primary is believed to account for a flight whistle.

> While indulging in this performance the wings are kept much depressed, like those of a drake about to land, while the head is held outstretched and carried in an almost erect position. Throughout this highly mannered flight one can distinctly hear a curious whistling sound. Although proof is lacking, there can be little doubt that this is caused by air passing through one or more of the gaps created by the abnormally-shaped fourth primary in each wing. In the male of this species, but not in the female [nor in the first-year male], this feather is appreciably shorter than either of its neighbours, while it is further characterised by having its web deeply and asymmetrically emarginate on both sides of the shaft.

In courtship flights especially, the wings of the male Wagler's Oropendola (*Zarhynchus wagleri*) make a "loud startling, rushing roar, such as might be produced by the sudden violent tearing of some textile" (Chapman, 1928). Some of the neotropical manakins (Pipridae) combine nonvocal sounds with courtship dances conducted in small open spaces ("leks") in the jungle. The mechanical sounds produced by these birds have been likened to the "muffled rattling of dried peas within their pod," "the crack of a whip," "a sharp explosive snap," and a "sharp percussive crack." All are presumed to result from specialized features of the wing feathers and muscles (Chapman, 1935; Lowe, 1942): the webs of the four outermost primaries are very narrow, leaving gaps between the feathers; there is a thickening of the shafts of the first four or five secondaries; and two of the forearm muscles (flexor carpi ulnaris and flexor digitorum superficialis) give rise to tendinous slips that insert on the bases of the secondaries (some other birds, however, possess a similar muscular arrangement). Sutton (1945: 241; and *in litt.*) referred to the Wedge-tailed Sabre-wing or Singing Hummingbird (*Campylopterus curvipennis*) as "a species notable for its curiously curved, much stiffened wing feathers" which produce "an almost frightening roar" as the bird flies about the undergrowth in which it "sings."

The tail feathers, also, may produce mechanical sounds during flight. The Common Snipe (*Capella gallinago*) engages in an aerial display involving a "bleating" flight, produced by the "relatively slow quivering of the half open wings superimposed on the much more rapid vibration of the tail-feathers" (Witherby *et al.*, 1949: 199).

Several unrelated birds make sounds by secondarily filling the esophagus with air from the lungs. During the breeding season the esophagus of the breeding male Sage Grouse (*Centrocercus*) is capable of distention to 25 times that of the esophagus of the mature nonbreeding male. The greatest increase in size, midway between glottis and crop, consists of a single enlargement which is almost spherical. The hypertrophy of the esophagus is accompanied by an enlargement of fleshy pads at the sides of the glottis and of the skin and bare areas of the neck. "By sudden contraction of the muscles of the neck, the air trapped in the distended portion of the esophagus causes the membranes of the bare areas to vibrate," and results in a "soft, hollow 'plopping' sound of considerable intensity" (Honess and Allred, 1942). Chapin (1922) described anatomical specializations in the male American Bittern (*Botaurus lentiginosus*), and concluded that the "pumping" of the bittern is accomplished by distending the esophagus with air (see also Maynard, 1928: 333). He further pointed out that certain other birds produce sounds in a similar manner: e.g., a rail (*Sarothrura elegans*), a bustard (*Neotis cafra*), the Pectoral Sandpiper (*Erolia melanotos*), many pigeons, two African sylviids (*Camaroptera superciliaris* and *Bathmocercus rufus*), and the Mocking-thrush (*Donacobius atricapillus*). Fuertes (1913: 342) had reported earlier that "both sexes of *Donacobius* possess an inflatable sac of bright yellow skin on the sides of the throat, which, when the bird sings, puffs out to the size of a cherry, and is a very queer and conspicuous character."

Vocal Sounds

The syrinx, as pointed out in Chapter 2, is the primary sound-producing organ in birds. Other anatomical structures may modify the voice, but usually are not responsible for it. That the mouth plays a minor role is suggested by the fact that some birds (e.g., Prothonotary Warbler, Kirtland's Warbler) habitually sing complete songs while carrying a billful of food. Certain specializations of the trachea were discussed on p. 34. Elongation and coiling of the trachea result in a trombone effect, adding resonance to the voice. In the Chachalaca (*Ortalis vetula*), in which the tracheal loop is absent in females and young males, "the old males sing a full octave lower than the females and young males . . ." (Sutton, 1951: 127). Dilatations of the trachea (as in some male ducks and in the cotingas *Cephalopterus* and *Perissocephalus*) also modify the sounds made by the syrinx.

Both sexes of the Emu (*Dromiceius novae-hollandiae*) possess a tracheal pouch, which reaches its full development during the breeding season, at which time, especially, deep booming sounds are produced. The thin-walled and voluminous pouch may be over a foot in length, but its slitlike opening into the ventral wall of the trachea is less than 3 inches long (Murie, 1867; see also Portmann, 1950: 265).

An apparently unique diverticulum from the interclavicular air sac has been described for the Brown Jay (*Psilorhinus*) by Sutton and Gilbert (1942). This small, subcutaneous "furcular pouch" lies in the interclavicular space and is thought to be responsible for the *hiccup,* a "part of the Brown Jay's vocabulary."

Classification of Vocal Sounds

The vocal sounds made by birds are classified as songs and call notes, depending on length and function. If one were to state that a call note is any vocal sound that is not a song, anyone thinking of the Wood Thrush (*Hylocichla mustelina*) or the Nightingale (*Luscinia megarhyncha*) would have little difficulty deciding which of the vocalizations were call notes. But the distinction is not so simple when considering *all* birds. The Song Sparrow, for example, has 21 "chief vocalizations" (Nice, 1943: 274). Thorpe (1956) informs us that "a bird's call note, in contrast to its song, is a brief sound with a relatively simple acoustic structure."

Call notes serve a multitude of purposes. The Bobwhite (*Colinus virginianus*) uses a special note as a gathering call when the members of a covey become separated. Both adults and young of such precocial species use similar calls to keep the brood together or to reunite it. Fledglings of altricial species, as well, give location notes. Nestlings may give distinctive food calls when hungry, and other calls when being fed; they utter soft notes of well-being when they are warm and adequately fed; they may give distress calls when cold or when handled (after a certain age). Voipio (1952) described a special call given by a young Green Sandpiper (*Tringa ochropus*). When Voipio picked up the young bird "it was heard to emit sounds at a very high pitch, approaching the upper limit of the sound range audible to the human ear. Therefore, although the author's ear only registered the cry of the young bird very faintly the mother bird reacted to it instantaneously from a distance of at least 50 metres." Fledgling and juvenile birds may, in addition, develop call notes unlike those of the nestling or the adult.

A species may utter several kinds of alarm notes, depending in part on the cause for alarm and the time of year. Colonial-nesting species and nonbreeding flocks have distinct warning notes. In describing the warning cry of Wagler's Oropendola, Chapman remarked that at times not only did the colony "act as one bird and plunge from their nests or perches into the forest" but birds of other species sometimes also responded to the warning call. The alarm notes of titmice often serve to alert all of the species found in winter feeding flocks.

Various other notes are associated with fear, anxiety, or pain; still others, with breeding behavior, such as threat and intimidation notes, or greeting notes between mated birds. Female Song Sparrows announce their sex "by various notes, used only by females and typically in connection with a mate and nest" (Nice, 1943: 172). Other birds have special notes given primarily during the nest-building or incubation periods. Special notes often accompany copulation. Blue-gray Gnatcatchers (*Polioptila caerulea*) carry on an almost continuous exchange of calls during nest construction. The female American Goldfinch (*Spinus tristis*) gives an easily identifiable warbling call during nest-building and incubation. Magpie-larks (*Grallina cyanoleuca*) give a stimulation note which is used principally "in nest-building and feeding of the young" (Robinson, 1947).

Grinnell (1920) spoke of the winter call notes of the Ruby-crowned Kinglet (*Regulus calendula*) as "sequestration notes"; they "serve to keep the foraging birds *apart*" because "each individual Kinglet *must cover much territory in limited time* in order to gather the food in sufficient quantity." Some nocturnal migrants use special call notes which are rarely heard at other times.

Song

Most of the discussion in literature has centered around the function of song and, in recent years, the types of song. Several definitions of bird song have been proposed, but as more has been learned about bird behavior they have proved to be either too restrictive or too broad to be of more than historical interest.

Nicholson (1929: 41) said that "bird song is properly a sustained, more or less uninterrupted repetition of one or more notes conforming recognisably to a constant specific type, and used by the male as an expression of independent sovereignty." Saunders (1929: 16) proposed that "a bird's song is a vocal performance usually confined to the male, and to a definite season of the year, that season including the time of courtship and mating," but he added that true song is not necessarily musical nor is it confined to the male. Tinbergen (1939: 73–74), recognizing the "enormous diversity of bird calls that are commonly labeled as song," commented that duration of the call and aesthetic appreciation are poor criteria for classifying bird sounds as call notes or as songs, and he emphasized the importance of function for understanding the vocal efforts of birds. Craig (1943: 169–172) analyzed the five criteria used in the definitions of Nicholson and Saunders and showed that there were exceptions to each one. He proposed, therefore, that the proper procedure in the study of bird song "is to develop a concept inductively." Craig's concept included the recognition that bird songs are true music and aesthetic art, and "that there is always some formality about the song." When formality is lacking in the song it can be found in the accompanying behavior. Thus, when "the male cowbird says 'glub glub kee he keek' we are sure that this is a song, because it is accompanied by a display toward the female."

Nicholson and Koch (1936) and Lister (1953a) distinguished between primary or true song and secondary or subsong. Nicholson and Koch reserved "the word 'song' for full or true songs consisting of a flow or pattern of notes warbled or otherwise delivered more or less at the top of the bird's voice, separating as sub-song all similar performances which are so inwardly or faintly delivered that they do not carry to anywhere near the distance over which the bird is physically capable of making itself heard."

The following classification is of value insofar as it enables one to develop a concept of bird song. Definitions are needed as a basis for uniformity in reporting observations, but one must remember that a definition is a tool, not the end product. The discussion which follows the definitions of the several song categories reveals the frequent overlap in functions of a particular song type (e.g., flight song, duetting) among different birds.

Primary Song

Advertising (or territorial) song is a "loud sound, given by a bird of one of the two sexes especially at the beginning of the reproductive period, that serves to attract a sex partner, to warn off a bird of the same sex, or both" (Tinbergen, 1939: 80). This type of song is inseparably related to territoriality in birds, and it is one of the biological isolating mechanisms that "guarantees the mating of individuals belonging to the same species" (Nice, 1943: 149). In the Song Sparrow advertising song serves equally for attracting a mate and for warning other males. In the Snow Bunting (*Plectrophenax nivalis*), on the other hand, attraction of a mate is the primary function; Tinbergen noted that a "conspicuous feature of the behavior of the newly mated male was the abrupt stopping of his song. During the first few hours after the arrival of a female that stayed with him no male sang a single note" (1939: 24; see also Nice, 1943: 173). Attraction of a mate seems also to be of primary import in the Brown Towhee (*Pipilo fuscus*) because "permanently mated males do not sing" (Quaintance, 1938). Advertising song in many tropical species, however, differs from the examples just cited, and the females of some temperate zone species (e.g., European Robin, Mockingbird) have territorial songs that are given primarily in the nonbreeding season. It should be noted also that mechanical sounds may fulfill the two functions of advertising song.

Signal song may be defined as any song that serves to co-ordinate the activities of birds, particularly of a mated pair. This definition arbitrarily excludes the song function of warning or threat to other males (or females) that is inherent in the concept of advertising song. Nice (1937: 129) found that under normal conditions a female Song Sparrow "may come off the nest two-thirds of the time in answer to 'signal songs' and one-third independently." Skutch (1954: 104) reported that members of a mated pair of Black-striped Sparrows (*Arremonops conirostris*), "when they alight side by side after a temporary separation, greet each other with a sort of song, albeit one devoid of melody." Signal songs may be an integral part of courtship behavior; still others may act as a stimulus to gaping by nestlings. Such songs may be the same as the territorial song, in which case only the function differs. Responsive singing in many species is a method used for co-ordinating the activities of mated birds.

Emotional song encompasses a variety of songs that cannot be associated directly with securing a mate and defense of territory. Excluding early anthropomorphic interpretations of bird song, many ornithologists have concluded that "song is a normal outlet of excess energy in many birds" even "when there is no special function to be served, nor on the other hand, any inhibitory influence" (Nice, 1943: 148). Twilight, postbreeding, and some winter songs may be included under this heading (see "Song Cycles"). Although most social singing is properly considered as signal song, serving to stimulate or co-ordinate physiological development and flock activities, it seems likely that some social singing may be, in part, an outlet for excess energy (which is to say, the function is unknown). Skutch (1954: 39) observed five male Yellow-faced Grassquits (*Tiaris olivacea*) singing in the same small bush at the height of the nesting season. In this species, as in the American Goldfinch, the male defends only a small area around the nest; the psychological aspects of the sociality of such species are poorly understood.

Secondary Song

Nicholson's secondary or subsong "is low and inward, often becoming so faint as to be inaudible at a few yards range"; it has no territorial significance, it may be sung by either sex, and it may be more varied than the primary song—in fact, "many species have a sub-song which have never developed a true song." Lister (1953a, 1953b) presented a "more exact terminology as a preliminary to further investigation" of secondary song. He proposed four major subdivisions, and, in addition, would include "other songs used only occasionally or so infrequently as not to justify their inclusion in the category of primary song, however loud or quiet they may be, e.g. the special courtship songs given by some species." The inclusion of courtship songs in this category seems to us to be unwarranted.

Whispering song is the "very quiet, inward rendering of the primary song, with or without slight variations or additions" and with "an audibility limit of no more than about 20 yards."

Subsong, less common than whispering song, is the "very quiet, inward rendering of song which is intrinsically different from the primary song."

Rehearsed song is the "random utterance of song-notes by young and sometimes old birds before they have attained perfection in the primary song. In the case of old birds this would cover the very imperfect versions of the primary song which can sometimes be heard in winter and spring (this does not include the full, primary songs uttered during the winter months by such birds as the Robin and the Song Thrush)." Lister thought it unnecessary to use a different phrase ("searching or exploratory song") to describe the first song attempts by young birds.

Female song, according to Lister, should be considered a type of secondary song but this certainly would be an inappropriate designation for female song in many species.

Many examples can be cited to demonstrate the inadequacy of early definitions of song, but the examples are of far greater importance as they reveal the complex relationships between song and behavior. Song is primarily a characteristic of passerine birds (the "songbirds"), but not all songbirds sing and some nonpasserine birds do (e.g., Bobwhite, Mourning Dove, Upland Plover). Song is typically the function of the male, but again there are many exceptions (see Nice, 1943: 129; Gerber, 1956). The females of certain species (e.g., European Robin, Mockingbird, Loggerhead Shrike, Bullock's Oriole, Violet-eared Waxbill, White-crowned Sparrow) sing occasionally or under special conditions. The female Orange-billed Sparrow (*Arremon aurantiirostris*) sings while incubating (Skutch, 1954: 94). Both sexes may sing elaborate songs "in courtship or to keep up the bond between the pair," as in some scrub-wrens (Sylviidae), several spinetails (Furnariidae), European Dipper (*Cinclus cinclus*), Gray-cheeked Thrush (*Hylocichla minima bicknelli*), Cardinal (*Richmondena cardinalis*), etc. In Australia, female song is very common "among resident territory-holders which appear to follow the pattern of the life cycle of the Wren-tits very closely" (Robinson, 1949). In a few species, in which the male incubates, the female has an elaborate song and the male may not sing at all: e.g., Variegated Tinamou (*Crypturus variegatus*), Hemipode-quails, Painted-snipe, Northern Phalarope (*Lobipes lobatus*).

Responsive or antiphonal singing and duetting have been reported in many species, in which both sexes sing either the same or different songs and either simultaneously or alternately. Here are some representative examples: the Marbled Wood-quail (*Odontophorus gujanensis*), Bar-tailed Trogon (*Heterotrogon vittatum*), Kookaburra (*Dacelo gigas*), a barbet (*Trachyphonus d'arnaudii*), many South American tyrant-flycatchers, Australian "butcher-birds" (Cracticidae), Magpie-lark (Grallinidae), certain timaliids (*Garrulax erythrocephalus, Macronus ptilosis, M. gularis, Pomatorhinus erythrogenys*), several Central American wrens (see Skutch, 1940: 295), California Thrasher (*Toxostoma redivivum*), Kenya Red-tailed Bush Chat (Turdidae), the scrub-warbler *Bradypterus usambarae* (Sylviidae), two bush-shrikes and the South African Bokmakierie (*Laniarius funebris, L. ferrugineus,* and *Telophorus zeylonus*), Buff-rumped Warbler (*Basileuterus fulvicauda*), Buff-throated Saltator (*Saltator maximus*). Wetmore (1926: 246), in speaking of the ovenbird (*Furnarius rufus*), reported that "the loud calls of the ovenbird never fail to announce its presence. One, presumably the male, with bill thrown up and wings drooped, gives vent to a series of shrieking, laughing calls, with distended, vibrating throat, and quivering wing tips. At about the middle of this strange song its mate chimes in with shrill calls of a different pitch, and the two continue in duet to terminate together." Young (1942) described duetting in a Malayan cuckoo (*Centropus bengalensis javanicus*) in which the "smooth 'whōō, whū, whū, whū, whū' of the male finds instant response in the higher-pitched 'kā, kā, kā, kā, kow' of the female." Haverschmidt (1947), however, asserted that one "can only speak of a duet when, in a mated pair of birds, both sexes utter the same sounds either simultaneously" or alternately; "community singing" cannot be called duetting. He considered true duetting to take place in *Certhiaxis, Donacobius,* and *Thamnophilus,* as well as in the White Stork (*Ciconia ciconia*), because "the well known bill-clattering is always uttered by the returning bird when landing on its nest." Most authors, however, have used the terms "duetting" and "responsive" or "antiphonal" singing interchangeably. It would seem more logical to refer to the simultaneous singing of two birds as duetting, the alternate singing as antiphonal or responsive singing.

The significance of female song remains obscure despite the many known examples. Nice and Ter Pelkwyk suggested that "song was originally present in both sexes, and that there were two lines of evolution, one where the male developed the more elaborate song, the other where the female did so" (Nice, 1943). The observed cases of female song fit into the pattern depicted by their table on the possible evolution of song in male and female birds. But the causes, physiological and psychological, of female song are little understood. It seems likely that part of the answer is to be found in the fact that female birds are heterogametic and that the gonads of each sex secrete both male and female sex hormones, but data are fragmentary and confined to a small group of experimental birds. That there is a delicate balance in the production of androgens and estrogens in both sexes of mammals is well known; the imbalance of these hormones results in changes in behavior and secondary sex characters. It has been demonstrated experimentally in ducks, by injection of sex hormones and by castration, that the ovary is responsible for the sexual dimorphism in the development of the osseus bulla and the genital tubercle. That is, the female sex hormone inhibits the development of the male-type syrinx and the penis (Lewis and Domm, 1948; Domm, 1955; Wolff, 1955). Little is known about possible sexual dimorphism in the syrinx of passerine birds, in which group we are especially interested, but female canaries injected with the male sex hormone (testosterone propionate or phenylacetate) develop song "indistinguishable from that of normal males" (Shoemaker, 1939; Herrick and Harris, 1957). Shoemaker also found that injected females achieved peck-dominance over untreated females and exhibited male-type courtship behavior. In speaking only of North American birds, Saunders (1929: 17) suggested that singing females were unusual individuals that possessed some trace of masculine characteristics, and Nice (1943: 132) observed that the two female Song Sparrows that sang most zealously were unusually aggressive in chasing male trespassers. It is doubtful, however, that all female singing can be explained on the basis of hormonal imbalance. Craig (1943: 151) suggested that "other things being equal, the species in which the male and female sing responsively must be regarded as higher psychologically and esthetically than those in which the male sings alone." And Thorpe (1956) has pointed out that the "possibility of birds singing for pleasure is by no means ruled out. The evidence is far from negligible that the songs of some thrushes, the warblers [Sylviidae] and the nightingale exhibit elaborate esthetic improvement far beyond what strict biological necessity requires."

Female song might have a similar psychological basis in some birds.

There is in general an ecological correlation with development of song. Many ocean birds tend to be silent, although some are noisy at breeding colonies, where shearwaters, especially, are noted for their vociferousness at night. Forest-inhabiting birds, where communication by eye is limited, are pre-eminent as songsters. Several authors have suggested that "birds of bright plumage have poor songs," and Nicholson (1929: 44) has said "that song is the expedient used by inconspicuous birds to compensate for the drawbacks of being inconspicuous." Skutch (1954: 177) reported that "it is perhaps not wholly without significance that the two tanagers that dwell in the undergrowth of the heavy forests of the valley of El General are less brilliant in plumage than most of the local representatives of their family and are here its most notable songsters." Nevertheless, many exceptions can be cited to the generalization that "birds of bright plumage have poor songs."

A flight song is featured by some birds that live in the open, especially arctic species that live beyond the tree limit; in many it serves as a territorial song. In the Song Sparrow, however, the flight song "has no direct relationship with any other bird" (Nice, 1943: 118). The Skylark (*Alauda arvensis*), Horned Lark (*Eremophila alpestris*), and Sprague's Pipit (*Anthus spragueii*) often sing at considerable heights (at least 800 feet). Bobolinks (*Dolichonyx oryzivorus*), Cassin's Sparrows (*Aimophila cassinii*), and Lapland Longspurs (*Calcarius lapponicus*) habitually sing during flight, and many other birds occasionally do so. The Streaked Saltator (*Saltator albicollis*) has a flight song which is most often undertaken "in the dusk at the day's end, well after the saltator and most other birds have ceased their ordinary or sedentary singing" (Skutch, 1954: 82). The flight song of Traill's Flycatcher (*Empidonax traillii*) is often given as a part of the evening song, less commonly as part of the morning song choruses (McCabe, 1951). Among birds inhabiting wooded areas, there are a few species such as the Ovenbird (*Seiurus aurocapillus*) and Blue-winged and Golden-winged warblers (*Vermivora pinus, V. chrysoptera*) which have flight songs, but this seems to be exceptional.

Phylogeny of Song

Several writers have speculated about the origin of voice in vertebrates in general and of bird song in particular. S. J. Holmes suggested that voice in vertebrates developed primarily as a sex call "as is now its exclusive function in the Amphibia." Charles Darwin, Eliot Howard, and others, however, imagined vocal sounds produced involuntarily under stress of fear and excitement. Hence, birds first gave alarm notes. These were followed by call notes having a social function and by distinctive sequestration notes, which were of special biological value during the breeding season. Song arose, these authors would propose, as a doubling of a single call note, followed later by the rapid repetition of a series of notes, particularly at the start of the nesting season. Saunders (1929: 111, 123) thought that the mating song preceded the development of territorial song. As evidence for this assumption he stated that the eastern and western species of the meadowlark (*Sturnella*) have dissimilar territorial songs but similar flight songs; he thought further that there was "some reason to suppose that flight songs are more or less primitive." He added that primitive song is soft, indefinite, infrequently uttered, and is much alike in different species. Territorial song, on the other hand, must be loud, definite, and specifically distinct, and it must be repeated frequently. Consequently, primitive song first increased in complexity but the "evolution of the territory song has proceeded from complex to simple" in many species. In a similar vein, Lister (1953a) thought it possible that "sub-song may be the basic utterance from which primary song has evolved."

Ontogeny of Song

The steps by which individual birds learn their species' song have been outlined by several writers. The first song is generally an indefinite warble, nonspecific in character, and is sometimes given by nestlings (e.g., *Cinclus cinclus, Turdus ericetorum, Sylvia atricapilla*). Nice (1943: 133) listed five stages in the development of the Song Sparrow's song, and stated that the first warbling songs in four hand-raised birds were given between the ages of 13 and 20 days; two birds had "adult songs of definite form" at 159 and 192 days of age, respectively. She stated that "young birds of 16 species are reported as starting to sing from the age of 13 to 24 days, and 15 species from the age of 4 to 8 weeks."

A problem that has intrigued ornithologists since the days of Daines Barrington in the eighteenth century is the method by which a species acquires its song: Is song inherited or is it learned by imitation? Scott (1904a) reported that hand-raised Bobolinks and Redwinged Blackbirds (*Agelaius phoeniceus*) did not sing the songs of their own species. He concluded that Rose-breasted Grosbeaks (*Pheucticus ludovicianus*) inherited the "call-notes of both pleasure and fear" but not the adult song (1904b). Sanborn's (1932) evidence for song was contrary to that presented by Scott, but Sanborn was not proficient in identifying the songs of American species. The conclusions reached by Scott and Sanborn are unreliable and their work is of historical interest only. Metfessel (1940) studied the development of song in canaries, which "while still in eggs, were placed in sound-proofed cages and were left thus in isolation until the end of the first year of life." His experiments demonstrated that it "was not necessary for a male canary to hear his species song in order to produce it." Metfessel conducted further experiments in which he introduced vibrato stimuli into the cages at spaced intervals starting with the first appearance of song. The species' song was modified by the insistent environmental tone in that the birds altered their songs by introducing elements similar in tone and rate to the environmental stimuli. These birds were then placed together in flight cages, where, after a period of time, the songs changed again. The fast-singing birds sang slower, the slow-singing birds faster, so that the birds "moved toward group uniformity in song, when they mutually stimulated each other." Thorpe (1955a) similarly reported that "first-year Chaffinches isolated as a unit from all other bird song during their first singing season will sometimes produce abnormal and very variable songs and sometimes fairly normal ones, but in either case will tend to develop a community song-pattern characteristic of the group."

Craig (1943: 141), Nice (1943: 142), and Thorpe (1951: 264–267) have summarized data on song-learning for many birds. Present evidence suggests that the call notes and songs of some species are entirely inherited, but that the songs of the Skylark and Linnet (*Carduelis cannabina*) are almost wholly learned, and that the European Robin and the Chaffinch (*Fringilla coelebs*) must learn their perfected song. "There is a short and critical six-week period, at about the 11th month of life, during which the chaffinch develops its song pattern. Once this critical learning period is over, the song is fixed for life" (Thorpe, 1956). Sauer (1954) hand-raised seven Whitethroats (*Sylvia communis*), including two males raised in isolation from the egg, and found that all of the 25 call notes and the three song-types characteristic of the species were entirely innate; "a bird lacking all acoustical experience, utters all these sounds in exactly the same manner, in the same phases of its life cycle and in the same specific moods as birds in the field." In another outstanding paper, Messmer and Messmer (1956) report that in the European Blackbird (*Turdus merula*) "the pure juvenile song is fully innate" but that the adult song is partly learned from other birds. Much additional experimental work of the caliber represented in the papers by Sauer and the Messmers is needed on other species. Thorpe (1955a) suggested that the study of subsong might throw further light on specific differences in song-learning ability, partly because subsongs probably have "little or no communicatory function."

Imitation has an additional role in bird vocalizations. Vocal mimicry is developed to a high degree in many birds, in which the songs or notes of other species are readily imitated, e.g., the Mockingbird and the European Marsh Warbler (*Acrocephalus palustris*). Van Someren (1956: 299–300) reported that the thrush *Cossypha heuglini* is one of the best mimics among African birds, "but on many occasions the calls are inappropriate to the time of day or the month of the year—the call of a nightjar at noon; that of the European bee-eater in June; that of the solitary cuckoo at a time when the cuckoos have long since left off calling and are silent or have departed." Chisholm (1932, 1937) commented that in Australia the most skilled and persistent mimics are the Bowerbirds (Ptilonorhynchidae) and ground-frequenting species of the families Menuridae, Atrichornithidae, Alaudidae, Oriolidae, Cracticidae, and Zosteropidae. Mimicry is well documented for the Starling (*Sturnus vulgaris*). The tyrant-flycatchers are a New World family, and starlings frequently adopt the "pewee" note in the United States but not in Europe. Starlings in Chicago are said not to use the "bobwhite" call. Parrots, crows, ravens, and magpies apparently mimic only when in captivity. The similarity between certain calls of the Blue Jay (*Cyanocitta cristata*) and the Red-shouldered Hawk (*Buteo lineatus*) is thought by some writers to be a matter of coincidence rather than of imitation.

The significance of vocal mimicry is not understood, but Thorpe speculated that "it may perhaps be regarded simply as evidence of a plasticity of behaviour which is of potential value in many circumstances." He also commented that "when we come to consider the parrots we are still more at a loss, for parrots in the wild seem to make little or no use of their vocal powers beyond uttering the stereotyped cries and calls which help to co-ordinate the flock behaviour, yet surely we must assume that a considerable proportion of brain substance must be in some way ear-marked for voice control and so not available for other purposes" (1955b: 216). There is little, if any, neurological basis for such an assumption.

Marshall (1950) reviewed the subject of mimicry with special reference to Australian birds. Over 50 mimetic Australian species have been classified as "master," "minor," and "casual" mimics. The best mimics inhabit wooded country and are strongly territorial. Marshall suggested that "lack of visibility places a premium on sound and that it is biologically advantageous for individuals to make more and more sound in order that territorial rivals and members of the opposite sex will be constantly aware of their presence." For the two species investigated at that time, Marshall also showed that there is a correlation between vocal mimicry and seasonal changes in the gonads. In *Ptilonorhynchus violaceus,* for example, "vocal mimicry is commonly heard only during the territorial and display season while spermatogenesis and interstitial modification are going on. Gonadectomy inhibits vocal mimicry in *P. violaceus,* and mimicry, along with other song and display, is re-established by injections of testosterone propionate." Mimicry has been considered primitive by some writers, but Thorpe (1955b) stated that "true vocal imitation must be regarded as a late development from inherited song patterns and is characteristic of the most highly evolved amongst the true song birds." Such a pronouncement, however, raises far-reaching questions concerning the evolution and relationships of passerine birds, and it must therefore be interpreted with caution. Casual reference to the widely divergent Australian families cited above, for example, suggests that Thorpe's phrase "most highly evolved" should be modified to read "most highly specialized," but this phrase, too, would be misleading. There is indeed much to be learned about vocal mimicry.

There is scant information on the question of inheritance of a particular song within a species. Nice (1943: 139) found with Song Sparrows "no case of a male having the song of his father or grandfather," and further that two males from the same nest "had no song in common."

Song Cycles

Few birds sing throughout the year, and those that do generally have periods of increased song activity. There is a daily cycle as well. Most species sing less during the middle of the day than they do in the early morning and late afternoon. A midday slackening of song is often correlated with high heat and wind, and is especially noticeable in desert areas. Midday singing does take place on cloudy days, and light rain in itself has little effect on singing. Robinson (1949: 303) noted that in Australia, "whisper songs are generally sung by 'unemployed' birds from a shady position on a hot day or from a sheltered position on a very windy day." There are a few species that sing more or less continuously throughout the day, and with little regard for weather or season. One of the best examples is the Red-eyed Vireo (*Vireo olivaceus*), a species which holds the world's record for number of songs given in one day—22,197 songs (de Kiriline, 1954).

In addition to a morning awakening song, many birds have special morning twilight (or dawn) and evening songs, which are correlated with changing light intensities, or perhaps with a specific intensity. Such songs given by members of the tyrant-flycatcher family have been described in great detail, particularly that of the Eastern Wood Pewee (*Contopus virens*), whose evening song is a mirror image of the morning song. Both Saunders (1929: 129) and Craig (1943: 154) stated that the Pewee's twilight song is neither a territorial nor a mating song. The most striking characteristics of the twilight song are "its great length and continuity, its complex and highly musical structure, its superiority to the daytime singing, its connection with the cycles and photoperiodism and the symmetrical relation between the morning and the evening song"; consequently, Craig added that "in explaining it we must refer to internal factors, partly nervous and psychological." The Red Ant Tanager (*Habia rubica*) has a dawn song entirely different from its daytime song, and the Blue Honeycreeper (*Cyanerpes cyaneus*) has a "dawn-song which he rarely if ever utters after sunrise" (Skutch, 1954: 390).

The thrushes (Turdidae) are noted for evening singing, mainly after sunset, and many daytime singing birds sing at night, some of them often, others only occasionally: e.g., American cuckoos, Bush-lark (*Mirafra javanica*), Magpie-lark (Grallinidae), Mockingbird, Nightingale, Willie Wagtail (*Rhipidura leucophrys*), Yellow-breasted Chat (*Icteria virens*), Field Sparrow (*Spizella pusilla*), Henslow's Sparrow (*Passerherbulus henslowii*). Similarly, night-singing birds such as the nightjars (Caprimulgidae) occasionally call during the day.

The seasonal song cycle begins in the spring for most birds of the Northern Hemisphere. American wood-warblers and sparrows sing during migration, but in a few cases (e.g., Fox Sparrow, *Passerella iliaca*) this may not be the full song. Some American thrushes, however, apparently do not sing at all during migration. In Australia, on the other hand, birds tend to sing year around. Robinson (1949) gave several reasons for this year-round singing: there are comparatively few migrants; a large number of the resident birds mate for life and hold a permanent territory throughout the year; except in social species, the average territory occupies about 20 acres; and some species have a prolonged breeding season—in one instance a pair of Magpie-larks was known to raise four broods in one year. Skutch (1954: 94) reported that in Costa Rica the male Orange-billed Sparrow sings throughout most of the year.

The song behavior of birds during the nesting season varies widely among different species. In many nonpasserine birds, display and accompanying sounds are discontinued after pairing is accomplished. In writing of Old-world warblers (Sylviidae), Howard (1920) commented on the temporary (from a few days to a few weeks) "partial or complete suspension of the song after pairing" as being the most interesting and noticeable feature in the relationship of song to the arrival of the female. Lack reported a similar decline in song for the European Robin after a mate has been obtained, and Tinbergen reported that the male Snow Bunting stops singing as soon as a mate is taken. Nice described a marked decrease in song during the prenuptial and preliminary stages of the nesting cycle in Song Sparrows, in which species the male begins to sing again as soon as nest-building commences. Few specific details are available for most passerine birds, but many wood-warblers and vireos sing during the incubation and nestling periods. Incubating male Warbling Vireos (*Vireo gilvus*) sing from the nest.

Saunders commented on the "lengthening, elaboration or sometimes complete change in the song" of certain species in late summer, but more information is needed. Among Saunders' examples were the flight song of the Ovenbird and the "second" song of the Blue-winged and Golden-winged warblers. Hann found that the season for the flight song of the Ovenbird "was practically the same as that for the 'teacher' song"; the so-called "second" song of the other two warblers is also given during courtship and incubation. Nearly all song stops during the molting period, but there may be a resurgence of song afterward.

Postbreeding and winter song have not been studied much.

Saunders thought that postbreeding song is improved because it no longer needs to remain in the simple form of the territory song, and Craig stated that the superiority of postbreeding song is "probably due to the fact that birds which sing outside the breeding season are more free to develop the song for its own sake." It has also been suggested that the "inactive" condition of the testes of autumn- and winter-singing birds "proves" that these songs are not sexually stimulated, but this is not "proof" at all. It is more within the realm of probability that postbreeding song is stimulated in part by the physiological changes that accompany decrease in gonad size after the breeding season; although spermatogenesis may stop, the interstitial cells are not "inactive." The entire answer is probably not so simple, however. The most persistent winter singers, both male and female, belong either to social species (e.g., Purple Finch, *Carpodacus purpureus*) or to those which defend a territory throughout the year. It is interesting to note that in their winter homes the migratory wood-warblers "do not often sing, but many, perhaps all, species deliver a few songs before their departure in the spring" (Skutch, 1954: 383).

Variation in Song

Variation in song is not only the rule among the members of a species but also within individuals of the species. Saunders reported that "each individual Field Sparrow usually sings but one song and varies it very little," but that "no two Song Sparrows sing songs that are just alike, and each individual Song Sparrow has from seven or eight to twenty or more different songs." Nevertheless, each species has a distinctive basic song pattern so that one can usually identify the species despite this variation; only rarely does one encounter a song that cannot be identified.

The song of certain species varies in different parts of their range, sometimes even within a small local area. The populations having different songs have been called "song races," and the songs, "song dialects." Song dialects have been reported for the European Blackbird, Snow Bunting, and the Chaffinch, and local variations in the Chaffinch's "rain-call" in Germany have been described by Sick (1939). One of the best examples of song dialects in the western United States is found in the races of the White-crowned Sparrow (*Zonotrichia leucophrys*), in which not only do the songs of the subspecies differ but in the race *nuttalli* the songs differ from one local population to another. Saunders described differences between the songs of Ruby-crowned Kinglets (*Regulus calendula*) in the eastern and western parts of the United States; Van Tyne noted that the calls of the White-breasted Nuthatch (*Sitta carolinensis*) in Michigan differ from those heard in the Chisos Mountains of Texas. Benson (1948) studied the songs of over 200 African species and found geographical variation in only 33 species. (For other examples see Chapman, 1940; Mayr, 1942: 54.)

Geographical variation of song within a species is of special interest because of its possible relationship to speciation, although it has not been shown yet that such variation is genetically determined. Thorpe (1951: 265) thought it likely that these variations "are based on a learned tradition and are not inherited."

Ways of Recording Song

As in other phases of bird study, the recording of bird song has gone through an evolution in methodology. Flowery literary descriptions, English words or phrases, and phonetic interpretations of bird song have been used for many years, and, with few exceptions, they have been of value primarily to their authors. We are, for example, still not sure whether the Alder (Traill's) Flycatcher says *fitz-bew* or *phe-be-o!* And yet, in rare cases, English words seem to fit bird calls, e.g., *bob-white, whip-poor-will,* and perhaps even the *hip-three-cheers!* of the Olive-sided Flycatcher. In his criticism of the phonetic method of depicting bird song, Saunders (1929: 136) said: "Suppose the first man to apply 'caw' to the Crow's note had instead applied 'taw.' Then we should all have been taught from early days that the Crow says 'taw' and we would hear it that way."

Saunders recognized the method of musical notation as a step in advance of the phonetic records, but there were weaknesses. The fact that some birds use quarter tones and other fractions not possible to record on our musical staff, that they use slurs and glides from one tone to another, and that the time factor is frequently too variable and nonrhythmic to be revealed in music were apparent to him. In addition, it was impossible to portray the phonetic sounds and the voice quality—that characteristic of a tone which distinguishes a violin from a horn when they are playing the same note. All these weaknesses prompted Saunders to propose a graphic method which made it possible to demonstrate the time, pitch, and intensity of the songs. As a part of the graphic record, Saunders included a phonetic rendering to reveal the consonant sounds, and descriptive words to indicate the quality of the voice. A good musical ear was prerequisite for success with the graphic method.

Phonographic recording of bird song, which was first demonstrated by Sylvester Judd before the 16th Congress of the American Ornithologists' Union in 1898, proved unsatisfactory for detailed laboratory study of songs "in which the high frequencies are prominent and long sustained" (Brand, 1935). Essentially nothing more was done in this area until 1929, when "sound pictures" of the songs of three common birds were recorded synchronously with motion pictures by A. A. Allen and the Fox-Case Company. Allen, Brand, and Kellogg then began an intensive study "by photographing bird sound on motion picture film" and examining the film under a microscope. The examination enabled them to measure the length of a song and of individual notes accurately to 1/500 second, to determine the pitch of a note with greater accuracy, and to see clearly extremely short notes and those of very high pitch, which often are inaudible to the human ear. Microscopic examination of the film and manual recording of data on a graph were very time-consuming, and amplitude or intensity of tone was difficult to measure accurately.

Within the last decade, several different types of instruments have been developed for making previously recorded sounds visible graphically. In general they all involve the same basic principle. Sounds are magnetically recorded on a metal disc and then are transmitted through various modulators and oscillators to a stylus which automatically writes upon a cylindrical drum. This drum is synchronized with the revolutions of a recorder disc. The stylus, electrically actuated, leaves a series of lines. Higher and lower tones are shown on a vertical axis, time or rhythm is recorded on a horizontal axis, and amplitude or loudness of the tones is revealed by the intensity of the line. The quality of the sound is portrayed by the spread of the frequency (e.g., a narrow frequency spread indicates a musical note to the human ear; a wide frequency spread indicates a note that sounds like a noise to us). One can learn to "read" the graphs just as a musician "hears" a musical score as he reads it. Fundamental frequencies and overtones inaudible or indistinguishable to the human ear also are depicted permanently, providing more reliable information in greater detail than can be obtained through purely auditory methods (see Borror and Reese, 1953; Collias and Joos, 1953; Thorpe, 1954).

References

Allen, Francis H. 1919. The Evolution of Bird-Song. *Auk,* 36: 528–536.

Bailey, C. E. G. 1950. Towards an Orthography of Bird Song. *Ibis,* 92: 115–122.

Ball, Stanley C. 1945. Dawn Calls and Songs of Birds at New Haven, Connecticut. *Trans. Conn. Acad. Arts Sci.,* 36: 851–877.

Benson, C. W. 1948. Geographical Voice-variation in African birds. *Ibis,* 90: 48–71.

Borror, Donald J., and Carl R. Reese. 1953. The Analysis of Bird Songs by Means of a Vibralyzer. *Wils. Bull.,* 65: 271–276.

Brand, A. R. 1935. A Method for the Intensive Study of Bird Song. *Auk,* 52: 40–52.

Chapin, James P. 1922. The Function of the Oesophagus in the Bittern's Booming. *Auk,* 39: 196–202.

Chapman, Frank M. 1928. The Nesting Habits of Wagler's Oropendola (*Zarhynchus Wagleri*) on Barro Colorado Island. *Bull. Amer. Mus. Nat. Hist.,* 58: 123–166.

———— 1935. The Courtship of Gould's Manakin (Manacus vitellinus vitellinus) on Barro Colorado Island, Canal Zone. *Bull. Amer. Mus. Nat. Hist.,* 68: 471–525.

———— 1940. The Post-Glacial History of *Zonotrichia capensis. Bull. Amer. Mus. Nat. Hist.,* 77: 381–438.

Chisholm, A. H. 1932. Vocal Mimicry among Australian Birds. *Ibis,* 1932: 605–624.

———— 1937. The Problem of Vocal Mimicry. *Ibis,* 1937: 703–721.

Collias, Nicholas, and Martin Joos. 1953. The Spectrographic Analysis of Sound Signals of the Domestic Fowl. *Behaviour,* 5: 175–188.

Cox, P. R. 1944. A Statistical Investigation into Bird-Song. *Brit. Birds,* 38: 3–9.

Craig, Wallace. 1943. The Song of the Wood Pewee *Myiochanes virens* Linnaeus: a Study of Bird Music. *N. Y. State Mus. Bull.,* 334: 1–186.

Domm, L. V. 1955. Recent Advances in Knowledge Concerning the Role of Hormones in the Sex Differentiation of Birds. In *Recent Studies in Avian Biology.* Univ. Illinois Press, Urbana, pp. 309–325.

Fuertes, Louis Agassiz. 1913. Impressions of the Voices of Tropical Birds. *Bird-Lore,* 15: 341–344.

Gerber, Robert. 1956. Singende Vogelweibchen. *Beiträge zur Vogelkunde,* 5: 36–45.

Grinnell, Joseph. 1920. Sequestration Notes. *Auk,* 37: 84–88.

Haverschmidt, Fr. 1947. Duetting in Birds. *Ibis,* 89: 357–358.

Herrick, E. H., and J. O. Harris. 1957. Singing Female Canaries. *Science,* 125: 1299–1300.

Honess, Ralph F., and Warren J. Allred. 1942. Structure and Function of the Neck Muscles in Inflation and Deflation of the Esophagus in the Sage Grouse. *Wyoming Game and Fish Dept. Bull. No. 2:* 5–12.

Howard, H. Eliot. 1920. *Territory in Bird Life.* John Murray, London.

Ingram, Collingwood. 1956. Mechanical Sounds in Bird Life, Part II. *Illustrated London News,* Oct. 20, 1956: 673.

Kellogg, P. 1938. Hunting the Songs of Vanishing Birds with a Microphone. *Jour. Soc. Motion Picture Eng.,* 30: 201–207.

Kiriline [Lawrence], Louise de. 1954. The Voluble Singer of the Treetops. *Audubon Mag.,* 56: 109–111.

Kullenberg, Bertil. 1946. Om fågellätenas biologiska funktion. *Vår Fågelvärld,* 5: 49–64. [English summary; "On the biological function of the song of birds."]

Laskey, Amelia R. 1944. A Mockingbird Acquires His Song Repertory. *Auk,* 61: 211–219.

Lewis, Lillian B., and L. V. Domm. 1948. A Sexual Transformation of the Osseus Bulla in Duck Embryos Following Administration of Estrogen. *Physiol. Zool.,* 21: 65–69.

Lister, M. D. 1953a. Secondary Song: A Tentative Classification. *Brit. Birds.,* 46: 139–143.

——— 1953b. Secondary Song of Some Indian Birds. *Jour. Bombay Nat. Hist. Soc.,* 51: 699–706.

Lowe, Percy R. 1942. The Anatomy of Gould's Manakin (*Manacus vitellinus*) in Relation to its Display . . . . *Ibis,* 1942: 50–83.

McCabe, Robert A. 1951. The Song and Song-flight of the Alder Flycatcher. *Wils. Bull.,* 63: 89–98.

Marler, P. 1952. Variation in the Song of the Chaffinch *Fringilla coelebs. Ibis,* 94: 458–472.

Marshall, A. J. 1950. The Function of Vocal Mimicry in Birds. *Emu,* 50: 5–16.

Maynard, Charles Johnson. 1928. *The Vocal Organs of Talking Birds and Some Other Species.* C. J. Maynard, West Newton, Mass.

Mayr, Ernst. 1942. *Systematics and the Origin of Species.* Columbia Univ. Press, New York.

Messmer, Egon, and Ingeborg Messmer. 1956. Die Entwicklung der Lautäusserungen und einiger Verhaltensweisen der Amsel (*Turdus merula merula* L.) unter natürlichen Bedingungen und nach Einzelaufzucht in schalldichten Räumen. *Zeitschr. f. Tierpsychologie,* 13: 341–441.

Metfessel, Milton. 1940. Relationships of Heredity and Environment in Behavior. *Jour. Psychol.,* 10: 177–198.

Miskimen, Mildred. 1951. Sound Production in Passerine Birds. *Auk,* 68: 493–504.

Moreau, R. E. 1941. "Duetting" in Birds. *Ibis,* 1941: 176–177.

Murie, James. 1867. On the Tracheal Pouch of the Emu (*Dromaeus novae-hollandiae,* Vieill.). *Proc. Zool. Soc. London,* 1867: 405–415.

Nice, Margaret Morse. 1937–1943. Studies in the Life History of the Song Sparrow. I, II. *Trans. Linn. Soc. N. Y.,* 4, 1937: vi +247 pp.; 6, 1943: viii + 329 pp.

Nicholson, E. M. 1929. *How Birds Live.* 2nd ed. Williams and Norgate, London.

——— and Ludwig Koch. 1936. *Songs of Wild Birds.* H. F. & G. Witherby, London.

Portmann, Adolphe. 1950. Les organes respiratoires. In Grassé's *Traité de Zoologie,* Vol. 15, Oiseaux. Masson et Cie, Paris, pp. 257–269.

Poulsen, Holger. 1954. On the Song of the Linnet (*Carduelis cannabina* (L.)). *Dansk Ornith. For. Tidsskr.,* 48: 32–37.

Quaintance, Charles W. 1938. Content, Meaning, and Possible Origin of Male Song in the Brown Towhee. *Condor,* 40: 97–101.

Robinson, Angus. 1947. Magpie-larks—A Study in Behaviour. Part 3. *Emu,* 47: 11–28.

——— 1949. The Biological Significance of Bird Song in Australia. *Emu,* 48: 291–315.

Sanborn, Herbert C. 1932. The Inheritance of Song in Birds. *Jour. Comp. Psychol.,* 13: 345–364.

Sauer, Franz. 1954. Die Entwicklung der Lautäusserungen vom Ei ab schalldicht gehaltener Dorngrasmücken (*Sylvia c. communis,* Latham) im Vergleich mit später isolierten und mit wildlebenden Artgenossen. *Zeitschr. f. Tierpsychologie,* 11: 10–93.
Saunders, Aretas A. 1929. Bird Song. *N. Y. State Mus. Handbook 7.* Albany.
——— 1948. The Seasons of Bird Song—The Cessation of Song After the Nesting Season. *Auk,* 65: 19–30.
——— 1951. *A Guide to Bird Songs.* Doubleday & Company, New York.
Scott, William E. D. 1904a. The Inheritance of Song in Passerine Birds. *Science,* 19: 154.
——— 1904b. The Inheritance of Song in Passerine Birds . . . . *Science,* 20: 282–283.
Shoemaker, Hurst H. 1939. Effect of Testosterone Propionate on Behavior of the Female Canary. *Proc. Soc. Exper. Biol. & Med.,* 41: 299–302.
Sick, Helmut. 1939. Ueber die Dialektbildung beim "Regenruf" des Buchfinken. *Jour. f. Ornith.,* 87: 568–592.
Skutch, Alexander F. 1940. Social and Sleeping Habits of Central American Wrens. *Auk,* 57: 293–312.
——— 1954. Life Histories of Central American Birds. *Pacific Coast Avifauna,* No. 31.
Sutton, George Miksch. 1945. At a Bend in a Mexican River. *Audubon Mag.,* 47: 239–242.
——— 1951. *Mexican Birds. First Impressions.* Univ. Oklahoma Press, Norman.
——— and Perry W. Gilbert. 1942. The Brown Jay's Furcular Pouch. *Condor,* 44: 160–165.
Thorpe, W. H. 1951. The Learning Abilities of Birds. Part 2. *Ibis,* 93: 252–296.
——— 1954. The Process of Song-Learning in the Chaffinch as Studied by Means of the Sound Spectrograph. *Nature,* 173: 465–469.
——— 1955a. Comments on 'The Bird Fancyer's Delight': together with notes on imitation in the sub-song of the Chaffinch. *Ibis,* 97: 247–251.
——— 1955b. The Analysis of Bird Song with Special Reference to the Song of the Chaffinch (*Fringilla coelebs*). *Acta XI Congr. Internatl. Ornith., 1954:* 209–217.
——— 1956. The Language of Birds. *Sci. American,* 195 (4): 128–138.
Tinbergen, N. 1939. The Behavior of the Snow Bunting in Spring. *Trans. Linn. Soc. N. Y.,* 5: 1–95.
Tyler, W. 1916. The Call-notes of Some Nocturnal Migrating Birds. *Auk,* 33: 132–141.
Van Someren, V. G. L. 1956. Days with Birds. Studies of Habits of Some East African Species. *Fieldiana: Zoology,* 38 (Chicago Nat. Hist. Mus.).
Voipio, Paavo. 1952. Disguised calls of birds as defence mechanisms. *Ornis Fennica,* 29: 63–67. (Finnish, with English abstract.)
Wetmore, Alexander. 1926. Observations on the Birds of Argentina, Paraguay, Uruguay, and Chile. *U. S. Natl. Mus. Bull. 133.*
Witchell, Charles A. 1896. *The Evolution of Bird-Song, with Observations on the Influence of Heredity and Imitation.* Adam and Charles Black, London.
Witherby, H. F., F. C. R. Jourdain, Norman F. Ticehurst, and Bernard W. Tucker. 1949. *The Handbook of British Birds.* Vol. 4. H. F. & G. Witherby, London.
Wolff, Etienne. 1955. Le rôle des hormones embryonnaires dans la différenciation sexuelle primaire des Oiseaux. *Acta XI Congr. Internatl. Ornith., 1954:* 86–103.
Wright, Horace W. 1913. Morning Awakening and Even-Song. *Auk,* 30: 512–537.
Young, Charles G. 1942. "Duetting" in Birds. *Ibis,* 1942: 110–111.

6. Bird distribution

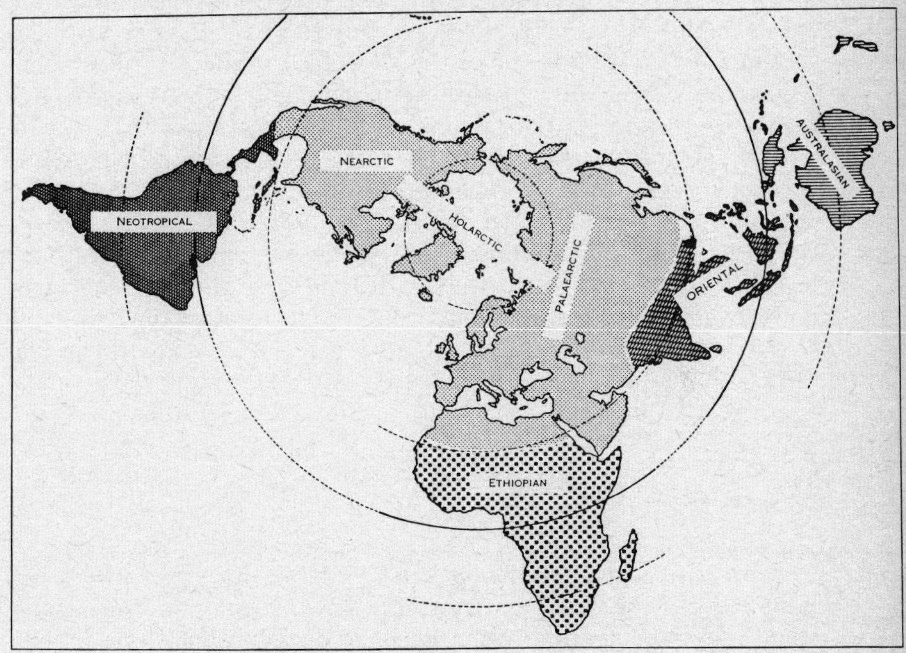

Fig. 1. The six zoogeographical regions of the world, approximately as conceived by Sclater. (By permission of *Encyclopaedia Britannica.* Vol. 23, 1949, p. 964.)

FOR MORE THAN a hundred years men have been systematically studying the distribution of birds and, for nearly as long, the factors that control it. The ranges of many species are, to be sure, still little known, but for an astonishing number of species the geographical distribution can be adequately described. Therefore ornithologists are perhaps better qualified than most zoologists to discuss this subject and to draw sound conclusions.

Zoogeography and Taxonomic Concepts

Correct interpretation of bird distribution is, of course, completely dependent upon correct classification. Our zoogeography can be only as good as our taxonomic system. For example, when Chapman and Griscom (1924) discussed the distribution of wrens (Troglodytidae), they believed that there were about 48 species and subspecies in Asia and Europe in addition to the numerous forms in the Western Hemisphere, but 22 years later it had been recognized that all but one of the 48 were not wrens, but timaliids. Therefore, when Mayr (1946) discussed the North American avifauna, he could treat the wrens as one great American group, of which a single species (*Troglodytes troglodytes*) has spread across Bering Straits, across all Asia and Europe, and westward as far as Iceland. Similarly, ornithologists have long called the wren-tits ("Chamaeidae") of California and Oregon the only family of birds peculiar to continental North America north of Mexico. Increased knowledge of bird classification now convinces most bird students that *Chamaea* is simply an isolated genus of the great babbler family (Timaliidae) and is closely related to certain timaliids of southern China.

Zoological Regions

Of the more than 8000 species of birds in the world, no two have exactly the same distribution (if we except a few species on small islands). Yet many species have distributions that coincide to a considerable extent, and this suggested to early ornithologists a way of organizing the facts of distribution.

Gadow (1913) interestingly summarized the history of zoogeography, beginning with Buffon's *Histoire naturelle* (1770); but for present purposes we may start with Sclater (1858, elaborated in 1891), who first proposed dividing the world into six major regions (Fig. 1). He named them: Palaearctic, Aethiopian, Indian (later called Oriental), Australian (called Australasian by Huxley and others), Nearctic, and Neotropical. Later, it was proposed that the northern regions of the Old and New Worlds (Palaearctic and Nearctic) be united and called the "Holarctic" (see Newton, 1893; Heilprin, 1883). Sclater frankly based his zoogeographical divisions on the class Aves, but he believed that they had a far wider application. (It is interesting to note that he also thought these divisions of the world to be "natural primary divisions of the earth's surface,"—"every species of animal must have been created within and over the geographic area which it now occupies"—and even as Sclater wrote these words, Charles Darwin was preparing for publication his revolutionary *Origin of Species,* which forever destroyed such quaint concepts.) Huxley (1868) proposed another zoogeographical classification system, which emphasized the differences between northern and southern faunas, but Wallace, in the first great monographs on animal distribution (1876, 1880), adopted Sclater's system, and it has remained a dominant concept ever since. Allen, who early showed a remarkable grasp of the problems of bird distribution (1871), proposed a quite different classification (1893), dividing the world into seven "realms": Arctic, North Temperate, American Tropical, Indo-African, South American Temperate, Australian, and Lemurian (= Madagascan), but his classification, although praised by various contemporary scientists, was not generally adopted.

Life Zones

Allen's (1893) division of North America into geographical areas (which he called subregions, provinces, and subprovinces) has much to commend it, but a very different basis of division—by transcontinental "life zones" (Fig. 2)—was developed by Merriam in a series of papers (1890, 1892, 1894, 1898) and quickly received widespread approval. It became the accepted system of the rapidly expanding government organizations and of naturalists generally. Beginning by criticizing Wallace's divisions of North America, Merriam showed that the greatest differences were between the north and the south. He observed apparent correlations between isotherms and the limits of distribution of many birds and mammals. He then decided that temperature was the most important limiting factor and proposed two temperature "laws."[1] Merriam (1894) tried to place the life zones on an exact basis by having the U. S. Weather Bureau calculate temperature "sums" for a large number of localities. These figures were later discovered to be erroneous (Merriam, 1899), but the promised corrected tables were never published. Merriam claimed, however, that owing to temperature factors the distribution of animals and plants could be expressed in terms of a few great transcontinental zones. These zones were named: Boreal (later subdivided into Arctic-Alpine,

[1] a. Animals and plants are restricted in northward distribution by the total quantity of heat during the season of growth and reproduction. b. Animals and plants are restricted in southward distribution by the mean temperature of a brief period covering the hottest part of the year (Merriam, 1894: 233–234).

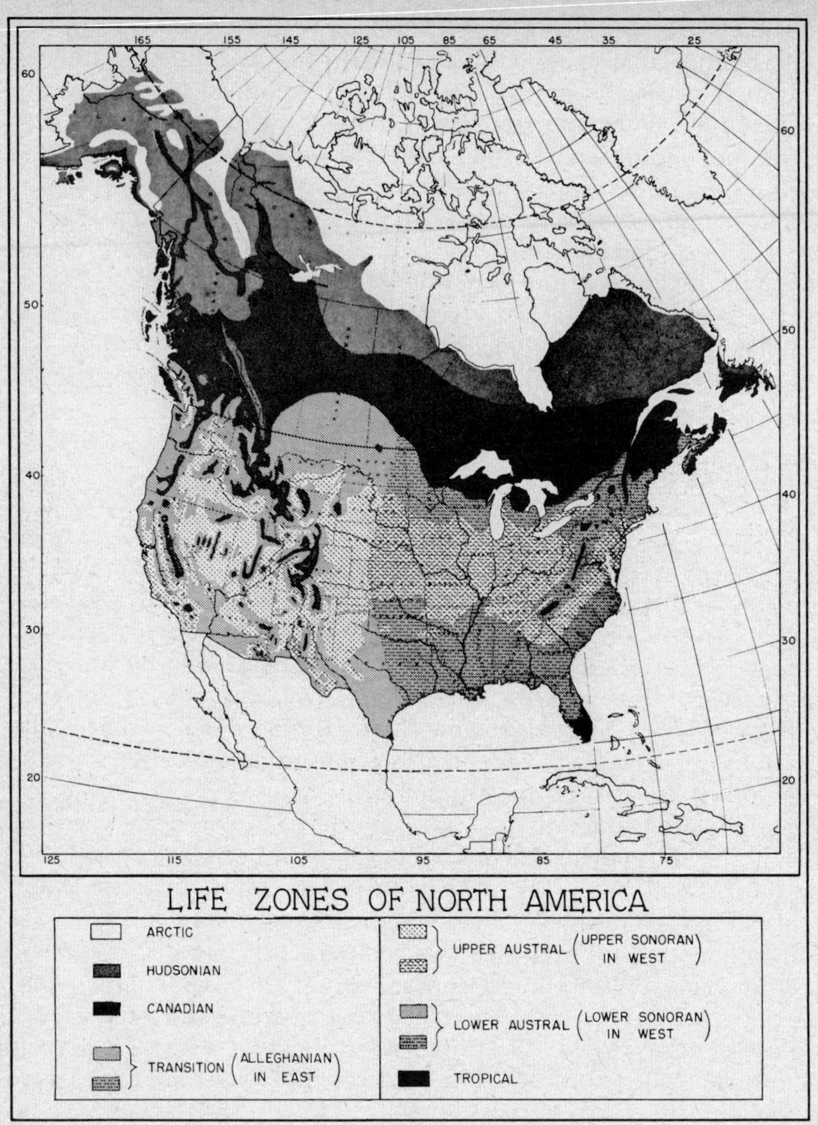

Fig. 2. Life zones of North America. (Courtesy of C. F. W. Muesebeck and Arthur D. Cushman, U. S. Bureau of Entomology and Plant Quarantine.)

Hudsonian, and Canadian), Transition, Upper Austral (called "Upper Sonoran" in the arid west), Lower Austral ("Lower Sonoran" in the arid west), and Tropical.

Shelford (1932), Kendeigh (1932), Daubenmire (1938), and others have presented serious criticisms of Merriam's life-zone concept. They show that these zones do not fit the known distribution of animals and plants except in limited mountain areas. Certainly the zones cannot be drawn across the continent as Merriam tried to do, and temperature is surely not the only factor controlling animal distribution.

Biomes

Another method of analyzing the distribution of animals and plants is by "biomes" (Fig. 3). According to this concept, North America is divided into about four natural areas ("biomes") in which, under conditions undisturbed by man, the vegetation eventually reaches a stable "climax" which theoretically will maintain itself indefinitely. Tundra, coniferous forest, deciduous forest, and grassland are examples. If destroyed, the vegetation in a given biome will pass through its characteristic succession of types, the early ones being called "seral" communities and the later ones "subclimax" communities. For example, Aldrich (1945) has described the plant stages (together with their characteristic birds) which occur in northeastern Ohio in the succession that leads from open-water vegetation to climax deciduous forest. He lists the stages (named from dominant plants which characterize them) as follows:

1. Water lily.
2. Loosestrife–cattail.
3. Buttonbush–alder.
4. Maple–elm–ash.
5. Beech–maple.

The transitional areas between biomes are called "ecotones." The biome concept was developed in North America largely by Clements and Shelford (1939) and was first applied seriously to American bird distribution by Pitelka (1941). A diagrammatic map which attempted to show both the life zones and the biomes of North America was published by Shelford (1945; also reproduced by Pough, 1946).

When analyzing the breeding birds of California according to the biome system (or "ecological formation"), Miller (1951: 540–591) found it necessary to employ units of lesser rank (actually com-

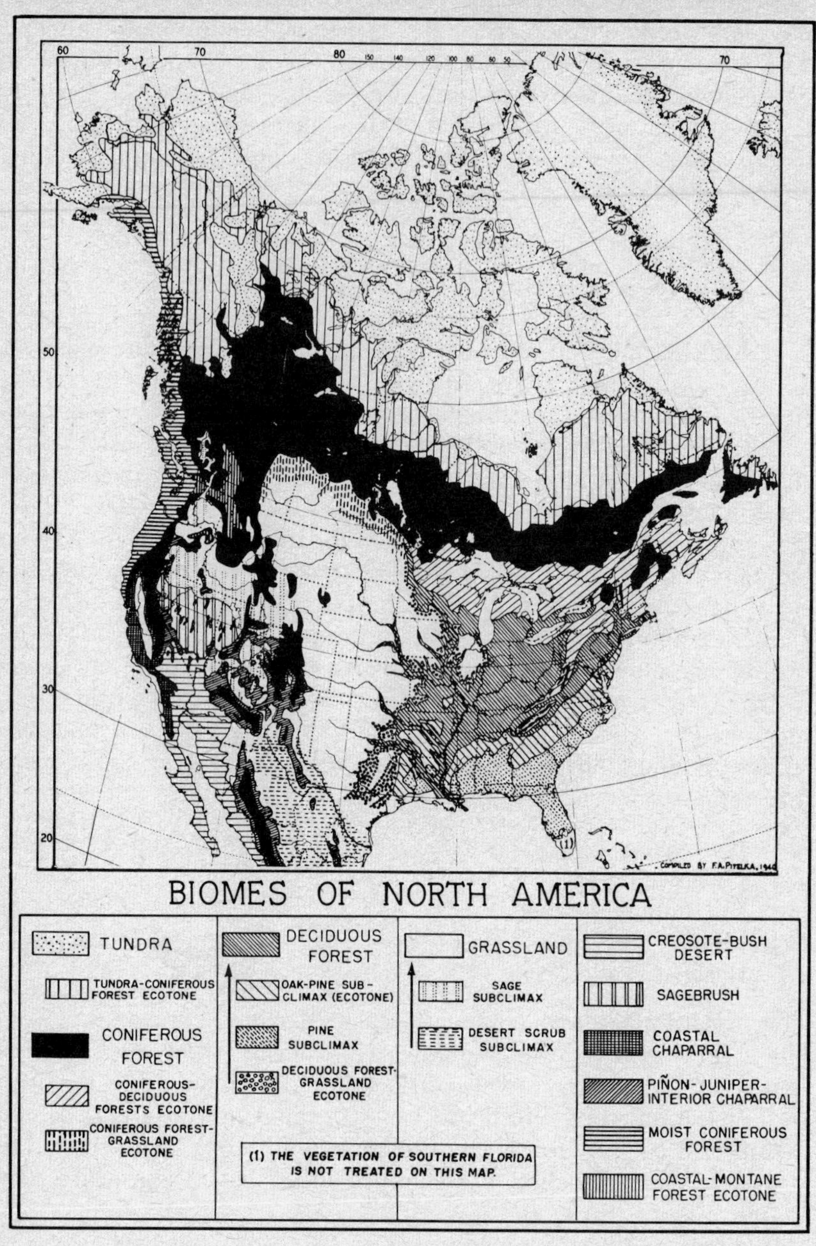

Fig. 3. Biomes of North America. (Courtesy of Frank A. Pitelka.)

parable to second- and third-order subdivisions in the system of Weaver and Clements, 1938). Even then, he stated, the biome concept does not express the facts in a completely satisfactory way. Kendeigh (1954) has published an excellent illustrated history and evaluation of the various concepts of plant and animal communities in North America; he concludes by recommending the biome system.

Biotic Provinces

A third analysis of plant and animal distribution uses "biotic provinces"—developed principally by H. M. Smith (1940), Dice (1943), and Goldman and Moore (1945). Dice divides North America into 29 "provinces" (Fig. 4). A "biotic province," according to

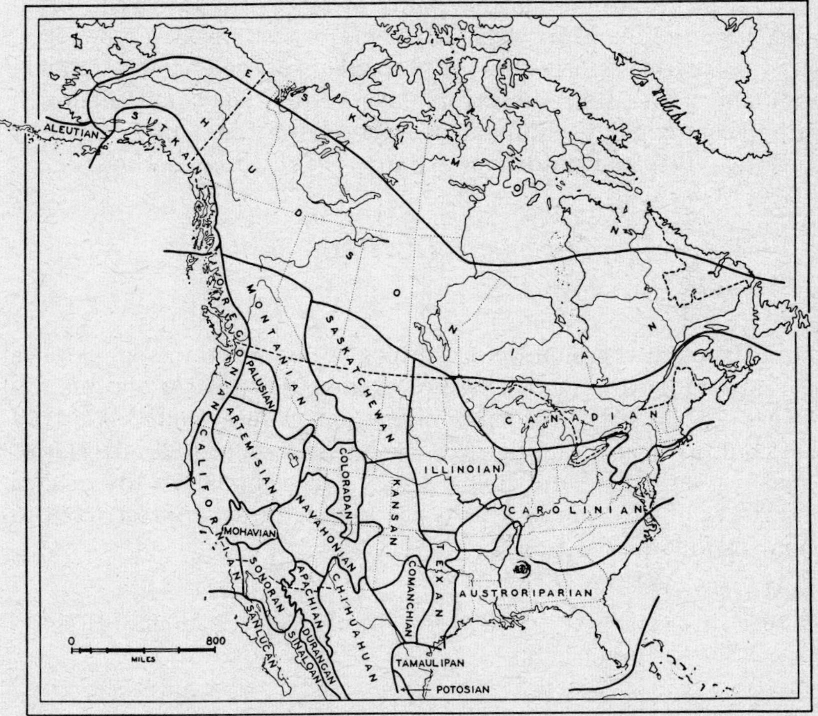

Fig. 4. Biotic provinces of North America. (Courtesy of University of Michigan Press.)

Dice, "covers a considerable and continuous geographic area and is characterized by the occurrence of one or more ecologic associations that differ, at least in proportional area covered, from the associations of adjacent provinces. In general, biotic provinces are characterized also by peculiarities of vegetation type, ecological climax, flora, fauna, climate, physiography, and soil." Subdivisions of the biotic provinces of Dice are (in descending order of importance): biotic districts, life belts, and ecologic associations. A biotic province differs from a biome in at least one very important respect: a biome is coincident with its vegetational climaxes, and these are often discontinuous; a biotic province is never discontinuous (on the mainland).

Critics of the biotic-province concept (such as Johnson *et al.*, 1948: 236–237) show that these provinces are largely subjective things which have never been adequately defined. This system probably overemphasizes the purely geographical aspect at the expense of an analysis of the faunas and floras themselves.

A. H. Miller, in his notable study of the avifauna of California (1951), points out that these three major systems are not necessarily mutually exclusive (as the proponents of each have commonly assumed). "Rather," he says, "each system has some, although perhaps not equal, usefulness and expresses certain truths." Miller then analyzes the Californian avifauna by all three methods.

The Breeding-Season Distribution of Some Bird Families

Although the modern ornithologist no longer attaches to the several zoological regions the importance that Sclater and his followers did, nevertheless some important general facts about the distribution of bird families can be concisely expressed in terms of those regions.[2] The ornithologist may, for example, list the regions and the families of birds which, as breeding birds, are restricted to them, as follows:

NEOTROPICAL

Rheidae—Rhea family

Tinamidae—Tinamou family

Cochleariidae—Boat-billed Heron family

[2] Barden (1941) has discussed this subject, but his definitions of many families do not take into account recent revisions of taxonomic concepts, and therefore his statements must be used with caution.

Anhimidae—Screamer family
Cracidae—Curassow family
Opisthocomidae—Hoatzin family
Psophiidae—Trumpeter family
Eurypygidae—Sunbittern family
Cariamidae—Cariama family
Thinocoridae—Seedsnipe family
Steatornithidae—Oilbird family
Nyctibiidae—Potoo family
Todidae—Tody family
Momotidae—Motmot family
Galbulidae—Jacamar family
Bucconidae—Puffbird family
Ramphastidae—Toucan family
Dendrocolaptidae—Woodcreeper family
Furnariidae—Ovenbird family
Formicariidae—Antbird family
Conopophagidae—Antpipit family
Rhinocryptidae—Tapaculo family
Cotingidae—Cotinga family
Pipridae—Manakin family
Oxyruncidae—Sharpbill family
Phytotomidae—Plantcutter family
Zeledoniidae—Wren-thrush family
Dulidae—Palmchat family
Cyclarhidae—Pepper-shrike family
Vireolaniidae—Shrike-vireo family
Tersinidae—Swallow-tanager family
Catamblyrhynchidae—Plush-capped Finch family

NEARCTIC plus NEOTROPICAL

No bird family is restricted to the Nearctic region. The following are *restricted to the New World* but occur in both the Neotropical and the Nearctic.

Cathartidae—American Vulture family
Meleagrididae—Turkey family
Aramidae—Limpkin family
Trochilidae—Hummingbird family
Tyrannidae—Tyrant-flycatcher family
Mimidae—Mockingbird family
Ptilogonatidae—Silky-flycatcher family
Vireonidae—Vireo family
Parulidae—American Wood-warbler family
Icteridae—Troupial family
Thraupidae—Tanager family

PALAEARCTIC

No bird family is restricted to the region.

HOLARCTIC (Palaearctic plus Nearctic)

Gaviidae—Loon family
Tetraonidae—Grouse family
Phalaropodidae—Phalarope family
Alcidae—Auk family
Bombycillidae—Waxwing family
Prunellidae—Hedge-sparrow family

ETHIOPIAN

Balaenicipitidae—Whale-billed Stork family
Scopidae—Hammerhead family
Sagittariidae—Secretarybird family
Numididae—Guineafowl family
Mesoenatidae*—Mesite family
Musophagidae—Touraco family
Coliidae—Coly family
Leptosomatidae*—Cuckoo-roller family
Phoeniculidae—Woodhoopoe family
Philepittidae*—Asity family
Hyposittidae*—Coral-billed Nut-hatch family
Vangidae*—Vanga-shrike family
Prionopidae—Wood-shrike family

* Restricted to Madagascar

ORIENTAL

Irenidae—Leafbird family

AUSTRALIAN

Casuariidae—Cassowary family
Dromiceiidae—Emu family
Apterygidae*—Kiwi family
Rhynochetidae—Kagu family
Aegothelidae—Owlet-frogmouth family
Acanthisittidae*—New Zealand Wren family
Menuridae—Lyrebird family
Atrichornithidae—Scrub-bird family
Cracticidae—Bellmagpie family
Grallinidae—Mudnest-builder family
Ptilonorhynchidae—Bowerbird family
Paradisaeidae—Bird-of-paradise family
Neosittidae—Australian Nuthatch family
Callaeidae*—Wattlebird family

* Restricted to New Zealand

The Origins of the North American Avifauna

The various types of zoogeographical divisions so far discussed have been based on animal distributions as found at any given period, but Mayr (1946) has shown that a more significant and fruitful basis for the study of a fauna is the examination of its origins. "Instead of thinking of fixed regions," he said, "it is necessary to think of fluid faunas." The following brief general account is based on his work and that of Bond (1948) and Griscom (1950).

There is very little paleontological evidence to help us decide where and when a given bird family originated. For the most part we must depend on indirect evidence, such as the number of related forms and their present distribution.

All authors have recognized that some families still defy analysis. For example, most families of oceanic birds are widely distributed around the world, since they are independent of continental boundaries. Many other waterbirds, fresh-water as well as marine, are now so widely distributed that we cannot make even a guess about their place of origin. Mayr leaves 29 families, including oceanic birds, shorebirds, fresh-water birds, and even landbirds (such as hawks, falcons, nightjars, swifts, woodpeckers, and swallows), in the unanalyzable category. Modifying Mayr's lists to take into account more recent findings and to use the slightly different classification employed in this book, we may group the families as follows:

OF OLD WORLD ORIGIN:*

Phasianidae–Pheasant family
Gruidae–Crane family
Columbidae–Pigeon family
Cuculidae–Cuckoo family
Tytonidae–Barn-owl family
Strigidae–Typical-owl family
Alcedinidae–Kingfisher family
Alaudidae–Lark family
Corvidae–Crow family
Paridae–Titmouse family
Sittidae–Nuthatch family
Certhiidae–Creeper family
Timaliidae–Babbler family
Turdidae–Thrush family
Sylviidae–Old-world Warbler family
Motacillidae–Pipit family
Laniidae–Shrike family

* Omitting families, such as the Prunellidae, which are of only casual occurrence in North America.

OF PAN-AMERICAN ORIGIN:

Cracidae–Curassow family
Trochilidae–Hummingbird family
Tyrannidae–Tyrant-flycatcher family
Thraupidae–Tanager family
Icteridae–Troupial family

OF SOUTH AMERICAN ORIGIN:

Tinamidae–Tinamou family
Eurypygidae–Sunbittern family
Furnariidae–Ovenbird family
Formicariidae–Antbird family
Nyctibiidae–Potoo family
Galbulidae–Jacamar family
Bucconidae–Puffbird family
Ramphastidae–Toucan family
Dendrocolaptidae–Woodcreeper family
Rhinocryptidae–Tapaculo family
Cotingidae–Cotinga family
Pipridae–Manakin family
Oxyruncidae–Sharpbill family

OF NORTH AMERICAN ORIGIN:

Cathartidae–American Vulture family
Tetraonidae–Grouse family
Meleagrididae–Turkey family
Aramidae–Limpkin family
Todidae–Tody family
Momotidae–Motmot family
Troglodytidae–Wren family
Mimidae–Mockingbird family
Bombycillidae–Waxwing family
Ptilogonatidae–Silky-flycatcher family
Dulidae–Palmchat family
Cyclarhidae–Pepper-shrike family
Vireolaniidae–Shrike-vireo family
Vireonidae–Vireo family
Parulidae–American Wood-warbler family

Factors Controlling Distribution

There are several types of factors which control the present distribution of a species, or larger category, of birds: past history, physical barriers, the ecological conditions which the birds can tolerate, and mobility.

Time and Geology

The importance of the historical factor is most strikingly demonstrated in certain isolated land masses. Some oceanic islands are so remote that very few kinds of birds have ever reached them. The ancestral Darwin's Finches (*Geospiza*) reached the Galápagos Islands at such an early period that there were probably no other small landbirds there. The existence of many vacant ecological niches on islands closely grouped but remote from the mainland provided optimal conditions for the rapid evolution of more than a dozen species with many subspecies. An even more extreme case is provided by the Hawaiian Honeycreepers (Drepaniidae). Here a presumed single ancestral species reached an unoccupied group of islands at a very early date and evolved some 22 species with very great diversity of form and habit, ranging from small, slender-billed insect- and nectar-eating forms to "grosbeaks," large birds with enormous bills used to crush hard seeds or even nuts.

Similarly, on a continental scale, the absence of woodpeckers (Picidae) and finches (Fringillidae) from Australia, where physical conditions are perfectly suitable for them, must be explained on purely historical grounds.

One of the earliest and most satisfactory studies of the historical basis of bird distribution in a particular region is found in Griscom's classic account of the bird life of Guatemala (1932: 72–77). He showed clearly that the present avifauna of Guatemala contains three major elements: (1) a very old preglacial element, (2) an element which invaded the region from the north when the glacial period forced it out of much of northern North America, (3) an element which, with the return of a warmer climate, invaded Guatemala from Central and South America.

Physical Barriers

Any considerable area or zone of unfavorable environment obviously constitutes a barrier to the expanding range of any bird species. Seabirds are limited by bodies of land, and landbirds by large bodies of water. Similarly, both forest and grassland form a barrier to birds of the other type of habitat. But such zones must be very wide indeed before they will serve as complete barriers to birds that are both strong-flying and tolerant of short periods of change. For example, the 50-mile-wide Isthmus of Panama is no barrier to certain strictly marine birds: Brown Pelicans (*Pelecanus occidentalis*) and Frigatebirds (*Fregata magnificens*) may be seen daily flying across the Isthmus. On the other hand, certain birds of equally powerful flight, e.g., the Common Booby (*Sula leucogaster*), apparently never venture across, and distinct subspecies are found on the two sides of the Isthmus.

Different races of a sedentary tropical bird may live on adjacent islands (as certain warblers and tanagers in the West Indies) without mingling, or broad rivers may provide impassable barriers. Describing the segregation of subspecies of the barbet *Capito auratus* (a tree-top bird with well-developed powers of flight), Chapman (1928: 2) said, "In Amazonia it is evident that this segregation is supplied by a river system whose broad streams cut this vast area into districts" where races may live completely separated though within sight of each other. The smaller rivers nearer the Andes prove to be no barriers to the barbets, and the same race lives on either side.

Even in the north a few very sedentary birds, such as the Ruffed Grouse (*Bonasa umbellus*) and Screech Owl (*Otus asio*), are apparently blocked by small zones of water. Both species are absent from most islands of the Great Lakes area, even those providing one to several square miles of suitable habitat. The Ruffed Grouse is absent even from Drummond Island (in Lake Huron), which is separated from the mainland by barely a mile of water.

Mobility

If we exclude the few birds that are flightless, most species seem perfectly capable of transporting themselves far beyond the boundaries of their present ranges. Indeed, we have some examples of birds which in historic time have suddenly jumped a wide gap and occupied new areas. In 1937 the Fieldfare (*Turdus pilaris*) invaded North America from Europe. A flock of these large, strong-flying thrushes, apparently stimulated by a severe cold spell, started on January 19 to migrate from Norway southwest toward England. Caught that night in a strong southeast wind, they seem to have been swept far off their course to the northwest: to Jan Mayen and the northeast coast of Greenland, at both of which places individuals were seen and collected on January 20. They then moved rapidly southward and by January 27 and 28 were reported on the coast of southwestern and southern Greenland. They became established as nonmigratory colonies in several southern Greenland localities, where the milder climate of recent years has permitted them to persist (Salomonsen, 1951). According to Bond (1948: 224), the Glossy Cowbird (*Molothrus bonariensis*) of South America was unknown in the Lesser Antilles until 1899, but has since become established as far north as St. Lucia. A good many other such cases could be cited.

The occurrence of any landbird at all on a true "oceanic island" (i.e., an island which has never been connected with existing continents) is striking proof of the extraordinary ability of birds to traverse considerable expanses of water. Yet no oceanic island is too remote to have been reached and colonized by even rather weak-flying landbirds.

In general, it appears that birds are limited in their distribution less by the problems of travel than by the difficulty of establishing and maintaining themselves in the new area after they reach it. In this situation the competition of other species already established in the ecological niche required by the invading species often seems to be the critical factor that prevents successful expansion of range.

Environmental Requirements

One of the first facts that strikes the student of bird distribution is that most birds, in spite of the very great mobility resulting from the power of flight, have sharply demarked distribution.

The physical factors which determine some of the geographical boundaries of many species are well known. In many instances these are clearly coasts, mountains, deserts, or other obvious geographical features, but more often we can only say that the bird's range ceases where certain necessary factors in the physical environment cease. Many attempts have been made to list the physical factors involved. Grinnell, an outstanding student of zoogeography, listed (1917) a number which affect the distribution of higher vertebrates. The following seem to be the ones that apply to birds:

- Vegetation
- Food supply
- Rainfall
- Humidity of the air
- Wetness or dryness of the soil
- Water (to land species)
- Land (to water species)
- Nature and availability of cover, or shelter from enemies
- Safety of breeding places
- Nature of the ground (coarse or fine soil, or rock)
- Insolation or light intensity
- Cloudiness

Temperature: in general; mean annual; of winter; of period of reproduction; of hottest part of year

Interspecific pressure, or competition

Parasitism

Some of the factors listed above apply to birds almost universally, others are of much less general validity, and still others may as a rule affect birds only indirectly. In the latter category are such factors as rainfall, humidity, and soil structure, which in most cases affect the vegetation and thus, indirectly, bird distribution.

Food has often been singled out as an important element in determining the limits of the range of bird species, but few cases can be documented as regards any one kind of food. However, there are a few striking examples recorded. For instance, the vulture *Gypohierax angolensis* feeds largely on the nuts of the oil palm (*Elaeis*), and in West Africa this vulture's range coincides with that of the oil palm (Chapin, 1932: 207, 522; Moreau, 1933). The Everglade Kite (*Rostrhamus sociabilis*) and the Limpkin (*Aramus guarauna*) live almost exclusively on the large fresh-water snail *Pomacea* ("*Ampullaria*") and the ranges of *Pomacea* and these birds coincide wherever they have been studied (Lang, 1924; Cottam, 1936; Harper, 1936). The Common Jay (*Garrulus glandarius*) of Eurasia feeds chiefly on acorns, and its range is closely correlated with that of the oaks *Quercus* (Turček, 1950); see Fig. 5.

Ecological Tolerance

It is important, however, not to overemphasize the fact that many bird species have strongly marked ecological requirements and often, as a result, restricted distribution. Equally striking, though less understood, are the examples of birds of very broad tolerance and very wide distribution.

For example, R. C. Murphy (1936: 109–110) says of the Olivaceous Cormorant:

> Still more remarkable . . . is the case of an American cormorant (*Phalacrocorax olivaceus*). The specific range is both inland and coastal from Cape Horn to the southern United States, but the birds occurring north of Nicaragua have been separated as subspecies *mexicanus*, while a third race seems to inhabit Tierra del Fuego. The typical South American form disregards not only latitude and climate, but also altitude, water temperature and salinity, precipitation, the nature or presence of vegetational groundcover, and almost every other obvious environmental factor. It lives and breeds along rocky, sandy, or muddy seacoasts. It is equally at home beside a glacier in southern Chile, on a barren rainless islet off Peru, among man-

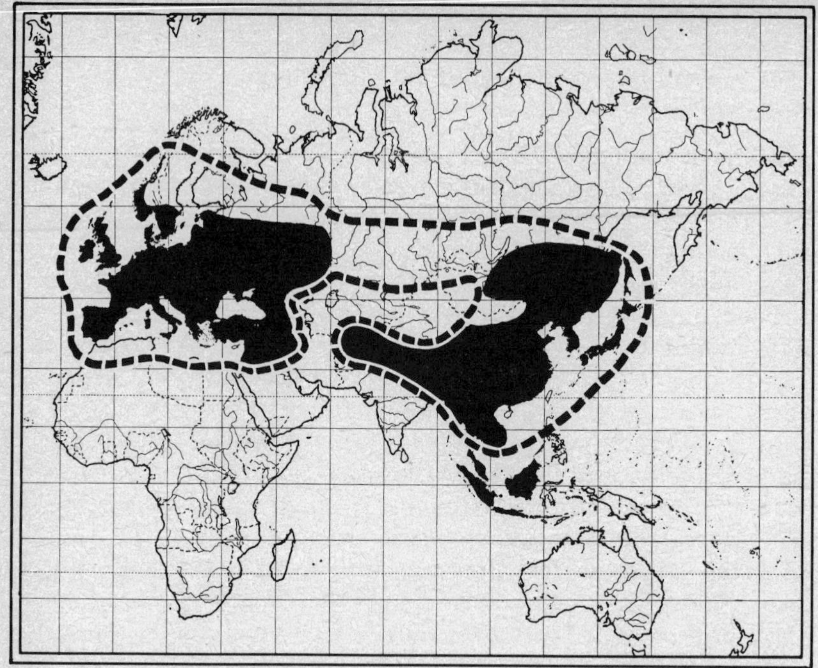

Fig. 5. The range of the Common Jay (*Garrulus glandarius*) (dotted line) and the oaks *Quercus* (in black). (After Turček.)

grove channels of the Caribbean coast, in the stump-filled lakes of Panama, on tepid rivers in the forested interior of the continent, or in lofty and frigid mountain lakes such as Titicaca and Junín. It is clear that this cormorant is superior to climate, in the ordinary sense. . . . The probable explanation of its freedom from environmental control, aside from its patent toleration of a wide range of heat and cold, is that it feeds upon almost any sort of bottom-living fish, of which there is no dearth in either salt or fresh water of various latitudes, temperatures, and composition.

Other wide-ranging species of the New World avifauna that largely ignore zonal restrictions include such well-known birds as the Turkey Vulture (*Cathartes aura*), Barn Owl (*Tyto alba*), Great Horned Owl (*Bubo virginianus*), Black Phoebe (*Sayornis nigricans*), Rough-winged Swallow (*Stelgidopteryx ruficollis*), and Meadowlark (*Sturnella magna*).

Psychological Factors

The psychological factor, although more difficult to test and to demonstrate, must also be considered when we study bird distribution. It is surely of primary importance in many cases.

Thus the Harlequin Duck (*Histrionicus histrionicus*) in Iceland is confined to swift, rocky streams, where it feeds by swimming against the current and poking its bill under the stones to secure insect larvae. It is absent from the lakes, where insect larvae are equally abundant and where many other ducks of more generalized habits are common. In captivity the Harlequin may be successfully reared on a diet of ant pupae, fresh-water shrimps, and insects, but its habitual method of feeding must be provided for (Lack, 1937: 130–131).

The Olive-sided Flycatcher (*Nuttallornis borealis*) in the coastal belt of California originally nested only in fairly open or interrupted stands of tall coniferous trees. But now that groves of introduced eucalyptus have reached a large size, this flycatcher adopts them as a nesting habitat. The chief thing the eucalyptus and the conifers have in common seems to be height. The insect fauna, the nest sites, and the perching places are all very different, but the plant forms are enough alike to satisfy the taste of the flycatchers (A. H. Miller, 1942: 30).

A forest Drongo (*Dicrurus ludwigii*) of Africa, which has quite unspecialized feeding and nesting habits, will cling to the scantiest vestige of original forest but has never been recorded in man's plantations or in second-growth forest, those habitats being taken over instead by a savannah species, *Dicrurus adsimilis* (Moreau, 1935: 182).

Ranges of Birds

Size of Range

The ranges of birds vary greatly in size. The smallest ranges are those of species that occur on only one small island. For example, *Calandrella razae,* a small species of lark that occurs only on Razo Island (Cape Verde Islands), has a range of about 3 square miles. Within that area it is said to be abundant.

Another small landbird whose breeding range is restricted to an island is the Ipswich Sparrow (*Passerculus princeps*) of Sable Island, Nova Scotia (about 20 sq. mi.).

A number of small oceanic islands have (or did have) species of rails peculiar to them, e.g., Wake Island (total of 3 sq. mi.), Laysan (2+ sq. mi.), and Henderson Island (about 5 sq. mi) in the Pacific; and Gough (about 30 sq. mi.), Inaccessible (less than 2 sq. mi.), and Tristan da Cunha (about 40 sq. mi.) in the Atlantic.

A few well-marked species of water birds are restricted to a sin-

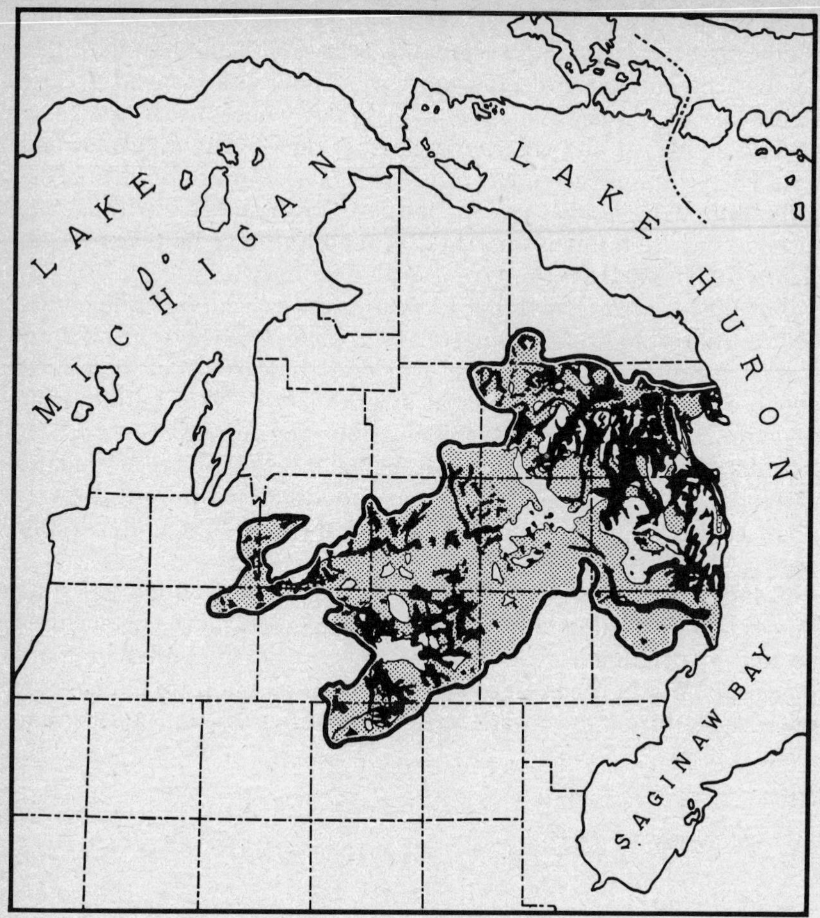

Fig. 6. The complete known breeding range of the Kirtland's Warbler (*Dendroica kirtlandii*) in an area less than 100 by 60 mi. in Michigan. (Van Tyne, 1951.)

gle lake, e.g., a grebe (*Podiceps rufolavatus*) and a duck (*Aythya innotata*), which are restricted to Lake Alaotra (40 mi. long) on Madagascar, and the flightless grebe (*Centropelma micropterum*), found only on Lake Titicaca (138 mi. long) in the Andes.

Small ranges are rare among continental species, but the Kirtland's Warbler (*Dendroica kirtlandii*) is one well-studied case. The total known breeding range in historic time is about 100 by 60 mi. (Van Tyne, 1951) (Fig. 6), but because of this warbler's peculiar ecological requirements, it has a shifting local distribution and occupies only part of that total range in any one year. An intensive survey in 1951 (Mayfield, 1953) revealed breeding pairs in but 92 sq. mi. sections.

Most species have much larger ranges than those so far mentioned. If we take our examples from among the landbirds of eastern North America, we find that the average species has a breeding range which is of the order of a thousand miles from east to west and the same, or a little less, from north to south. The breeding ranges of other North American species extend completely across the continent from Atlantic to Pacific.

A few species extend over a large part of the world. Those with the largest ranges are a small, curiously assorted group, and no one seems to have suggested what they have in common which puts them in this exclusive category. Omitting a few species whose taxonomic boundaries are still being debated, the following striking cases may be mentioned:

Golden Eagle (*Aquila chrysaëtos*)—Mountainous areas of much of the northern Temperate Zone.

Osprey (*Pandion haliaetus*)—Australia, Celebes, and most of the northern Temperate Zone, extending into the tropics at some points (Fig. 7).

Peregrine Falcon (*Falco peregrinus*)—Most of the Northern Hemisphere, Chile and the Falkland Islands, southern Africa and Madagascar, much of the East Indies, Australia, and some of the Pacific Islands.

Barn Owl (*Tyto alba*)—South America and the West Indies, North America and Eurasia except the northernmost areas, East Indies, Australia, and many oceanic islands.

Common Gallinule, or "Moorhen" (*Gallinula chloropus*)—The Americas (except the extreme north), including the West Indies, the Galápagos, and the Hawaiian Islands; Africa, including Madagascar; Eurasia, except the extreme north.

Horned Lark (*Eremophila alpestris*)—Africa north of the Sahara; much of Eurasia (wherever aridity or severe climate produce the necessary bare or nearly bare ground); North America, south through Mexico, and the Bogotá area of Colombia.

House Wren (*Troglodytes aedon* and *musculus*)—Chapman and Griscom (1924) have pointed out that the House Wren (considering *aedon* and *musculus* members of a single species) has a range exceeded by no other American passerine bird. It is found through South and North America (except the far north) and on many of the adjacent islands.

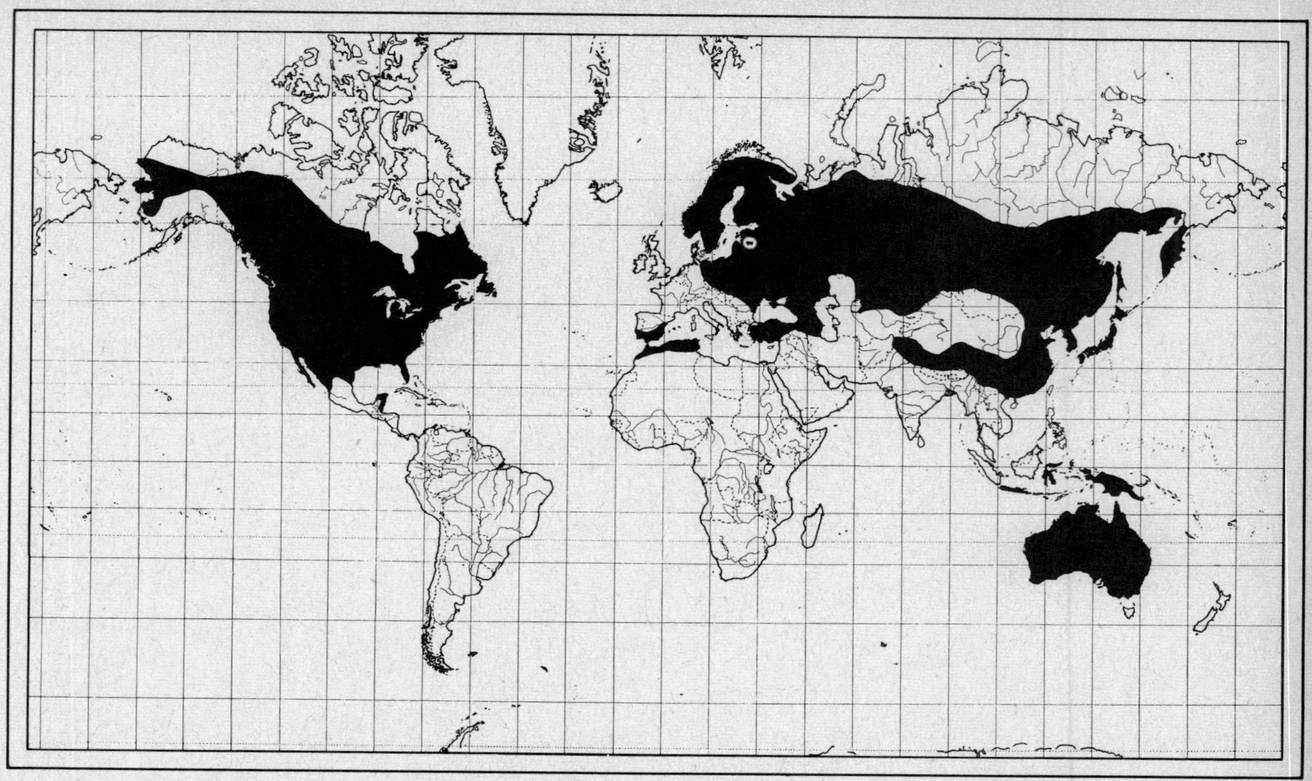

Fig. 7. The vast breeding range of the Osprey (*Pandion haliaetus*).

It is notable that another small wren of the same genus, *Troglodytes troglodytes,* has a similarly vast range. It occurs from Newfoundland across the northern states (and down the Appalachians to Georgia); across most of Eurasia and the northern mountains of Africa to Great Britain, the Faroes, and Iceland.

Discontinuity of Range

There are many striking cases of discontinuous distribution known among birds. They may perhaps be considered to be of three main types:

1. Species presumed to have had a far wider distribution in ancient times, but which have now shrunk in numbers and disappeared from much of their old range, surviving in widely separated "islands" of relict population. (This statement, of course, expresses the extreme case; the populations of certain other species have shrunk only a little, leaving a moderate gap in the range, as in the case of the Hudsonian Curlew, Fig. 8.)

Examples are:

Caspian Tern (*Hydroprogne caspia*)—Breeds very locally in widely separated parts of North America, Eurasia (Denmark to northern China), Africa, Australia, and New Zealand.

Southern Pochard (*Netta erythrophthalma*)—Western South America from Venezuela to Peru, also eastern and south Africa (Abyssinia and Angola to the Cape).

Fulvous Tree-duck (*Dendrocygna bicolor*)—Occurs in Mexico and southwestern United States, northern and southeastern South America, southeastern Africa, and India.

Azure-winged Magpie (*Cyanopica cyanus*)—Occurs in southern and central Spain and Portugal, and eastern Asia (China, Japan, Manchuria, and a little of adjacent Siberia).

2. Species with much smaller ranges, the continuity of which has been broken by some such factor as glaciation, vulcanism, forest loss, forest growth, or changed humidity.

Examples are:

Black Tanager (*Diglossa carbonaria brunneiventris*)—Occurs along the Andes from Bolivia to northern Peru. The bird has never been recorded in Ecuador or southern Colombia, but is found in the eastern and western Andes of northwestern Colombia. (Fig. 9.)

Red-shouldered Hawk (*Buteo lineatus*)—Undetermined factors

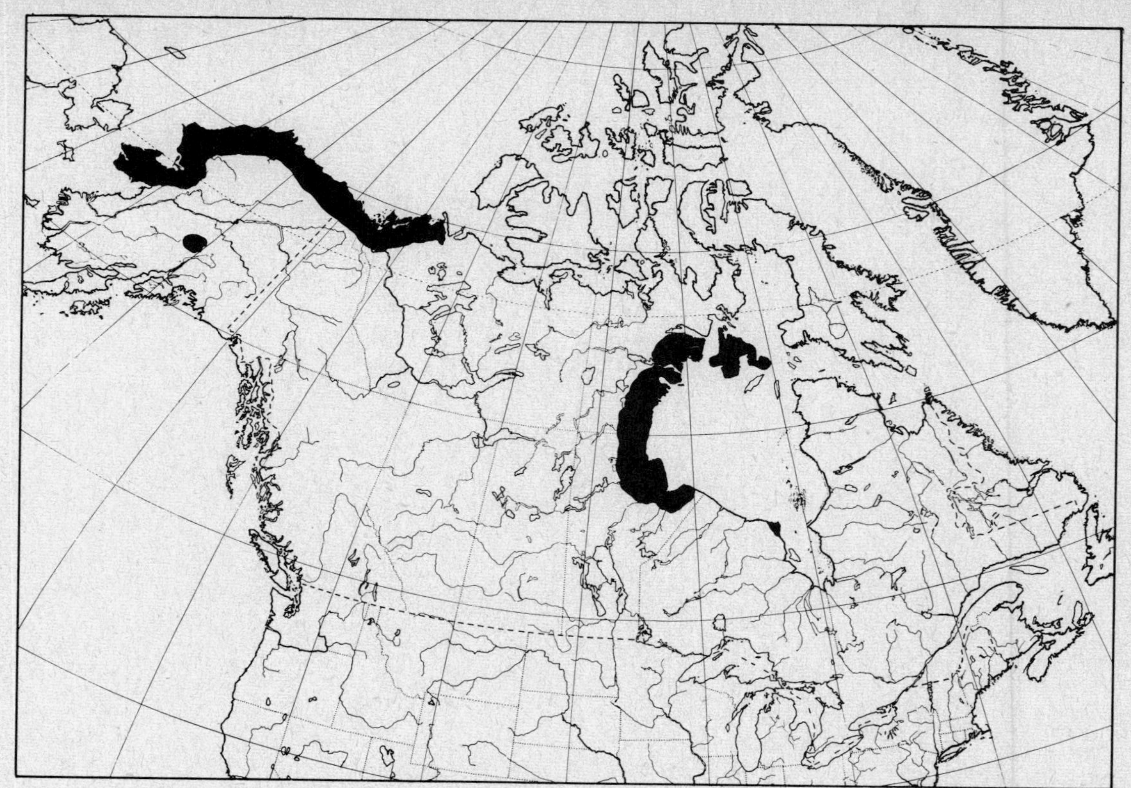

Fig. 8. The discontinuous breeding range of the Hudsonian Curlew (*Numenius phaeopus hudsonicus*). (After Taverner.)

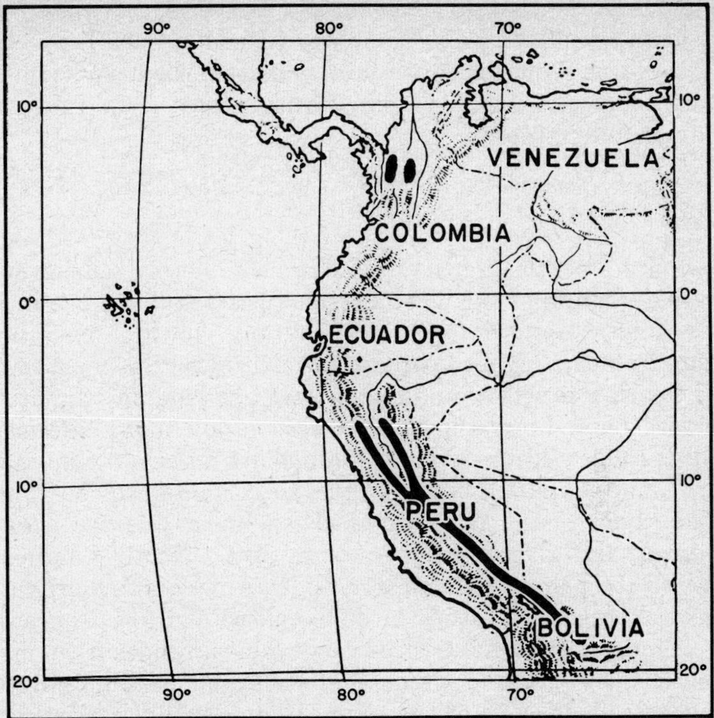

Fig. 9. The discontinuous range of the Black Tanager (*Diglossa carbonaria brunneiventris*). (After Chapman.)

(perhaps altitude and aridity) have made a thousand-mile gap in the range of this species. Occurs throughout the eastern half of North America (south of about 48°) and on the west coast (California west of the Sierra, and northern Baja California).

3. Species of strong flight which have probably wandered, colonizing certain remote outposts where conditions are favorable.

Examples are:

Hispaniolan White-winged Crossbill (*Loxia leucoptera megaplaga*)—This outpost subspecies in the mountains of Hispaniola in the West Indies is doubtless derived from the Common White-winged Crossbill (*Loxia leucoptera leucoptera*) of Canada and the northern edge of the United States. The narrowest gap is now between Hispaniola and the Adirondacks, New York; during the greatest extension of the Pleistocene glaciers the gap was probably much less.

Bogotá Horned Lark (*Eremophila alpestris peregrina*)—This representative of the great complex of Horned Lark forms which inhabit North America south into southern Mexico is isolated in the highlands of Colombia. The forms nearest to its range occur in Oaxaca and Veracruz.

Changes in Range

Seasonal. Some species of birds are completely sedentary, but the greater number (at least outside of the tropics) are in some degree migratory. A few species simply contract their range, retiring from the higher latitudes (or altitudes), but most of them move to other territory in a region that has a milder climate or is otherwise more favorable at that season. In many species, the breeding range and the wintering range are far—even many thousands of miles—apart. For example, some shorebirds such as the Pectoral, Baird's, and White-rumped sandpipers (*Erolia melanotos, E. bairdii,* and *E. fuscicollis*) nest in arctic North America but winter on the pampas of southern South America, more than 8000 mi. away. Such migratory birds have two distinct geographical ranges; indeed, they have three geographical ranges if we include the extensive regions in which they occur as "passage migrants" during certain seasons of the year. (The complicated subject of bird migration is treated more fully in Chapter 7.)

Sporadic "flights." Mammals, insects, and especially birds are subject to occasional sporadic movements whose causes are largely unknown, and which result in temporary changes in distribution.

In some cases these "flights" are cyclic. The flights of the Snowy Owl (*Nyctea scandiaca*) into northern United States and adjacent Canadian provinces are perhaps the best recorded (Gross, 1947; Snyder, 1947); see Fig. 10. These great flights are definitely cyclic in nature and occur on the average every 4 years. The owls appear rather suddenly in the late fall, and during a big flight the numbers are astonishing. For example, in the flight of 1945–1946 a total of 14,409 was reliably reported. The Northern Shrike (*Lanius excubitor borealis*) invades the same area, but its cycle seems to be a 4- to 6-year one (Davis, 1949).

Other northern species make great southward invasions at intervals without evidence of regular cycles. In America such flights have been reported, for example, for the Arctic or Black-backed Three-toed Woodpecker, *Picoïdes arcticus* (Van Tyne, 1926), the Great Horned Owl, *Bubo virginianus* (Soper, 1918), and the Dove-

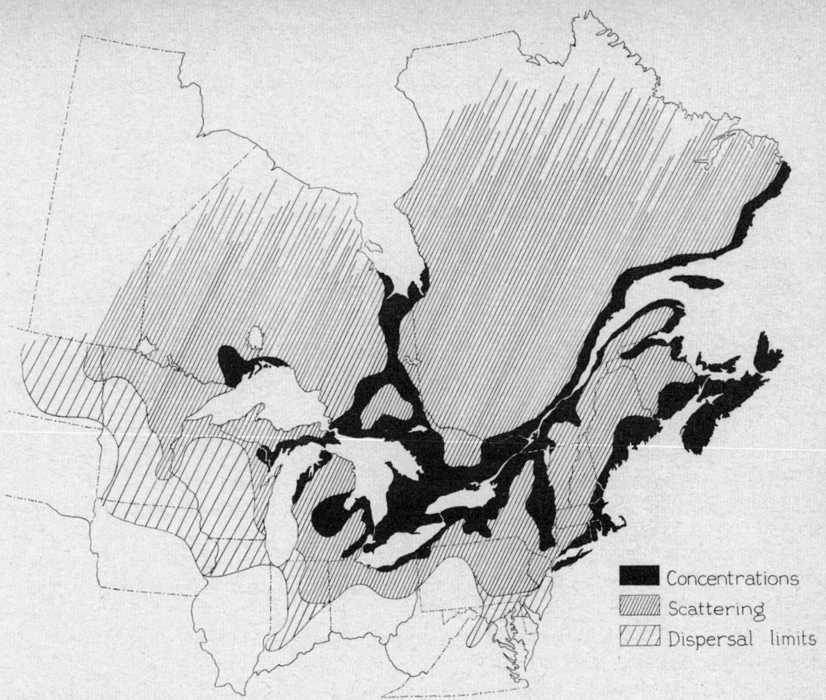

Fig. 10. The great "flight" of the Snowy Owl (*Nyctea scandiaca*) into northern United States in 1941–1942. (Courtesy of L. L. Snyder.)

kie, *Plautus alle* (Murphy and Vogt, 1933). The most striking example in Europe is the Pallas Sandgrouse (*Syrrhaptes paradoxus*), which has a number of times swept southwestward across Europe from its normal range in northern Asia; strangely, these Sandgrouse flights take place in spring.

References

Aldrich, John W. 1945. Birds of a Deciduous Forest Aquatic Succession. *Wils. Bull.,* 57: 243–245.

Allen, J. A. 1871. On the Mammals and Winter Birds of East Florida . . . . *Bull. Mus. Comp. Zoöl.,* 2: 161–450.

——— 1893. The Geographical Origin and Distribution of North American Birds, Considered in Relation to Faunal Areas of North America. *Auk,* 10: 97–150.

Barden, Albert A., Jr. 1941. Distribution of the Families of Birds. *Auk,* 58: 543–557.

Bond, James. 1948. Origin of the Bird Fauna of the West Indies. *Wils. Bull.*, 60: 207–229.
Chapin, James P. 1932. The Birds of the Belgian Congo. Part I. *Bull. Amer. Mus. Nat. Hist.*, 65, x + 756 pp.
Chapman, Frank M. 1928. Mutation in *Capito auratus*. *Amer. Mus. Novitates, No. 335.*
——— and Ludlow Griscom. 1924. The House Wrens of the Genus *Troglodytes*. *Bull. Amer. Mus. Nat. Hist.*, 50: 279–304.
Clements, Frederic E., and Victor E. Shelford. 1939. *Bio-ecology.* John Wiley & Sons, New York.
Cottam, Clarence. 1936. Food of the Limpkin. *Wils. Bull.*, 48: 11–13.
Daubenmire, Rexford F. 1938. Merriam's Life Zones of North America. *Quart. Rev. Biol.*, 13: 327–332.
Davis, David E. 1949. Recent emigrations of northern shrikes. *Auk*, 66: 293.
Dice, Lee R. 1943. *Biotic Provinces of North America.* Univ. Michigan Press, Ann Arbor.
Gadow, Hans. 1913. *The Wanderings of Animals.* Cambridge Univ. Press, London.
Goldman, Edward A., and Robert T. Moore. 1945 [1946]. The Biotic Provinces of Mexico. *Jour. Mamm.*, 26: 347–360.
Grinnell, Joseph. 1917. Field Tests of Theories Concerning Distributional Control. *Amer. Nat.*, 51: 115–128
——— 1928. Presence and Absence of Animals. *Univ. Calif. Chron.*, 30: 429–450.
Griscom, Ludlow. 1932. The Distribution of Bird-Life in Guatemala. *Bull. Amer. Mus. Nat. Hist.*, 64: ix + 439 pp.
——— 1950. Distribution and Origin of the Birds of Mexico. *Bull. Mus. Comp. Zoöl.*, 103: 341–382.
Gross, Alfred O. 1947. Cyclic Invasions of the Snowy Owl and the Migration of 1945–1946. *Auk*, 64: 584–601.
Harper, Francis. 1936. The Distribution of the Limpkin and Its Staple Food. *Oriole* (Atlanta, Ga.), 1: 21–23.
Heilprin, Angelo. 1883. On the Value of the "Nearctic" as One of the Primary Zoological Regions . . . . *Proc. Acad. Nat. Sci. Phila.*, 1883: 266–275.
Huxley, T. H. 1868. On the Classification and Distribution of the *Alectoromorphae* and *Heteromorphae*. *Proc. Zool. Soc. London*, 1868: 294–319.
Johnson, David H., Monroe D. Bryant, and Alden H. Miller. 1948. Vertebrate Animals of the Providence Mountains Area of California. *Univ. Calif. Publ. Zool.*, 48: 221–375.
Kendeigh, S. Charles. 1932. A Study of Merriam's Temperature Laws. *Wils. Bull.*, 44: 129–143.
——— 1954. History and Evaluation of Various Concepts of Plant and Animal Communities in North America. *Ecology*, 35: 152–171.
Lack, David. 1937. The Psychological Factor in Bird Distribution. *Brit. Birds*, 31: 130–136.
Lang, Herbert. 1924. Ampullarius and Rostrhamus at Georgetown, British Guiana. *Nautilus*, 37: 73–77.
Mayfield, Harold. 1953. A Census of the Kirtland's Warbler. *Auk*, 70: 17–20.
Mayr, Ernst. 1946. History of the North American Bird Fauna. *Wils. Bull.*, 58: 3–41.
Merriam, C. Hart. 1890. Results of a Biological Survey of the San Francisco Mountain Region and Desert of the Little Colorado, Arizona. *N. Amer. Fauna, No. 3.*
——— 1892. The Geographic Distribution of Life in North America, with Special Reference to the Mammalia. *Proc. Biol. Soc. Wash.*, 7: 1–64.

Merriam, C. Hart. 1894. Laws of Temperature Control of the Geographic Distribution of Terrestrial Animals and Plants. *Natl. Geogr. Mag.*, 6: 229–238.

——— 1898. Life Zones and Crop Zones of the United States. *U. S. Dept. Agric. Bull. No. 10*

——— 1899. Zone Temperatures. *Science*, 9: 116.

Miller, Alden H. 1942. Habitat Selection among Higher Vertebrates and Its Relation to Intraspecific Variation. *Amer Nat.*, 76: 25–35.

——— 1951. An Analysis of the Distribution of the Birds of California. *Univ. Calif. Publ. Zool.*, 50: 531–643.

Moreau, R. E. 1933. A Note on the Distribution of the Vulturine Fish Eagle, *Gypohierax angolensis* Gmel. *Jour. Animal Ecol.*, 2: 179–183.

——— 1935. A Critical Analysis of the Distribution of Birds in a Tropical African Area. *Jour. Animal Ecol.*, 4: 167–191.

Murphy, Robert Cushman. 1936. *Oceanic Birds of South America.* 2 vols. American Mus. Natural History, New York.

——— and William Vogt. 1933. The Dovekie Influx of 1932. *Auk*, 50: 325–349.

Newton, Alfred. 1893. Geographical Distribution. In *A Dictionary of Birds*, A. Newton and H. Gadow. Adam and Charles Black, London, part 2, pp. 311–363.

Peterson, Roger T. 1932. Life Zones, Biomes, or Life Forms? *Audubon Mag.*, 44: 21–30.

Pitelka, Frank A. 1941. Distribution of Birds in Relation to Major Biotic Communities. *Amer. Midl. Nat.*, 25: 113–137.

Pough, Richard H. 1946. *Audubon Bird Guide: Eastern Land Birds.* Doubleday & Company, New York.

Salomonsen, Finn. 1951. The Immigration and Breeding of the Fieldfare (*Turdus pilaris* L.) in Greenland. *Proc. 10th Internatl. Ornith. Congr., 1950:* 515–526.

Sclater, Philip Lutley. 1858. On the general Geographical Distribution of the Members of the Class Aves. *Jour. Linn. Soc. London*, 2: 130–145.

——— 1891. On Recent Advances in our Knowledge of the Geographical Distribution of Birds. *Ibis*, 1891: 514–557.

Shelford, Victor E. 1932. Life Zones, Modern Ecology, and the Failure of Temperature Summing. *Wils. Bull.*, 44: 144–157.

——— (ed.). 1945. Bird Distribution and Ecological Concepts. A Symposium. *Wils. Bull.*, 57: 191–201, 243–252.

Smith, Hobart M. 1940. An Analysis of the Biotic Provinces of Mexico, As Indicated by the Distribution of the Lizards of the Genus *Sceloporus*. *Anal. Escuela Nac. Cien. Biol.*, 2: 95–110. (English and Spanish.)

Snyder, L. L. 1947. The Snowy Owl Migration of 1945–46: Second Report of the Snowy Owl Committee. *Wils. Bull.*, 59: 74–78.

Soper, J. Dewey. 1918. Flight of Horned Owls in Canada. *Auk*, 35: 478–479.

Turček, Frantisek J. 1950. [The Continental Jay in relation to the oak and its distribution.] *Lesnická Práce*, 29: 385–396. (English summary.)

Van Tyne, Josselyn. 1926. An Unusual Flight of Arctic Three-toed Woodpeckers. *Auk*, 43: 469–474.

——— 1951. The Distribution of the Kirtland Warbler (*Dendroica kirtlandii*). *Proc. 10th Internatl. Ornith. Congr., 1950:* 537–544.

Wallace, Alfred Russel. 1876. *The Geographical Distribution of Animals.* 2 vols. Harper and Brothers, New York.

——— 1880. *Island Life.* Macmillan and Co., London.

Weaver, John E., and Frederic E. Clements. 1938. *Plant Ecology.* 2nd ed. McGraw-Hill Company, New York.

7. Migration

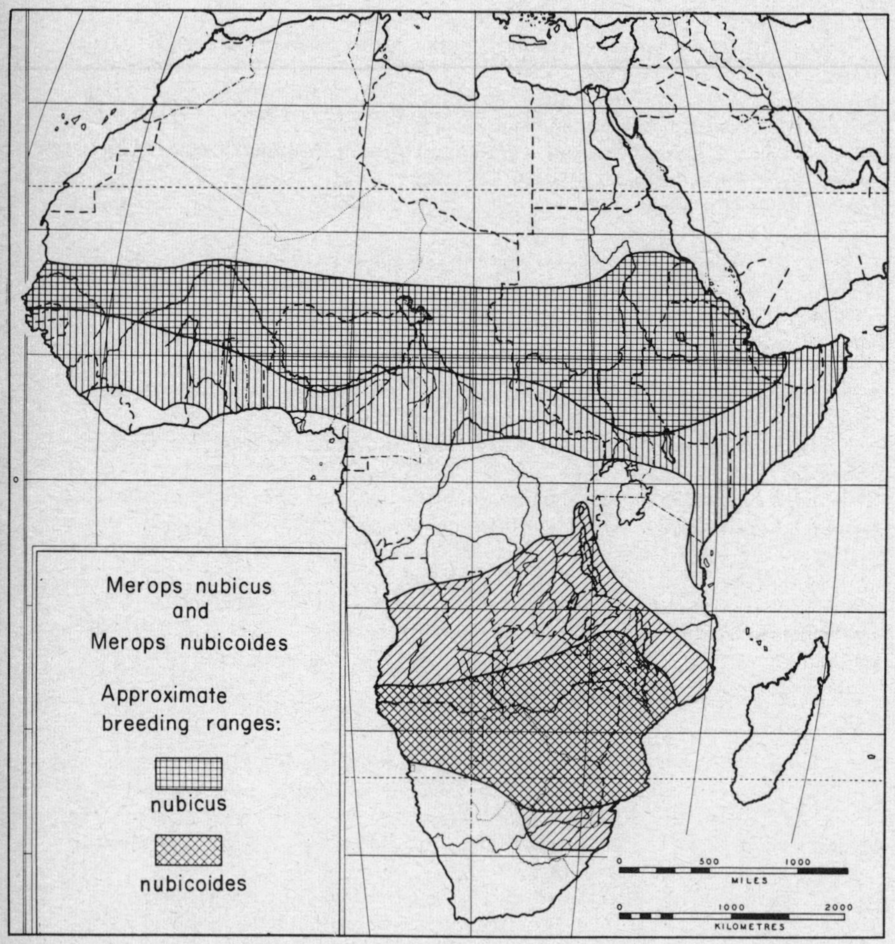

Fig. 1. Two species of tropical bee-eaters (*Merops*) which migrate toward the equator after their respective breeding seasons. (After Chapin, 1932.)

AN IMPORTANT PHASE of the science of zoology is concerned with the ways in which animals adapt themselves to their environment. Every conceivable environment has certain unfavorable aspects for any given animal inhabitant. Often these unfavorable factors are in part seasonal. The seasonal changes of temperature in the northern United States commonly range over 100° F.; yet a few birds, such as the Ruffed Grouse (*Bonasa umbellus*), live there the year round, adapting themselves in various ways to a summer heat of over 90° F. and a winter extreme of −40° F. The Ruffed Grouse, for example, adapts to the very low temperatures by spending nights and mornings under the snow, coming out to feed during a few hours in the afternoon.

But perhaps the most remarkable and effective solution to the problem posed by a seasonally changing environment is migration. The animal does not attempt to combat the unfavorable environment; it simply moves to an environment that *is* favorable. Several groups of animals, such as insects (butterflies, dragonflies), fish (eels, salmon, smelt, etc.), and mammals (caribou, bison, bats), have developed the migratory habit, but birds, with their great mobility, have become migratory far beyond all others.

World-wide Scope of Bird Migration

The bulk of the literature on bird migration deals with the birds of the Northern Hemisphere—especially with those of Europe and North America—for that is where the phenomenon is best developed and also where the great majority of ornithologists have lived and carried on most of their work. But bird migration is nevertheless a world-wide phenomenon and not limited to northern species. Many years ago W. H. Hudson (1872: 534) described the migration of certain Argentine birds northward toward the equator at the onset of the cold season and back again at the beginning of the Argentine "summer." Wetmore (1926: 19–22), however, was one of the first to give a general account of bird migration in the Southern Hemisphere (southern South America). Chapin (1932) documented and mapped many instances of bird migration in Africa, a number of them entirely within tropical latitudes; for example, two species of bee-eater (*Merops nubicus* and *M. nubicoides*) nest, respectively, north and south of the equator, and both migrate toward the equator after breeding (Fig. 1). Chapin recorded (p. 350) four species (a heron, a cuckoo, a roller, and a bee-eater) that leave tropical Madagascar after breeding and cross a water gap of 230 mi. to winter in Africa; Rand (1936: 300) added a falcon to this list. Very remarkable migrations have been mapped for two species of New Zealand cuckoos: the Bronze Cuckoo (*Chalcites l. lucidus*) migrates northward toward the equator, more than 2000 mi. across the ocean, to winter in the region of the Solomon Islands (Fell, 1947) (see Fig. 2); and the Long-tailed Cuckoo (*Eudynamis taitensis*) makes an even longer transocean migration—to Pacific islands as much as 4000 mi. to the northwest, north, and northeast (Bogert, 1937).

Possible Causes of Migration

Failure of Food Supply on the Breeding Ground

It is often assumed that the winter scarcity of food in the north is the simple explanation for most bird migration. It is indeed true that in the extreme north of the Northern Hemisphere available food supplies are insufficient in the winter for the vast numbers of birds that breed there. But we find many species leaving the north long before there is the slightest reduction in the food supply and we must therefore assume that other factors are involved.

Cold Weather of Winter

However plentiful food and shelter might be, cold would certainly prevent many birds from wintering in the north. But we observe species after species leaving the northern United States in July or early August before the heat of summer is over, and, also, there are many cases of extended migration within the tropics, as mentioned above.

Fluctuations of the Pleistocene Ice Front

To bird students in the North Temperate Zone the complex of many major and minor advances and recessions of the Pleistocene

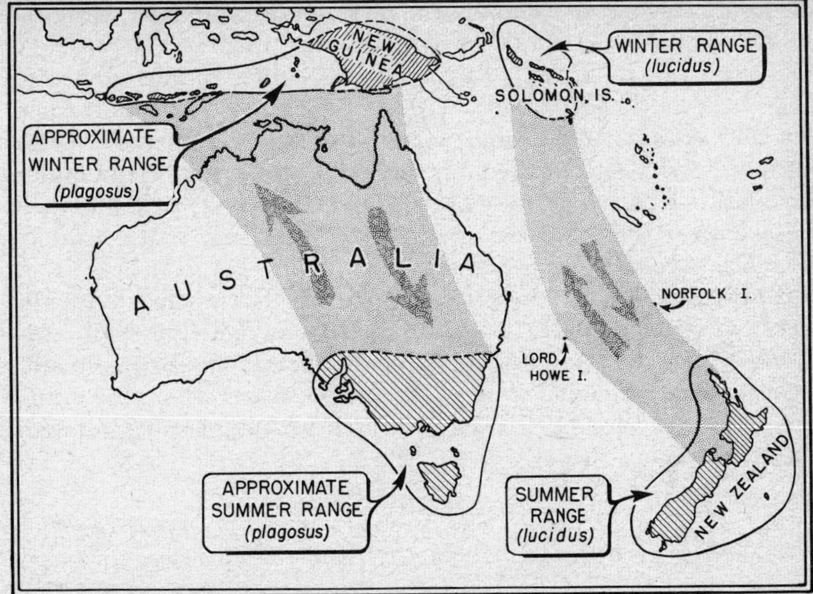

Fig. 2. The migration paths of two geographical races (*plagosus* and *lucidus*) of the Bronze Cuckoo, *Chalcites lucidus*. The New Zealand race traverses more than 2000 mi. of ocean. (After Fell, 1947.)

ice front has always loomed large as a probable cause of bird migration, but this is now generally conceded to have been greatly overemphasized. Moreau (1951), reviewing the complete world picture of the migrations of birds, concluded that bird migration is probably as old as bird flight itself, that the Pleistocene climatic fluctuations did "no more than determine the details of the specific migrations" we now see. The whole Pleistocene glaciation, Moreau observed, occupied "a period less than one hundredth part of the age of the class Aves."

Return to "Ancestral Home" in the South

Some have postulated the Southern Hemisphere as the original home of many species of birds that now breed only in the far north. Wolfson (1948), the latest advocate of this theory, accepts the Wegener hypothesis of two great original land masses which split into the present continents and then gradually drifted apart (an idea strongly opposed by many geologists and paleontologists).

According to Wolfson's theory, the original southern land mass was the home of a bird population which later spread to the northern land mass but regularly returned to the southern one to winter. The birds continued this practice, Wolfson thinks, even after the two land masses began to split into the present continents. As the northern segments drifted far into the Northern Hemisphere the migration routes of these birds were gradually stretched to their present great lengths (from the Arctic to southern South America or to New Zealand, for example).

However, Wegener, the geologist principally responsible for the theory of continental drift, placed the time of splitting of the supposed original continental land masses before the Jurassic—the earliest period in which we find the fossils of even the most primitive birds. Amadon (1948) has presented further strong arguments against Wolfson's theory.

Annual Stimulus for Migration

The exact nature of the stimulus that annually initiates the notably regular migration of birds is very difficult to uncover. The first experimental study of this problem was begun by Rowan (1925, 1926b). He detained two groups of Slate-colored Juncos (*Junco hyemalis*) in outdoor aviaries at Edmonton, Alberta. Though this was well north of their normal winter range and the temperature reached an extreme of −52° F., the birds—supplied with adequate food—seemed to maintain themselves in good condition. Rowan simulated increasing day-length in one aviary by electric lights, these being turned on for a period of 5 minutes following sunset on October 2, for 10 minutes on October 3, etc., the day-length increasing about 3 minutes for each 24-hour period (allowing for the progressively later time of sunrise). In the other aviary no lights were used. Beginning October 15, birds from each aviary were killed at intervals and dissected. The testes of those in the unlighted cage remained in normal winter condition, but the testes of birds from the lighted cage, after first diminishing rapidly and reaching minimum at the end of October (sooner than those of the control birds), began to recrudesce. By the end of December the gonads were larger than those of wild Slate-colored Juncos on their return in spring. Later, Rowan (1946) liberated individuals from both aviaries during the period between early December and mid-February. The number of birds was small and the results not decisive, but in most cases untreated birds remained in the vicinity, whereas light-treated birds disappeared and were thought to have migrated. Then Rowan (1932, 1946), in two experiments, banded and released in early winter about 350 Crows (*Corvus brachyrhynchos*), including both treated and untreated birds. Over 60 per cent of the Crows were retaken, but results were not wholly satisfactory. Some light-treated birds migrated as much as 100 mi. to the northwest; untreated birds remained in the vicinity. Rowan suggested that the increased exercise resulting from the increasing day-length caused the gonads to develop and that the developing gonads, in turn, actuated northward migration. Since only birds whose gonads were changing in size (increasing or decreasing) migrated, and since interstitial tissue occurred most abundantly in the gonads during periods of change, Rowan suggested that the secretions of the interstitial cells may provide the primary stimulus of migration.

Subsequent experiments by other investigators have fully confirmed Rowan's discovery that artificial increase in day-length in fall and winter results in the recrudescence of birds' gonads, but there has been no corroboration of his theory that migration is controlled by the gonads and is thus a part of the breeding cycle, nor of his theory that exercise rather than light itself is the factor that directly causes recrudescence in the gonads.

Bissonnette (1931, 1935, 1937) thought that light as such was the stimulating factor and that the anterior pituitary controlled the changes in gonad size; he agreed with Rowan that migration occurs during recrudescence or regression of the gonads. Bissonnette also postulated an inherent seasonal rhythm in the activity of a bird's pituitary gland and a correlated, similar rhythm in the activity of the gonads. Birds migrate in the fall because of decreasing pituitary (and hence gonadal) activity and do not breed on the wintering ground because the pituitary remains in the "refractory phase." When the pituitary again becomes active and the gonads begin to recrudesce, the bird migrates back to its breeding ground and breeds as soon as the gonads reach a certain point in their development. Detention on the wintering ground, according to both Rowan and Bissonnette, should result in a breeding cycle there and in complete failure to migrate if the gonads reach full size before the bird is released.

To test this theory, Wolfson (1940) detained juncos, of a species (*J. oreganus*) closely related to Rowan's birds, at Berkeley, California (their wintering ground), until their gonads reached full size

(May 23 one year, June 5 another). When released, these birds disappeared and apparently migrated. After the breeding season many of them returned with the southward migration of normal wild birds. Wolfson (1940, 1945) also brought out the importance of the heavy deposition of fat by migratory birds just before the time of migration. Nonmigratory subspecies which he studied showed no change even when subjected to the same change in day-length. Wolfson regarded fat deposition as a "primary part of a general, metabolic internal stimulus and as an excellent indicator of a readiness to migrate." The response of the endocrine system to progressive changes in day-length is a change in metabolism leading to a heavy deposition of fat. Apparently air temperature is not a controlling factor in the deposition of fat. From his own experiments on several migratory and nonmigratory races of juncos and from results obtained by other workers, Wolfson (1945: 122) concluded that neither the gonads nor the reproductive system can be considered "the primary source of the annual stimulus" and that the theory of migration as a "phase" of the reproductive cycle is without factual basis—"Migration and breeding involve different patterns of behavior and are separate entities in the avian cycles." Wolfson (1942: 262) explained the effect of increasing day-length on the gonads as follows: "As the days increase in length, birds are awake for longer periods of time because the state of wakefulness, at least in some birds, is a conditioned response to light; the concomitant activity of the hypothalamus [a ventral part of the fore-brain that includes the pituitary gland] causes an increased production, or release, or both, of the gonadotropic hormones of the pituitary; these in turn stimulate gonadial recrudescence . . . and the deposition of large amounts of fat."

[Benoit and Assenmacher (1953) have lately shown that light, as such, can stimulate gonadal development through its action on the hypothalamus and rhinencephalon, both through the eye and—independently of the eye—through "deep light-receptors" in the head.]

A major objection to the acceptance of this explanation in its simplest form is the fact that many species that breed in the northern parts of the world spend their winter in the equatorial regions or even cross the equator and winter in lands far to the south where the season's (of lengthening and of lessening) days are reversed. Wolfson later (1952), however, suggested that it is the *summation* of day-lengths, rather than increasing day-lengths, that is the critical factor, and he presented the results of some experiments with Slate-colored Juncos and White-throated Sparrows (*Zonotrichia albicollis*) that strongly substantiate the theory. His results seem to show also that there is no inherent "refractory phase" (such as that postulated by Bissonnette and others) during which birds are unresponsive to light, but rather a period of regression and inactivity of the gonads during which short day-lengths are required before another period of activity can occur.

Influence of the Weather on Migration

The problem of the relation between weather (as contrasted with *seasonal* climatic change) and bird migration is exceedingly difficult. It is not enough to note the correlation between the weather at a given place (e.g., on a spring day) and large numbers of migrant birds at the same place. The principal cause of the bird's being there (assuming weather to be the dominant cause) may be yesterday's weather conditions hundreds of miles to the south of the point of observation or today's weather conditions immediately to the north. These and similar complications so obscure the problem that as recently as 1950 an authority on bird migration remarked that "the state of the weather at any point has little if anything to do with the time of arrival of migratory birds. This is contrary to the belief of observers who have thought that they could foretell the appearance of various species by a study of the weather conditions" (Lincoln, 1950: 80).

Our present data provide no evidence that birds anticipate changes in the weather. The initiation of migratory flights, insofar as it is correlated with the weather, seems to depend on the weather conditions at the point of origin of the flight.

Rudebeck (1950: 20–26; 43–54), studying migration at the famous Falsterbo station at the southwestern tip of Sweden, described a great range of variation among migratory birds in sensitivity to weather changes. Of all Swedish migratory birds the Common Swift (*Apus apus*) is the most sensitive to weather changes; it may make a southward migration during an unseasonable cold spell even in the very midst of the breeding season. Other birds that react quickly to changing weather are the soaring hawks, especially the Honey-buzzard (*Pernis apivorus*). When in migration time the weather at Falsterbo begins to improve at the end of a period of low clouds and rain (i.e., when a high-pressure area moves in from the west), transient Honey-buzzards immediately appear. If the fair weather continues for a long period, more and more species begin to migrate; finally, at the end of a very long period of fair weather, Rudebeck has recorded "migratory excitement" even in the Common Nuthatch (*Sitta europaea*) and the Partridge (*Perdix perdix*), both normally nonmigratory.

An apparently valid general distinction has been made by students of migration between "weather migrants" (of early spring) and "instinct migrants" (of late spring). The former are greatly influenced by weather, the latter only a little. Nice (1937: 43–56) found that Song Sparrows (*Melospiza melodia*) arrived in southern Ohio in spring in two main flights: an early flight of males (most of the local breeding population) and a later flight which included females of the local population, the balance of the breeding males, and transient individuals. The time of the early flight was dependent on the occurrence of warm weather in late February or early March; the later flight came in mid- or late March and was less dependent on a rise in temperature. Very cold weather in either period seemed to stop all migration.

The nocturnal telescopic observations by Lowery (1951) and his associates have given us our first comprehensive data on the numbers and flight direction of nocturnal migrants; these data show "a striking correlation . . . between air currents and the directional flight trends" of night migrants, suggesting "a system of presssure-pattern flying" (i.e., the birds apparently move with the favorable winds). Bagg, Gunn, *et al.* (1950) show that during spring migration in eastern North America pronounced movements of migrant birds regularly take place into or through any given region during the interval between the passage of a "warm front" through that region and the subsequent arrival of a "cold front." Bennett (1952) found that in autumn all important waves of night migrants at Chicago were associated with cold fronts and the northerly winds that follow them. He considered that the important factor was the direction of the wind, not the changing temperature or the cold.

Routes

It is quite clear now that individual birds migrate regularly back and forth between a definite breeding spot and an equally definite wintering spot. It is therefore reasonable to suppose that the same route is followed year after year, but since most species have breeding and wintering grounds that cover thousands of square miles, a species advancing in migration is commonly rather widely and evenly spread over a front hundreds of miles in breadth. That this is generally characteristic of the small night-migrating land-birds is confirmed by Lowery's observations (1951) made with a telescope trained on the face of the moon. Day migrants, although advancing in general on an equally wide front, are much influenced by major topographic features—seacoasts, mountains, large lakes, and rivers. Such conformations often strongly "funnel" diurnal migrants; i.e., the migration route becomes locally very narrow, which strengthens the popular notion that bird migrants travel as a rule along narrow avenues like the roads of man. (See also "Diurnal and Nocturnal Migration," p. 198.)

A few species of North American waterfowl are known to have restricted summer and winter ranges connected by rather narrow migration routes (though the routes may shift laterally to some degree from year to year). For example, the little Ross' Goose (*Chen rossii*), the smallest goose in the world, nests in the Perry River region on the central arctic coast of Canada and migrates south and then southwest, along a very narrow route, to winter in the Great Valley of California (Fig. 3). The Blue Goose and Lesser Snow Goose (*Chen caerulescens* and *Ch. hyperborea*—perhaps actually a single species) breed north of Hudson Bay, on Southampton Island and Baffin Island, and migrate by a narrow route to their wintering ground on the Gulf coast of Louisiana and Texas, returning by a somewhat different, but also narrow, route in spring.

Some species, restricted by their narrow ecological requirements, migrate along extremely narrow routes determined by the seacoast. The Ipswich Sparrow (*Passerculus princeps*), for example, migrates from Sable Island, Nova Scotia, down the Atlantic coast to its wintering ground (Massachusetts to Georgia), which also is closely restricted to the shore line. The route apparently is rarely so much as a mile wide and along many stretches may be only a few hundred yards across. Other coastal species, such as the Sharp-tailed and Seaside Sparrows (*Ammospiza caudacuta* and *A. maritima*), have similar narrow migration routes along the Atlantic coast of the United States.

Even in northern latitudes, not all migration routes are north and south. Many years ago W. W. Cooke (1915: 20) showed that the White-winged Scoter (*Melanitta deglandi*) migrates from its central Canada breeding ground almost due east and due west to the Atlantic and Pacific coasts. Later, Magee (1934) demonstrated by banding that the Evening Grosbeak (*Hesperiphona vespertina*)

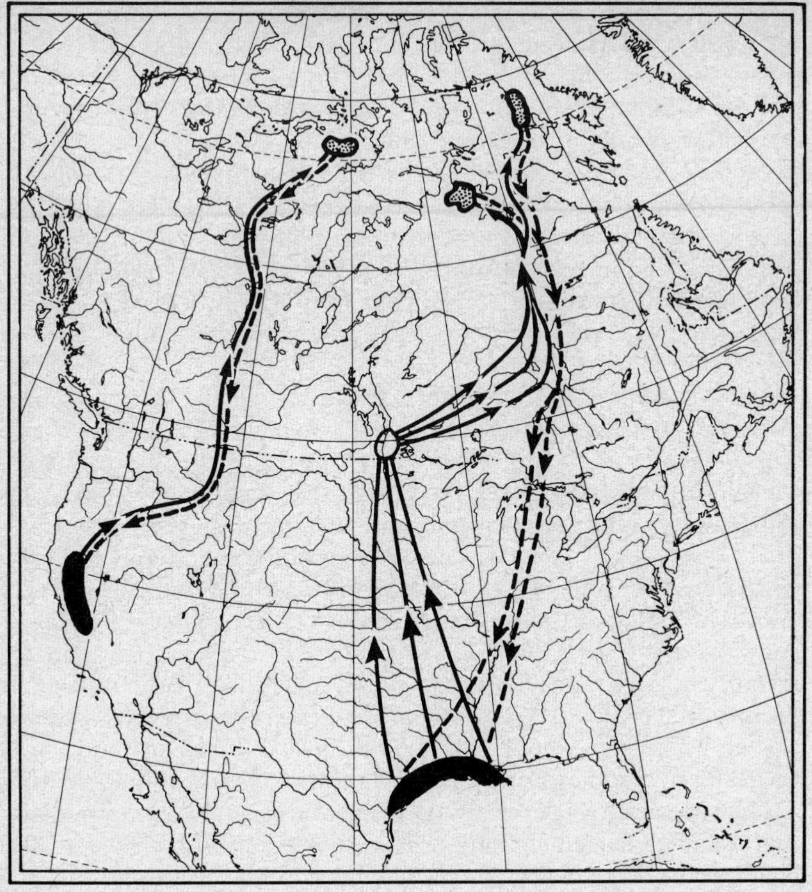

Fig. 3. The narrow migration paths of the Ross' Goose (between Mackenzie and California) and of the Blue and Snow Geese (between the Southampton–Baffin Island region and the Gulf coast). (After W. W. Cooke, 1915; and Soper, 1942.)

of northern Michigan migrates directly east, to winter in New England (Fig. 4).

The routes followed by migrating birds involve quite clearly in some cases the retracing of paths by which the species historically reached a given breeding area. For example, the Yellow Wagtail (*Motacilla flava*) of Eurasia has spread across Bering Strait into Alaska. The New World population has been breeding there so long that a well-marked subspecies (*tschutschensis*) has developed, but after the breeding season the whole population goes back across Bering Strait and migrates down the Pacific coast of Asia to winter in the Philippines and New Guinea (Grant and Mackworth-Praed, 1952). Similarly, the Wheatear (*Oenanthe oenanthe*) of Europe has spread into Greenland and Labrador and developed a geographical race (*leucorhoa*) there. At the end of the nesting season the Labrador individuals start their migration to their tropical winter home by flying northward to Greenland (along the route by which their ancestors doubtless reached Labrador); there the Labrador Wheatears turn westward to Europe and finally southward along the European coast to Africa, where they winter. (The Wheatear has also spread into Alaska from northeastern Asia, and, similarly, retreats in winter to its ancestral home.)

Some young birds are known to use a migration route in autumn that is very different from that used by the adults. Since W. W. Cooke's classic account of the two-route migration of the Eastern Golden Plover (*Pluvialis d. dominica*) northward through the Mississippi Valley, but southward from Labrador over the Atlantic to the Lesser Antilles, Rowan (1926a: 34–37) and others have shown that the young migrate southward through the interior of the

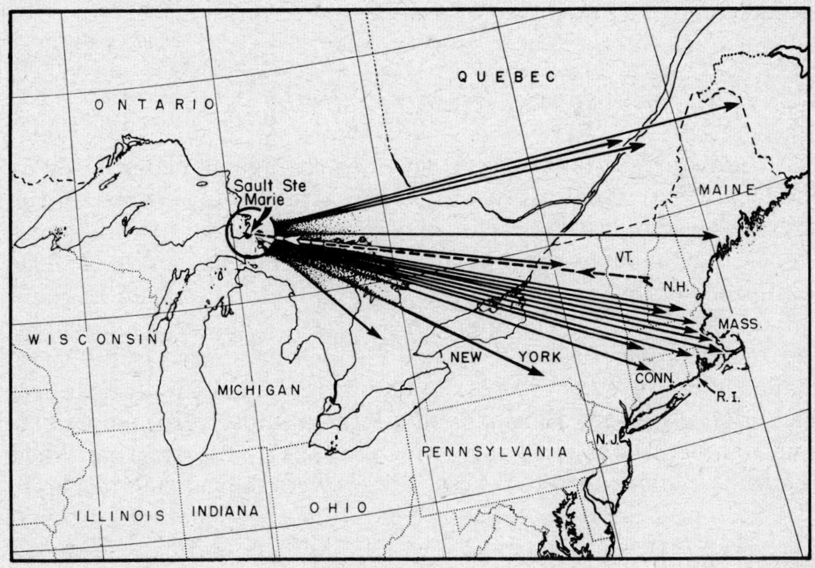

Fig. 4. The east-west migrations of Evening Grosbeaks between their breeding ground in Michigan and the New England wintering ground, as demonstrated by the recovery of banded individuals. (After Magee, 1934.)

country—presumably the ancient, ancestral spring migration route of all the Eastern Golden Plover.

Emlen (1943) found that the two sexes of the Gambel White-crowned Sparrow (*Zonotrichia leucophrys gambelii*) tend to migrate to different wintering grounds in California, males predominating west of the Sierras, females east of the Sierras.

Some mention must be made under this heading of the much-publicized "flyway" theory (Lincoln, 1950: 46–52), according to which populations of North American waterfowl (and even "all populations" of North American migratory birds) "adhere with more or less fidelity" to one or another of four "flyways" (the Atlantic, Mississippi, Central, or Pacific). This doubtless has a considerable value as a legal concept for classifying game administrative areas, but when Lincoln (1950: 48, and figs. 13 to 16) maps his concept of the four flyways and admits that "during the nesting season extensive areas may be occupied by birds of the same species but which belong to different flyways," and when Aldrich *et al.* (1949) show us by actual banding records (cf. Mallard, Baldpate, and Lesser Scaup) that the ducks banded on their breeding grounds in Alberta, for example, go south on all four flyways, we cannot give the flyway theory much weight as a biological concept.

Determination of "Homing" Point

Some attention has been given to the age at which birds fix the locality to which they will return after their absence on the wintering ground. The classic experiment, reported by Välikangas (1933), demonstrated that in the Mallard (*Anas platyrhynchos*), at least, it is not determined by heredity. Mallard eggs from England (where the species is nonmigratory) were hatched in Finland and the young raised there and banded for identification. In fall these Mallards migrated southwest to the wintering ground of Finnish Mallards in western Europe, and a large number returned to Finland to breed the next spring. McCabe (1947) reported that Wood Ducks (*Aix sponsa*) from central Illinois were moved 200 mi. north, to Madison, Wisconsin, at the age of 3 to 5 weeks and raised there. They were released at about 7 weeks, and they left with the fall migration a couple of months later. A number returned to Madison and nested there in subsequent seasons. In another experiment, young Wood Ducks were sent from the same Illinois point

180 mi. eastward to Indiana and made that their breeding area. In neither experiment did any of the young return to their hatching place in Illinois. Further experiments are needed to test other species and to learn the maximum age and minimum acclimatization period involved.

Altitudinal Migration

Many species that live in mountainous regions adjust to the changing seasons with a minimum of migratory effort by making an altitudinal migration. These altitudinal migrations are, of course, usually downward to lower altitudes and milder climates in winter, with a return to the higher breeding ground in spring. Many examples could be given: the Junco (*Junco hyemalis*) of the Great Smoky Mountains of Tennessee makes only a shift in altitude, though its relatives in nonmountainous parts of the eastern United States regularly migrate many hundreds of miles southward in the fall.

Mountain Quail (*Oreortyx pictus*) nest at altitudes up to 9500 feet in the central California mountains, but in September they leave the region of deep snow, little parties of 10 to 30 individuals migrating on foot single file down to areas below 5000 feet. In spring they return, again on foot, to the higher altitudes.

In a few cases altitudinal migration may be in the reverse direction: a few birds migrate from lower to higher altitudes to spend the winter. One example is the Blue Grouse (*Dendragapus obscurus*), which winters in the fir and pine forest of the northern Rocky Mountains well above its nesting grounds. This movement is apparently correlated with food supply and absence of predators. (Ninety-nine per cent of their food in winter in Idaho consists of the needles and buds of Douglas fir, *Pseudotsuga taxifolia,* and the Grouse spend that season almost exclusively in these trees—Marshall, 1946.)

Another example is furnished by the Ibis-bill (*Ibidorhyncha struthersii*), a long-billed "shorebird" of the high plateaus of central Asia. According to LaTouche, the Ibis-bill breeds almost at sea level in Chihli, northeastern China, but retires in winter to the Shanhaikuan Mountains, where warm springs and the swiftness of the streams ensure open water all winter, when the lowland streams are frozen hard.

Partial Migration and Variation in the Urge to Migrate

Among many birds we find what Thomson (1926: 243) called "individual migration"; Lack (1943–44: 44), thinking in terms of species, used the better term "partial migration." Briefly, it appears that some individuals of a species stay through the winter on their breeding grounds, whereas others migrate—in some instances to distant countries.

Nice (1937: 32–42) found that some Song Sparrows (*Melospiza melodia*) of a southern Ohio population migrated and others did not. A few individuals migrated some years, remained resident other years. Thomson (1926: 301) had suggested that there might prove to be migratory and nonmigratory genetic strains in such mixed populations, but Nice found that the offspring of two regularly migratory parents might be either migratory or resident.

Variation in the urge to migrate is in some species apparently correlated with age, with sex, or with both age and sex. Eaton (1933), studying American Herring Gulls (*Larus argentatus*) of the Atlantic coast, and Thomson (1939), studying British Gannets (*Morus bassanus*), found that first-year birds made a long migration, second-year birds a shorter migration, third-year and older birds apparently did not migrate at all. Deelder (1949) found that in the European Chaffinch (*Fringilla coelebs*) females were much more strongly migratory than males (and in part even used different migration routes). In the Tree Sparrow (*Spizella arborea*), the females of the populations wintering in the Middle West migrate farther south on the average than males (Heydweiller, 1936: 66–67). Lack (1943–44) made an excellent analysis of the rich bird-banding data gathered in England, where the mild climatic conditions make possible a wide variation in migration habits. He found that some individuals of several passerine and shorebird species remained in the region where they had been banded as breeding adults or nestlings, whereas others migrated south to France and the Iberian Peninsula or west to Ireland. Females and (except in westward migration) immature males showed a greater tendency to migrate than adult males.

Physical Proportions of Birds in Relation to Migration

There is a close correlation between the physical proportions of birds and migratory habits. Averill (1920) showed that among related species and subspecies of North American birds the migratory forms have smaller bills, feet, and tails; the wings of the migrants are significantly longer and frequently also characterized by a reduced outermost primary.

Chapman's classic study (1940) of the Crowned Sparrow (*Zonotrichia capensis*) of South America strikingly illustrates the correlation of wing form with migratory habits; see Fig. 5. The Crowned Sparrow ranges over South America generally (except the Amazon basin) and north into Central America and the West Indies. Twenty-two geographical races have been named, all but two of which are nonmigratory birds with short, rounded wings. The race (*Z. capensis australis*) which inhabits the cold southern tip of South America makes an annual migration of over 1800 mi., and its wing is long and pointed. The remaining form, *Z. capensis sanborni* of northern Chile, has a wing almost as long, but it is a bird of high mountains where wind conditions may necessitate strong powers of flight (in addition, this subspecies may, on further investigation, prove to be an altitudinal migrant).

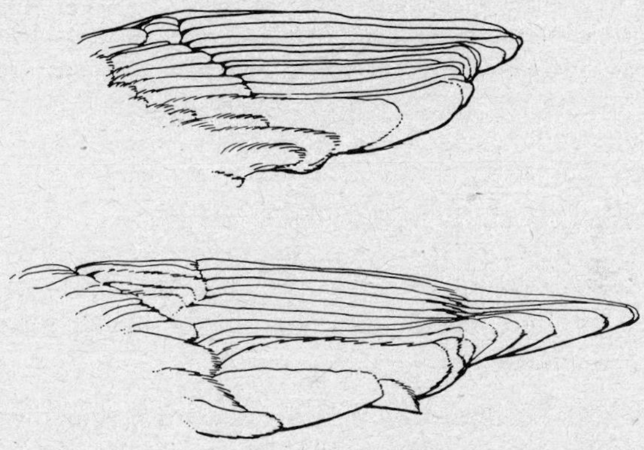

Fig. 5. The folded wings of two races of Crowned Sparrows (*Zonotrichia capensis*): a relatively sedentary form (*costaricensis,* Colombia; upper figure) and a highly migratory form (*australis,* Chile; lower figure). (After Chapman, 1940.)

Discussing this correlation in his recent review of Old World larks (Alaudidae), Meinertzhagen (1951: 82–83) reported that migratory species of larks have the wing long and pointed—the primaries (except the outermost) are longer and the secondaries shorter than in resident species, though the wing area in relation to weight is actually less in the migrant larks (Fig. 6).

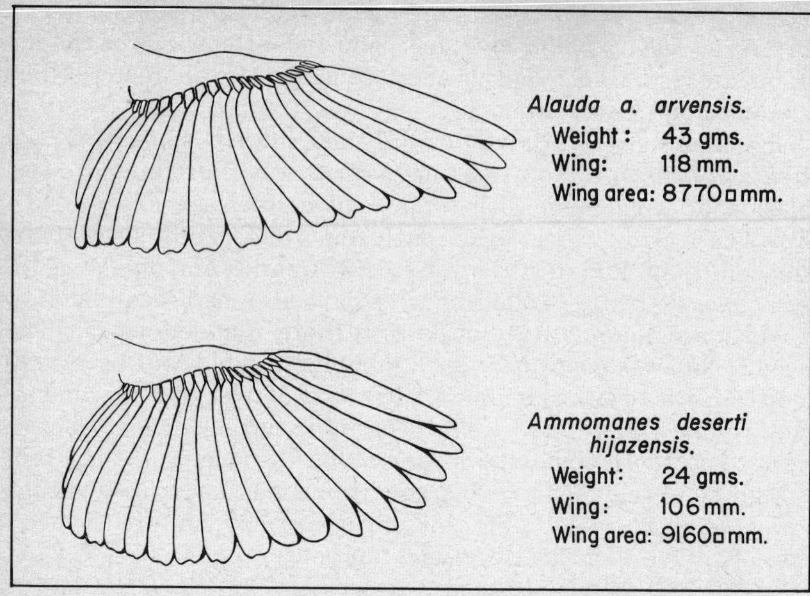

Fig. 6. Spread wing of the highly migratory Skylark (*Alauda*) of Europe compared with that of the nonmigratory Sandlark (*Ammomanes*) of Arabia. The migratory lark has a long, pointed wing, but actually *less* wing area per weight. (After Meinertzhagen, 1951.)

Diurnal and Nocturnal Migration

In his classic paper on "Bird Migration," William Brewster (1886: 19–21) divided North American birds into groups according to their hour of migration.

1. The greater number of small birds (and larger birds that are shy and secretive) migrate by night, viz.:

Rails (*Rallidae*)
Woodcock (*Philohela*) and Spotted Sandpiper (*Actitis*)
Cuckoos (Cuculidae)
Woodpeckers (Picidae)
Tyrant-flycatchers (Tyrannidae) except the Kingbird (*Tyrannus*)
Titmice (Paridae)*
Nuthatches (Sittidae)
Creepers (Certhiidae)
Wrens (Troglodytidae)
Thrushes (Turdidae) except the strong-flying Robin (*Turdus migratorius*) and Bluebird (*Sialia*)
Kinglets (*Regulus*)
Vireos (Vireonidae)

* Black-capped Chickadees (*Parus atricapillus*), however, are now known to migrate by day (Van Tyne, 1928).

Wood-warblers (Parulidae)
Meadowlarks (*Sturnella*) and orioles (*Icterus*)
Tanagers (Thraupidae)
Finches (Fringillidae) except the strong-flying Snow Bunting (*Plectrophenax*)

2. Among birds which migrate "chiefly, or exclusively" by day, Brewster listed:

Hawks (Accipitridae; Falconidae)
Pigeons (Columbidae)
Swift (*Chaetura*)
Hummingbird (*Archilochus*)
Horned Lark (*Eremophila*)
Swallows (Hirundinidae)
Crows and jays (Corvidae)
Robin (*Turdus migratorius*) and Bluebird (*Sialia sialis*)
Pipits (*Anthus*)
Waxwings (*Bombycilla*)
Shrikes (*Lanius*)
Blackbirds and orioles (Icteridae) except *Sturnella* and *Icterus*
Pine Grosbeak, and other carduelines

3. Many other birds, Brewster reported, migrate "more or less equally" by day or night. For example:

Loons (Gaviidae)
Ducks and geese (Anatidae)
Shorebirds (Charadriidae; Scolopacidae) except those listed under group 1
Auks and murres (Alcidae)

According to Brewster, the time of day of migration is in most cases obviously correlated with "habitual manner of procuring food, disposition, and wing power." "Bold, restless, and strong-winged birds migrated chiefly, or very freely, by day," presumably because of their greater security from winged enemies and, in some instances, their ability to feed on the wing as they travel. Conversely, more timid, sedentary species devote their days to feeding in their usual cover and migrate by night; they are thus safer from the hawks, gulls, and other enemies that threaten them by day. Small birds use up their food reserve very rapidly and cannot go long without feeding. Large birds need not feed so frequently. In fact, hawks and vultures regularly go many hours, or even several days, without food. Chapman (1933) made a very good case for his theory that Turkey Vultures (*Cathartes aura*) migrate by day from Panama to Michigan and Minnesota (some 3600 mi.) in about 10 days, traveling without stopping for food. The same seems to be true of the great flocks of Swainson's and Broad-winged Hawks (*Buteo swainsoni* and *B. platypterus*) that migrate through Central America every spring and fall on their travels between the United States and South America (Skutch, 1945).

Except for the Alcidae, which migrate only over water, the birds listed in group 3 above are, in general, strong-flying birds which feed freely by either night or day and which do not customarily seek safety in concealment. Some species in group 3 seem to migrate by day only when traveling over water, in which they can take refuge if need be.

Diurnal migration is most readily seen and studied at certain promontories which have the effect of concentrating the migrants, often to a spectacular degree. Day migrants (unlike night migrants) are strongly affected by topography and often seem reluctant to start out across large expanses of water. Famous points of concentration of diurnal migrants are Point Pelee, Ontario; Cape May, New Jersey; and Falsterbo, Sweden—studied, respectively, by Taverner and Swales (1907–1908), Stone (1937: 38–46), and Rudebeck (1950). Diurnal migration can also be studied to advantage where a stream of migrants is concentrated in a mountain pass (D. and E. Lack, 1951; Beebe, 1947), along highland escarpments (D. and E. Lack, 1949), or along seacoasts (Deelder, 1949). Hawks, eagles, ospreys, and vultures greatly depend on soaring, which requires rising air currents; thus, where a mountain ridge deflects winds upward, migrating birds of the soaring type will follow the ridge closely for great distances even though this carries them far out of the direct and shortest route to their destination (Broun, 1939; 1949).

Moreau (1938) demonstrated brilliantly how much can be learned of diurnal bird migration by observers on ships at sea.

Thomson (1953) has given us a masterful summary of recent progress in the study of bird migration, with special emphasis on the study of day migrants.

Nocturnal migration can often be detected by the sound of the call notes of the birds passing overhead. Frequently, it is even possible to identify thus the species of birds that are migrating (Tyler, 1916); and Ball (1952), studying the migrant birds of the Gaspé Peninsula, has demonstrated that much may be learned this way. In the past, lighthouses have provided most of our exact information on nocturnal migration. Brewster (1886) spent several weeks at the Point Lepreaux, New Brunswick, lighthouse in the fall of 1885 and made the first scientific study of the phenomena involved. Gätke (1895) on Heligoland in the North Sea, and Clarke (1912) at the lighthouses and lightships of Great Britain, spent many months studying nocturnal migration. More recently, important data have been gathered at floodlighted monuments, such as the Washington

Monument (District of Columbia) and the Perry Monument (Put-in-Bay, Ohio). Lowery (1951) has taken the long-neglected method of telescopic observation of night migrants passing across the face of the moon and, with Newman (1952), has developed it into a method of considerable precision, employing the data gathered by hundreds of co-operating observers scattered across the continent.

Postbreeding Northward Migration

A few species of North American birds, notably herons and Bald Eagles, migrate many hundreds of miles northward immediately after the nesting season. In July and August of some years, great numbers of American (Common) Egrets (*Casmerodius albus egretta*) and Little Blue Herons (*Florida caerulea*) and a few Snowy Egrets (*Leucophoyx thula*) appear in northern United States and southern Canada. The flights consist mainly of young of the year, and it was once thought that these northward-migrating young herons might be simply the northern component of an explosive dispersal in all directions (which would be observable only where the great white birds invaded an area beyond their normal range). However, Townsend (1931) showed that banding demonstrates a strong northward flight of the young of another species—the Black-crowned Night Heron (*Nycticorax nycticorax*) from Massachusetts; 79 per cent of the August and September recoveries of young banded on Cape Cod were made at points to the north (up to 500 mi. distant from the nest). Broley (1947) has shown by banding that the young Bald Eagles (*Haliaeetus l. leucocephalus*) fledged in Florida move northward immediately after leaving the nest; by May many of them are 1000 mi. north of the nesting ground; a number have been found 1500 mi. north by June (Fig.7). Apparently, adults also migrate northward, but for shorter distances, at the same season.

No plausible explanation for the heron northward migrations has yet been proposed, but we may surmise that the summer heat of Florida is too great for the Bald Eagle, a northern species which has probably only recently spread into Florida—able to profit during the cooler season by the abundant food and plentiful nesting sites, but not adapted to the higher temperatures of the Florida summer.

The term "abmigration" was proposed by A. L. Thomson (1931) for "a spring movement by a bird which has performed no autumn

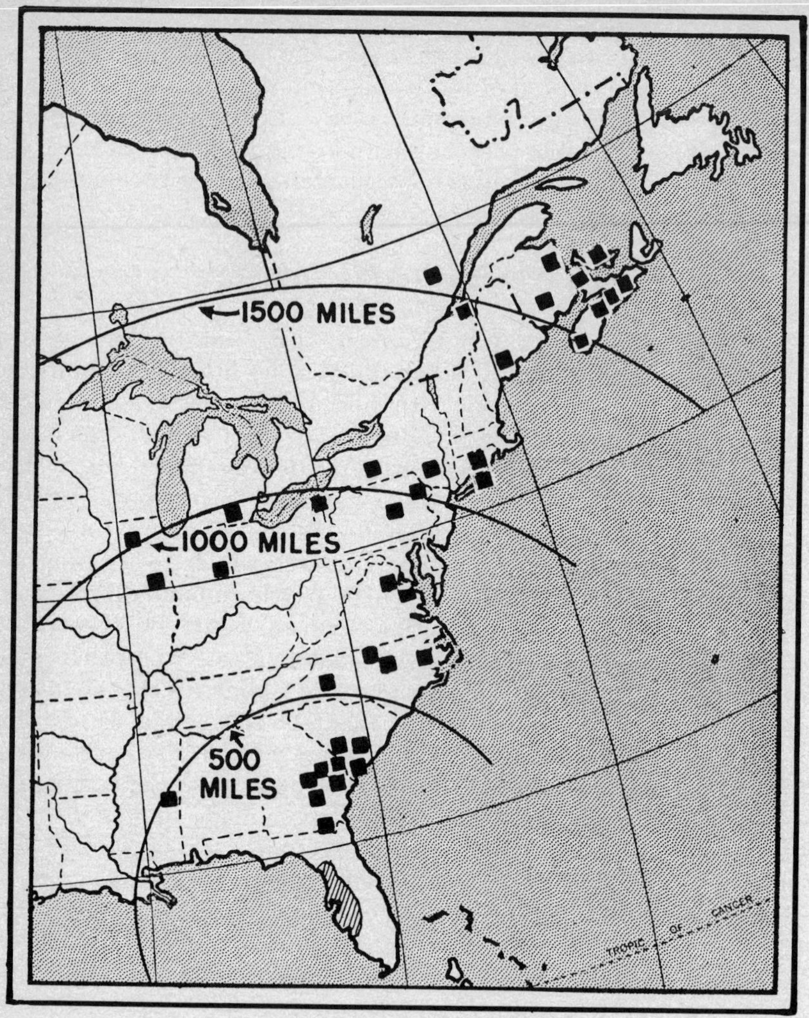

Fig. 7. Young Bald Eagles banded in the nest in west Florida and recovered in the north during their first year. (Broley, 1947.)

movement at all but has passed the winter in its native area." Thus a bird native to one area may be found in a subsequent summer in quite a different area. (The term is not meant to apply to the movement of birds which migrate southward in fall and merely miss their way on the return journey in spring, with the result that they are found breeding in a geographical region different from their native one.) Abmigration apparently occurs with some frequency among ducks but perhaps only very rarely among other birds.

Altitude

Early writers, such as Gätke (1895), were inclined to believe that birds usually migrate at very great heights (20,000 or even 40,000 feet), but modern studies have not borne out that theory. The first considerable amount of exact data was furnished by Ingram (1919) and Meinertzhagen (1920), who gathered their figures largely from the aviators of World War I. Earlier, Stebbins (1906) and then Carpenter (1906) published some figures on the altitude of night-migrating birds determined by the use of two telescopes (a method devised by Stebbins). Lowery (1951: 389), however, has recently cast doubt on the accuracy of the results, contending that the technique has serious inherent limitations. Sinding (1947) reports excellent success with a military range finder.

In general, the results of recent studies indicate that most migrating birds fly at very moderate heights. Very few seem to fly above 3000 feet, and the majority probably travel below 1300 feet. In Europe, the Lapwing (*Vanellus*) is the species most frequently found at greater altitudes. Many of these strong-flying shorebirds have been recorded at 5000 and 6000 feet, an extreme record being 8500 feet. Ducks have been recorded at 7500 feet, geese at 9000 feet, and Rooks (*Corvus frugilegus*) at 11,000 feet. Two large birds (probably cranes) at 15,000 feet are the highest-flying birds so far recorded except over mountainous country.

All these altitude records refer to regions where the level of the land is not significantly above sea level. It is well known that considerable numbers of birds go up to 18,000 feet to migrate through passes in the Himalayan Mountains. Such birds as the Snow-partridge (*Lerwa lerwa*), the Snow Pigeon (*Columba leuconota*), and the Yellow-billed Chough (*Pyrrhocorax graculus*) even nest up to 15,000 feet in those ranges. The Mount Everest expedition of 1924 recorded these choughs up to 27,000 feet.

On the other hand, migrants may fly very low, especially when flying against the wind. For example, Moreau (1938: 18–19), watching migrating birds from a ship in the Mediterranean, reported Ortolan Buntings (*Emberiza hortulana*) flying over the water at 10 to 15 feet, Turtle Doves (*Streptopelia turtur*) at 5 to 30 feet, and pipits only a "few feet" above the sea.

Flight Velocity During Migration

Two quite distinct phenomena are involved: The migrating speed of individual birds and the rate of advance of the "species front."

For obvious reasons, very little is known of the rate at which individual birds migrate. Actual flying speeds of birds, measured over short distances, are now known for enough species to give us some idea of the average figures to be expected among a number of families of birds. Meinertzhagen's early findings (1921), which have been well borne out by later writers, provide a good index to flight speeds. He summarized the "normal and migratory rate of flight in miles per hour" thus:

Crow family	31–45	Geese	42–55
Smaller passeres	20–37	Ducks	44–59
Starlings	38–49	Shorebirds	34–51
Tame pigeons	30–36	Falcons	40–48

(A more detailed discussion of flight speed is given in Chapter 8.)

Bird banding provides a method of tracing the individual bird, but obviously the odds are heavily against us. If we are to learn the true migrating speed of an individual bird, it must be captured immediately before its departure from the nesting area and immediately after its arrival on the wintering grounds (by someone who will record the time carefully and report the details accurately to the central record bureau). Naturally this does not happen often, but after banding several million birds we have accumulated a few records which may meet these requirements. There is, for example, the oft-cited case of the Lesser Yellowlegs (*Totanus flavipes*) banded at North Eastham, Cape Cod, Massachusetts, on August 28, 1935, and killed 6 days later 1900 miles away at Martinique in the West Indies; the average distance traveled was about 316 mi. per day. M. T. Cooke (1940) gives additional records: Two Mallards (*Anas platyrhynchos*) traveled over 500 mi. (510 and 550) in 2 days; Chimney Swifts (*Chaetura pelagica*) traveled 80 mi. in 1 day, and 600 mi. in 4 days. A Wheatear (*Oenanthe oenanthe*) banded at Skokholm, Wales, on August 16, 1949, was recovered at Capbreton, southwestern France, 43 hours later, having traveled about 600 mi. (Conder, 1954).

The species front, on the other hand, advances northward in the spring much more slowly. Wells W. Cooke, the pioneer student of bird migration in North America, published data and maps in 1915 on the migration rates of a number of species. These have been much copied and never yet improved upon. In general, he found, the earlier migrants (which are doubtless often held back by unfavorable weather) advance into the north more slowly than species that start later in the spring. The Robin (*Turdus migratorius*) takes 78 days, he reported, to advance from the edge of its winter range in Iowa to its northwestern outpost in Alaska, 3000 mi. away (a rate of about 38 mi. per day). The Black-and-White Warbler (*Mniotilta varia*) averages 20 to 25 mi. per day in its migration from southern Florida to Lake Superior. A much more rapid migrant is the Gray-cheeked Thrush (*Hylocichla minima*), which starts late in spring and travels to its northernmost breeding areas at about 130 mi. per day. The Blackpoll Warbler (*Dendroica striata*) Cooke mapped as starting late in spring and advancing at an ever-increasing rate (increasing from 30 to more than 200 mi. per day)—a habit characteristic, in varying degree, of most migrants that have been studied (Fig. 8).

This information on the rate of advance on a continent-wide front of the vanguard of several species is a triumph of co-operative study, for it represents the labors of many hundreds of volunteers who for decades have made faithful reports to a central bureau, and yet it is only a beginning. We still know almost nothing about the main body's rate of advance in either spring or fall, almost nothing about even the vanguard's rate in fall.

Pattern of Migration in the Americas

The migrations of American birds are extremely varied. The principal types of postbreeding migrations to winter quarters (Fig. 9) may be summarized thus:

a. Many North American species migrate southward. The distance covered varies from only a few miles to 7000 or even 8000 mi. (Arctic American shorebirds that winter in Patagonia).

b. A few species leave the tropical West Indies, Mexico, and even Central America and migrate to South America at the end of their breeding season. The Gray Kingbird (*Tyrannus dominicensis*) and the Black-whiskered Vireo (*Vireo altiloquus*), for example, leave Cuba to winter in South America; the Sulphur-bellied Flycatcher (*Myiodynastes luteiventris*) nests in Mexico and throughout Central America to Costa Rica, but after breeding leaves all

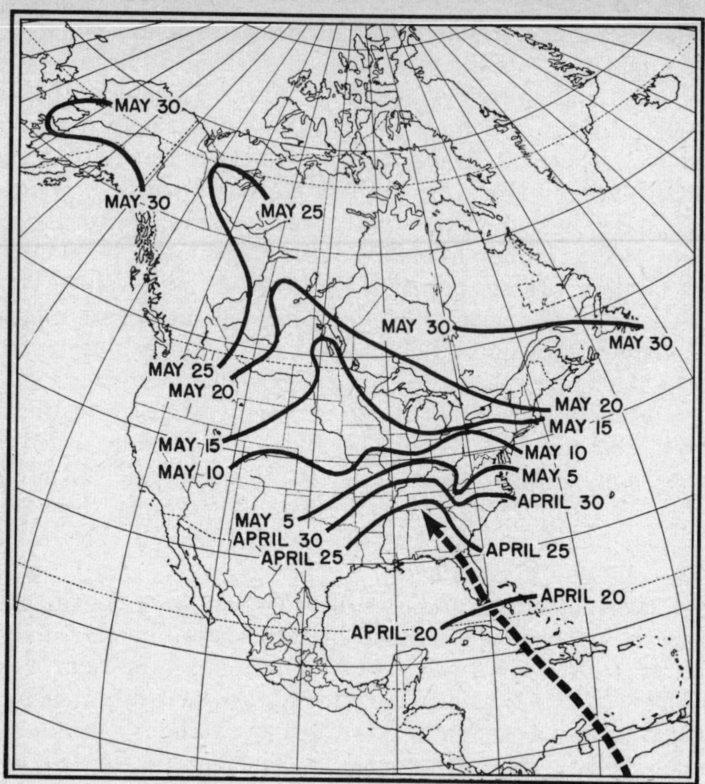

Fig. 8. Migration of the Blackpoll Warbler, a species which starts late in spring and then migrates more and more rapidly as the season progresses. (After W. W. Cooke, 1915.)

the area north and northwest of Costa Rica, moving into Panama and South America (south to Bolivia).

c. A number of species which nest in the South Temperate Zone of South America migrate northward after breeding, "wintering" as far north in some cases as the Caribbean coast of that continent (Chapman, 1929; Zimmer, 1938). Here also there is every gradation from short to long distances. Note, however, that no South American species is known to migrate into North or even Central America.

d. Certain petrels and shearwaters (e.g., the Sooty Shearwater, *Puffinus griseus*), which nest on southernmost South America (and the subantarctic islands), migrate in their "winter" to the north Atlantic (Greenland) and Pacific (Alaska) oceans.

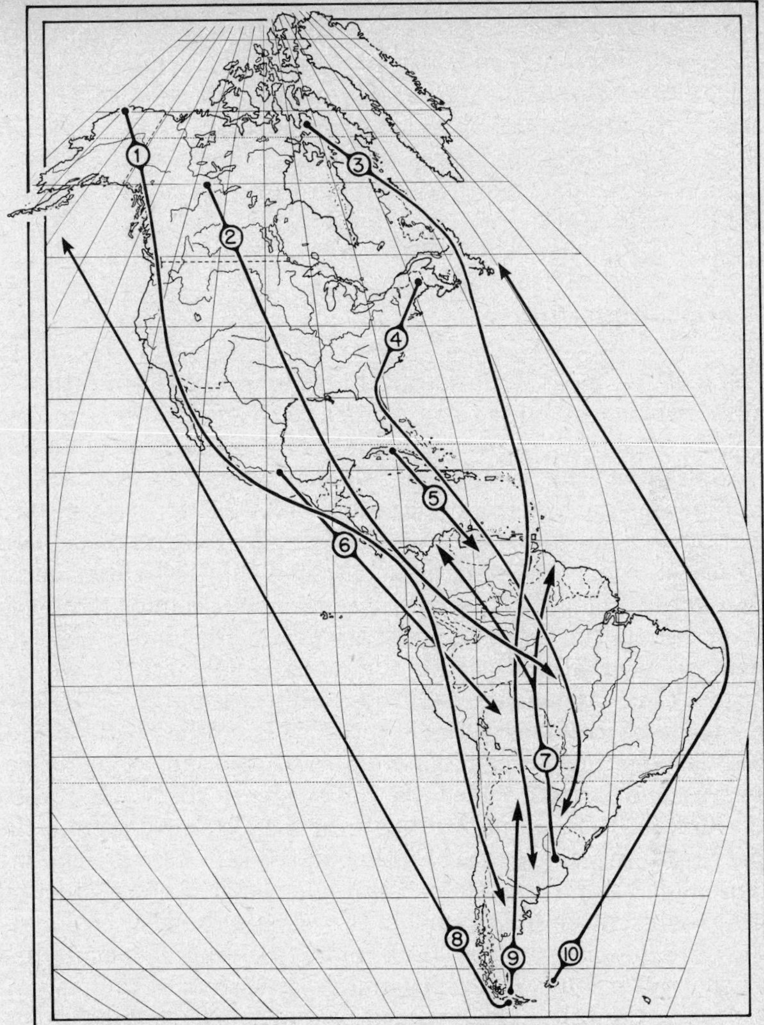

Fig. 9. The postbreeding migrations of some American birds.

1. Sanderling (*Crocethia alba*). Northern Alaska to s. Argentina.
2. Red-eyed Vireo (*Vireo o. olivaceus*). Mackenzie to Mato Grosso.
3. Golden Plover (*Pluvialis d. dominicus*). Melville Peninsula to Argentina.
4. Bobolink (*Dolichonyx oryzivorus*). Maine to s. Brazil.
5. Gray Kingbird (*Tyrannus dominicensis sequax*). Cuba to Venezuela.
6. Sulphur-bellied Flycatcher (*Myiodynastes l. luteiventris*). S. Mexico to Bolivia.
7. Brown-chested Martin (*Phaeoprogne tapera fusca*). Argentina to British Guiana.
8. Sooty Shearwater (*Puffinus griseus*). Magellanic Islands to Alaska coast.
9. Rufous-backed Ground-tyrant (*Lessonia rufa*). Tierra del Fuego to n. Argentina.
10. Wilson's Petrel (*Oceanites oceanicus*). Falkland Islands to Newfoundland.

e. At least one species, *Vireo olivaceus,* breeds from northern North America to southern South America, and the migrants from Canada (*Vireo olivaceus olivaceus*) mingle in tropical South America with individuals of another subspecies (*Vireo olivaceus chivi*) which migrate north from Argentina. Further, the wintering ground also supports other, nonmigratory, forms of this same species (Zimmer, 1941).

Bird Navigation

One of the most remarkable things about bird migration is the ability shown by birds to navigate a route of hundreds or even thousands of miles to an exact point. The curiosity of man has been aroused by the wonder of bird navigation as far back as human records go; yet the remarkable precision of the best bird navigation was not apparent until bird banding began to be used as a research tool. Banding demonstrated that individual birds not only return regularly from distant wintering grounds to nest in nearly or exactly the same spot used the year before, but that many of them go year after year to the same small area to winter. Baldwin (1919) demonstrated that White-throated Sparrows (*Zonotrichia albicollis*) repeatedly returned from the north to winter on the same few acres in Georgia; later the same type of behavior was demonstrated for birds that winter in the tropics, when Indigo Buntings (*Passerina cyanea*) were found returning from the United States to winter a second time in the same jungle clearing in Guatemala (Van Tyne, 1932). But even after the introduction of bird banding, attempts to explain the physical basis of bird navigation were for some years little more than pure speculation. Then, soon after 1940, there began a great rush of actual experimental work, doubtless the result in part of D. R. Griffin's important survey (first published in 1944; revised in 1952). Only a few of the fast-changing trends of current research can be indicated here.

It has so far not proved possible to experiment with long-range migrants traveling their natural routes; most experimentation has consisted of removing birds to a distance from their natural "home" (usually the nest area) and studying the percentage of returns, the speed of return, and sometimes—by airplane observation—even the path followed.

It seems certain that there are great differences among species in the ability to navigate. Hinde (1952: 38) surveyed many tests of homing ability in nonmigratory titmice (of the genus *Parus*) and concluded that these birds find their way home over distances of only a few miles (maximum of about 7 mi. in the studies listed), the returns seeming to "depend on the bird coming by chance into known country." Similarly, Wojtusiak (1949: 103), experimenting in Poland with the nonmigratory European Tree Sparrow (*Passer montanus*), found that no birds removed from the nest area returned home from distances greater than about 7 mi. On the other hand, the same technique has demonstrated extraordinary powers of navigation in certain migratory seabirds. For example, Lack and Lockley (1938) reported that Manx Shearwaters (*Puffinus puffinus*), removed from their nesting burrows in Wales, returned successfully from points outside their normal geographical range and as remote as 930 mi. airline over land; or 3700 mi. over water—the route probably used. Later, Mazzeo (1953) took a single breeding adult from the same colony to Boston, Massachusetts, by airplane and released it there—3200 land mi. airline from its nest; it was recaptured at the nest 12 days and 12½ hours later! This shearwater returned from outside the range of the species, along an east-west route (at right angles to its normal migration), and at a rate of more than 250 mi. per day, a speed that leaves little time for any deviation from the shortest possible route.

Types of Homing

Griffin (1952) has outlined three types of homing in birds:

Type I is homing through reliance on visual landmarks within familiar territory and the use of wandering "exploration" when the bird is released in unfamiliar country.

Type II depends on the ability to maintain a certain direction even when crossing unfamiliar territory.

Type III depends on the additional ability which some birds show, when released in unfamiliar territory, to choose approximately the correct direction to their destination. This is the most remarkable type, and though Griffin speaks of it as demonstrated only by Matthews' (1951) experiments on pigeons, it is necessarily the type used by all birds that migrate long distances between limited areas. For example, the Kirtland's Warbler (*Dendroica kirtlandii*) winters exclusively in the small Bahama island group and breeds exclusively in a small area of central Michigan, migrating annually between them; in spite of 100 years of observation, we have not the slightest evidence that even rare individuals ever fail in the navigation of the rather lengthy course (at least 1375 mi.) over land and sea. A similar instance is the migration of the Bronze Cuckoo (*Chalcites l. lucidus*) between New Zealand and the Solomon Islands.

Bird Navigation and the Coriolis Force

Ising (1946) has proposed that bird navigation may depend upon the mechanical effects which result from the rotation of the earth (the "Coriolis force"). There is no question that as a result of the earth's rotation the weight of a flying bird would change, depending on the direction of the bird's flight (which would either add to or subtract from the velocity of its rotation about the axis of the earth) and its latitude. The Coriolis force is strongest at the poles and is zero at the equator. Therefore, theoretically a bird might thus judge its latitude. However, the force is so small and the confusing factors—such as variation in the speed of the bird, effects of wind and air turbulence—are so great that the detection and measurement of the extremely small changes which the theory requires seem well outside the sensitivity of the bird's sense organs. For example, according to Wynne-Edwards (1948: 610), a change of speed from 40 to 39 mi. per hour in a bird's flight speed could alter the Coriolis effect by 2.5 per cent, the same change that would be registered by a geographical displacement of about 150 mi.

Bird Navigation Related to Infrared Light

Reporting on migration studies made in Poland, Wojtusiak (1949) has brought forward again the old theory that birds may be sensitive to infrared rays. If the theory is correct, birds would be able to see not only through fog but also at night. Wojtusiak suggests that "during autumn migrations the birds would be guided towards warmer regions having stronger radiation and thus appearing brighter." However, there appears to be no satisfactory experimental proof of such sensitivity in birds, and Griffin (1952: 369) dismisses this theory of bird navigation as scarcely deserving serious consideration.

Bird Navigation Related to Terrestrial Magnetism and Coriolis Force

Theories of bird navigation based on terrestrial magnetism have been in circulation since the middle of the nineteenth century, but no one has yet produced experimental proof that any animals are sensitive to a magnetic field. However, Yeagley (1947, 1951) has published accounts of elaborate experiments with homing pigeons which he believes are evidence of the use of both terrestrial magnetism and the Coriolis force in bird navigation. He suggests that birds sense their "latitude" by the effects of the Coriolis force and their "longitude" by the strength of the vertical component of the earth's magnetic field. In North America the variation in these two forces constitutes a grid, one set of lines being the parallels of latitude (lines of equal Coriolis force) and the other being arcs drawn about the North Magnetic Pole as a center.

Yeagley reported on experiments with pigeons trained to return to a home loft in central Pennsylvania; the pigeons were released in Nebraska with the expectation that they would (if they were indeed homing by means of the above-described grid) return to a "conjugate point" in Nebraska where the lines of the two forces intersect exactly as they do at the home loft in Pennsylvania. Only a very few pigeons actually reached even the vicinity of the Nebraska loft, but Yeagley presented evidence for what he considered to be a significant "tendency" to fly in that direction. Other experiments of Yeagley's compared the homing ability of two groups of pigeons: some with magnets attached to their wings (which would prevent any detection or measurement of the earth's magnetic field), and others with unmagnetized copper bars attached in a similar manner. One set of results seemed to show that pigeons without magnets return more rapidly and in larger numbers, but subsequent tests both by Yeagley and by several other investigators failed to show any difference between those with and those without magnets. Wynne-Edwards (1948), Thorpe (1949: 92–93), and Griffin (1952: 364–368) have presented fundamental criticisms of Yeagley's work which have not as yet been answered.

Bird Navigation Related to Vision

There can be no question about the importance of vision in bird navigation. All published accounts of diurnal migration include many details that point unmistakably to the use of vision in modifying the migration route in relation to local physiography.

A series of remarkable experiments with captive Starlings (*Sturnus vulgaris*), pigeons (*Columba livia*), and other birds, made by Kramer (1952) and his associates in Germany, have demonstrated that birds have a strong tendency to orient in relation to the sun. By the use of elaborate experimental equipment which included a series of windows opening on the sky, artifical light, mirrors, and an "environment" which could be easily revolved about the cage, it was possible to show that the birds oriented their migratory efforts ("migration restlessness") very definitely in relation to source of light, natural or artificial. Starlings oriented continuously toward a given compass direction regardless of the time of day, even when their view of the out-of-doors was limited to six square equally spaced windows, in a circular wall, each subtending about 20° and revealing only a patch of sky well above the horizon. Kramer then taught Starlings to find food in closed containers placed in a fixed relation to the light source. When the light source was shifted 90° by the use of mirrors, the Starlings made a corresponding shift in their orientation. When artificial light was substituted, the Starlings continued to react in the same manner, seeking food in a direction relative to the artificial sun and correcting for the passage of time as they had for the real sun. A heavy cloud cover prevented sun orientation, though a medium cover did not, the birds' ability to estimate the sun's position behind the clouds being apparently no better than man's. Kramer believes his study to demonstrate beyond question not only that birds orient strongly in relation to light sources but also that the daily movement of the sun "is mastered by the bird superlatively well."

Matthews (1952) studied the homing of Lesser Black-backed Gulls (*Larus fuscus graellsii*) in England. Of 194 gulls that were removed to distances of 130 to 330 mi., a large percentage (57 to 75 per cent, varying with distance) returned successfully to their nesting grounds; when released, a significant number showed an immediate orientation toward home when the sun was visible but not when it was obscured by clouds. Working with Manx Shearwaters, Matthews (1953b) was the first to provide complete evidence for navigational ability in a wild bird. Continuing the earlier work of Lack and Lockley, Matthews and his collaborators took from their nesting burrows 338 marked shearwaters (a large, hardy bird accustomed to fasting for several days at a time while incubating) and released them at distances of 200 to 400 mi. largely at inland points, which would be completely strange to these pelagic birds. A significantly large number of the shearwaters not only flew home with a promptness that demonstrated great navigational ability, but they were also observed to turn in the correct compass direction within 3 minutes of their release. Of very great interest is the additional fact that these shearwaters, like the pigeons and gulls studied earlier by Matthews (1952, 1953a), were able to navigate thus only when the sun was visible; cloudy weather greatly reduced their homing ability.

Matthews (1955), critically reviewing the various theories of bird navigation, makes a good case for the hypothesis that the bird uses the sun-arc for direction finding. The hypothesis requires, as Matthews points out, that the bird have an accurate memory of the sun-arc characteristics at its home locality, an accurate chronometer mechanism (for which, indeed, there seems to be satisfactory evidence), and an eye capable of measuring small angles.

Matthews (p. 120) reminds us that "the primary stimuli for the onset of migration appear to be changes in day-length, which are governed by the rising and sinking of the sun-arc. Again, one of the main purposes of migration appears to be to take advantage of the longer days in higher latitudes, which allow more food to be collected for the young. The length of day is correlated with the inclination of the sun-arc. Thus it seems possible that the sun-arc may provide the purpose, cause and guide of migration."

References

Aldrich, John W., *et al.* 1949. Migration of Some North American Waterfowl. *U. S. Fish and Wildl. Serv. Spec. Sci. Rept. (Wildlife) No. 1.*

Amadon, Dean. 1948. Continental Drift and Bird Migration. *Science,* 108: 705-707.

Averill, C. K. 1920. Migration and Physical Proportions. A Preliminary Study. *Auk,* 37: 572–579.

Bagg, A. M., W. W. H. Gunn, *et al.* 1950. Barometric Pressure-Patterns and Spring Bird Migration. *Wils. Bull.,* 62: 5–19.

Baldwin, S. Prentiss. 1919. Bird-Banding by Means of Systematic Trapping. *Proc. Linn. Soc. N. Y.,* 31: 23–56.

Ball, Stanley C. 1952. Fall Bird Migration on the Gaspé Peninsula. *Peabody Mus. Nat. Hist., Yale Univ., Bull. 7.*

Beebe, William. 1947. Avian Migration at Rancho Grande in North-central Venezuela. *Zoologica,* 32: 153–168.

Bennett, Holly Reed. 1952. Fall Migration of Birds at Chicago. *Wils. Bull.,* 64: 197–220.

Benoit, J., and I. Assenmacher. 1953. Action des facteurs externes et plus particulièrement du facteur lumineux sur l'activité sexuelle des oiseaux. *Réunion Endocrin.,* 1953: 33–80.

Bissonnette, Thomas Hume. 1931. Studies on the Sexual Cycle in Birds.... *Jour. Exper. Zool.,* 58: 281–318.

——— 1935. Sexual Photoperiodicity. *Jour. Heredity,* 27: 170–180.

——— 1937. Photoperiodicity in Birds. *Wils. Bull.,* 49: 241–270.

Bogert, Cardine. 1937. The Distribution and the Migration of the Long-tailed Cuckoo (*Urodynamis taitensis* Sparrman). *Amer. Mus. Novitates, No. 933.*

Brewster, William. 1886. Bird Migration. *Mem. Nuttall Ornith. Club, No. 1.*

Broley, Charles L. 1947. Migration and Nesting of Florida Bald Eagles. *Wils. Bull.,* 59: 3–20.

Broun, Maurice. 1939. Fall Migrations of Hawks at Hawk Mountain, Pennsylvania, 1934–1938. *Auk,* 56: 429–441.

———— 1949. Hawks Aloft: The Story of Hawk Mountain. Dodd, Mead Co., New York.

Carpenter, Frederic W. 1906. An Astronomical Determination of the Heights of Birds during Nocturnal Migration. *Auk,* 23: 210–217.

Chapin, James P. 1932. The Birds of the Belgian Congo. Part I. *Bull. Amer. Mus. Nat. Hist.,* 65: x + 756 pp.

Chapman, Frank M. 1929. Relationships of the Races of Phaeoprogne tapera and their Probable Significance. *Auk,* 46: 348–357.

———— 1933. The Migration of Turkey Buzzards as Observed on Barro Colorado Island, Canal Zone. *Auk,* 50: 30–34.

———— 1940. The Post-Glacial History of *Zonotrichia capensis. Bull. Amer. Mus. Nat. Hist.,* 77: 381–438.

Clarke, William Eagle. 1912. *Studies in Bird Migration.* 2 vols. Gurney and Jackson, London.

Conder, P. J. 1954. Wheatear. In Reports on the Movements of Certain Migrants at British Bird Observatories in 1952. *Brit. Birds,* 47: 17–18.

Cooke, May Thacher. 1940. Notes on Speed of Migration. *Bird-Banding,* 11: 21.

Cooke, Wells W. 1915. Bird Migration. *U. S. Dept. Agric. Bull. No. 185.*

Deelder, C. L. 1949. On the autumn migration of the Scandinavian Chaffinch (*Fringilla c. coelebs* L.). *Ardea,* 37: 1–88.

Eaton, Richard Jefferson. 1933. The Migratory Movements of Certain Colonies of Herring Gulls . . . . Part I. *Bird-Banding,* 4: 165–176.

Emlen, John T., Jr. 1943. Sex Ratios in Wintering Gambel White-crowned Sparrows. *Condor,* 45: 196.

Fell, H. Barraclough. 1947. The Migration of the New Zealand Bronze Cuckoo, *Chalcites lucidus lucidus* (Gmelin). *Trans. Proc. Roy. Soc., N. Z.,* 76: 504–515.

Gätke, Heinrich. 1895. *Heligoland as an Ornithological Observatory.* David Douglas, Edinburgh.

Grant, D. H. B., and C. W. Mackworth-Praed. 1952. On the Species and Races of the Yellow Wagtails from Western Europe to Western North America. *Bull. Brit. Mus.* (*Nat. Hist.*) *Zool.,* 1: 255–268.

Griffin, Donald R. 1944. The Sensory Basis of Bird Migration. *Quart. Rev. Biol.,* 19: 15–31.

———— 1952. Bird Navigation. *Biol. Rev.,* 27: 359–400.

Heydweiller, A. Marguerite. 1936. Sex, Age and Individual Variation of Winter Tree Sparrows. *Bird-Banding,* 7: 61–68.

Hinde, R. A. 1952. The Behaviour of the Great Tit (*Parus major*) and Some Other Related Species. *Behaviour,* Suppl. 2. (Also separately publ. by E. J. Brill, Leiden.)

Hudson, W. H. 1872. On the Birds of the Rio Negro of Patagonia. *Proc. Zool. Soc. London,* 1872: 534–550.

Ingram, Collingwood. 1919. Notes on the Height at which Birds migrate. *Ibis,* 1919: 321–325.

Ising, Gustav. 1946. Die physikalische Möglichkeit eines tierischen Orientierungssinnes auf Basis der Erdrotation. *Ark. f. Matematik, Astronomi, Fysik,* 32A, No. 18.

Kramer, Gustav. 1952. Experiments on Bird Orientation. *Ibis,* 94: 265–285.

Lack, David. 1943–44. The Problem of Partial Migration. *Brit. Birds,* 37: 122–130, 143–150.

——— and Elizabeth Lack. 1949. Passerine Migration through England. *Brit. Birds,* 42: 320–326.

——— 1951. Migration of Insects and Birds through a Pyrenean Pass. *Jour. Animal Ecol.,* 20: 63–67.

Lack, David, and R. M. Lockley. 1938. Skokholm Bird Observatory Homing Experiments. 1. 1936–37. Puffins, Storm-Petrels and Manx Shearwaters. *Brit. Birds,* 31: 242–248.

Lincoln, Frederick C. 1950. Migration of Birds. *U. S. Fish and Wildl. Serv. Circ. 16.*

Lowery, George H., Jr. 1951. A Quantitative Study of the Nocturnal Migration of Birds. *Univ. Kans. Publ. Mus. Nat. Hist.,* 3: 361–472.

McCabe, Robert. 1947. The Homing of Transplanted Young Wood Ducks. *Wils. Bull.,* 59: 104–109.

Magee, M. J. 1934. The Distribution of Michigan Recovered Eastern Evening Grosbeaks Near the Atlantic Seaboard. *Bird-Banding,* 5: 175–181.

Marshall, William H. 1946. Cover Preferences, Seasonal Movements, and Food Habits of Richardson's Grouse and Ruffed Grouse in Southern Idaho. *Wils. Bull.,* 58: 42–52.

Matthews, G. V. T. 1951. The Experimental Investigation of Navigation in Homing Pigeons. *Jour. Exper. Biol.,* 28: 508–536.

——— 1952. An Investigation of Homing Ability in Two Species of Gulls. *Ibis,* 94: 243–264.

——— 1953a. Sun Navigation in Homing Pigeons. *Jour. Exper. Biol.,* 30: 243–267.

——— 1953b. Navigation in the Manx Shearwater. *Jour. Exper. Biol.,* 30: 370–396.

——— 1955. *Bird Navigation.* Cambridge Univ. Press, Cambridge, England.

Mazzeo, Rosario. 1953. Homing of the Manx Shearwater. *Auk,* 70: 200–201.

Meinertzhagen, R. 1920. Some preliminary remarks on the Altitude of the Migratory flight of Birds, with special reference to the Palaearctic Region. *Ibis,* 1920: 920–936.

——— 1921. Some preliminary remarks on the Velocity of Migratory Flight among Birds, with special reference to the Palaearctic Region. *Ibis,* 1921: 228–238. (Republ. in *Smithsonian Rept. for 1921.*)

——— 1951. Review of the Alaudidae. *Proc. Zool. Soc. London,* 121: 81–132.

——— 1955. The Speed and Altitude of Bird Flight (with Notes on Other Animals). *Ibis,* 97: 81–117.

Moreau, R. E. 1938. Bird-Migration over the North-western Part of the Indian Ocean, the Red Sea, and the Mediterranean. *Proc. Zool. Soc. London,* 108A: 1–26.

——— 1951. The Migration System in Perspective. *Proc. 10th Internatl. Ornith. Congr., 1950:* 245–248.

Newman, Robert J. 1952. Studying Nocturnal Bird Migration by Means of the Moon. Louisiana State Univ., Museum of Zoology, Baton Rouge (mimeographed).

Nice, Margaret Morse. 1937. Studies in the Life History of the Song Sparrow, I. *Trans. Linn. Soc. N. Y.,* 4: vi + 247 pp.

Rand, A. L. 1936. The Distribution and Habits of Madagascar Birds. *Bull. Amer. Mus. Nat. Hist.,* 72: 143–499.

Rowan, William. 1925. Relation of Light to Bird Migration and Developmental Changes. *Nature,* 115: 494–495.

Rowan, William. 1926a. Notes on Alberta Waders Included in the British List, Part II. *Brit. Birds,* 20: 34–42.

———— 1926b. On Photoperiodism, Reproductive Periodicity, and the Annual Migrations of Birds and Certain Fishes. *Proc. Boston Soc. Nat. Hist.,* 38: 147–189.

———— 1932. Experiments in bird migration. III. The effects of artificial light, castration and certain extracts on the autumn movements of the American Crow (*Corvus brachyrhynchos*). *Proc. Natl. Acad. Sci.,* 18: 639–654.

———— 1946. Experiments in Bird Migration. *Trans. Roy. Soc. Canada,* 40 (ser. 3, sect. 5): 123–135.

Rudebeck, Gustaf. 1950. Studies on Bird Migration. Based on Field Studies in Southern Sweden. *Vår Fågelvärld,* Suppl. 1, 1950.

Sinding, Erik. 1947. [Determination of the Altitude of the Passage of Birds by Means of a Range-Finder]. *Dansk Ornith. For. Tidsskr.,* 41: 56–60.

Skutch, Alexander F. 1945. The Migration of Swainson's and Broad-winged Hawks through Costa Rica. *Northwest Sci.,* 19: 80–89.

Soper, J. Dewey. 1942. Life History of the Blue Goose, *Chen caerulescens* (Linnaeus). *Proc. Boston Soc. Nat. Hist.,* 42: 121–222.

Stebbins, Joel. 1906. A Method of Determining the Heights of Migrating Birds. *Popular Astronomy,* 14: 65–70.

Stone, Witmer. 1937. *Bird Studies at Old Cape May.* Vol. 1. Delaware Valley Ornithological Club at the Academy of Natural Sciences of Philadelphia.

Taverner, P. A., and B. H. Swales. 1907–1908. The Birds of Point Pelee. *Wils. Bull.,* 19: 37–54, 82–99, 133–153; 20: 79–96, 107–129.

Thomson, A. Landsborough. 1926. *Problems of Bird-Migration.* H. F. & G. Witherby, London.

———— 1931. On "Abmigration" Among the Ducks: An Anomaly Shown by the Results of Bird-marking. *Proc. 7th Internatl. Ornith. Congr., 1930:* 382–388.

———— 1939. The Migration of the Gannet: Results of Marking in the British Isles. *Brit. Birds,* 32: 282–289.

———— 1953. The study of the visible migration of birds: an introductory review. *Ibis,* 95: 165–180.

Thorpe, W. H. 1949. A Discussion on the Orientation of Birds on Migratory and Homing Flights: Recent Biological Evidence for the Methods of Bird Orientation. *Proc. Linn. Soc. London,* 160: 85–94.

Townsend, Charles Wendell. 1931. The Post-breeding Northern Migration of North American Herons. *Proc. 7th Internatl. Ornith. Congr., 1930:* 366–369.

Tyler, Winsor M. 1916. The Call-Notes of Some Nocturnal Migrating Birds. *Auk,* 33: 132–141.

Välikangas, Ilmari. 1933. Finnische Zugvögel aus englischen Vogeleiern. *Vogelzug,* 4: 159–166. (Summarized in English by M. M. Nice in *Bird-Banding,* 5, 1934: 95.)

Van Tyne, Josselyn. 1928. A Diurnal Local Migration of the Black-capped Chickadee. *Wils. Bull.,* 40: 252.

———— 1932. Winter Returns of the Indigo Bunting in Guatemala. *Bird-Banding,* 3: 110.

Wetmore, Alexander. 1926. Observations on the Birds of Argentina, Paraguay, Uruguay, and Chile. *U. S. Natl. Mus. Bull. 133.*

Wojtusiak, Roman J. 1949. Polish Investigations on Homing in Birds and their Orientation in Space. *Proc. Linn. Soc. London,* 160: 99–108.

Wolfson, Albert. 1940. A Preliminary Report on Some Experiments on Bird Migration. *Condor,* 42: 93–99.

Wolfson, Albert. 1942. Regulation of Spring Migration in Juncos. *Condor,* 44: 237–263.

——— 1945. The Role of the Pituitary, Fat Deposition, and Body Weight in Bird Migration. *Condor,* 47: 95–127.

——— 1948. Bird Migration and the Concept of Continental Drift. *Science,* 108: 23–30.

——— 1952. Day Length, Migration, and Breeding Cycles in Birds. *Sci. Monthly,* 74: 191–200.

Wynne-Edwards, V. C. 1948. Yeagley's Theory of Bird Navigation. *Ibis,* 90: 606–611.

Yeagley, Henry L. 1947. A Preliminary Study of a Physical Basis of Bird Navigation. *Jour. Appl. Phys.,* 18: 1035–1063.

——— 1951. A Preliminary Study of a Physical Basis of Bird Navigation. Part II. *Jour. Appl. Phys.,* 22: 746–760.

Zimmer, John T. 1938. Notes on Migrations of South American Birds. *Auk,* 55: 405–410.

——— 1941. Studies of Peruvian Birds. No. XXXIX. The Genus *Vireo. Amer. Mus. Novitates, No. 1127.*

8. Flight

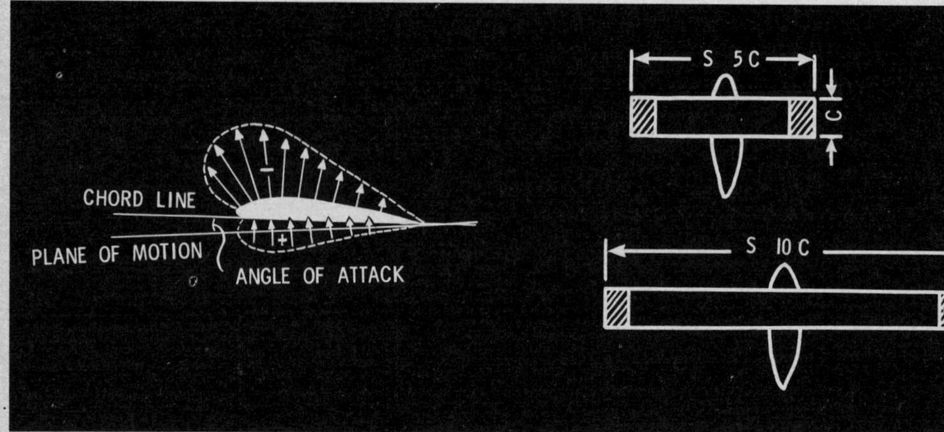

Fig. 1. Left: Section through wing to show the approximate magnitude and direction of lift at different points on the surface. Right: Effect of increased aspect ratio in decreasing the ineffective proportion of the wing. S = span; C = chord; shading shows ineffective area at wing tip. The ineffective area in the upper aircraft (S/C = 5) is twice as great as in the lower one (S/C = 10). (Modified by courtesy of D. B. O. Savile and the Editor of *Evolution.*)

NO ONE HAS FOUND it possible to give a complete explanation of the manifold factors concerned in bird flight, although much information has been compiled and some general principles have been proposed. Nearly all investigators have encountered apparent contradictions among data obtained from the analyses of single parts of the total flight mechanism. This is due in part to the fact that the primary modifications and adaptations of the forelimb for flight tend to conceal phylogenetic characters among the orders of birds. This makes it extremely difficult to sort out and analyze structural differences some of which may be a reflection of flight pattern, others a reflection of phylogenetic relationships, still others a combination of the two. Engels (1941), Fisher (1946, 1955), and others have pointed out that many factors—aerodynamic, mechanical, and psychobiological—must be considered in any attempt to relate structure with flight habit.

Let us note briefly a few simple aerodynamic principles as they pertain to the different adaptations seen in the wings of birds. Flight is possible because of certain phenomena associated with air pressure and the movement of air around a streamlined structure—one which follows the natural design of air flow. The pressure on the surface of such a streamlined structure is reduced to a minimum so long as the force of the moving air strikes it "head-on" and exactly midway between the upper and lower surfaces. Pressure on the two surfaces will be unequal if the contour of one surface differs from the other, e.g., one surface straight, the other curved. The stream of air passing around the more curved surface must move farther and therefore faster to keep up with the air passing the flatter surface. With higher velocity, less pressure (negative pressure) is exerted on the curved surface. A change in pressure on the surfaces may be effected by tilting upward (or downward) the nose of the streamlined object; this causes greater resistance to the moving air and greater pressure on the more exposed area. If, by construction and/or tilting, there is greater pressure (positive pressure) against the lower surface and therefore less pressure (negative pressure) on the upper surface, *lifting force* or *lift* results.

The construction of a bird's wing is such that during flight there is greater pressure on the lower surface than on the upper surface. In addition, the lifting force can be increased by tilting the wing (i.e., raising the leading edge of the wing) so that more of the air stream is deflected to strike the lower surface and increase the pressure on it. The amount of tilt in the wing with respect to the direction of the relative wind is called the *angle of attack*. The air flow and the relative pressures on the two surfaces of the wing are affected by changes in the angle of attack. If this angle becomes too great, the air stream cannot follow the upper surface and the air flow breaks away and results in a turbulent wake with less negative pressure, hence a loss of lift. The angle at which this occurs is called the *stalling angle*. *Drag* is backward pressure or the force of the air opposing the wing in its movement through the air. Both lift and drag are affected by the shape and area of the wing, by the angle of attack, and by speed (Fig. 1). As approximations it may be said that lift increases in about the same proportion as the wing area and the angle of attack (up to the stalling point). An increase in speed gives a much greater increase in lift—approximately proportional to the square of the speed, *i.e.,* three times the speed produces nine times the lift. Drag, too, varies in proportion to the wing area and the square of the speed, but it increases much more rapidly with an increase in the angle of attack than lift does.

One serious drag on the wing is caused by air which, having passed along the lower surface of the wing, flows up over the trailing edge of the wing and into the lower pressure area on the upper surface. This upflow is especially strong at the end of the wing, and is spoken of as *wing-tip vortex.* The circulation or flow induced by the wing-tip vortex spreads inward along the trailing edge of the wing, interrupting the desired smooth movement of air for a considerable distance (see J. H. Storer, 1948). Loss of power or efficiency due to wing-tip vortex can be reduced by increasing the wing span so as to allow the greatest possible undisturbed area between the wing tips. If, in addition, the width of the wing is increased, there will be less interference with the negative pressure on the upper surface of the wing. This is important because the negative pressure on the upper surface of the wing has been estimated to account for two-thirds to three-fourths of the total lifting force. Lifting power can be improved by *wing slots* which increase the rate of air flow over a wing by forcing the air to pass through a restricted space or slot. When the stalling point is reached, wing slots make it possible to delay stall and restore lift without changing the angle of attack.

A bird can control the direction of its flight either by increasing the frequency of beat or by changing the angle of attack of one wing, thus increasing lift on the one side. Some birds steer by twisting the tail to one side or by elevating or depressing the tail; others (e.g., murres, puffins, herons, cranes) use the feet for steering. The tail may be spread to increase lifting power or to serve as a brake in preparation for landing.

J. H. Storer (1948) has likened the take-off of the Wood Ibis to a helicopter: "The wings sweep forward and back nearly horizontally, producing a climb that takes more power than forward flight requires." The American Egret uses its legs to catapult itself into the air, and its wings operate like a variable propeller, in which the wings concentrate on forward speed: "With wings beating fast, the pressure against the air twists most of their surface into propellers, leaving little surface to supply lift. The tail, spread wide, helps by acting as a flap and making a slot behind each wing to add lift till the bird gains speed. The propellers appear more than twice as big as in normal flight." Some loons, coots, swans, and many ducks run or "patter" along the water for some distance in order to become air-borne. Frigatebirds, some condors, and other birds that are masters at soaring are helpless or nearly so on land. However, the factors involved in landing are more complicated than those operating in taking off or in maintaining flight. Many young birds that can fly well have great difficulty in securing an adequate perch.

The Feathers

The structure of a flight feather (Chapter 3) takes on new meaning when considered in terms of the interaction between the feather and air pressures in flight. It is the distal segment of the wing—the hand and the primary feathers—that serves as the propeller in bird flight. The secondaries, "tertials," and scapulars, plus the body area and tail area, provide the supporting or lifting surface. The outermost primary is attached to the distal phalanx of digit II and, therefore, can function independently. The remaining primaries act as a group because of their mode of attachment and the relationship of their quills to the elastic tissue along the posterior margin of the hand. The tips of all the primaries, however, respond individually to air pressures, and J. H. Storer (1948) has pointed out that during a single wing beat "each of the outer primary feathers goes through a series of different shapes and sizes." Depending upon their structure, therefore, several of the primaries may act as individual propeller blades, which must be controlled in take-off, landing, and in aerial maneuvering. The critical periods during flight occur at take-off and landing, as mentioned above. The presence of wing slots increases lift, which is needed especially at the take-off. The alula functions as a wing slot when it is drawn forward away from the rest of the hand (see Fisher, 1955: 85). The outermost primary, because of its capacity for independent action, may also function as a slot. According to the pattern of emargination of the outer primaries, an additional series of V-shaped, U-shaped, or square slots may be present and used when needed; see Figs. 2 and 3. Savile (1957) reported that

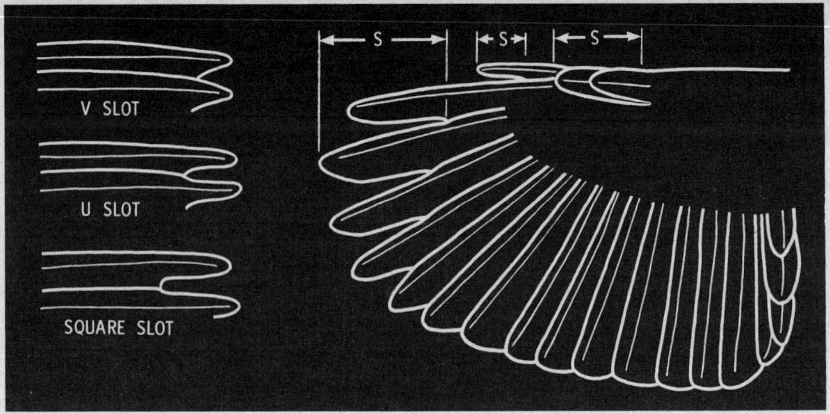

Fig. 2. Left: Types of slot formed by emargination of the primaries; V slot is primitive; the more efficient U slot is found in many woodland birds; the highly efficient square slot is found in birds of prey. Right: Diagrammatic plan view of the Catbird's wing, in which the slotted portions (S) make up 55 per cent of the total wing length. (Modified by courtesy of D. B. O. Savile and the Editor of *Evolution*.)

the slotted length of a Catbird's (*Dumetella*) wing may be as much as 55 per cent of the total length of the wing.

The ratio of length of wing to width of wing (i.e., the aspect ratio) varies greatly among birds. The shape and size (area) of a wing depends largely on the length and shape of the remiges. Wing shape varies with type of flight pattern. Generalizations such as these are subject to many exceptions. Fully cognizant of exceptions and gradations, Savile (1957) has described four basic wing types in birds. His analysis of wing form and function is very helpful in considering the adaptive features of certain wing characteristics. The following discussion is based upon his presentation.

The elliptical wing is characterized by a low aspect ratio, an unusually uniform pressure distribution over the wing surface, and only a slight amount of wing-tip vortex or induced flow. This type of wing is found in birds which "must move easily through restricted openings in vegetation": gallinaceous birds, doves, woodcocks, woodpeckers, and most passerine birds. The amount of slotting (number, size, shape) in the wings varies with the size and habits of the birds. Slots are well developed in gallinaceous birds and in corvids; the extreme example of slotting in the Catbird was mentioned above. Slots are better developed in small active birds (e.g., wood-warblers) than in more sedentary species (House Sparrow).

The high-speed wing is characterized by having a lower camber (flatter section) than is general in bird wings, a moderately high aspect ratio, a taper to a relatively slender elliptical tip, pronounced sweepback of the leading edge and sometimes even of the trailing edge, lack of wing-tip slots, and the development of a pronounced "fairing" at the root of the wing that blends the trailing edge of the wing into the body. The best examples of the high-speed wing are found in plovers, sandpipers, swifts, hummingbirds, swallows, and falcons. Although falcons possess wing-tip slots, which Savile correlates with the need to carry prey, the slots are closed in rapid flight. Intermediate stages are seen in ducks, terns, and jaegers.

The high-aspect-ratio wing is, by definition, one in which the length greatly exceeds the width. Savile gave approximate aspect ratios of 15 to 18 for two species of albatross; by comparison, the aspect ratio of the Catbird's wing is 4.7. Wing-tip slots, in general,

Fig. 3. Yellowbreasted Sunbird (*Leptocoma jugularis microleuca*) returning to its nest; note slotting in the wing and the position of feet. (Courtesy of Loke Wan Tho, Singapore.)

are poorly developed. The high-aspect-ratio wing is characteristic of oceanic soaring birds: albatrosses, frigatebirds, tropicbirds.

The high-lift or slotted soaring wing results from the combination of a moderate aspect ratio with pronounced slotting and camber. This produces an efficient soaring wing for large birds that, in general, "inhabit forested areas or other impeded terrain." Within this group, the degree of slotting is "markedly greater in proportion to size in the large than in the small birds." Savile reported that "the eagles, ospreys and harriers, of relatively open habitats, seem usually to have appreciably higher aspect ratios than the woodland hawks and owls, but I have not been able to examine enough species to be sure that a correlation with habitat is invariable." Savile would include the owls in this group because "their wings have evolved similarly to develop exceptionally high lift."

The basis for soaring is found in the interaction of air currents. Rising columns of air are produced when wind is deflected upward by striking some obstruction or when masses of cold and warm air meet. The differential in the heat absorption properties of water, forested areas, and open fields also results in variation in the air currents over even relatively small areas. The relative air and water temperature and wind velocity are important factors in producing rising air currents over large bodies of water (Woodcock, 1940). Whatever the source, all soaring birds are dependent on rising air currents, and much can be learned about the currents by observing the behavior of the birds. J. H. Storer (1948) has pointed out that birds, such as pelicans, that fly in formation take advantage of the rising currents produced by the wing-tip vortex phenomenon: "The inner wing of each bird in a V formation gains support from the upward rising side of the whirl left by the outer wing of the bird ahead. Thus the energy wasted by each bird in making the vortex is passed on and used by the bird behind it."

The Bony Framework

The two main theories concerning the origin of flight in birds were discussed in Chapter 1, and selected osteological characters were described in Chapter 2. Little mention was made of the appendicular skeleton and the high degree of specialization for flight in the bird skeleton. Avian flight could develop, it would seem, only after the forelimbs were released from use as legs; therefore, we concluded that bipedal progression long preceded flight. Some of the principal adaptations to bipedal locomotion in birds are these:

1. The body (but not the neck) is shortened and the center of gravity is moved toward the rear.

2. The whole thoracic framework tends to be fused and strengthened.

3. The pelvic girdle becomes fused to a long section of the vertebral column.

4. The ilia have become long and fused to the ischia.

5. In the legs there is a reduction in the number of bones and much fusion of bones.

The principal adaptations to flight in birds are:

1. The bones are light and often pneumatic; there is much fusion of bones.

2. There often is much fusion of the dorsal vertebrae (but not in flightless running birds).

3. The thoracic cage is very strong and much fused, thus supporting the pectoral appendage in spite of the strain of flight.

4. The sternum is strong and keeled, the keel being more highly developed in birds which use flapping flight (as contrasted with soaring flight).

5. The whole pectoral girdle is very firmly attached to the thorax.

6. The coracoid is very robust (opposing the pull of the great pectoral muscle).

7. The clavicles are fused (forming the furcula) in most flying species.

8. The supracoracoideus muscle (which raises the wing) is on the ventral side of the sternum and by running over a sort of pulley in the shoulder accomplishes the same result as though it were on the dorsal side of the wing. Thus the center of gravity remains low.

9. The process of breathing is effectively correlated with the movements of the wings in flight.

10. The bones of the wing are reduced in number; two free carpals instead of seven; three (fused) metacarpals instead of five independent bones.

11. The tail is shortened and there is fusion of some of the coccygeal vertebrae.

The pectoral girdle forms a rigid support for the wing. In a few birds (p. 24), the several elements of the pectoral girdle may be fused, but in most birds the three bones articulate with each other by true joints. The coracoid typically fits into a groove in the anterior edge of the sternum and is firmly attached to that bone by ligaments. The strong coracoid forms a strut opposing the pull of M. pectoralis; it is assisted by the furcula in most instances. It has been said that a bird cannot fly if its furcula is broken, but some weak-flying birds do not have functional clavicles at all.

The most obvious differences in the bony elements of the wing among birds are the relative lengths of the several segments of the wing skeleton: arm (humerus), forearm (radius and ulna), and hand or manus (carpometacarpus and the digits, specifically digit II). Böker (1927, 1935) studied flight patterns in relation to food-getting and general habits of birds. He proposed four main "biological types" of flight (Flatterflug, Hubflug, Schwirrflug, Segelflug) based primarily on intramembral proportions of the bony wing segments. His instructive "bildliche Armindices" (histograms) illustrating the relative proportion of arm, forearm, and hand stimulated further analysis of the correlation between the bony wing proportions and flight pattern.

Engels published a series of papers (1938a, 1938b, 1940, 1941) in which he attempted to answer two questions raised by Böker's thesis: (1) How reliable are conclusions regarding intramembral proportions based on only a few skeletons? (2) Are the differences in wing element proportions among the four basic types of flight based on functional differences or on phylogenetic relationships? In a statistical study of coot skeletons, Engels showed that the variability in limb proportions "is usually less than 3%," and he stated that "a few specimens, even single specimens, will suffice *to reveal strongly contrasting patterns of proportion;* but that large series of individuals and statistical treatment are necessary to demonstrate the reliability of slight differences" (italics ours). As to the second question, Engels (1941) concluded that "the intramembral proportions of the wing skeleton are not an infallible index to flight habits, except perhaps where they indicate an extreme pattern." In his analysis of the wing skeleton in a series of hawks, Engels found several patterns, not only in intramembral proportions but also in relative length of the wing. In one group (*Coragyps, Accipiter, Falco*) the total wing length is *less* than three times the trunk length, whereas in a second group (*Cathartes, Buteo, Aquila, Haliaeetus, Pandion*) the wing is *more* than three times the trunk length. Moreover, the intramembral wing proportions vary within both the short-winged and the long-winged groups of hawks. Among the genera in the short-winged group, for example, the manus may be either the shortest or the longest segment of the bony wing. Fisher (1946) presented further data in his excellent study of the American vultures, in which he noted that the "proportions within the wing are variable and are apparently correlated with the mode of flight."

The Wing Muscles

Approximately 50 different muscles and muscle slips have been described as effecting the movements of the wing. Some of the more proximally located muscles (e.g., pectoralis, supracoracoideus, biceps brachii, deltoideus major, tensores patagii longus et brevis) have been studied in some detail in a large number of birds, but the intrinsic musculature, especially that in the manus, is less adequately known. Differences among birds in the absence or the relative development of some of these muscles appear to indicate phylogenetic relationships, but most of the differences seem to be correlated with flight habits.

Nair (1954b) compared data on a series of Indian birds with respect to three previously proposed generalizations concerning muscle development and flight pattern: (1) the motor power (primarily Mm. pectoralis and supracoracoideus) varies inversely to the surface area of the wings; (2) sailing birds have the minimum weight of pectoral musculature; (3) there is an inverse relation between the weight of M. supracoracoideus and wing area. And to be sure, in each case Nair found exceptions based on the weight of these two flight muscles. The fallacy of placing too much reliance on a single morphological feature of a muscle and of attempting to "explain" flight patterns on the basis of the relative development of two or three muscles has been pointed out by Fisher (1946, 1955) and others. Information on the volume and weight (either wet or dry) of all the wing muscles may be used satisfactorily in certain comparisons, but such data alone reveal nothing about gross and microscopic structure, which are correlated with the functional demands made on the muscles (see Chapter 2). For example, a pennate muscle and a muscle in which the fibers are arranged parallel to each other and to the direction of pull could be of equal weight and volume, but the pennate muscle, with shorter but more numerous fibers per cross section, would be more efficient for power of movement. High levels of blood sugar and fat have been reported for the few birds studied, and it has been suggested that the percentage of fat in the pectoral muscles "has a direct relation to the ability of the bird for sustained flight" (Menon, 1954).

As long ago as 1886 Edwards tabulated the ratio of body weight to the weight of the pectoral musculature (Mm. pectoralis and supracoracoideus) of over 50 species of North American birds. He reported, for example, that the pectoral muscles of the Broad-winged Hawk equaled about 6 per cent of the body weight; that of the Tree Sparrow, 10 per cent; and that of the Mourning Dove, about 16 per cent. It remained for Fisher (1946), however, to present the first thorough analysis of osteology and myology in relation to flight pattern in a group of closely related birds, the American vultures, which have a high-lift wing adapted for soaring. Cognizant of the many factors contributing to the over-all flight pattern, Fisher not only described in detail the skeleton and all the appendicular and tail muscles, but also considered the volume of the muscles, the body weight, and, where possible, the total supporting surface of the wing, tail, and body. Fisher's data demonstrate admirably how great may be the differences in structure among birds that are closely related and that have a very similar locomotor pattern. The ratio of length of bony wing to body weight in *Gymnogyps* is 31.9; in *Coragyps,* 93.3; and in *Cathartes,* 110.1. In this same series, the ratio of the volume of the wing musculature to body weight is 24.7, 33.1, and 52.3. A comparison of body weight and the total supporting surface of the wings, tail, and body revealed that the "California condor has a supporting surface of 497 square centimeters per pound; in the turkey vulture the ratio is 1125 square centimeters per pound." Fisher correlated these and other differences with the amount of wing flapping, relative stability when in flight, and manner of take-off.

Engels (1938b) and Berger (1954) studied limb proportions and wing muscles in three genera of American cuckoos that have very different locomotor habits. The Roadrunner (*Geococcyx californianus*) is primarily a terrestrial bird, capable of running at a speed of 10 to 15 mi. per hour. It uses its wings when leaping into the air and for gliding to the ground from perches. At the other extreme, the Black-billed Cuckoo (*Coccyzus erythropthalmus*) is almost entirely arboreal, skilled in flying through the thickets it usually inhabits. The Groove-billed Ani (*Crotophaga sulcirostris*) is a somewhat sluggish bird, using its wings in short flights and long glides. A fairly nice correlation is seen in the intramembral proportions of bony wing elements among the three genera. The wing is relatively shorter in *Geococcyx* than in *Crotophaga* and *Coccyzus*. In this series, the greatest reduction is seen in the manus (carpometacarpus plus digit II). The manus is progressively shorter from *Coccyzus* to *Geococcyx:* the manus shows a 12.9 per cent decrease from *Coccyzus* to *Crotophaga;* a 17.6 per cent decrease from *Coccyzus* to *Geococcyx*. Although Berger found apparently significant differences in the power arm and in the relative development (length of belly) of a few of the wing muscles, the over-all wing myology was surprisingly similar in pattern and development among the three genera. Comparisons of the wing area and body size in the specimens examined revealed that the Roadrunner is nearly ten times as heavy as the Black-billed Cuckoo but it has a wing area only three times larger than that of the Black-billed Cuckoo. Consequently, it was concluded that differences in flight pattern among the three genera could be explained more satisfactorily in terms of a progressive reduction in relative wing area and a progressive increase in body size from *Coccyzus* to *Geococcyx* than in terms of differences in muscle development. Such studies, incomplete as they are, focus attention on some of the many variables that influence the patterns of bird flight.

Examination of certain peculiarities in the hummingbird wing reveals that the actions of individual muscles or of muscle groups cannot be understood without reference to the wing bones and their mode of articulation. Extreme differences in relative proportions of wing segments can be seen by comparing the bony wing of a hummingbird with that of a pelican (Fig. 4). The manus of the hummingbird *is longer than the arm and forearm* combined; the manus of the pelican is short, and both the arm and the forearm are very long. Stolpe and Zimmer (1939) presented a detailed analysis of the "hovering" flight in hummingbirds, in which the wing tip traverses a figure-eight pattern in the course of a single complete cycle of wing beat. During the backward stroke, the under (ventral) surface of the wing is turned *upward.* Then at the rearmost reversal point in the stroke, the wing moves upward and rotates so that the under surface is turned downward for the forward stroke. The primaries form most of the functional wing, the secondaries being few in number and telescoped together. While hovering at a flower, the body of a hummingbird may "hang" in a vertical position, and the bird can even fly backwards (see J. H.

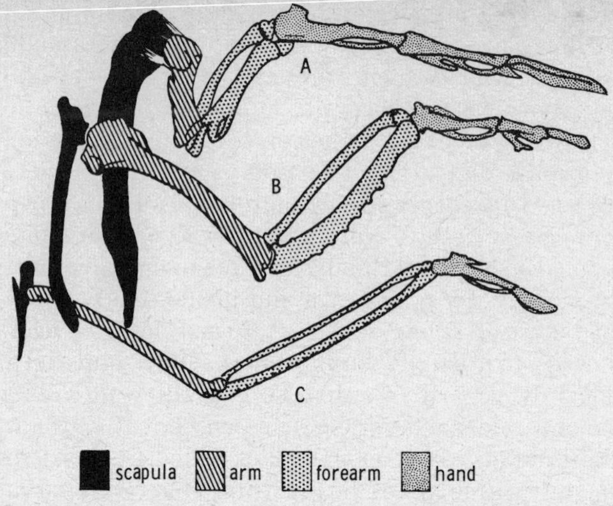

Fig. 4. Comparison of the wing skeleton of a hummingbird (A), the Roadrunner *Geococcyx* (B), and a pelican (C), to show the relative proportions of the wing segments to total wing length. (Based on Stolpe and Zimmer, 1939.)

Storer, 1948: 35). The hummingbird's humerus is extremely short and robust and is much modified in configuration. The proximal articular surface is very small and is displaced to the inner side of the "articular" head of the humerus, so that rotation of the humerus is facilitated. Moreover, the relationship of the tendon of the supracoracoideus muscle to the head of the humerus is such that the muscle appears to function primarily in rotating the humerus, rather than in elevating it. The articular surfaces at the distal end of the humerus, the weak collateral ligaments, and the lateral displacement of the tendon of the triceps muscle all favor sliding and rotatory movements rather than simple flexion and extension at the elbow. These osteological characters are correlated with several peculiar myological features. The deltoideus major muscle (of importance in wing elevation in other birds) and the biceps brachii muscle (the main flexor of the forearm) are said to be absent in hummingbirds. The absence of the biceps is compensated for in part, at least, by the very high origin of M. extensor metacarpi radialis and by the hypertrophy and peculiar insertion of M. tensor patagii brevis. M. pectoralis is only about 1.7 times as large as M. supracoracoideus; the ratio between these muscles in the Black-backed Gull is 15:1 (Stolpe and Zimmer, 1939). The problems connected with the analysis of hummingbird flight are, of course, much more complicated than is indicated by this brief discussion of a few anatomical features.

Flight Speed

The numerous anatomical and aerodynamic features of a bird's wings determine the type of flight and flying ability. Flying ability is not the same thing as flight speed. Flying ability is affected by the age of the bird, its physical condition, and the state of its plumage. Flight speed is dependent upon the type of flight, flying ability, and a variety of other factors: velocity and direction of the wind, air currents, thermal updrafts, presence of moving automobiles or airplanes, pursuit of prey, escape from predator, etc. The flight speed of small passerine birds has been reported to vary from about 15 to 55 mi. per hour. Several ducks have been timed at speeds of 50 to 60 mi. per hour when followed by airplanes. Under similar conditions, a Duck Hawk is reported to have flown at a rate of about 175 mi. per hour, but Broun and Goodwin (1943) gave the average speed as 30 mi. per hour for migrating birds. McCabe (1942) described his experience of flying in an airplane at 90 mi. per hour and being overtaken by two flocks of sandpipers, which he estimated were flying at least 110 mi. per hour. Cottam *et al.* (1942), clocked a "cruising" Great Blue Heron at a speed of 18 to 29 mi. per hour; a heron flew 36 mi. per hour when "pressed." Broun and Goodwin timed the flight speed of 16 Ospreys along a measured course of $\frac{2}{3}$ mile at Hawk Mountain Sanctuary in Pennsylvania. They computed the wind velocity above the treetops on the crest of the ridge, recorded the wind direction, and described the birds' flight activities. In addition, they noted the birds' location in relation to the valley and the ridge: along crest, high over valley, above the crest, low over valley, etc. The average speed of the Ospreys was 41.5 mi. per hour, but one bird made a speed of 80 mi. per hour with a wind of only 4 mi. per hour. It sailed continuously except for two half flaps of its wings. They noted that it was evidently making use of a strong thermal updraft. All these records report flying or sailing speeds under varying conditions; none have measured flying ability *per se*. The speeds reported for some birds would be startling indeed if the conditions at the time of the observations had not been recorded. It is obvious that if one is to compare flight speeds, it is essential that one know as much as possible about the factors contributing to the speed attained.

Blake (1947) reported wing-flapping rates varying from 2 to 3 per second in a series of birds, including the Double-crested Cormorant, Black Duck, Sparrow Hawk, Killdeer, Herring Gull, Mourning Dove, and Belted Kingfisher. Wing-beat frequencies of "up to 200 strokes per second" have been attributed to hummingbirds, but studies based on stroboscopic methods and slow-motion pictures have revealed much lower frequencies: 36 to 39 wing beats per second for *Chlorostilbon;* 50 to 51, for *Phaethornis* (see Stolpe and Zimmer, 1939; Stresemann and Zimmer, 1932).

Many interesting adaptations are seen in those birds that use their wings for propelling themselves under water. The most completely water-adapted birds are the penguins, which have lost the power of flight in air. Nevertheless, the highly modified penguin wing, with its broadly rounded leading edge and a finely tapered trailing edge, approximates an airplane wing. Based on motion picture studies of captive penguins in specially constructed tanks, Neu (1931) found that the King Penguin makes about 120 wing beats per minute. There appears to be good evidence that wing-beat frequency of wild penguins, especially the smaller species, may be much higher. The leading edge of the wing is depressed during the downstroke, as it is in flying birds. As a result, the water is pushed backward by the concave lower surface of the wing; during underwater swimming the wing usually is raised only a little above the horizontal plane. In this respect the pattern of wing movement differs from that of air flight. The effective surface of the wing can be changed by rotation either at the shoulder or the elbow. The humeroradial and humero-ulnar joints are modified so that flexion and extension are limited at the elbow. M. biceps brachii, a powerful flexor of the forearm in other birds, is absent, but some of its function is accomplished by specializations of Mm. pectoralis and tensor patagii longus.

Of greater interest in some respects, however, are the birds that use their wings both in the air and under water: the diving-petrels, some shearwaters (*Puffinus*); cormorants; Razorbills, murres, puffins, and other alcids. The diving-petrels, especially, are noted for their habit of diving into the water from the air and then literally flying under water in search of their food. By contrast, many other birds (e.g., loons, grebes, coots, ducks) that secure their food under water propel themselves with their feet alone, in most instances keeping their wings pressed close to the body. An interesting variation in wing position has been described for certain scoters which use the feet as paddles under water. In describing the diving of the White-winged Scoter (*Melanitta deglandi*),

Brooks (1945) wrote: "The wings are flipped upward as the bird plunges, but under water the tips of the primaries can be seen crossed over the tail, the secondaries are somewhat expanded, showing the white patch conspicuously, but the alula is extended to its utmost, giving the appearance of small, sharp-pointed wings held out rigidly on each side during the whole period of the dive." Common Scoters (*Oidemia nigra*), however, do not extend the alula when under water.

Flightlessness

It was pointed out in Chapter 1 that changes from the Archaeornithes to the Neornithes involved primarily modifications which improved the basic anatomical structure for flight, and that almost all ornithologists believe that the ratites and the penguins secondarily lost the power of aerial flight. A number of other birds have become flightless, and, although there are exceptions, most of them (both living and extinct) are island forms. Among the best known flightless birds are these: the grebe *Centropelma,* the cormorant *Nannopterum,* two Steamer Ducks (*Tachyeres brachypterus, T. pteneres*), several species of island-inhabiting rails, and the extinct Great Auk (*Pinguinus impennis*). In addition, members of several other families (e.g., the mesite *Monias,* the Kagu, one species of New Zealand wren) are either flightless or nearly so. Stonor (1942) spoke of the three species of wattlebirds as being "'half-way' towards becoming flightless." Their legs are well developed, and they hop from branch to branch; their infrequent flight is described as being labored and of short duration.

In his description of *Atlantisia rogersi,* the flightless rail from Inaccessible Island, Lowe (1928) reported it to be the "smallest flightless bird known to exist, or to have existed." The sternum of this diminutive bird is only 14 mm. long; an unusually long, but thin, furcula is attached to the anterior end of the sternum. Lowe described only a few of the proximal wing muscles, but he reported the forearm muscles to be "extremely well developed, perhaps rather more proportionately well developed than the corresponding muscles in a specimen of *Rallus aquaticus.*" Moreover, he found "no hint of degeneration" in certain shoulder and arm muscles (e.g., deltoideus major, supracoracoideus, biceps brachii). Both Lowe and Stresemann (1932) discussed certain microscopic features of the feathers of flightless rails.

Atlantisia is an exception to the usual correlation between flightlessness and increased body weight. Such a correlation is demonstrated clearly in a comparison of the flightless and the flying Steamer ducks. The Flightless Steamer Duck (*Tachyeres brachypterus*) is said to weigh almost twice as much as the Flying Steamer Duck (*T. patachonicus*), whereas the wing length in the two species is nearly the same (Lowe, 1934; Stonor, 1942). Lowe found the wing muscles (including pectoralis and supracoracoideus) of *brachypterus* to be better developed than those of *patachonicus*. The well-developed muscles of *brachypterus* account for the "violent flapping motion" of the wings as the birds "steam" through the water at a speed variously reported as 8 to 15 mi. per hour.

References

Allen, Francis H. 1939. Effect of Wind on Flight Speeds. *Auk,* 56: 291–303.

Aymar, Gordon C. 1935. *Bird Flight.* Dodd, Mead Co., New York.

Berger, Andrew J. 1954. The Myology of the Pectoral Appendage of Three Genera of American Cuckoos. *Misc. Publ. Univ. Mich. Mus. Zool.,* 85, 35 pp.

Blake, Charles H. 1947. Wing-flapping rates of birds. *Auk,* 64: 619–620.

Böker, Hans. 1927. Die biologische Anatomie der Flugarten der Vögel und ihre Phylogenie. *Jour. f. Ornith.,* 75: 304–371.

——— 1935. *Einfuhrung in die Vergleichende Biologische Anatomie der Wirbeltiere.* Bd. I. Gustav Fischer, Jena.

Brooks, Allan. 1945. The Under-water Actions of Diving Ducks. *Auk,* 62: 517–523.

Broun, Maurice, and Ben V. Goodwin. 1943. Flight-speeds of Hawks and Crows. *Auk,* 60: 487–492.

Brown, R. H. L. 1951. Flapping Flight. *Ibis,* 93: 333–359.

——— 1953. The Flight of Birds. II. Wing Function in Relation to Flight Speed. *Jour. Exper. Biol.,* 30: 90–103.

Cooke, May Thacher. 1937. Flight Speed of Birds. *U. S. Dept. Agric. Cir. No. 428.*

Cottam, Clarence, Cecil S. Williams, and Clarence A. Sooter. 1942. Flight and Running Speeds of Birds. *Wils. Bull.,* 54: 121–131.

Daneel, A. B. 1943. The Speed and Height of Bird Flight. *Ostrich,* 14: 61–64.

Edwards, Charles L. 1886. The Relation of the Pectoral Muscles of Birds to the Power of Flight. *Amer. Nat.,* 20: 25–29.

Engels, William Louis. 1938a. Variation in Bone Length and Limb Proportions in the Coot (Fulica americana). *Jour. Morph.,* 62: 599–607.

——— 1938b. Cursorial Adaptations in Birds. Limb Proportions in the Skeleton of *Geococcyx. Jour. Morph.,* 63: 207–217.

——— 1940. Structural Adaptations in Thrashers (Mimidae: Genus Toxostoma) with Comments on Interspecific Relationships. *Univ. Calif. Publ. Zool.,* 42: 341–400.

——— 1941. Wing Skeleton and Flight of Hawks. *Auk,* 58: 61–69.

Fisher, Harvey I. 1945. Flying Ability and the Anterior Intermuscular Line on the Coracoid. *Auk,* 62: 125–129.

Fisher, Harvey I. 1946. Adaptations and Comparative Anatomy of the Locomotor Apparatus of New World Vultures. *Amer. Midl. Nat.,* 35: 545–727.

——— 1955. Avian Anatomy, 1925–1950, and Some Suggested Problems. In *Recent Studies in Avian Biology,* Univ. Illinois Press, Urbana, pp. 57–104.

——— 1956a. The Landing Forces of Domestic Pigeons. *Auk,* 73: 85–105.

——— 1956b. Apparatus to Measure Forces Involved in the Landing and Taking Off of Birds. *Amer. Midl. Nat.,* 55: 334–342.

——— 1957a. Bony Mechanism of Automatic Flexion and Extension in the Pigeon's Wing. *Science,* 126: 446.

——— 1957b. The Function of M. Depressor Caudae and M. Caudofemoralis in Pigeons. *Auk,* 74: 479–486.

George, C. J., and K. R. Menon. 1954. The Physiological Lag of the Domestic Fowl. *Jour. Animal Morph. & Physiol.* (Bombay), 1: 77.

Graham, R. R. 1932. The Part played by Emarginated Feathers and the Alula in the Flight of Birds. *Bull. Brit. Ornith. Club,* 52: 68–79.

——— 1934. The Silent Flight of Owls. *Jour. Roy. Aeronaut. Soc.,* 38: 837–843.

Gray, James. 1955 [1951]. The Flight of Animals. *Smiths. Inst. Publ. 4200* (*Smiths. Rept. for 1954:* 285–303). Reprinted from *How Animals Move,* Cambridge Univ. Press, England, 1951.

Heim, Arnold. 1937. Fliegertypen der Natur. *Vjschr. Naturf. Ges. Zürich,* 82: 143–160.

Horton-Smith, C. 1938. *The Flight of Birds.* H. F. & G. Witherby, London.

Kaelin, J. 1941. Über den Coracoscapularwinkel und die Beziehungen der Rumpfform zum Lokomotionstypus bei den Vögeln. *Rev. Suisse Zool.,* 48: 553–557.

Kelso, J. E. H. 1922. Birds Using their Wings as a Means of Propulsion under Water. *Auk,* 39: 426–428.

Lorenz, Konrad. 1933. Beobachtetes über das Fliegen der Vögel und über die Beziehungen der Flügel- und Steuerform zur Art des Fluges. *Jour. f. Ornith.,* 81: 107–236.

Lowe, Percy R. 1928. A Description of *Atlantisia rogersi,* the Diminutive and Flightless Rail of Inaccessible Island (Southern Atlantic), with some Notes on Flightless Rails. *Ibis,* 1928: 99–131.

——— 1934. On the Evidence for the Existence of Two Species of Steamer Duck (*Tachyeres*), and Primary and Secondary Flightlessness in Birds. *Ibis,* 1934: 467–495.

McCabe, T. T. 1942. Types of shorebird flight. *Auk,* 59: 110–111.

Madsen, Harry. 1945. On the Different Position of the Legs of Birds during Flight and in Cold Weather. *Dansk Ornith. For. Tidsskr.,* 39: 98–105.

Menon, K. R. 1954. The Glucose and Fat Levels in the Blood of Five Representative Vertebrates. *Jour. Animal Morph. & Physiol.,* 1: 65–68.

Nair, K. K. 1954a. A Comparison of the Muscles in the Forearm of a Flapping and a Soaring Bird. *Jour. Animal Morph. & Physiol.,* 1: 26–34.

——— 1954b. The Bearing of the Weight of the Pectoral Muscles on the Flight of Some Common Indian Birds. *Jour. Animal Morph. & Physiol.,* 1: 71–76.

Neu, Wolfgang. 1931. Die Schwimmbewegungen der Tauchvögel (Blässhuhn und Pinguin). *Zeitschr. f. vergl. Physiol.,* 14: 682–708.

Petrides, George A. 1943. Variation in the outermost greater primary covert as related to method of flight. *Auk,* 60: 264–265.

Poole, Earl L. 1938. Weights and Wing Areas in North American Birds. *Auk,* 55: 511–517.

Richardson, Frank. 1943. Functional Aspects of the Inner Vane of Remiges. *Auk,* 60: 44–50.

Savile, D. B. O. 1950. The Flight Mechanism of Swifts and Hummingbirds. *Auk,* 67: 499–504.

——— 1957. Adaptive Evolution in the Avian Wing. *Evolution,* 11: 212–224.

Schneider, Hannes. 1942. Aufbau und Funktion der Patagien gut fliegender Vögel. *Morph. Jahrb.,* 87: 27–84.

Schorger, A. W. 1947. The Deep Diving of the Loon and Old-squaw and Its Mechanism. *Wils. Bull.,* 59: 151–159.

Slijper, E. J., and J. M. Burgers. 1950. *De Vliegkunst in het Dierenrijk.* E. J. Brill, Leiden.

Smith, J. Maynard. 1953. Birds as Aeroplanes. *New Biol.,* No. 14: 64–81.

Sooter, Clarence. 1947. Flight speeds of some south Texas birds. *Wils. Bull.,* 59: 174–175.

Stolpe, M., and K. Zimmer. 1937. Physikalische Grundlagen des Vogelfluges. *Jour. f. Ornith.,* 85: 147–164.

——— 1938. Die flugmechanische Bedeutung des Daumenfittichs am Vogelflügel. *Jour. f. Ornith.,* 86: 485–496.

——— 1939. Der Schwirrflug des Kolibri im Zeitlupenfilm. *Jour. f. Ornith.,* 87: 136–155.

Stonor, C. R. 1942. Anatomical Notes on the New Zealand Wattled Crow (*Callaeas*), with especial Reference to its Powers of Flight. *Ibis,* 1942: 1–18.

Storer, John H. 1948. The Flight of Birds Analyzed through Slow-motion Photography. *Cranbrook Inst. Sci., Bull. No. 28.*

Storer, Robert W. 1955. Weight, Wing Area, and Skeletal Proportions in Three Accipiters. *Acta. XI Congr. Internatl. Ornith. 1954:* 287–290.

Stresemann, Erwin. 1932. La Structure des Rémiges chez quelques Rales Physiologiquement Aptères. *Alauda,* 1932: 1–5.

——— and K. Zimmer. 1932. Ueber die Frequenz des Flügelschlages beim Schwirrflug der Kolibris. *Ornith. Monats.,* 40: 129–133.

Sy, Maxheinz. 1936. Funktionell-anatomische Untersuchungen am Vogelflügel. *Jour. f. Ornith.,* 84: 199–296.

Townsend, Charles W. 1909. The Position of Birds' Feet in Flight. *Auk,* 26: 109–116.

——— 1924. Diving of Grebes and Loons. *Auk,* 41: 29–41.

Trautman, Milton B. 1943. Normal Flight of a Black Duck after Healing of Wing Fractures. *Wils. Bull.,* 55: 126.

Tucker, B. W. 1942. Aerial Evolutions and Soaring of Cormorants. *Brit. Birds,* 36: 114–115.

Warner, Lucien H. 1931. Facts and Theories of Bird Flight. *Quart. Rev. Biol.,* 6: 84–98.

Woodcock, Alfred H. 1940. Observations on Herring Gull Soaring. *Auk,* 57: 219–224.

9. Food and feeding habits

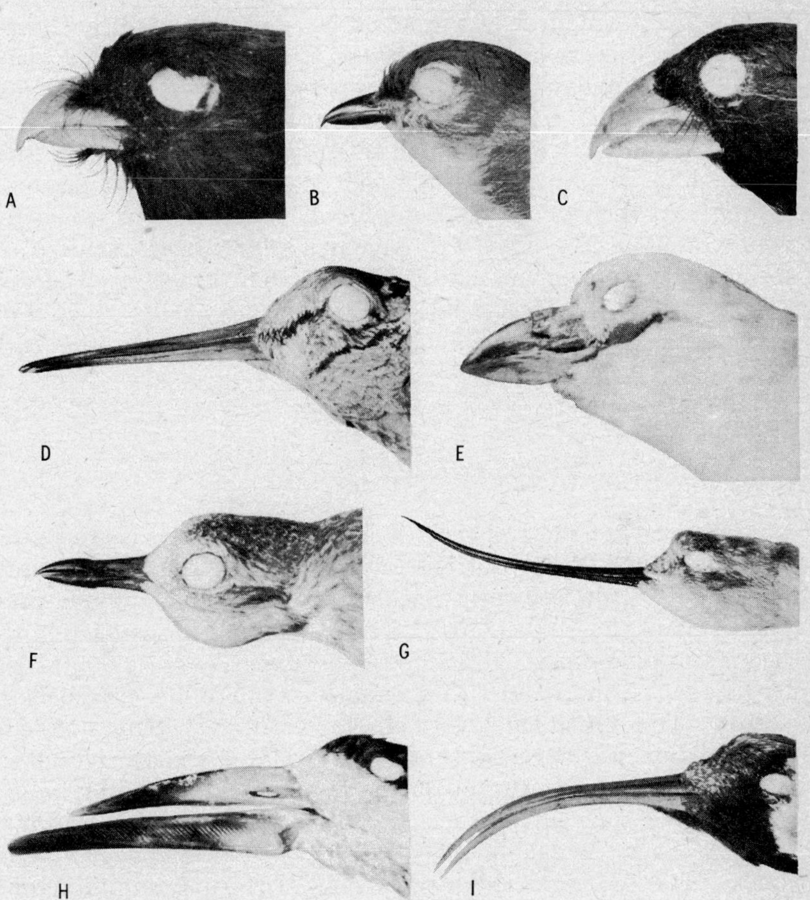

Fig. 1. A selected series of different types of bills: A—*Trogon collaris;* B—*Vireo flavifrons;* C—*Pitylus grossus;* D—*Philohela minor;* E—*Chionis alba;* F—*Squatarola squatarola;* G—*Recurvirostra americana;* H—*Rynchops nigra;* I—*Ibidorhyncha struthersii.*

IT IS A familiar fact that all animals are directly or indirectly dependent on plants for nourishment. Only green plants can manufacture food from the chemical elements. But birds, as a group, seem to feed mainly on animals and only a rather small proportion of the birds of the world have become sufficiently specialized to utilize plant food firsthand. One indication that plant-eating is a secondary specialization is found in the fact that most plant-eating birds start their newly hatched young on an animal diet, then gradually change them to a plant diet. Only a few birds—such as that highly specialized plant-feeding family, the pigeons—do not start their young on animal food. Pigeons feed their small young on a special secretion ("pigeon's milk") from the crop. A specialized condition is found in certain highly vegetarian carduelline birds (e.g., the American Goldfinch, *Spinus tristis*) which bring to the young in their crop a finely chopped mass of seeds, apparently already partly digested.

Anatomical Specializations

Some of the most obvious differences among birds are seen in the numerous bill adaptations for feeding (Fig. 1); in hawks and owls the feet, too, are specialized for grasping and carrying prey. The nomadic crossbills (*Loxia*) are bill-adapted for extracting the seeds from pine cones. Grackles (*Quiscalus*) have a "palatal keel" in the roof of the mouth that enables them to cut the shells of acorns. The bill shape is very similar within the genera of some families, but in other groups of closely related genera the bill exhibits wide adaptive specialization for particular feeding habits. Examples of such adaptations in bills are seen in the Hawaiian Honeycreepers (Amadon, 1950: pls. 9–12), the Galápagos Finches (Lack, 1947: 57), larks (Meinertzhagen, 1951), and hummingbirds (Fig. 2). Parallelism or convergence in bill shape is well illustrated by certain members of the woodcreeper family (Dendrocolaptidae) with genera of other families: e.g., *Campylorhamphus trochilirostris* with *Hemignathus procerus* (Drepaniidae); *Xiphorhynchus*

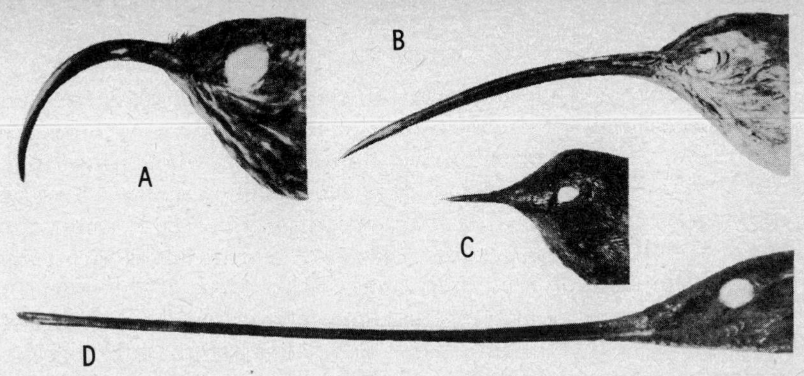

Fig. 2. Bill specialization for different types of flowers in four genera of hummingbirds: A—*Eutoxeres aquila;* B—*Phaethornis superciliosus;* C—*Ramphomicron microrhynchum;* D—*Ensifera ensifera.*

flavigaster and certain woodpeckers; *Sittasomus griseicapillus* and *Certhia familiaris* (Certhiidae).

Although most birds carry food in their bills, food may also be carried in a gular pouch (pelicans) or in a crop. The Rosy Finch (*Leucosticte tephrocotis*) has a pair of buccal food pouches, which apparently are used only during the breeding season (Miller, 1941). The efficiency of the gizzard in grinding up food in some birds is truly remarkable. Some ducks (e.g., Mallard, Wood Duck) swallow acorns, and even harder nuts, whole; eiders and other diving ducks swallow mussels and other shellfish. Many seed-eating birds eat grit, which facilitates the grinding process in the gizzard. According to Meinertzhagen (1954), quartz is most often ingested as grit, but when it is not available birds eat small rounded stones; small shells and the "stones" of fruits also serve the same purpose. Meinertzhagen reported a seasonal variation in grit-eating by the Bramble Finch. Grit is ingested along with a grain diet in the winter, but during the autumn the bird eats large quantities of fruit and no grit. The gizzard of some fruit-pigeons (*Muscadivores*), which feed on nutmegs and similar fruits, contains a series of horny, conelike projections (Garrod, 1881; Wood, 1924). McAtee (1917) remarked that, among birds with a muscular gizzard, shedding of the lining probably occurs more or less regularly and is necessary to maintain the efficiency of the food-triturating process. Certain hornbills are said to slough the epithelial lining of the stomach, which, with the stomach contents, is cast up as a bag-like structure.

Types of Food

It is probable that all phyla—all classes—of living things have, at least occasionally, furnished food for birds. Not many birds are known to eat the more primitive plants such as algae and fungi, but a Pygmy Parrot (*Micropsitta*) of New Guinea apparently subsists largely on fungus in rotten wood (Rand, 1942: 450), the Glaucous Gull (*Larus hyperboreus*) eats marine algae (Cottam, 1944), and ptarmigan feed on lichens. Also, most of the types of specialized parts developed by the higher plants have been recorded in the food of birds: root tubers of many water plants (ducks, geese, and swans), eelgrass (Brant), grass and leaves of many herbaceous plants (geese), sage brush leaves (Sage Grouse), spruce needles (Spruce Grouse), mast (Passenger Pigeon), acorns (Band-tailed Pigeon, Acorn Woodpecker, jays, grackles), buds (grouse, Galápagos finches, Purple Finch), petals (*Phainopepla,* Cedar Waxwing), pollen (hummingbirds), nectar (hummingbirds, honey-eaters, sunbirds, some American orioles), sap (sapsuckers, hummingbirds, wood-warblers, kinglets, etc.), and many different seeds and fruits.

In the tropics, where there is a year-round supply, many birds eat the pulp of fruit: e.g., trogons, toucans, parrots, oropendolas, some honeycreepers, and even some woodpeckers and tyrant-flycatchers. In northern climates, as well, the fruit of numerous trees and shrubs is eaten by many birds during certain periods of the year. Some well-known examples are Catbirds (*Dumetella carolinensis*), thrushes, waxwings, and Myrtle Warblers (*Dendroica coronata*). Some tanagers (*Tanagra*), flowerpeckers (*Dicaeum*), silky-flycatchers (*Phainopepla, Ptilogonys cinereus*), the Cedar Waxwing, and a South American tyrant-flycatcher (*Phaeomyias*) feed, occasionally or usually, on mistletoe berries. An entire chapter might be devoted to a discussion of the great variety of plants whose seeds are eaten by a host of different birds.

So many animals, both vertebrate and invertebrate, serve as food for birds that only a brief summary can be given here (see also Chapter 13). Rodents provide a large share of the diet of many hawks and owls. Bats are eaten by the White-throated Falcon (*Falco albigularis*), sloths by the Harpy Eagle (*Harpia harpyja*), and monkeys by the Philippine Monkey-eating Eagle (*Pithecophaga jefferyi*). Many birds, from swallows to ducks, serve as food for some of the large owls, hawks, and falcons (e.g., Sharp-shinned and Cooper's hawks, Prairie and Peregrine falcons, Pigeon Hawk), and the Roadrunner includes birds as well as reptiles in its diet. Reptiles are eaten mainly by raptors and herons but representatives of many other families sometimes eat them: cariamas, trogons, kingfishers, motmots, toucans, tyrant-flycatchers, birds-of-paradise, vanga-shrikes, shrikes, etc. Groups that feed to some extent on amphibians are cormorants, anhingas, herons, storks, hawks, rails, avocets, thick-knees, woodcreepers, and certain corvids and icterids. Fish are eaten by many birds from penguins to kingfishers and by a few passerine birds (dippers, grackles, some tyrant-flycatchers). Flatworms, annelid worms, mollusks, crustaceans, ticks, spiders, and a host of other invertebrates serve as food for birds. Certain honeyguides (Indicatoridae) eat large quantities of beeswax. Birds obtain insects from every available source: on the ground, in the ground, on water, under water, on tree trunks, in tree trunks, on branches, twigs, and leaves, and in the air. Finally, American vultures, especially, and some gulls regularly feed on carrion and/or garbage.

Food-Finding and Capture

Some birds watch for the appearance of their prey and then descend upon it: the familiar pictures of the vulture circling high watching for carrion; of the owl in silent flight awaiting the emergence of small nocturnal mammals; flycatchers perched on bare twigs or wires and making quick outward flights for passing insects.

Other birds actively seek food through obstacles. Some ground birds rake away with their bill the forest litter that hides their food; others scratch with the feet alternately (the Bobwhite, *Colinus*); some small birds, like the Towhee (*Pipilo*), jump up in the air and scratch rapidly with both feet at once—in a fashion that must be seen to be believed.

Still other birds flush their food from hiding or follow moving objects, both animal and mechanical, which habitually perform that service for them. Mud- and ground-feeders that pat and probe the earth as they move across their feeding grounds are presumed to be "flushing" to the surface the small animals on which they feed.

Mixed flocks of small birds follow the hordes of army ants, feeding on the insects disturbed by the ants' passage. Other birds follow cattle for the same purpose. Even fire is recognized by birds as a food-bringer. White-tailed Hawks (*Buteo albicaudatus*) in Texas quickly gathered from a radius of some 10 mi. to feed on the rodents and grasshoppers exposed by a grass fire (Stevenson and

Meitzen, 1946). In Ceylon the Red-rumped Swallow (*Hirundo daurica*) has learned to come quickly to the grass fires set by tea-planters and there hawk for the insects that are flushed by the fires (Phillips, 1953).

The Lesser Flamingo (*Phoeniconaias minor*) of Kenya skims the surface of the water with a semicircular motion of its inverted bill, and with the fine, almost hairlike serrations along the edge of the bill sifts from the water the blue-green algae and diatoms on which it subsists almost exclusively (Ridley, 1954). The feeding technique of the American Flamingo (*Phoenicopterus ruber*) is illustrated in Fig. 3.

Turnstones (*Arenaria interpres*) regularly feed along beaches, flipping over stones, sticks, and other objects by means of their strong, somewhat wedge-shaped bill and stout, muscular neck, securing the animal life lurking beneath them. Other sandpipers, especially Sanderlings (*Crocethia alba*), sometimes attend a Turnstone closely and dart in when a stone is turned and steal some of the food. These Sanderlings have been observed to attack sharply others which tried to join their poaching operations, but the Turnstones gave no evidence of resentment (Norris-Elye, 1946). In the Colorado desert of California, Jaeger (1947) watched a Roadrunner turn over large pieces of caked, dry mud in its search for food.

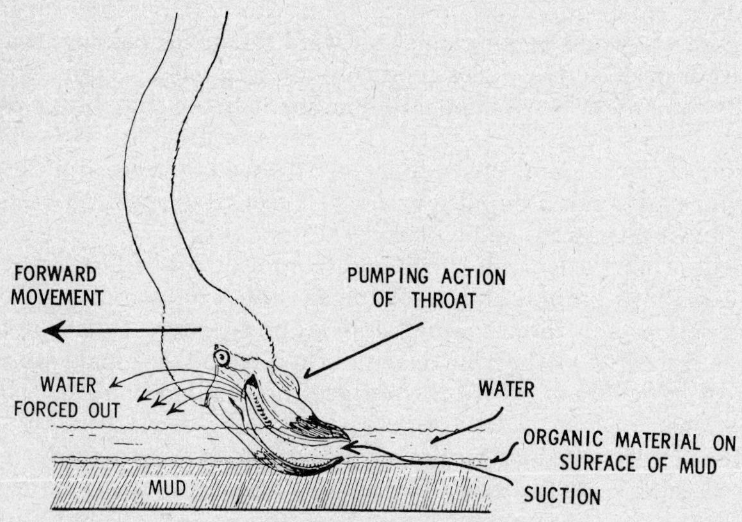

Fig. 3. Feeding technique of the American Flamingo (*Phoenicopterus ruber*). (Courtesy of Robert P. Allen and the National Audubon Society.)

Darwin's Tree-finch (*Camarhynchus pallidus*) holds a twig or thorn in the bill and thrusts it into crannies of bark, or into holes it has itself excavated. When an insect emerges, the bird drops its probe and seizes the insect (Lack, 1947: 58–59).

Food Preparation

Food preparation in birds is very often left entirely to the digestive system. A Secretarybird (*Sagittarius*), for example, may swallow as much of a snake as it can, wait for the digestive processes to act upon that part, then swallow the rest. Owls swallow small mammals whole, and regurgitate indigestible portions—hair, bone, etc.—in neat pellets.

On the other hand, some of the most remarkable bird behavior is connected with food preparation. Ravens and gulls seize mollusks or crabs in their bill, fly to a height, drop the hard shell, and quickly descend to retrieve the broken animal. If the first attempt does not break open the food, the bird may repeat the process several times, without, however, rising to a greater height on subsequent attempts or even discriminating between rocky surfaces and sand (Oldham, 1930). Insect-eating birds often batter large or hard insects upon a branch before swallowing them.

The Micheners (1945) describe as an "anvil" the forked branch or other object that the California Jay (*Aphelocoma coerulescens*) employs to hold a nut while opening it with blows of its bill; and Law (1929: 234) uses the term "chopping block" for a barked section of tree where the Lewis' Woodpecker (*Asyndesmus lewis*) wedges acorns while chucking them. These "tools," however, might better be termed "vises." The European Song-Thrush (*Turdus ericetorum*) does use the anvil principle, hammering the snails which are an important part of its diet onto stones in order to smash the shell.

The Moreaus (1941: 17) reported that the male Silvery-cheeked Hornbill (*Bycanistes cristatus*) "always regurgitates" fruits which are then passed to the incubating female, though it apparently is not known to what extent digestion may have begun.

Food Storage

Birds generally require an almost continuously available supply of food, but a few, notably the crow family (Corvidae), store some food in time of plenty and use it when supplies are scarce. For example, Brewster (1937: 504–508) watched Canada Jays (*Perisoreus canadensis*) storing food in the Maine woods in autumn. They filled their throats and bills to capacity with the food put out for them, flew off into the woods to store it, and then hurried back for more. Brewster found that the jays were going a half mile or more to store the food in crevices in trees or in holes made by woodpeckers. However, the most striking and most thoroughly known example of this habit is provided by Swanberg's study (1951) of Nutcrackers (*Nucifraga*) in Sweden. These large jaylike birds fly considerable distances (up to $3\frac{3}{4}$ miles) from their haunts in the evergreen-forested hills to gather hazelnuts in the lowland. Filling their throats with nuts, the nutcrackers fly back to the evergreen forest, bury and carefully hide the load of nuts in a single hole which they dig in the ground, and then hasten for another load. This process is carried on with hardly a break from sunrise to sunset during two or three autumn months. Then all through the winter and early spring they feed on these nuts, digging down through as much as 18 inches of snow to recover them. Swanberg believes that in their very successful search for these caches (86 per cent, or better) they depend entirely on memory.

The Acorn Woodpecker (*Melanerpes formicivorus*) of western North America stores a great number of acorns, each neatly fitted into a specially excavated hole in the trunk of a tree (Ritter, 1938: 20).

In higher latitudes of Eurasia and North America certain shrikes (*Lanius*) store some of their prey (large insects and small mammals and birds) by hanging it on thorns or in forked branches. The significance of this habit has been much debated, but it now seems clear that shrikes follow this habit only in unfavorable climates (where they experience periods of food scarcity) and that they do frequently return to the stored food during periods of stress (Durango, 1951).

A few nuthatches, titmice, and owls also store food more or less regularly.

Amounts of Food Required

Despite numerous bird studies tabulating minute measurements and elaborately calculated percentages, little reliable information is available on the quantitative analysis of birds' food. Before making analyses and before using those of others, a student should read Hartley's article (1948) and van Koersveld's note (1951) on the factors that complicate this sort of research.

Because of their high metabolic rate most birds require large amounts of food at relatively frequent intervals. This is especially true for small birds which, in proportion to their weight, eat more food per day than do large birds. Lack (1954: 131) gave the following approximate ratios between body weight and daily food consumption. Landbirds weighing between 100 and 1000 grams eat from 5 to 9 per cent of their body weight daily; songbirds weighing 10 to 90 grams eat from 10 to 30 per cent of their own weight daily; and hummingbirds may eat twice their weight in syrup in a day. Kendeigh (1934: 383) reported that adult seed-eating birds eat about 10 per cent of their weight and that insectivorous birds eat an amount equal to 40 per cent of their weight daily, though the high water content of larvae largely accounts for this high percentage. Calculations based on the dry weight of grains and meal worms indicated that granivorous and insectivorous birds eat about the same relative amounts of food. Lack suggested that the quantity be expressed in calories rather than grams.

The quantity of food eaten varies not only with type of food but also with the air temperature and with time of year. Experiments with captive passerine birds have revealed that the average time for the passage of artificially stained food through the digestive tract is about 1½ hours, whether the food be grain, fruit, or insects (Stevenson, 1933). Nice (1941: 60) found that various fruits passed through the tract of a young Cedar Waxwing in from 16 to 40 minutes. The contents of a full stomach may be completely digested in 2½ hours, so that small birds must spend much time securing food. Under experimental conditions, a House Sparrow will starve in about 67 hours if deprived of food at an air temperature of 84°F., and within a much shorter period at a lower temperature (Kendeigh, 1945). By comparison, a raptorial bird in the laboratory may live for over 3 weeks without food. Much less is known about wild birds which, unlike experimental birds, expend considerable energy searching for food. Nuthatches, titmice, House Sparrows, Tree Sparrows, Cardinals, etc., regularly go without eating for 15-hour periods during the winter months in such northern states as Michigan. The deposition of fat aids birds in surviving northern winters, but such fat deposits may become exhausted during prolonged cold periods coupled with inadequate food supplies.

In their study of the Red-tailed Hawk (*Buteo jamaicensis*) in California, Fitch *et al.* (1946: 231) followed a juvenal female for 21 full, but not consecutive, days, during which the bird made only five kills. For one 5-day period the hawk apparently did not eat at all. The average food intake during the 21-day period was estimated to be slightly less than 100 grams per day.

Incubating birds undergo the longest periods without food. The female Common Eider (*Somateria mollissima*) does not eat during an incubation period lasting over 3 weeks, and the male Emperor Penguin (*Aptenodytes forsteri*) incubates for 60 days without eating (Lack, 1954: 139).

It is well known that nestlings are fed large amounts of food, but few quantitative data are available. Based on known amounts of food given to nestling Starlings at individual feedings, Kluijver estimated that a nestling received about six-sevenths of its own weight in food per day during the last part of the nestling period (see Lack, 1954). The Lacks (1951) found that a nestling Common Swift (*Apus apus*) may be given a single meal equal to 10 per cent of its weight, and that in good weather a nestling weighing between 15 and 50 grams may be fed from 15 to 20 or more grams of insects per day. The total daily weight increase, however, rarely exceeds 7 grams, partly because the rate of defecation increases markedly with an increase in feeding rate. Unlike passerine birds, nestling swifts revert to poikilothermy and their feather development is retarded when inadequate amounts of food are received during periods of bad weather. Nestling Belted Kingfishers (*Megaceryle alcyon*) will eat from 1 to 1¾ times their weight in fish daily (White, 1939). Richdale (1942: 20) reported that the weight of a Royal Albatross (*Diomedea epomophora*) chick, when 93 days old, increased 4½ pounds after being fed by both adults; when 199 days old the chick was fed at 10:00 a.m. and again at 1:20 p.m., gaining a total of 6½ pounds.

Variation in the Food of Birds

Seasonal

The food of many birds varies greatly according to season. In a few instances this has been conclusively documented by detailed studies of the contents of a large number of stomachs gathered from a great area. For example, Kalmbach (1918) based his conclusions on 2118 stomachs of the American Crow (*Corvus brachy-*

rhynchos) taken in more than 40 states and provinces of the United States and Canada. For the same author's study (1927) of the Magpie (*Pica pica*) of western America 547 stomachs from 13 states and provinces were available. As shown graphically in Fig. 4, the Magpie's diet varies greatly according to season. Some classes of food make up more than half of the diet at one season but are nearly or completely missing at another season of the year. Beer (1943), analyzing the stomach contents of 128 Blue Grouse (*Dendragapus*) from the northwestern states, found that adults subsist on 98 per cent vegetable matter—nearly 64 per cent conifer needles! Less than 2 per cent of the annual total is animal food, but during August it may rise to more than 20 per cent.

Wagner (1946) summarized his observations on feeding habits of 19 species of hummingbirds and reported that "a given species may feed mainly on nectar or mainly on insects, depending on the time of year." The Smooth-billed Ani (*Crotophaga ani*) lives primarily on vegetable matter during the dry season in Cuba, but shifts to a diet of animal food (insects, lizards, etc.) during the rainy season. Seasonal variation in diet is well illustrated by the Great Spotted Woodpecker (*Dendrocopos major*) of Finland, which subsists primarily on pine and spruce seeds during the winter but on ants and other insects during the summer (Lack, 1954: 127). Many species of Galápagos finches feed on buds and leaves at the beginning of the rainy period, but as the season progresses they turn to caterpillars, then to fruit, and later to seeds (Lack, 1947).

Annual

Despite the food preferences of birds, availability also is a factor in determining the diet over a period of years. Annual differences in diet have been studied more in hawks and owls than in other birds. Banfield (1947) analyzed nearly 3000 Short-eared Owl (*Asio flammeus*) pellets over a period of 6 years in an area where two genera of rodents constituted about 99 per cent of the food. The percentage of *Peromyscus* remains in the pellets varied from about 5 to 30 per cent; of *Microtus,* from 68 to 95 per cent. During four summers in Germany, the vole *Microtus arvalis* formed from 21 to 77 per cent, small birds from 2 to 34 per cent, of the food of Long-eared Owls, *Asio otus* (Zimmerman, 1950). Seasonal, annual, and geographical variation in food habits are well shown by studies of the Marsh Hawk, *Circus cyaneus* (Errington and Breckenridge, 1936; Randall, 1940).

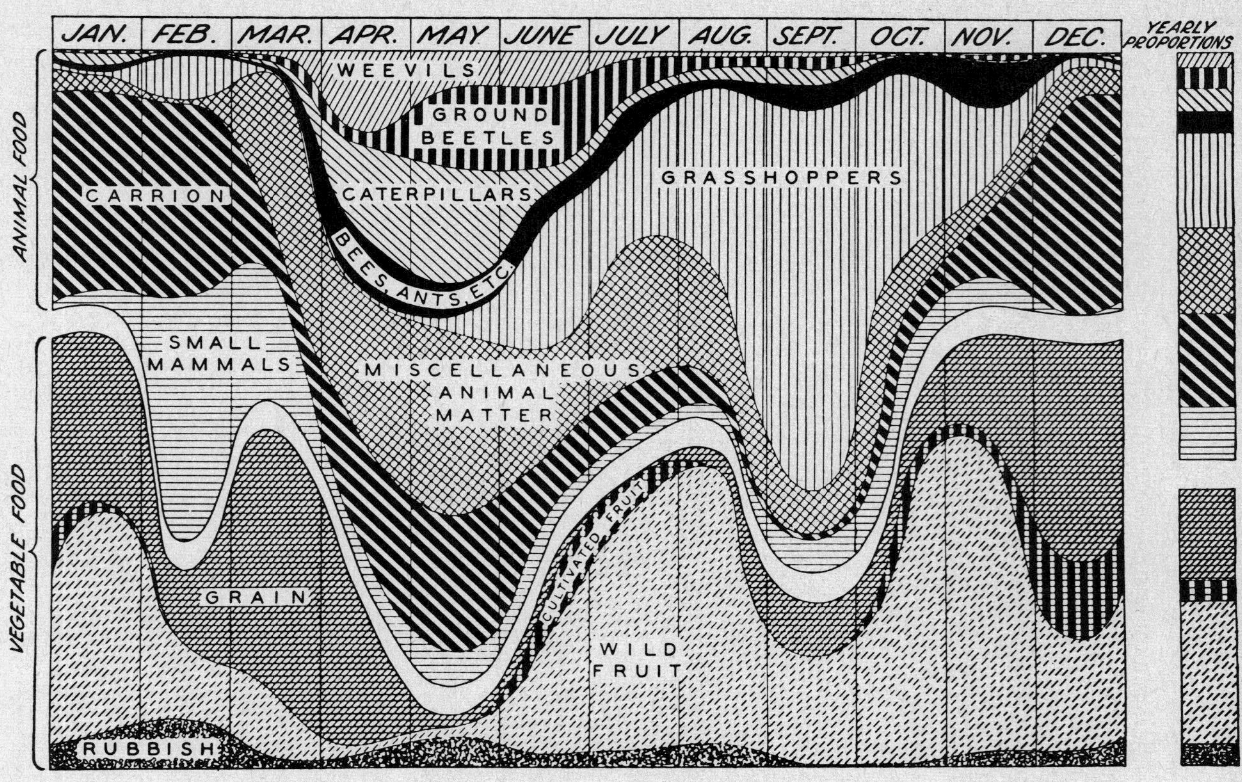

Fig. 4. Principal food items of the adult Black-billed Magpie (*Pica pica*) throughout the year, based on the contents of 313 stomachs (from Kalmbach, 1927).

Geographical

In Finland the winter food of the Great Spotted Woodpecker is mainly conifer seeds; in England, mainly insects. Adult insects form the main diet for nestling titmice (*Parus*) in Lapland, whereas defoliating caterpillars form the bulk of their diet in England (Lack, 1954). Korschgen (1948) found that the fall and winter food habits of the Bobwhite in Missouri varied for birds living in three different ecological regions. The percentage (by volume) of *Lespedeza* in a large series of crops from the different regions varied from less than 4 to nearly 30 per cent, and of corn, from 5 to 45 per cent. Similar ecological differences in food habits have been reported for other gallinaceous birds, and geographical variation has been reported for hawks and owls.

With Age

Reference was made above to the frequent difference in food taken by adults and that given to nestlings. Van Tyne (1951) reported observations of a male Cardinal that came to a feeding shelf with a billful of larvae. The male put the larvae on the shelf and began to eat sunflower seeds, but later picked up the larvae and flew toward the bird's nest containing young. White (1938, 1939) reported both a size difference and a species difference in fish eaten by adult kingfishers and those given to the nestlings. He further called attention to the interesting difference in the digestive processes on the same type of food between young and adult kingfishers. There is complete digestion of the bones and scales of fish for about 1 month after hatching. With the development of the flight feathers, the digestion of bones and scales becomes incomplete and stomach pellets are cast up by the nestlings. Both fledglings and adults cast pellets containing bones and scales in such excellent condition that they may be used for determining the species and age of the fish. An interesting problem about which little is known is the relationship between food and growth in nestling Cowbirds (*Molothrus ater*), whose food depends on the food preference of the host species.

Food as a Limiting Factor

Many writers have assumed that the numbers of birds are limited by the available food supply and that the development of territoriality resulted from the special need to provide adequate food during the nesting season. There is, however, little direct evidence that this is so. Such evidence is difficult to obtain because one must collect quantitative data on the abundance and availability of the food in relation to the number of birds over a period of years. One also must have precise information on the causes of mortality in wild bird populations. It has been estimated for a number of bird species that during outbreaks of a prey species (insect or mammal) the birds eat only from 0.05 to less than 5 per cent of the available prey. When the population of the prey species is not abnormally high, the birds may take as much as 25 per cent of the available food (Lack, 1954). Lack discussed four types of indirect evidence which "suggest that many species are limited in number by their food supply."

1. Few adults appear to die from predation or disease, so that food shortage seems to be the likeliest cause of density-dependent loss. Lack points out that many large birds have no serious predators as adults, nor do certain small secretive or fast-flying birds. Although disease may be important in reducing the number of birds on a local basis, Lack concludes that disease probably is not an important factor in regulating the number of most wild birds.

2. Birds usually are more numerous where their food supply is abundant, both during and outside the breeding season. The best example of this is found in the distribution of ocean birds, which are more abundant where plankton and fish are abundant (Murphy, 1936). Cottam *et al.* (1944) described the interesting case of the Brant (*Branta bernicla*) when its usual winter food of eelgrass became drastically reduced. The population of the Brant decreased to one-tenth its former number and the remaining birds changed their food habits, either by taking other marine plants or by eating true grasses on meadows 100 or more yards from water.

3. Related species living in the same region have different feeding habits. The different species may take the same types of food but of a different size range. Lack (1946) reported that congeneric species of various falconiform and strigiform birds in Germany did not compete for food in the same habitat. Food competition may be eliminated because closely related species live in different habitats or occupy different niches in the same habitat. For example, Hartley (1953) found that each of five species of titmice exhibited preferences not only for certain species and parts of trees but also for different heights for their foraging activities (see also

Lack and Southern, 1949). Thus Lack stated (1954: 148): "If food were not limiting numbers, it is hard to see why such differentiation in feeding habits should have been evolved, but its evolution is essential to survival if food is limiting, since if two species compete for food, the chance of both being equally well adapted is negligible, so that one will eliminate the other." That certain birds of prey and passerine species do eat the same foods when it is abundant is considered further evidence that the normal differentiation in feeding habits has been evolved to avoid competition for food. A number of hawks and owls, for example, feed largely on voles (*Microtus*), which are considered superabundant most of the time.

4. Fighting for food as a "regular feature" of the winter behavior has been described for certain species of the families Paridae and Corvidae—"Presumably such behaviour would not have been evolved unless the birds were short of food."

These four types of indirect evidence for the thesis that food is the limiting factor in determining the numbers of a species appear very attractive at first glance, but Lack rightly emphasized the great dearth of information on several critical aspects of the problem. Little is known about the role of disease or of starvation in normal winters in wild populations, or of their effect on the populations over a long period of time. The inadequately explained drastic "crash" and rapid rise in numbers of cyclic species is a case in point. The interrelationships between cyclic predator and prey species are little understood. Further, food might be a critical factor at certain periods of the year but not at other periods, in some years but not in other years. Moreover, the effect on the food supply depends in part on the nature of the food. A small mammal population, for example, may be affected by the number of adults killed before the breeding season, but the number of conifer seeds eaten during the winter has no influence on seed production the following year.

Social Feeding Habits

There are many interesting interrelationships between feeding birds (Rand, 1954). There may be some form of co-operation between birds engaged in seeking food, or it may be a parasitic or at least symbiotic relationship between birds, or between birds and other animals.

1. Mixed flocks of insectivorous birds, so familiar to American bird observers, are also recorded in many other parts of the world. Oddly enough, these flocks have been more carefully analyzed in the tropics, where there are few ornithologists, than in the Temperate Zone of the United States. Davis (1946) in Brazil and Winterbottom (1949) in South Africa, for example, have described mixed flocks of forest birds made up of four to nine species which travel through the forest together, feeding as they go. A considerable group of species contribute to the formation of these flocks on occasion, but certain "nucleus species" which seem to be essential to the formation of such flocks are always included. Gannon (1934), in his discussion of Australian birds, spoke of "primary association formers" and "secondary association formers." Various explanations for these flocks have been offered. Perhaps these social habits provide mutual aid in securing food; they may also help to prevent a surprise attack by predatory birds. Other observers have pointed to the "confusion effect" produced on a predator confronted by a mixed flock of rapidly moving birds. Whatever may be their significance, there is no doubt of the occurrence of these flocks in woodlands in many parts of the world.

In the Southern Hemisphere mixed flocks of oceanic birds are often seen. The flocks are commonly composed entirely of members of the Procellariiformes (petrels, shearwaters, and albatrosses), but nevertheless the species vary greatly in size—from small to very large. Probably this great range in size is of ecological and even evolutionary significance, for the small species survive and flourish on the "crumbs" dropped by the larger ones. Their food, whether carrion or schools of fish and other marine life, is often concentrated in small areas of the vast expanse of ocean, and this habit of gathering quickly at food found by other birds must be of great survival value.

2. Feeding flocks made up of one species of bird vary in type from those whose members forage individually, though at the same time and place, to those which work as a group, the individual members benefiting from the activity of the flock. The Cedar Waxwing (*Bombycilla cedrorum*) is an example of the first type. Except during the nesting season, waxwings are almost invariably found in flocks, but we can see no obvious benefit to their feeding activities from this association. At the other extreme is the Double-crested Cormorant (*Phalacrocorax auritus*), whose autumn

feeding habits have been studied in San Francisco Bay (Bartholomew, 1942). Concerted fishing activities develop when a dozen or more cormorants congregate, but there are often many hundred (up to a record 1900) in a fishing flock. These flocks form long, closely packed lines on the water, usually at right angles to the direction of movement, as illustrated in Fig. 5. As the line advances, cormorants throughout the flock keep making short dives, a quarter to a half of the total number being under water at any given moment. The line apparently drives the fish steadily forward and limits their dodging. Thus each member of the flock is aided in making his capture.

Another kind of co-operative feeding is that of the Herring Gull (*Larus argentatus*), which was analyzed in a study made on the coast of Maine (Frings *et al.,* 1955). The gulls do not search for food in a close flock. Scattered individuals cruise up and down the shore, only a few actively searching at any one time. Small quantities of food discovered by a gull are usually consumed without vocal announcement, but when a gull finds a large supply it instantly utters a special "food-finding" call, audible to other gulls as much as 5 kilometers away. All hungry gulls within range hasten to the feast, and these too broadcast the call. A figure-eight pattern of descending flight performed when a cruising gull discovers food is also recognized by other gulls as a food indicator.

Parasitic or Symbiotic Feeding Relationships

Preying on organisms flushed (or exposed) by another animal (or by some moving object, such as a vehicle). Our American Brown-headed Cowbird (*Molothrus ater*) was closely associated with bison herds in primitive times and now has transferred its attachment to domestic cattle. The exact nature of the advantages derived by the Cowbird from this association has never been really settled, but in tropical America a black cuckoo called the Groove-billed Ani (*Crotophaga sulcirostris*) similarly associates with cattle and horses, feeding on the insects flushed by the grazing animals. Rand (1953), tabulating the feeding activities of Anis in Salvador both with cattle and without, concluded that the birds secured their insect prey about three times as effectively when they accompanied cattle. Several herons associate with cattle; best known is the Cattle Egret (*Bubulcus ibis*) of the Old World, which has recently reached America and is rapidly spreading through the United States. In Florida it is almost invariably seen in company

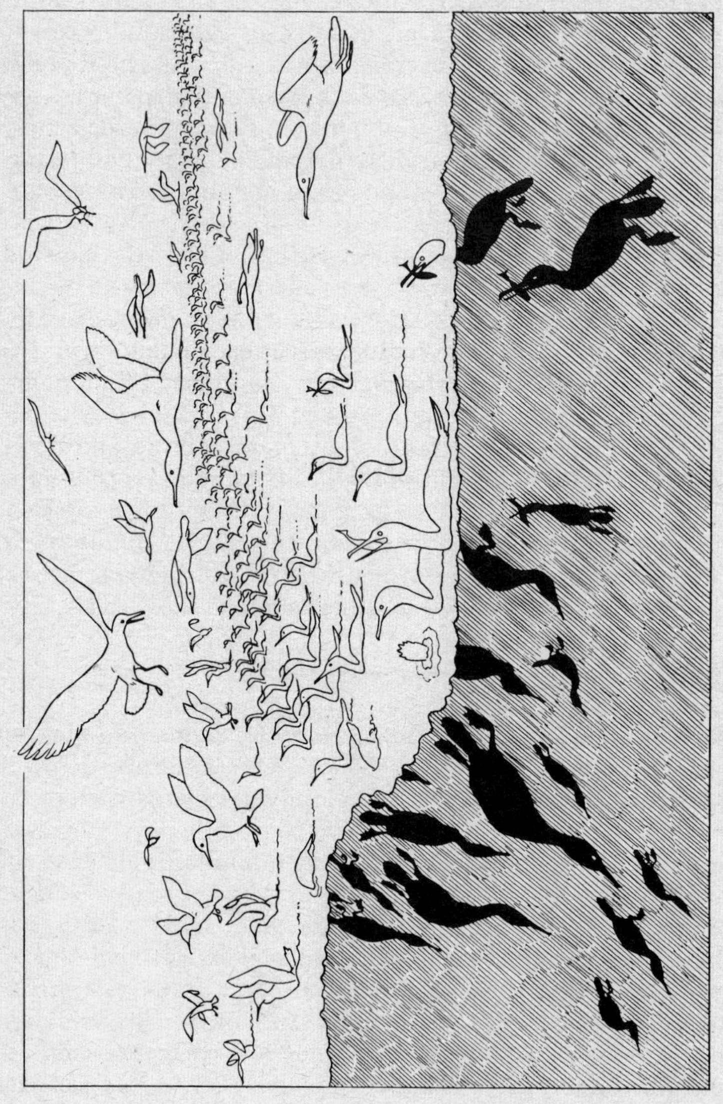

Fig. 5. Co-operative autumn feeding habits of the Double-crested Cormorant (*Phalacrocorax auritus*). (Courtesy of George A. Bartholomew.)

with cattle, actively pursuing the grasshoppers disturbed by the grazing animals (Sprunt, 1955: 272). North (1944) has described the behavior of the Carmine Bee-eater (*Merops nubicus*) of Africa, which habitually perches on the backs of bustards (*Choriotis*) as they walk through the grass flushing many of the cryptically colored grasshoppers in their path. The Bee-eater flies down to seize the grasshopper and then returns to the back of the bustard. Chapin (1939: 352) and Stott (1947) have reported that certain hornbills, drongos, and leafbirds (*Irena*) accompany troops of monkeys, apparently obtaining insects disturbed by them.

Sometimes the prey is flushed, not by another animal, but by one of man's vehicles. From several parts of the world come reports of hawks that have learned to accompany railroad trains and swoop on the birds that are flushed by the locomotive. Kenyon (1942), for example, saw six Pigeon Hawks (*Falco columbarius*) hunt in this way in Sonora and—except for one hampered by darkness—all of them successfully.

The honeyguides (Indicatoridae) of Africa provide the most remarkable example of birds' benefiting by the activities of other animals (Friedmann, 1955). Two African species of honeyguides are known to have the habit of leading a mammal (usually a badger or man) to a bees' nest. The bird chatters noisily in the presence of the mammal and makes short flights, waiting or returning if the mammal does not follow promptly. The bird may travel a half mile or more but stops when it comes to the beehive, and after the mammal has broken into the beehive the honeyguide enthusiastically eats the wax; no other bird is known to have a comparable appetite for wax.

Hummingbirds, kinglets, and other birds often are attracted to sap and insects at holes made in trees by woodpeckers.

Preying "helpfully" on the parasites of another animal. A few birds prey upon the external parasites of certain large mammals and, apparently, reptiles. In the western United States, Magpies (*Pica pica*) have often been seen picking insects from the heads and backs of deer and elk, and of domestic livestock as well (Linsdale, 1946: 149).

Two African starling-like birds, the oxpeckers (*Buphagus*), seem to represent the extreme of this line of specialization. Living only in regions where there are large numbers of big game (or cattle), they spend most of their time on the animals, climbing actively about by means of their strongly curved claws and stiff-pointed tail and clipping off the bloodsucking parasites with their very strong, sharp-edged bills. Since the mammals benefit by the removal of these parasites and also by the alarms which the keen-eyed birds sound at the approach of danger, this can clearly be called a symbiotic relationship (Moreau, 1933).

Stealing from other animals. Some species of birds have developed great ability in securing certain difficult prey. An excellent example, familiar to everyone, is the American Robin (*Turdus migratorius*) pulling worm after worm from the lawns of our towns (discovering the worms by some obscure means which man does not yet understand). Starlings (*Sturnus vulgaris*), Brown Thrashers (*Toxostoma rufum*), House Sparrows, and other birds sometimes also utilize this easy source of food (Van Tyne, 1946). Quietly accompanying the foraging Robin, the Starlings, for example, make a quick dash when the Robin pulls up a worm, and they are often successful in snatching the worm and making away with it. Strangely, the Robin shows no resentment, but simply resumes its search for worms. Starlings also rob the Blackbird (*Turdus merula*) in a similar manner, and the Blackbird steals snails from the Song-Thrush, *Turdus ericetorum* (Morris, 1954).

Certain waterfowl that do not dive well are known to steal habitually from species that get food easily from considerable depths. Cartwright (Shortt and Cartwright, 1948: Baldpate) says, "I have seen a pond covered with a scattering of Coots [*Fulica americana*] with two or three Baldpates or Baldpates [*Mareca americana*] and Gadwalls [*Anas strepera*] in attendance on each Coot. Up would come the diver with pondweed trailing from his bill and there would be a concerted rush to grab as much as possible by each of the poachers."

Robbing other animals by force. Most birds vigorously resist attempted robbery, usually by dodging or trying to outfly—or outswim—the enemy. Frigatebirds (*Fregata*) are swift and aggressive robbers. When weather conditions are unfavorable for their fish-catching technique, Frigatebirds resort to robbing boobies (*Sula*) and gulls, attacking them savagely and injuring or even killing birds that strongly resist. As a rule, the booby or gull quickly drops its food and the Frigatebird dexterously catches it, usually before it strikes the water (Murphy, 1936: 933, 936–937).

Under certain local conditions American Bald Eagles (*Haliaeetus*) habitually rob Ospreys (*Pandion*) of the fish they have just captured by plunging from the air. "The eagle, from some favorable perch, watches for the return to its nest of this industrious fisherman, heavily laden with its prey. As the eagle starts in pursuit, the osprey mounts into the air in an endeavor to escape, but the eagle is too swift and powerful for him, and the weaker bird is eventually forced to drop his prize, which his pursuer often dives down and catches before it falls to the ground. Sometimes the struggle is quite prolonged, but rarely does the osprey escape" (Bent, 1937: 329).

One whole family of gull-like birds, the jaegers and skuas (Stercorariidae), has specialized as robbers. All hunt for their own food in part, but frequently subsist largely on what they take from their less agile and less aggressive relatives, the gulls and terns. Attacking a successfully fishing gull or tern in the air, the jaeger makes the weaker bird disgorge its fish and then the jaeger catches it in mid-air. In Shetland the Great Skua even attacks the Gannet (*Morus bassanus*), seizing the tip of its wing and causing it to crash into the sea, where the Skua retains its hold until the Gannet disgorges (Tucker, in Witherby *et al.,* 1941: 123).

Water and Salt

Water Requirements

Birds are often seen drinking, especially where man provides a regular supply of water, and it is therefore commonly assumed that at least "in summer birds must have . . . water" (Forbush, 1907: 384). A more critical study of the facts seems to show that most birds remain in good health without any water except that contained in a diet that includes some animal and some green-plant food. California Quail (*Lophortyx californicus*) kept experimentally without water for a year in a large outdoor enclosure remained healthy, nested, and raised a family of young (Sumner, 1935: 193). Stoddard (1931: 501) similarly raised Bobwhite (*Colinus virginianus*) in Georgia without any supply of water except green food and dewdrops.

On the other hand, certain vegetarian birds which live on dry seeds must have a regular supply of surface fresh water. In Australia, parrots and pigeons come in flocks from points as much as 10 mi. away to drink at tanks and water holes (Cameron, 1938). Bowen (1927) analyzed the remarkable watering habits of African sandgrouse, which "come to drink with clockwork-like regularity." Certain species come to drink between 7 and 9 in the morning and again about 2 hours before sunset, whereas other species come to water only after sunset. Irwin (1956) summarized the drinking habits of many passerine birds in desert areas. He noted that genera of certain families (e.g., Timaliidae, Zosteropidae, Prionopidae, Paridae, Laniidae) apparently never came to available water supplies.

Cormorants and many gulls that live along the edge of the sea not only prefer to drink fresh water but even seem to require it. Many of the Alcidae, such as Thick-billed Murres (*Uria lomvia*), are more fully adapted to life on the sea and normally drink salt water all their lives. However, that they can drink either salt or fresh water seems to be demonstrated by their ability to survive for long periods on fresh-water lakes to which their occasional irruptive migratory flights bring them (Wynne-Edwards, 1935: 242). Petrels and shearwaters are apparently obligatory salt-water drinkers and will die of thirst even in the presence of abundant fresh water (Coles, 1925). Murphy (1936: 337) has pointed out that such penguins as the Peruvian (*Spheniscus humboldti*) normally live out their lives drinking only salt water, and a chick was killed by giving it fresh water, but it is known that adults in captivity adjust to drinking fresh water. The Adélie Penguin (*Pygoscelis adeliae*) drinks salt water most of its life but abruptly changes to the purest of fresh water (antarctic snow) during its month of courtship on land; after the eggs are laid it resumes drinking sea water. The nature of these adaptations to sea water presents physiologists with a challenging problem.

Salt-eating

Little is known about the physiological basis of salt-eating in birds, but relatively small quantities of salt may be lethal to chickens and pigeons, and there seems little doubt that tolerance to salt varies among birds. Cannibalism in captive Bobwhites may often be treated successfully by adding salt to the diet (Nestler *et al.,* 1945).

The salt-eating habit appears to be best developed in those birds which subsist largely on seeds or fruit during certain periods of the year. The best-known examples are found among the gallinaceous birds, doves, colies, and carduelines (Ploceidae). Gorsuch (1934: 39), for example, thought that there might be a relation between salt consumption and a diet of mesquite beans, which are especially abundant during November and December. He reported that coveys of Gambel's Quail (*Lophortyx gambelii*) "have frequently been seen to drop from their roosts in the early morning and run at top speed in a direct line to a block of salt at which they pecked greedily for as much as five minutes." Colies, which eat large quantities of fruit, also seek salt (Chapin, 1939: 473). The propensity for salt by North American carduelines is well known. Tordoff (1954: 17) believed that the habit in this group of birds represents more than a correlation between salt-eating and a seed-eating diet because "the quantity of salt observed to be eaten by many carduelines appears to be far in excess of that which would be supplied by a carnivorous diet." A few other birds have been observed to eat salt: e.g., woodpeckers (*Asyndesmus, Dendrocopos*), crows, jays (*Cyanocitta*), Black-billed Magpie (*Pica pica*), White-breasted Nuthatch (*Sitta carolinensis*), Rock Wren (*Salpinctes obsoletus*), and House Sparrow.

Methods of Study

The serious study of the food habits of birds in the United States began when Stephen Forbes, in a series of papers (1880–1883), devised methods for reporting by percentages the food remains found in stomachs. Interest in such studies increased so rapidly that on July 1, 1885, the Federal Government established a Division of Economic Ornithology and Mammalogy under the direction of C. Hart Merriam. A great deal was learned about the food of American birds during the following 50 years, but the primary aim was to ascertain whether a species was beneficial or harmful to man's interests (see Bryant, 1914; McAtee, 1933).

The early studies were largely confined to determining the percentage by bulk, or by numbers, of different food remains found in stomachs. Students of gallinaceous birds, especially, have examined the droppings in order to learn something about food habits. The standard method for studying the food of owls has been the examination of pellets, in which the skulls of rodents particularly provide a reliable indication of the food eaten. The pellets cast by some birds (e.g., hawks, herons, gulls, bee-eaters) do not provide a reliable sample of their food (see Hibbert-Ware, 1940). Some workers have tethered young hawks so that a careful study could be made of the prey brought by the adults (Hamerstrom and Hamerstrom, 1951). Special attention in recent years has been paid to the food of nestlings and several techniques have been devised. One of the most ingenious is that used by certain European workers who have constructed dummy nestlings. Smith (1945: 78) described a dummy with an electrically operated bill, which opens when an adult alights on a perch; the food then falls through the open gape into a bottle of preservative. Metal collars have been placed around the throats of certain passerine birds so that the nestling was unable to swallow the food given it by the adults. The young of some species (cormorants, hawks, herons, swifts) can be forced to regurgitate a recent meal, and the Lacks (1951) found that an adult Common Swift when caught on the nest would eject the entire food-ball it had for the young. Hartley (1948) and Lack (1954) have discussed the effectiveness of these and other methods used in the study of food habits.

References

Amadon, Dean. 1950. The Hawaiian Honeycreepers (Aves, Drepaniidae). *Bull. Amer. Mus. Nat. Hist.,* 95: 151–262.

Baldwin, S. Prentiss, and S. Charles Kendeigh. 1938. Variations in the Weight of Birds. *Auk,* 55: 416–467.

Banfield, A. W. F. 1947. A Study of the Winter Feeding Habits of the Short-eared Owl (*Asio flammeus*) in the Toronto Region. *Canad. Jour. Res. D.* 25: 45–65.

Bartholomew, George A., Jr. 1942. The Fishing Activities of Double-crested Cormorants on San Francisco Bay. *Condor,* 44: 13–21.

——— Thomas R. Howell, and Tom J. Cade. 1957. Torpidity in the White-throated Swift, Anna Hummingbird, and Poor-will. *Condor,* 59: 145–155.

Beer, James. 1943. Food Habits of the Blue Grouse. *Jour. Wildl. Manag.,* 7: 32–44.

——— and Wayne Tidyman. 1942. The Substitution of Hard Seeds for Grit. *Jour. Wildl. Manag.,* 6: 70–82.

Bent, Arthur Cleveland. 1937. Life Histories of North American Birds of Prey: Order Falconiformes, Part 1. *U. S. Natl. Mus. Bull.* 167.

Berger, Andrew J. 1953. Remains of Banded Birds Found in Screech Owl Pellets. *Bird-Banding,* 24: 19.

Bowen, W. Wedgewood. 1927. Remarks on the Classification of the Pteroclidae. *Amer. Mus. Novitates, No. 273.*

Brewster, William. 1937. The Birds of the Lake Umbagog Region of Maine. *Bull. Mus. Comp. Zoöl.,* 66, part 3.

Brian, M. V., and A. D. Brian. 1947. Starlings robbing Blackbirds of worms. *Brit. Birds,* 40: 340.

Bryant, Harold Child. 1914. A Determination of the Economic Status of the Western Meadowlark (*Sturnella neglecta*) in California. *Univ. Calif. Publ. Zool.,* 11: 377–510.

Cadow, G. 1933. Magen und Darm der Fruchttauben. *Jour. f. Ornith.,* 81: 236–252.

Cameron, A. C. 1938. Birds Drinking in the Dry Interior. *Emu,* 38: 336–337.

Chapin, James P. 1939. The Birds of the Belgian Congo. Part II. *Bull. Amer. Mus. Nat. Hist.,* 75: vii + 632 pp.

Chitty, Dennis. 1938. A Laboratory Study of Pellet Formation in the Short-eared Owl (*Asio flammeus*). *Proc. Zool. Soc. London,* 108A: 267–287.

Coles, Russell J. 1925. Sea-birds at Cape Lookout, North Carolina. *Auk,* 42: 123–124.

Cottam, Clarence. 1944. Gulls as Vegetarians. *Condor,* 46: 127–128.

——— John J. Lynch, and Arnold L. Nelson. 1944. Food Habits and Management of American Sea Brant. *Jour. Wildl. Manag.,* 8: 36–56.

Cottam, Clarence, C. S. Williams, and Clarence A. Sooter. 1942. Coöperative Feeding of White Pelicans. *Auk,* 59: 444–445.

Coujard-Champy, R. 1953. Sur un dispositif neuro-vasculaire du jabot du pigeon soumis a la prolactine. *C. R. Assoc. Anat.* (Paris), 39: 358–363.

Davis, David E. 1946. A Seasonal Analysis of Mixed Flocks of Birds in Brazil. *Ecology,* 27: 168–181.

Durango, S. 1951. Om törnskatans (*Lanius collurio* L.) spetsning av bytesdjur. *Vår Fågelvärld,* 10: 49–65. (English summary.)

Eisenmann, Eugene. 1946. Acorn Storing by *Balanosphyra formicivora* in Panamá. *Auk,* 63: 250.

Errington, Paul L. 1946. Predation and Vertebrate Populations. *Quart. Rev. Biol.,* 21: 144–177; 221–245.

——— and W. J. Breckenridge. 1936. Food Habits of Marsh Hawks in the Glaciated Prairie Region of North-Central United States. *Amer. Midl. Nat.,* 17: 831–848.

Fitch, Henry S., Freeman Swenson, and Daniel F. Tillotson. 1946. Behavior and Food Habits of the Red-tailed Hawk. *Condor,* 1946: 205–237.

Forbush, Edward Howe. 1907. Useful Birds and Their Protection. Mass. State Board of Agric., Boston.

Friedmann, Herbert. 1955. The Honey-guides. *U. S. Natl. Mus. Bull. 208.*

Frings, Hubert, Mable Frings, Beverly Cox, and Lorraine Peissner. 1955. Auditory and Visual Mechanisms in Food-Finding Behavior of the Herring Gull. *Wils. Bull.,* 67: 155–170.

Gannon, G. R. 1934. Associations of Small Insectivorous Birds. *Emu,* 34: 122–129.

Garrod, Alfred Henry. 1881. *The Collected Scientific Papers of the Late Alfred Henry Garrod.* Ed. by W. A. Forbes. R. H. Porter, London.

Gorsuch, David M. 1934. Life History of the Gambel Quail in Arizona. *Univ. Arizona Biol. Sci. Bull. No. 2.*

Hall, E. Raymond. 1927. A Commensal Relation of the California Quail with the California Ground Squirrel. *Condor,* 29: 271.

Hamerstrom, F. N., Jr., and Frances Hamerstrom. 1951. Food of Young Raptors on the Edwin S. George Reserve. *Wils. Bull.,* 63: 16–25.

Hartley, P. H. T. 1948. The Assessment of the Food of Birds. *Ibis,* 90: 361–381.

——— 1953. An Ecological Study of the Feeding Habits of English Titmice. *Jour. Animal Ecol.,* 22: 261–288.

Haugen, Arnold O. 1952. Trichomoniasis in Alabama Mourning Doves. *Jour. Wildl. Manag.,* 16: 164–169.

Hibbert-Ware, A. 1940. An Investigation of the Pellets of the Common Heron (*Ardea cinerea cinerea*). *Ibis,* 1940: 433–450.

Hindwood, K. A. 1937. The Flocking of Birds with Particular Reference to the Association of Small Insectivorous Birds. *Emu,* 36: 254–261.

Irwin, Michael P. Stuart. 1956. Notes on the Drinking Habits of Birds in Semi Desertic Bechuanaland. *Bull. Brit. Ornith. Club.,* 76: 99–101.

Jaeger, Edmund C. 1947. Stone-turning Habits of Some Desert Birds. *Condor,* 49: 171.

Jensen, G. H., and L. J. Korschgen. 1947. Contents of Crops, Gizzards, and Droppings of Bobwhite Quail Force-fed Known Kinds and Quantities of Seeds. *Jour. Wildl. Manag.,* 11: 37–43.

Johnson, R. A. 1954. The Behavior of Birds Attending Army Ant Raids on Barro Colorado Island, Panama Canal Zone. *Proc. Linn. Soc. N. Y.,* 63–65: 41–70.

Kalmbach, E. R. 1918. The Crow and Its Relation to Man. *U. S. Dept. Agric. Bull. 621.*

——— 1927. The Magpie in Relation to Agriculture. *U. S. Dept. Agric. Tech. Bull. 24.*

Kendeigh, S. Charles. 1934. The Rôle of Environment in the Life of Birds. *Ecol. Monog.,* 4: 299–417.

——— 1944. Effect of Air Temperature on the Rate of Energy Metabolism in the English Sparrow. *Jour. Exper. Zool.,* 96: 1–16.

——— 1945. Resistance to Hunger in Birds. *Jour. Wildl. Manag.,* 9: 217–226.

Kenyon, Karl W. 1942. Hunting Strategy of Pigeon Hawks. *Auk,* 59: 443–444.

Koersveld, E. van. 1951. Difficulties in Stomach Analysis. *Proc. 10th Internatl. Ornith. Congr., 1950:* 592–594.

Korschgen, Leroy J. 1948. Late-fall and Early-winter Food Habits of Bobwhite Quail in Missouri. *Jour. Wildl. Manag.,* 12: 46–57.

Lack, David. 1946. Competition for Food by Birds of Prey. *Jour. Animal Ecol.,* 15: 123–129.

——— 1947. *Darwin's Finches.* Cambridge Univ. Press, London.

——— 1954. *The Natural Regulation of Animal Numbers.* Oxford Univ. Press, London.

——— and Elizabeth Lack. 1951. The Breeding Biology of the Swift Apus apus. *Ibis,* 93: 501–546.

Lack, David, and D. F. Owen. 1955. The Food of the Swift. *Jour. Animal Ecol.,* 23: 120–136.

Lack, David, and H. N. Southern. 1949. Birds on Tenerife. *Ibis,* 91: 607–626.

Law, Eugene J. 1929. Another Lewis Woodpecker Stores Acorns. *Condor,* 31: 233–238.

Leopold, A. Starker. 1953. Intestinal Morphology of Gallinaceous Birds in Relation to Food Habits. *Jour. Wildl. Manag.,* 17: 197–203.

Linsdale, Jean Myron. 1946. American Magpie. In A. C. Bent, Life Histories of North American Jays, Crows, and Titmice. *U. S. Natl. Mus. Bull. 191.*

Lovell, Harvey B. 1945. Reaction of American Mergansers to Herring Gull Depredations. *Wils. Bull.,* 57: 202.

McAtee, W. L. 1911. Remarks on the Food of Young Cowbirds. *Condor,* 13: 107.

——— 1917. The Shedding of the Stomach Lining by Birds, Particularly as Exemplified by the Anatidae. *Auk,* 34: 415–421.

——— 1933. Economic Ornithology. In *Fifty Years' Progress of American Ornithology, 1883–1933.* Amer. Ornith. Union, Lancaster, Pa.

Madsen, F. Jensenius. 1954. On the Food Habits of the Diving Ducks in Denmark. *Danish Rev. Game Biol.,* 2: 157–266.

Marshall, William H. 1946. Cover Preferences, Seasonal Movements, and Food Habits of Richardson's Grouse in Southern Idaho. *Wils. Bull.,* 58: 42–52.

Martin, A. C., R. H. Gensch, and C. P. Brown. 1946. Alternative Methods in Upland Gamebird Food Analysis. *Jour. Wildl. Manag.,* 10: 8–12.

Matthews, L. Harrison. 1949. The Origin of Stomach Oil in the Petrels, with Comparative Observations on the Avian Proventriculus. *Ibis,* 91: 373–392.

Mayaud, Noël. 1950. Alimentation. In Grassé's *Traité de Zoologie,* Vol. 15, Oiseaux. Masson et Cie, Paris, pp. 654–688.

Meinertzhagen, R. 1951. Review of the Alaudidae. *Proc. Zool. Soc. London,* 121: 81–132.

———— 1954. Grit. *Bull. Brit. Ornith. Club,* 74: 97–102.

Michener, Harold, and Josephine R. Michener. 1945. California Jays, Their Storage and Recovery of Food, and Observations at One Nest. *Condor,* 47: 206–210.

Miller, Alden H. 1941. The Buccal Food-carrying Pouches of the Rosy Finch. *Condor,* 43: 72–73.

Moreau, R. E. 1933. The Food of the Red-billed Oxpecker, *Buphagus erythrorhynchus* (Stanley). *Bull. Entomol. Res.,* 24: 325–335.

———— and Winifred M. Moreau. 1941. Breeding Biology of Silvery-cheeked Hornbill. *Auk,* 58: 13–27.

Morris, Desmond. 1954. The Snail-eating Behaviour of Thrushes and Blackbirds. *Brit. Birds,* 47: 33–49.

Murphy, Robert Cushman. 1936. *Oceanic Birds of South America.* 2 vols. Amer. Mus. Nat. Hist., New York.

———— 1955. Feeding Habits of the Everglade Kite (*Rostrhamus sociabilis*). *Auk,* 72: 204–205.

Nestler, Ralph B. 1946. Mechanical Value of Grit for Bobwhite Quail. *Jour. Wildl. Manag.,* 10: 137–142.

————, Don R. Coburn, and Harry W. Titus. 1945. Picking Among Pen-reared Bobwhite Quail. *Jour. Wildl. Manag.,* 9: 105–115.

Nice, Margaret Morse. 1941. Observations on the Behavior of a Young Cedar Waxwing. *Condor,* 43: 58–64.

Norris-Elye, L. T. S. 1946. Symbiotic Tendencies Among Birds. *Canad. Field-Nat.,* 59: 174.

North, M. E. W. 1944. The Use of Animate Perches by the Carmine Bee-eater and other African Species. *Ibis,* 86: 171–176. (See also Jackson, *Ibis,* 87: 284–286.)

Oldham, Charles. 1930. *The Shell-smashing Habit of Gulls. Ibis,* 1930: 239–243.

Packard, Fred Mallery. 1946. Some Observations of Birds Eating Salt. *Auk,* 63: 89.

Parmenter, Henry E. 1941. Prairie Falcon Parasitizing a Marsh Hawk. *Condor,* 43: 157.

Pearson, Oliver P. 1950. The Metabolism of Hummingbirds. *Condor,* 52: 145–152.

Phillips, W. W. A. 1953. A Grass-fire Association of the Ceylon Swallow *Hirundo daurica hyperythra. Ibis,* 95: 142.

Rand, A. L. 1942. Birds of the 1938–1939 New Guinea Expedition. *Bull. Amer. Mus. Nat. Hist.,* 79: 425–516.

———— 1953. Factors Affecting Feeding Rates of Anis. *Auk,* 70: 26–30.

———— 1954. Social Feeding Behavior of Birds. *Fieldiana: Zoology,* 36: 1–71.

———— 1956. Foot-stirring as a Feeding Habit of Wood Ibis and Other Birds. *Amer. Midl. Nat.,* 55: 96–100.

Randall, Pierce E. 1940. Seasonal Food Habits of the Marsh Hawk in Pennsylvania. *Wils. Bull.,* 52: 165–172.

Richardson, Frank. 1947. Water-surface Feeding of Blackbirds. *Condor,* 49: 212.

Richdale, L. E. 1942. The Royal Albatross, *Diomedea epomophora sandfordi.* Dunedin, New Zealand, 23 pp. (Published privately.)

———— 1947. Seasonal Fluctuations in Weights of Penguins and Petrels. *Wils. Bull.,* 59: 160–171.

Ridley, M. W. 1954. Observations on the Diet of Flamingoes. *Jour. Bombay Nat. Hist. Soc.,* 52: 5–7.

Ritter, William Emerson. 1938. The California Woodpecker and I. Univ. California Press, Berkeley.

Schmidt-Nielson, Knut, C. Barker Jörgensen, and Humio Osaki. 1958. Extrarenal Salt Excretion in Birds. *Amer. Jour. Physiol.,* 193: 101–107.

Shortt [Angus Henry], and [B. W.] Cartwright. 1948. *Sports Afield Collection of Know Your Ducks and Geese.* Sports Afield Publ. Co., Minneapolis.

Smith, Stuart. 1945. *How to Study Birds.* Collins, London.

Sprunt, Alexander, Jr. 1955. The Spread of the Cattle Egret. *Smiths. Report for 1954:* 259–276.

Stevenson, James. 1933. Experiments on the Digestion of Food by Birds. *Wils. Bull.,* 45: 155–167.

Stevenson, James O., and Logan H. Meitzen. 1946. Behavior and Food Habits of Sennett's White-tailed Hawk in Texas. *Wils. Bull.,* 58: 198–205.

Stoddard, Herbert L. 1931. *The Bobwhite Quail: Its Habits, Preservation, and Increase.* Charles Scribner's Sons, New York.

Stott, Ken, Jr. 1947. Fairy Bluebird–Long-tailed Macaque Association on Mindanao. *Auk,* 64: 130.

Sumner, E. Lowell, Jr. 1935. A Life History Study of the California Quail, With Recommendations for its Conservation and Management. *Calif. Fish & Game,* 21: 164–342.

Sutton, George Miksch. 1951. Dispersal of Mistletoe by Birds. *Wils. Bull.,* 63: 235–237.

Swanberg, Olof. 1951. Food Storage, Territory and Song in the Thick-billed Nutcracker. *Proc. 10th Internatl. Ornith. Congr., 1950:* 545–554.

Swynnerton, C. F. M. 1915. Mixed Bird-parties. *Ibis,* 1915: 346–354.

Thomson, A. Landsborough, and R. E. Moreau. 1957. Feeding Habits of the Palm-nut Vulture Gypohierax. *Ibis,* 99: 608–613.

Tordoff, Harrison B. 1954. A Systematic Study of the Avian Family Fringillidae Based on the Structure of the Skull. *Misc. Publ. Univ. Mich. Mus. Zool.,* No. 81.

Van Tyne, Josselyn. 1946. Starling and Brown Thrasher stealing food from Robins. *Wils. Bull.,* 58: 185.

——— 1951. A Cardinal's, *Richmondena cardinalis,* Choice of Food for Adult and for Young. *Auk,* 68: 110.

Wagner, Helmuth O. 1946. Food and Feeding Habits of Mexican Hummingbirds. *Wils. Bull.,* 58: 69–93.

White, H. C. 1938. The Feeding of Kingfishers: Food of Nestlings and Effect of Water Height. *Jour. Fish. Res. Bd. Canada,* 4: 48–52.

——— 1939. Change in Gastric Digestion of Kingfishers With Development. *Amer. Nat.,* 73: 188–190.

Wilson, Kenneth A. 1938. Owl Studies at Ann Arbor, Michigan. *Auk,* 55: 187–197.

Winterbottom, J. M. 1949. Mixed Bird Parties in the Tropics, with Special Reference to Northern Rhodesia. *Auk,* 66: 258–263.

Witherby, H. F., *et al.* 1941. *The Handbook of British Birds.* Vol. 5. H. F. & G. Witherby, London.

Wood, Casey A. 1924. The Polynesian Fruit Pigeon, *Globicera Pacifica,* its Food and Digestive Apparatus. *Auk,* 41: 433–438.

Woppert, Joseph N. 1934. Unusual Bird Behavior. *Wils. Bull.,* 46: 200.

Wynne-Edwards, V. C. 1935. On the Habits and Distribution of Birds on the North Atlantic. *Proc. Boston Soc. Nat. Hist.,* 40: 233–346.

Zimmerman, Klaus. 1950. Jährliche Schwankungen in der Ernährung eines Waldohreulen-Paares zur Brutzeit. *Vogelwelt,* 71: 152–155.

10. Breeding behavior

Fig. 1. Parula Warbler (*Parula americana*) at nest; Luce County, Michigan. (Courtesy of L. H. Walkinshaw.)

The nests and eggs of birds have long held a special fascination for many people. Much of the early information, however, was obtained by individuals who were interested primarily in collecting eggs and not in studying the birds themselves. A. A. Allen (1914) and W. H. Bergtold (1913) were among the first Americans to undertake detailed studies of nesting activities. Their pioneering work still merits examination by the student of breeding behavior.

In view of the vast number of books on birds, the uninitiated person is apt to think that nearly everything is known about birds, but this is far from true. Excellent data are available for a few species, but comparative data are fragmentary in most instances. The need for more accurate and complete information is shown clearly in Bent's (1953) "Life Histories of North American Wood Warblers," in which the incubation and/or nestling periods are said to be unknown for almost 60 per cent of the 56 "best known" species. The statements on incubation and nestling periods for most of the other species had to be based either on a few nests (in some instances, on one nest) or on old records, most of which are unreliable. Some new information has been published since Bent's manuscript was finished, but even today the breeding behavior of less than ten species of wood-warblers can be said to be known even moderately well.

Here is an opportunity for wisely selected and carefully executed research. Certain indispensable techniques have been developed for obtaining accurate information. Failure to adopt them results in papers filled with unwarranted and unacceptable conclusions. One now assumes, for example, that the student will base most of his observations on color-marked birds, whether he is investigating nesting habits or populations of nonbreeding birds. In either case it is necessary to be able to recognize individual birds. The use of colored leg bands is highly satisfactory for many species but not for all. Some workers have attached colored feathers to the tail for ease of identification of a particular bird (Baumgartner, 1938; Young, 1951). Tail or wing feathers may be painted with "airplane dope" or sprayed with various dyes (Wadkins, 1948). Colored skin tags and plastic collars have been used for marking game birds (Helm, 1955). The young of precocial species have been marked by injecting the eggs with dyes so that the young are already color-marked at hatching (Evans, 1951). Other standard practices are mentioned in the discussions of "Eggs" and "The Young," and in Pettingill's excellent manual (1956). A great asset in life history studies is the observer's ingenuity in designing new methods, or adapting old ones, to fit the needs of a particular problem.

The modern study of breeding behavior involves the accumulation of precise information. The wise use of statistical methods applied to a large number of data contributes much to one's understanding of the information obtained in field studies. Statistical analyses, like definitions, however, are merely a means to an end; they do not justify, or compensate for, publishing inadequate observations. In presenting numerical data, one should include the number in the sample (the larger the better), the range, mean, standard deviation, and other computations where their use is indicated. There are relatively few studies where such information is available on egg weight, egg size, clutch size, incubation period, etc.

One can appreciate more fully the significance of the breeding behavior of a particular species if one is aware of the great diversity in pattern exhibited throughout the orders of birds. With this thought in mind, therefore, we have presented examples which illustrate this diversity; many others will be found in Chapter 13.

Territory

Territoriality among birds, especially breeding birds, was noted by Aristotle and by many later naturalists. Bernard Altum, a German zoologist, published a book in 1868 on *Birds and their Life* in which he developed the territory concept in great detail (Mayr, 1935), but, although the book was popular in Germany and was many times reprinted, the idea seems not to have influenced bird study in Germany nor to have spread to ornithologists outside that country. Eliot Howard, quite unaware of the work of Altum and others, published a large work (1907–1914) on the British Warblers which brought out the importance of territory among birds, and in 1920 he published a small book, *Territory in Bird Life,* which caught the attention of ornithologists everywhere, and the territory concept quickly became a major stimulating and guiding factor in field work on breeding birds.

Territory Defined

By "territory" we mean a limited area defended by a bird (usually a male) especially against members of its own species and sex during at least part of the breeding cycle. However, so many exceptions and special cases are now known that Noble reduced the definition of territory to "any defended area," and Nice (1941) accepted this as the most satisfactory definition. To reduce the phenomenon to simple terms, we might paraphrase Nice (1941) and say that, "It is characterized by a positive reaction to a particular place and a negative reaction to other individuals."

A Classification of Territories

Hinde (1956: 342) has suggested grouping territorial manifestations under the following headings:

Type A. Large breeding area within which courtship and copulation, nesting, and food-seeking usually occur. Examples: many spp. including American Wood-warblers, Old-world Warblers, Mockingbird, and Song Sparrows.

Type B. Large breeding area, which, however, does not furnish most of the food. Examples: Willet, Redwinged Blackbird, and Yellow-headed Blackbird.

Type C. Small nesting territories of colonial and some noncolonial birds—a small area around the actual nest. Examples: Herons, gulls, murres, etc.; House Sparrow; some doves, etc.

Type D. Pairing and/or mating territories. Small areas used for these purposes, not for nesting. Examples: some grouse, some birds-of-paradise, and manakins.

Of a somewhat different nature are winter territories and roosting territories (Nice, 1941: 464–465).

Some species occupy territories of more than one type, either in different parts of the breeding cycle or at the same time. Likewise, there may be a difference between the sexes, the male defending a large area (or a very small one of Type D), and the female defending only the immediate nest. A few species apparently show no territorial behavior (e.g., the Redshank, *Totanus totanus;* Hale, 1956).

Functions of Territorial Behavior

One might expect to find an immediate and easy answer to the question of what need is filled by such nearly universal behavior as territorialism, but it now appears that a considerable number of functions are served and the degree of importance of each varies greatly among different species (Hinde, 1956). Furthermore, other factors may exist and may be more important than some of those listed below.

Food. Early studies were largely concerned with species of Type A, and Howard and his early disciples emphasized the importance of ensuring an adequate food supply for the young. Modern studies have greatly reduced our belief in the general importance of this interpretation.

Pair-bond. Territorial behavior is surely important in many species in the formation and maintenance of the bond between a pair of birds.

The reduction of interference by other individuals of the species in the reproductive activities is certainly important in most territorial species.

Regulation of the density of a species in a favorable habitat is one result of territorial behavior.

Reduction in loss to predators doubtless results both from dispersion and from the territorial birds' thorough familiarity with every detail of the terrain.

Disease prevention by dispersion has been urged as another interpretation of territory, but there is little evidence for this view.

Object Defended

The defense of the nest site was the subject of most earlier studies, but Hinde (1956: 346) points out that the object defended may be: the mate; the family; the covey; the song or lookout post; the display ground; or a food source.

Methods of Defense

Territories are defended against intruders by the "owner" not only by physical attack, or threat of it, but often merely by song and even by mere conspicuous presence of the defending bird. Nice (1937: 57) described five phases in the establishment of territory by Song Sparrows: assuming the role; staking out the claim; the chase; the fight; and finally the proclamation of ownership of each bird on his own bit of land. One of the frequently observed phenomena of territorial behavior is that the bird defending a territory is more aggressive than the intruder and usually is successful in driving it away. However, Young (1951) reported that a "Robin's success is enhanced by its being within its own territory, but battles here are frequently lost." If, in the course of chasing and physical attack, the two fighting birds should fly into the territory of the intruder, the roles of defender and intruder may become reversed at once. "Song is the chief means of proclaiming territory" in Song Sparrows and some other Temperate Zone species that establish territory before the arrival of the females (Nice, 1937: 59). In certain tropical species, however, song and nest-building begin simultaneously, and "the birds have been long established with their mates upon their nesting territory (as in *Myiozetes*), or they hold no territory (as in *Ramphocelus*), or they fail to pair (as in *Pipromorpha*) . . ." (Skutch, 1950a: 197).

Size of Territory

The size of the area defended by Type A species varies with many factors. Song Sparrow territories studied by Nice ranged from 0.5 to 1.5 acres "depending partly on the pugnacity of the owner and partly on the amount of space available," i.e., partly on the size of the population in relation to the amount of suitable habitat. The average territory of Red-eyed Vireos varied from 1.4 to 2.1 acres, again depending on the number of pairs on the study area (Lawrence, 1953). By studying populations of Red-eyed Vireos, Yellow Warblers, and Song Sparrows on a series of islands, Beer *et al.* (1956) found that the "minimum amount of space used by a pair to raise their young successfully may be much smaller when the boundaries are strictly physical barriers rather than invisible lines determined by intraspecific conflict." For example, they found Song Sparrows utilizing areas "as small as one-tenth the minimum size defended by birds on the mainland and in contact with others of their own species." In a specially favorable habitat (open aspen woods), MacQueen (1950) found 19 pairs of nesting Least Flycatchers (*Empidonax minimus*) on 7 acres in 1942 and 14 pairs on the same area in 1944; on a nearby area in 1946, however, Hofslund (1946, unpublished manuscript) found only 9 pairs on a 160-acre tract of beech-maple forest. Walkinshaw (1953) reported the average territory of the Prothonotary Warbler (*Protonotaria citrea*) to be 3.66 acres, with extremes of 1.9 and 6.38 acres. Young (1951) found that Robin territories varied from about 0.11 to 0.60 acre the average being 0.30 acre. Territories of Black-capped Chickadees studied by Odum (1941) varied from 8.4 to 17.1 acres, with an average of 13.2 acres per pair.

The distance between active nests of the same species depends partly on the type and size of the territory and partly on the location of the nest with respect to the territorial boundaries set up by the males. The distance between nests of different species depends largely on the tolerance of the more strongly territorial species. Many examples of different species nesting in close proximity have been reported (see Gross, 1935: pl. 21; Chapman, 1928: 161; Hoyt, 1948; Skutch, 1951).

Pair Formation

Duration of the Bond

Heinroth (1928) and Lack (1940) have shown that at least five categories can be distinguished among the birds that have been studied.

1. The sexes meet only at the time of copulation.
   a. The males meet at a communal display ground (a "lek"). Examples: Prairie Chicken (*Tympanuchus*), Sharp-tailed Grouse (*Pedioecetes*), Sage Grouse (*Centrocercus*), Ruff (*Philomachus pugnax*), Hermit Hummingbirds (*Phaethornis*), Gould's Manakin (*Manacus vitellinus*), some birds-of-paradise (*Paradisaea*).
   b. The males remain isolated and display alone. Examples: Ruffed Grouse (*Bonasa*), Spruce Grouse (*Canachites*), Blue Grouse (*Dendragapus*), bowerbirds (Ptilonorhynchidae).

2. The sexes remain together for only a few days or until incubation begins. Examples: Ruby-throated Hummingbird (*Archilochus colubris*), Penduline Tit (*Remiz pendulinus*), the Philippine Weaverbird (*Ploceus philippinus*). In certain cases where the male incubates, the female leaves him at the start of incubation—e.g., hemipode-quails (*Turnix*), Northern Phalarope (*Lobipes lobatus*). Wagler's Oropendola (*Zarhynchus wagleri*) appears to be intermediate between this category and the next in that the males attend and protect the females for a period of 3 to 4 weeks while the nests are being built but leave after incubation begins.

3. The sexes remain together for weeks or months but separate when the eggs have been laid and incubation begins. Examples: most ducks.

4. The sexes remain together throughout the breeding season, usually until the young have been raised. Pairing in these species typically takes place after the male has selected a territory, but it may occur before the territory is chosen or even while the birds are still in winter flocks. This category includes a very large number of species. A few intermediate species connect this category with the preceding and the following group.

5. The sexes pair for life and remain together both during and outside the breeding season. Although a number of birds (especially hawks and owls) have been said to pair for life, there is little proof that this is so. Proof can be obtained only by following

populations of color-banded birds throughout the year for many years. The Wrentit (*Chamaea fasciata*) and the Thick-billed Nutcracker (*Nucifraga caryocatactes*) may perhaps pair for life, and Lack (1940: 271) stated that some other passerine birds are "suspected" of doing so—e.g., Crested Lark (*Galerida cristata*), European Nuthatch (*Sitta europaea*), White-breasted Nuthatch (*S. carolinensis*), Brown Creeper (*Certhia familiaris*), Black Redstart (*Phoenicurus gibraltariensis*), Stonechat (*Saxicola torquata*), and lyrebirds (Menuridae). Robinson (1949) stated that many of the resident birds in Australia hold a permanent territory throughout the year and presumably pair for life, but the birds studied were not banded.

Copulation

D. E. Davis (1955) called attention to the ambiguity of the term "mating," which has been used by authors to mean pairing, courtship, or copulation. In order to avoid confusion it seems desirable to refer to the actual process of introducing sperm into the female as copulation or coition. Copulation may take place on the ground, in trees or bushes, on telephone wires, nests or nest boxes, or in the air (some swifts, *Apus*). M. Davis (1938) reported that copulation in captive Flightless Cormorants (*Nannopterum harrisi*) took place in the water and near or on the nest. Many passerine species copulate during the nest-building period and at least the first part of the egg-laying period. Allen and Nice (1952: 621) said that in the Purple Martin (*Progne subis*) "copulation ceases with the laying of the first egg"; Emlen (1954: 32) reported that the latest observed copulation of Cliff Swallows (*Petrochelidon pyrrhonota*) took place on the "afternoon preceding the laying of the last (fourth) egg." Swallow-tanagers (*Tersina viridis*) generally copulate only after the nests are completed and before egg-laying has begun (Schaefer, 1953). In the House Sparrow, however, copulation may take place 2 months before the eggs are laid and continue during incubation (Summers-Smith, 1955; Berger, 1957). Coition in the Royal Albatross may occur as much as 27 days before egg-laying; coition tends to cease 1 or 2 days before the egg is laid (Richdale, 1950). Black-headed Gulls and Common Terns are said to copulate after the eggs hatch. Double-brooded species may start to copulate again when the young of the first brood are still in the nest: e.g., Cedar Waxwing, American Goldfinch.

Little is known about infertility in the eggs of wild birds because most statements about "infertile" eggs mean only that the eggs failed to hatch and not that they were unfertilized (but see Putnam, 1949). That the percentage of infertile eggs is low in certain species, however, is suggested by the high hatching success, but in only a few instances is such information available on a large number of nests and eggs. Because of the high rate of nest mortality, the life of viable sperm must be of considerable significance for those species in which the sexes meet only for copulation and in those which separate when incubation begins. Elder and Weller (1954) conducted experiments with domestic Mallards in order to determine the length of sperm life in the female reproductive tract. They found that the number of fertile eggs laid after separation from the drakes decreased from 64 per cent the first week to 3 per cent the third week (last fertile egg laid on 17th day) and that the hatchability of fertile eggs decreased from 73 per cent to zero during that period.

Number of Mates

The majority of birds are monogamous, i.e., copulation takes place only between the members of the pair. Certain species, however, are known to be polygynous, i.e., one male fertilizes the eggs of several females: e.g., Ring-necked Pheasant, Bittern (*Botaurus stellaris*), several icterids (*Agelaius phoeniceus, A. tricolor, Xanthocephalus xanthocephalus, Zarhynchus wagleri*), weaverbirds (*Euplectes hordeacea, E. nigroventris, Hyphantornis capensis, Ploceus philippinus*), and the Corn Bunting (*Emberiza calandra*). A few species, in which only the male incubates, are said to be polyandrous: some tinamous (*Crypturus*), hemipode-quails (*Turnix*), painted-snipe (*Rostratula*), and possibly some phalaropes. Less is known about species which are sometimes said to be polygamous or promiscuous (see Lack and Emlen, 1939; Lack, 1940). For example, the Brown-headed Cowbird (*Molothrus ater*) has been said to be promiscuous, but Laskey (1950), working with color-banded birds, found evidence only for monogamous relations in this species. Deviation from normal monogamous relationships has been described for several species (see Hann, 1937, 1940; Lack 1940; Nice, 1943: 206; Laskey, 1947).

Age at Sexual Maturity

The age at which birds first breed has been determined for some species and certain generalizations have been made. Ducks, many gallinaceous birds, pigeons, some owls, and most passerines breed the year after they hatch (they may be a little less than 1 year old); geese, many hawks and owls, most gulls, swifts, and a few passerines, when 2 years old; large birds of prey and storks, when 4 to 6 years old; and the Royal Albatross (*Diomedea epomophora*) probably does not breed until it is at least 8 years old (Richdale, 1950: 64). Individual variation in the time of first breeding has been proved from banding studies of certain species. Thus Richdale (1949) reported that female Yellow-eyed Penguins may breed for the first time when 2, 3, or 4 years old. Several authors have reported age variation in time of breeding from studies based on the assumption that certain morphological characters offer reliable criteria of breeding (e.g., Wright and Wright, 1944; Johnston, 1956).

Nests

"In many ways, it would be difficult indeed, from the standpoint of the student of instinct and behavior, to find a more unsatisfactory class of scientific literature than that which deals with the nests of birds" (Herrick, 1911: 160). Apparently very few ornithologists were disturbed by Herrick's statement, because detailed behavioral studies of actual nest construction are still uncommon. Nevertheless, there are many features about nests and nest-building which are of interest to the student of breeding habits.

Nest-Site Selection

A relatively few species, notably some of the larger birds of prey, use the same nest for many years, adding more material annually; a few use the same nest for successive broods in a single breeding season. The majority of birds, however, build a new nest for each clutch of eggs, both during the same and in later breeding seasons. This raises the question of which sex selects the nest site. The Nethersole-Thompsons (1943) summarized considerable information on this subject for British birds. The extent of individual variation in this behavior within a species and a family is poorly known, but certain tendencies are suggested. The nest site may be selected by the female (e.g., grouse, pheasants, wagtails, buntings of the genus *Emberiza*); by the male (*Sturnus vulgaris, Passer domesticus*); or by both sexes (doves, corvids, titmice). The Nethersole-Thompsons described the behavior of Scottish Crossbills (*Loxia curvirostra scotica*) as follows: "Nest-site normally chosen in course of a most distinctive selection-tour by both birds. Female tests and broods in various crotches. Substitute activities —bill-stropping, 'false-feeding,' preening, etc.—are common features." Nice (1938) had the following to say about nest-site selection by a pair of Mourning Doves: "The male gave the nest-call in a crotch, constantly flipping his wings; his mate came and preened him, then got into the crotch herself and flipped her wings, but gave no note. He preened her and soon was back in the crotch." A female Mistle-Thrush (*Turdus viscivorus*) may spend much time "brooding" in a nest site for periods up to 3 weeks before actual nest construction begins; the male Starling, sometimes the female also, may roost in a future nest site for over a month before the nest is built. Middleton and Johnston (1956) reported that the Eastern Phoebe (*Sayornis phoebe*) sometimes roosts on a future nest site, as well as in unfinished nests.

It is well known that some birds always nest on the ground and that other species never do so. Still others (e.g., Rufous-sided Towhee, Field Sparrow, Song Sparrow) typically build early nests on the ground and later ones in low bushes. Many species exhibit ecological and geographical differences in their choice of a nest site or nest height. The Brown Thrasher (*Toxostoma rufum*), for example, usually builds in low bushes in the eastern part of the United States, but often on the ground in the western part of its range; it nests in bushes in southern Michigan, on the ground in the Jack-Pine plains of northern Michigan. Preston and Norris (1947) analyzed the nesting heights of a number of Pennsylvania species and concluded that nest density "is greatest at ground level in examples of typical woodland and bush-grown countryside, and falls off rapidly with height" (see also Preston, 1946).

Among species nesting in the same habitat, competition for nest sites may be reduced because the species begin to nest at different times. This is true for three southern Michigan species which sometimes use the same shrub in succession in certain habitats. Competition is reduced because the Yellow Warbler begins to nest in May, the Alder (Traill's) Flycatcher in June, and the American Goldfinch in July (Berger, 1954).

Nest-Building

Ryves (1944) listed four major categories to which species may be assigned according to the role of the sexes in building the nest; three others might be added.

1. Both sexes build the nest.

   a. Male and female share more or less equally in nest construction: kingfishers, woodpeckers, swallows (*Riparia*), waxwings.

   b. Male builds "dummy" or "cock" nests: many wrens.

2. The female builds but only the male provides the material: Wood-Pigeon (*Columba palumbus*), Mourning Dove.

3. The female builds without help from the male: hummingbirds, manakins, Wagler's Oropendola, Red-eyed Vireo, Ovenbird.

4. The female builds but both sexes gather the material: Raven, Rook.

5. The male builds but the female provides the material: frigatebirds.

6. The male alone builds the nest: some shrikes, the Philippine Weaverbird (*Ploceus philippinus*); mainly by the male *Phainopepla*. Lack (1935) described the interesting habits of the Crimson-crowned Bishop-bird (*Euplectes hordeacea*), in which species the male alone

Fig. 2. Common Nighthawk (*Chordeiles minor*) incubating eggs on ground; Alger County, Michigan. (Courtesy of L. H. Walkinshaw.)

builds the main structure of the nest and then leaves to build a nest for another female. The females continue to add to the nest throughout the incubation period.

7. No nest is built: tropicbirds, pratincoles, auks, nightjars.

Time Required to Build

A species which lays its eggs on the ground or on bare rock may spend no time in preparation of the site, whereas some species work on a nest for weeks. Most of the small passerines, however, build their nests in a matter of days. The average number of days spent in nest construction by three species is: Prothonotary Warbler, 3.3 days (54 nests, Walkinshaw, 1941); Cedar Waxwing, 5.6 days (11 nests, Putnam, 1949); American Goldfinch, 9 days (45 nests, Stokes, 1950). Skutch (1945c) found that nests of the Costa Rican Orange-bellied Redstart (*Myioborus miniatus aurantiacus*) were constructed in 3 to 5 days. The Turquoise-browed Motmot (*Eumomota superciliosa*) may dig nesting burrows over 5 feet long in less than 5 days (Skutch, 1947). The female Wagler's Oropendola spends from 3 to 4 weeks in constructing its baglike nest, which may be over 3 feet long (Chapman, 1928).

Many birds devote less time to nest-building as the season progresses. Stokes found that American Goldfinch nests built during the first 2 weeks of July required an average of 13 days, whereas those built during the last 2 weeks of August required but 5.6 days. Early in the season the House Sparrow may carry materials to a nest box for a period of 6 weeks before the first egg is laid, but later may build a nest in a week.

There is variation also in the amount of time the birds spend building on different days. Van Tyne (in Bent, 1953: 419) described the construction of a Kirtland's Warbler's (*Dendroica kirtlandii*) nest as follows:

On June 10

> the female (who had searched the whole territory most of the day on June 8) began investigating the site a half hour after sunrise. An hour later she brought what was quite surely the first piece of nest material. Except for short periods devoted to feeding, she worked hard through the remainder of the day, obtaining most of the material at certain favored spots 50 to 70 feet from the site. She made 131 trips that day and 59 on the following, thus completing the main structure of the nest. On the third day she made 7 trips, and on the fourth day 6 trips, for the lining (a total of 203 trips with nest materials).

The pace of nest-building tends to be more rapid in the North—especially in the Arctic—where the nesting season is very short. Some tropical birds may spend many days in constructing a nest, working only a few hours each day.

Comparative Nidification

Among the orders of birds are species that lay their eggs or build their nests in nearly every conceivable location (see Chapter 13). A multitude of different materials are used to construct nests which vary in diameter from less than 1 inch to 5 or 6 feet. Standard references and many life history studies give data on the inside and outside diameters of the nest-cup, depth of the cup, and over-all depth of the nest. The diversity in nesting habits within the same family and between different families can be illustrated with a few selected examples. King and Emperor penguins hold a single egg on top of their feet and incubate it in this position; other penguins lay their eggs in burrows or caves. Potoos lay a single egg on the top of a broken tree stub and incubate in an erect position. The megapodes bury their eggs in sand or mounds of decaying vegetation, and the adults do not incubate at all. The conelike nest of the oilbird *Steatornis* is built of seeds and droppings; the nest of the swift *Collocalia* is said to be made entirely from salivary secretions. The Palm-Swift (*Cypsiurus parvus*) of Africa builds a vertical nest pad of plant floss and feathers of other birds, attaching the materials to the surface of a palm frond with saliva. A flange at the bottom of the nest pad is narrower than the long axis of the eggs, and the two eggs are "glued" to the nest with the bird's saliva. The adults, of necessity, incubate in a vertical position (Moreau, 1941). Tailor-birds (*Orthotomus*) and some wren-warblers (*Prinia*) of the family Sylviidae sew together the edges of one or more leaves and then build their nests in the resulting folds; the nests of some sunbirds are sewn to the under side of a large leaf. Most pigeons and doves build a somewhat flimsy platform of twigs, but a few nest in tree cavities and burrows in the ground. Skutch (1945b) reported that Blue-throated Green Motmots (*Aspatha gularis*) laid their eggs "in burrows which had already been in use for months as dormitories." After the motmots dig new burrows, the old ones often are used for nesting by Cobán Swallows (*Notiochelidon pileatus*). Many hole-nesting species use abandoned cavities excavated by woodpeckers. In Africa the White-rumped Swift (*Apus caffer*) uses the mud ball nests of the

Fig. 3. Longtailed Tailor-bird (*Orthotomus sutorius maculicollis*) at nest; Singapore. (Courtesy of Loke Wan Tho.)

swallow *Hirundo abyssinica* and lines them with feathers (Moreau and Moreau, 1940: 313). The Bay-winged Cowbird and some tyrant-flycatchers (notably *Legatus albicollis* and *L. leucophaius*) may take the nests of other species by force. After the eggs hatch, many rails, coots, and gallinules build "brood" nests in which the young are brooded. Some of the most elaborate nests are made by the weaverbirds. Friedmann (1922) described in detail the process of nest construction by captive Red-billed Weaverbirds (*Quelea quelea*), which pick up and weave the nest materials with their bills but hold the materials in place with their feet.

Nesting Associates

Brief mention was made on p. 270 to different species of birds nesting close together. Birds also nest in close association with a number of kinds of insects. So many different types of relationships have been reported that several writers have classified them (Chisholm, 1937, 1952; Durango, 1949). The following is a composite classification adapted from several sources.

1. Nesting associations among different species of birds.
   a. *Mixed colonies.* These are of two general types. In one type large numbers of two or more species nest together: gull and tern colonies; herons, ibises, and anhingas nesting in "heronries"; etc. In the other type, one or more pairs of one species build nests in the midst of a large colony of other species: Tufted Ducks and Turnstones often nest in large colonies of terns and Black-headed Gulls.
   b. *"Protective" nesting.* A number of small birds have been found nesting in close association with larger birds, often birds of prey. Grackles sometimes nest in the side of Osprey nests; Cliff Swallows, near Prairie Falcon nests. Certain African weaverbirds build near nests of the Jackal Buzzard (*Pterolestes rufofuscus*), and the Pygmy Falcon (*Polihiërax semitorquatus*) has been reported to nest in the large co-operative nests of the Sociable Weaver.
   c. *"Proximity" nesting.* There are many reports of different genera and species building their nests unusually close together. One of the most interesting is that cited by Hoyt (1948) who found active nests of the Pileated Woodpecker (*Dryocopus pileatus*) and Yellow-shafted Flicker (*Colaptes auratus*) on opposite sides of the same stump. Skutch (1951) described instances of congeneric species of tyrant-flycatchers nesting in the same tree.
2. Nesting associations between birds and invertebrates.
   a. *Birds nesting in termitaria.* Chisholm (1937) reported that in Australia three species of parrots and five species of kingfishers regularly excavate nesting burrows in termites' nests.

Fig. 4. Whitecollared Kingfisher (*Halcyon chloris humii*) at its nest in a live nest of termites; Singapore. (Courtesy of Loke Wan Tho.)

b. *Birds building their nests near the nests of hymenopterous insects* (primarily ants and wasps; rarely, bees). Chisholm (1952) said that the Black-throated Warbler (*Gerygone palpebrosa*) of Australia so often nests near hornets' nests that it is called the "Hornet-nest bird." Maclaren (1950) reported that the African weaverbird *Spermestes cucullatus* more often than not builds in trees containing nests of a red ant (*Oecophylla smaragdina*).

c. *Insects inhabiting birds' nests.*

(1) *Parasites on nestlings or adults.* The obligatory blood-sucking larvae of several genera of insects have been found on the young of many species of birds (George and Mitchell, 1948; Chisholm, 1952; Nolan, 1955). Nolan, for example, said that 54 species of birds are known to be parasitized by *Protocalliphora metallica.* Genera of Mallophaga, Siphonaptera, and Hippoboscidae also are parasitic on birds.

(2) *Nest-cleaning insects.* D. F. Thomson (1934) described a commensal relationship between the Golden-shouldered Parrot (*Psephotus chrysopterygius*) and the larvae of a moth (*Neossiosynoeca scatophaga*). The parrot digs a nesting burrow in a termitarium and lays its eggs on the bare ant bed. According to Thomson, the larvae feed on the feces of the nestling parrots. (See also Chisholm, 1952; Nolan, 1955.)

(3) *Miscellaneous insect inhabitants.* Many other insects have been found in birds' nests (over 400 insects representing eight species from a single nest), including insects parasitic on other insects.

d. *Invertebrates other than insects.* Nolan found one snail and seven genera of mites (two of which are parasitic on birds) in nine nests of the Prairie Warbler (*Dendroica discolor*).

3. *Secondary uses of birds' nests.* Abandoned nests frequently are appropriated by mice (especially *Peromyscus*) and remodeled for their use. It seems likely that mice sometimes eat the eggs in active nests and then make their own nests in them. Nests also are used as storage places and feeding platforms by small mammals and as roosting shelters by other birds (Nickell, 1951).

Eggs

The following discussion is deliberately restricted to what J. Arthur Thomson (1923) called the natural history of birds' eggs. Those who wish other sorts of information should turn to books on avian embryology or the Romanoffs' classic volume on the avian egg (1949).

Color and Pattern

Many kinds of birds lay white or near-white eggs, as do the reptiles. Plain white eggs are characteristic of many whole orders of birds, such as the albatrosses and petrels; the parrots; the owls; the kingfishers, motmots, and rollers; and the woodpeckers. White eggs are likewise found in many smaller groups and even in occasional species in families which otherwise have colored eggs. As has often been remarked, a large proportion of these birds nest in dark holes where color would have no function anyway. Another

Fig. 5. Redwattled Lapwing (*Hoplopterus indicus*) at nest. (Courtesy of Loke Wan Tho.)

interesting correlation was pointed out by Averill (1924), who showed that among many groups of North American birds the species with plain white eggs were the more southern, and therefore less migratory and, perhaps, less vigorous species.

However, much the greater number of birds have colored eggs, either solid colors or with various patterns, often very elaborate. These colors, which are deposited on the shell in the lower part of the oviduct, usually appear as spots or as irregular lines. The whole shell may be evenly marked or, very frequently, the marks are largely confined to one end or to a band about one end (in both cases it is usually the larger end). The usual background of birds' eggs of the colored types is green or blue or one of the browns—from pale buff to very deep reddish brown. The beautiful polished eggs of tinamous may be green, blue, yellow, pink, or purplish brown. A few eggs are nearly black.

The pigments which color birds' eggs are quite closely related to those of the blood and the bile, and it has even been suggested that the pigments on the bird's egg may be purely by-products or waste products with no more usefulness or significance than the colors that appear on autumn leaves (J. A. Thomson, 1923: 277).

The lines of pigment on the egg must result from movements of the egg in the oviduct while the color is being deposited, but there are curiously diverse arrangements of the lines and no satisfactory explanation of the mechanism seems to have been offered. Thus, some eggs of birds-of-paradise are streaked the length of the egg; those of a tropical finch, *Saltator albicollis,* are marked about one end with lines that parallel the equator (Benoit, 1950: pl. 1); those of some terns and other birds have spiral lines; and those of some American orioles (Icteridae) are boldly marked with completely irregular lines that do not even parallel each other.

Fig. 6. Nest and eggs of the American Golden Plover (*Pluvialis dominica*); Johnson River, Alaska. (Courtesy of L. H. Walkinshaw.)

Excellent color plates that illustrate a great many types of egg color and pattern may be found in the works of Bendire (1892–1895), Bent (1919–1921), and Benoit (1950: pl. 1); colored figures of British birds' eggs are readily available in Hollom's book (1952), and of several species of parasitic cuckoos and their hosts in Baker's book (1942). Uncolored figures of most North American birds' eggs may be consulted in Reed (1904).

The texture of the shell varies and often is very characteristic for certain groups of birds. The eggs of most birds are smooth, with a dull surface, but the surface is glossy in woodpeckers and most tinamous; pitted in the ostrich, storks, and toucans; rough or corrugated in emus and some chachalacas; greasy in ducks; and chalky in grebes, boobies, and anis.

The markings of a species' eggs are similar and some writers have thought that they could identify a given female over a period of years solely by the color pattern of her eggs, but this is an unwise assumption to make. Variation in pigmentation (both in amount and pattern) of eggs occurs among the members of a species and also in the clutch of an individual, as shown by Preston (1957) for the Laughing Gull (*Larus atricilla*) and the Common Tern (*Sterna hirundo*). Birds which typically lay unmarked eggs (e.g., Eastern Phoebe, American Goldfinch) sometimes produce eggs with light markings, usually around the larger end of the egg.

Size

Birds' eggs range in length from about $\frac{1}{4}$ inch (some hummingbirds) to about 13 inches (the extinct *Aepyornis*). There is a relationship between body size and egg size, but a number of factors modify this relationship in different groups of birds. Thus small birds lay relatively larger eggs than do most large birds. Precocial species, however, lay much larger eggs than altricial species of a similar weight: compare the eggs of the meadowlark (*Sturnella*) with those of the Upland Plover (*Bartramia*). A kiwi (*Apteryx*) weighing about 4 pounds may lay an egg 5 inches in length. Many parasitic cuckoos lay relatively small eggs, but a single egg of a nonparasitic cuckoo (*Crotophaga major*) has been known to equal a third of the female's weight. Amadon (1943) studied the relationship between body size and egg size in a series of fringillids and concluded that in this group it is possible "to calculate the size (weight) of a bird from the weight (or measurements) of its eggs."

Fig. 7. Eggs of the Bicolored Antbird (*Gymnopithys leucaspis*); Barro Colorado Island. (Van Tyne.)

Shape

The majority of birds' eggs are oval-shaped, but at least 11 other terms may be used to describe less frequently encountered shapes. Round (spherical) eggs are laid by some sedentary species such as owls and toucans. Elliptical or long elliptical eggs are laid by highly migratory birds with rapid flight (swifts, swallows, etc.) and by some other birds. Murres, auks, and shorebirds lay pear-shaped (pyriform) eggs; for seabirds that lay a single egg on rock ledges, this shape is often said to be an adaptation which reduces the chances of the egg rolling off the ledge. It has long been known that the eggs of a clutch vary both in size and shape, but only recently has this matter been investigated mathematically (Preston, 1953; Preston and Preston, 1953).

Clutch Size

The number of eggs laid by different birds for a single nesting varies from 1 to about 20. A single egg is laid by most penguins, albatrosses, shearwaters, petrels, tropicbirds, crabplovers, some auks, potoos, some nightjars, crested-swifts, lyrebirds, some sunbirds, and a few others; Moreau (1944: 305–307) discussed exceptional 1-egg species in a dozen African families of landbirds. Two eggs constitute the clutch of some penguins, loons, boobies, gannets, most pigeons, hummingbirds, and many tropical passerine birds; some of these species (e.g., Adélie Penguin, loons, boobies) may typically raise only one young from the 2 eggs laid. Many plovers, sandpipers, avocets, and phalaropes lay a clutch of 4 eggs. Many small birds in the Temperate Zone lay 4 or 5 eggs, but others (especially wrynecks, wrens, chickadees, titmice, nuthatches) lay 6 to 13. Most ducks and gallinaceous birds lay from 6 to 15 or more eggs, but with the larger clutches it is not always certain that all are laid by one female. In his study of the Bobwhite, Stoddard (1931) found clutches ranging from 7 to 28, but in this species two or three hens sometimes lay in the same nest.

Despite the fact that a few species invariably lay the same number of eggs, the number laid by the majority of birds varies. Geographical, seasonal, and annual variations in average clutch size occur both in nonpasserine and in passerine species. Many tropical species lay fewer eggs per clutch than do Temperate Zone species. Two eggs form the clutch for many Central American tyrant-flycatchers, troupials, tanagers, and fringillids (Skutch, 1949; 1954), whereas members of these families breeding in the United States usually lay 4 to 6 eggs. Similarly, the clutch of the Purple Gallinule (*Porphyrula martinica*) increases from 3 or 4 eggs in the tropics to 5 to 10 in more northern parts of its range. Each of the many species of pigeons, however, apparently lays a constant number of eggs (either 1 or 2; rarely 3?), and the Common Swift lays 2 or 3 eggs throughout much of its range. Moreau (1944) reported that equatorial African clutches were smaller than South African clutches for 54 (38 per cent) of 141 species, but that for almost two-thirds of the 54 species the difference amounted to less than one full egg. However, in about one-half of the closely related birds common to South Africa and Britain, clutch size of the British genera averaged at least 1.5 times larger than those of the South African genera. Lack (1947) found in many, but not all, orders a

Fig. 8. Nest and eggs of the Yellow-bellied Flycatcher (*Empidonax flaviventris*) on the ground; Schoolcraft County, Michigan. (Courtesy of L. H. Walkinshaw.)

tendency for increase in average clutch size from the tropics outward and also from west to east in Europe.

Seasonal variation in clutch size is well illustrated by Kluijver's (1951) outstanding study of over 1800 clutches of the Great Tit (*Parus major*) in Holland. For early nests (April 4–12), he found the average number of eggs to be 10.3; for later nests (June 6–14), only 7.4 eggs per clutch. It has been shown for the European Blackbird, European Robin, and the Yellowhammer (*Emberiza citrinella*) that early and late clutches are slightly smaller than those laid during the middle of the nesting season (Lack, 1947; 1954: 34). Decrease in average clutch size during the season has been reported also for a number of American species.

Annual differences in the average clutch have been demonstrated for some birds of prey, in which the clutch size seems to vary with the relative abundance of the rodents that serve as prey. Certain birds (e.g., bustards, some starlings and weaverbirds, Banded Landrail) in Africa and Australia lay smaller clutches in very dry years than in years of ample rainfall (Lack, 1947; Gilbert, 1936).

Clutch size may vary also with the age of the individual, the average being smaller for birds laying for the first time. This has been shown to be true for the Yellow-eyed Penguin, Common Swift, Great Tit, Redstart (*Phoenicurus*), and Song Sparrow, but Laskey (1943) found no difference in average clutch size between first-year and older Eastern Bluebirds (*Sialia sialis*).

Significance of clutch size. Four main theories have been proposed to explain differences in clutch size among birds.

1. The number of eggs laid is limited by the physiological capacity of the bird.
2. A bird lays as many eggs as it can cover with its brood patch.
3. Clutch size is correlated with the mortality rate of the species; if the mortality is low, the clutch is small, as in some birds of prey.
4. The clutch size for most birds represents the largest number of young that the parents can feed.

Lack (1954) subscribes to the fourth theory, and he presents data on several species to show that as the number of young per brood increases the number of feedings per hour and per day for each nestling decreases. The crux of the matter is the assumption that since the individuals in large broods supposedly receive less food they are less able to survive after leaving the nest than are the members of small broods of the same or similar species. Substantiating evidence for this assumption is scarce, and data on the Song-Thrush and the Great Tit are contrary to it (Lack, 1954: 29). The best support for the feeding-rate theory is found in Lack's own excellent work on the swifts *Apus apus* and *A. melba,* which may be considered highly vulnerable species with respect to food supply. One would conclude that the Chimney Swift (*Chaetura pelagica*), with its clutch of 4 to 6 eggs, has available a much better food supply in Canada and the United States than has the Common Swift in Britain.

Skutch (1949) presented considerable evidence against the feeding-rate theory in tropical species. Only the females of many species of hummingbirds, manakins, cotingas, tyrant-flycatchers, and icterids feed the young, but most of these raise the same number of young (2) as do species in which both parents feed the nestlings. By transferring nestling Song Tanagers (*Ramphocelus passerinii*) from one nest to another, Skutch found that the parents adjusted their feeding rate to the number of young in the nest (see also Wagner, 1957). Adjustment of feeding rate to the needs of the young was also observed at a nest of the Tyrannine Antbird (*Cer-*

comacra tyrannina). The young were not fed at all for over $1\frac{1}{2}$ hours, but during the following 69 minutes they were fed 23 times, 4.5 times the average feeding rate.

Both Lack and Skutch commented on problems of interpretation raised by certain nidifugous birds in which the young begin to pick up their own food shortly after hatching but in which there is a considerable difference in clutch size between tropical and Temperate Zone species. There are many puzzling exceptions to generalizations about clutch size, and all who have written about its significance are agreed that many more reliable data are needed, not only on the number of eggs laid but also on feeding habits, nesting success, and survival rates of both young and adults.

Indeterminate laying. Many years ago Phillips (1887) discovered that by removing an egg each day from the nest of a Flicker

Fig. 9. Nest, egg, and young of Sandhill Crane (*Grus canadensis*); Jackson County, Michigan. (Courtesy of L. H. Walkinshaw.)

(*Colaptes auratus*) the bird did not stop when the typical clutch had been laid, but laid a total of 71 eggs in a 73-day period. Such species are called indeterminate layers. Similar experiments have revealed other indeterminate layers: e.g., ducks, gallinaceous birds, wrynecks, House Wren, House Sparrow (see Kendeigh *et al.,* 1956). Pigeons, doves, charadriiform birds, and others, however, appear to be determinate layers; they cannot be induced to lay additional eggs. Emlen (1941), for example, removed eggs from nests of the Tricolored Blackbird (*Agelaius tricolor*) and added eggs to incomplete clutches, and found that this species is a determinate layer. D. E. Davis (1942c) was unable to induce Herring Gulls to lay anything but a typical clutch of 3 eggs, either by adding or removing eggs. The factors that control the cessation of laying, or its initiation after destruction of a nest, are little understood.

Time of laying. The interval between completion of the nest and laying of the first egg may be short or long. Some birds begin to lay the day following completion of the nest; others wait 2 or 3 days; and a few (e.g., American Goldfinch, some redstarts of the genus *Myioborus*) may wait a week or more before egg-laying begins.

Many birds lay 1 egg each day until the clutch is complete. A large number of these species lay early in the morning: e.g., Purple Martin, Cedar Waxwing, Red-eyed Vireo, Brown-headed Cowbird, American Goldfinch, Song Sparrow (see Table 2 in Putnam, 1949). Skutch (1952), writing about Costa Rican birds, reported that tanagers, most finches, wood-warblers, honeycreepers, wrens, and hummingbirds "usually lay early, from before to soon after sunrise," but that the finch *Atlapetes torquatus* and tyrant-flycatchers lay later in the morning and the nocturnal Pauraque (*Nyctidromus albicollis*) lays after 2:00 p.m. Some species (Neotropic House Wren, tanagers, Yellow-faced Grassquit, Variable Seedeater, Buff-rumped Warbler) lay at 24-hour intervals; others (Black-striped Sparrow, Buff-throated Saltator), at intervals of 25 or 26 hours. Schaefer (1953) found that some Swallow-tanagers laid at intervals of 23 to 26 hours, whereas others ("obviously younger females") laid on alternate days. During the early part of the laying period, American Coots lay "shortly after midnight" (Gullion, 1954). Stoddard (1931: 26) found that the Bobwhite may lay "progressively at a later hour each day till laying time comes late in the evening, when the day is skipped and laying is resumed at an early hour the next morning." The European Cuckoo (*Cuculus canorus*) and the Smooth-billed Ani (*Crotophaga ani*) lay on alternate days, usually in the afternoon; the Groove-billed Ani (*C. sulcirostris*), at 2- to 4-day intervals (Chance, 1940; Skutch, 1952). An African swift (*Apus caffer streubelii*) lays 2 eggs, usually 3 days apart, and some hornbills lay at 5- to 7-day intervals (Moreau and Moreau, 1940).

During their first breeding season, the members of some species begin to lay a little later in the season than the older birds: e.g., Tree Swallow (*Iridoprocne bicolor*), Great Tit, Starling, Eastern Bluebird. Among Eastern Bluebirds hatched in a given season, however, Laskey (1943) found that those hatched late (August) laid as early (sometimes earlier) the following season as their contemporaries who had hatched early (April).

Incubation

To incubate is to apply heat to the eggs. Most birds (exceptions: ratites, pelecaniform and anseriform birds) develop incuba-

Fig. 10. Incubating Piping Plover (*Charadrius melodus*); Muskegon County, Michigan. (Courtesy of L. H. Walkinshaw.)

tion (or brood) patches in the skin of the ventral abdominal wall a short time before incubation begins. The patches develop almost exclusively in the apteria and they differ in size, location, and number throughout the orders of birds (Tucker, 1943; Bailey, 1952). The two chief characteristics of incubation patches are defeatherization (usually involving down feathers only) and increased vascularization of the skin. In birds without down feathers the change may involve vascularization only, but sometimes also the loss of contour feathers. In general, only the sex that incubates develops an incubation patch, but so many genera have not been studied at all that reliance on the presence or absence of a brood patch for deciding which sex incubates is a questionable practice (see Skutch, 1957).

The *incubation period* is the elapsed time between the laying of the last egg in a clutch and the hatching of that egg when all the eggs hatch (Nice, 1954a). This is, as several writers have pointed out, a working definition made necessary because of the difficulty in obtaining precise data on each egg and the need for standardization in reporting information. It has now been shown for several species that the adult bird may sit on the eggs without applying heat to them. Therefore it is not safe to assume that incubation has begun simply because an adult has spent the night on its nest. The most precise method for determining the onset of incubation is by the use of thermocouples placed between the eggs in the bottom of the nest, but such equipment is available to very few of those interested in the breeding activities of birds. There is evidence to show that even when all external conditions are apparently the same—as in incubators with controlled temperature and humidity—there is variation in the time required for hatching a series of eggs of a single species. Data obtained in the field as well reveal that there is a normal range of variation in the incubation time for a species' eggs. Although hatching sequence sometimes differs from laying sequence, the last egg laid usually is the last egg to hatch. Until masses of reliable data on incubation time can be compiled, the working definition given above seems to be the most acceptable for the majority of birds.

In general, the eggs hatch in the order laid but there are exceptions. It is axiomatic, therefore, that the eggs should be marked individually as soon after laying as possible. By applying nail polish, India ink, or gentian violet with a brush, eggs can be numbered without danger of damaging them. Although this is a simple procedure, field ornithologists recognize that it is difficult in actual practice to obtain precise incubation periods on large numbers of eggs. Many nests are found after they contain complete clutches or young; still other nests are nearly inaccessible; and the high rate of nest destruction makes it difficult to follow many nests through the entire cycle.

D. E. Davis (1955) called attention to the distinction between incubation—"from the viewpoint of the egg"—and incubation behavior, the former applying to the egg, the latter to the adult birds. The urge to incubate—"broodiness" behavior—is controlled by incompletely understood physiological processes. The eggs may be incubated by the female only, by the male only, by both, or neither (megapodes and parasitic species). A family-by-family summary of the role of the sexes in incubation is given in Chapter 13. Through correspondence with ornithologists in many countries every effort was made to obtain new information and to clarify contradictory statements in the literature. Nevertheless, there still remain over 20 families for which there appears to be no reliable information on which sex incubates. In approximately 54 per cent of the remaining families incubation usually is performed by both sexes; in 25 per cent, by the female alone; in 6 per cent, by the male alone; and in 15 per cent, by the female, the male, or both. It should be emphasized, however, that there are very few families for which it has been proved that the incubation pattern is the same for all genera or species. Moreover, in some families, incubation is performed *mainly* by the female but she is sometimes assisted by the male. Skutch (1957) has given ornithologists another stimulating paper based on his long experience with Central American birds. He suggests that "incubation by both sexes was the primitive method among birds"; he gives a synopsis of the incubation patterns among birds; and he discusses theories pertaining to the role of the sexes in incubation.

Some birds (e.g., hawks, owls, storks, hornbills, crows, the Swallow-tanager) begin to incubate with the laying of the first egg, and the eggs hatch over a period of several days. It has been suggested that this behavior aids in protecting the eggs from predators, but Lack (1947: 325) believed that it is an adaptation "to bring brood-size and available food supply into correspondence." In order to prevent freezing of the egg, incubation (or covering of the egg, at least) of the first egg would appear necessary for birds nesting in February and March in northern climates. Many birds begin to incubate with the laying of the penultimate egg, others with the laying of the last egg. Walkinshaw (1938) noted that, usually, the American Goldfinch began to incubate with the laying of the antepenultimate egg, i.e., with 4-egg clutches the day the second egg was laid and 5-egg clutches the day the third egg was laid. Some birds (e.g., Mallards, Crested Flycatchers, titmice) cover the eggs with nest material when off the nest during the egg-laying period.

For some species in which both sexes incubate (and in hornbills), the eggs may be covered almost constantly during the incubation period, but in the majority of species the eggs are incubated only part of the time each day. *Attentiveness* is the term used to refer to the time a bird spends on the nest; *inattentiveness,* the time the bird is off the nest. Presumably because of the gradual physiological changes that result in broodiness behavior, birds spend short periods on the nest during the egg-laying period. Similarly, there may be an increase in the time spent on the nest on successive days during the laying period (see Putnam, 1949: 163). Attentiveness for different species ranges from less than 50 to 100 per cent of the total incubation period. Attentiveness may vary geographically, seasonally, with the stage of the incubation period, as an individual characteristic, and, sometimes, with air temperature. Odum (1944) suggested that circulatory congestion might be a factor in regulating the incubation rhythm. Richdale (1942: 17) reported that a male Royal Albatross "sat on one occasion for 14 days without relief and without food. This was followed by a period of ten days when the female was in charge, and then by another spell of nine days for the male." By contrast, Moreau (1940) found that Rough-wing Bank Martins (*Psalidoprocne holomelaena*) at five nests incubated from 31 to 66 per cent of the total observation periods. Paradise Flycatchers (*Terpsiphone perspicillata*), however, incubated from 91 to 100 per cent of the time (Moreau, 1949). Skutch (1945a) also reported attentive periods amounting to less than 60 per cent of the observed time, but these were for parts of one day only. Data are badly needed on the ratio of attentive to inattentive periods throughout the incubation period based on continuous observation rather than on "representative" time spans.

Among different birds the incubation period varies from a minimum of about 11 days to almost 12 weeks. The presumed 10-day incubation period for the Brown-headed Cowbird has been shown to be incorrect (Hann, 1937; Nice, 1953). At the other extreme, the eggs of the Royal Albatross require an incubation period of $77\frac{1}{2}$

to $80\frac{1}{4}$ days (Richdale, 1942, 1952). Summaries of present knowledge of incubation periods may be found in papers by the Moreaus (1940), Skutch (1945a, 1954), Nice (1953, 1954a, 1954b), and Kendeigh (1952).

Nice (1954a) discussed several theories (body temperature and longevity of the adults, size of egg and bird, condition of young at hatching) which have been postulated to explain differences in length of incubation time throughout the orders of birds. She concluded that "the critical factor determining length of incubation is rate of development of the embryo." Several writers have commented that long incubation and nestling periods are found in birds that are relatively safe from predation and other dangers: e.g., birds of prey and birds nesting on islands or in holes (but not woodpeckers). Skutch (1945a: 31) said that among tyrant-flycatchers it seems that "the less accessible the nest, the slower the development of the eggs and young."

Not very much is known about the environmental factors that exert a modifying influence on the inherent rate of embryonic development. A few writers have presented evidence suggesting that air temperature affects incubation time and the incubation rhythm of the adults, but Moreau (1940, 1949) concluded that temperature did not affect the incubation rhythm of two species of swallows and a Paradise Flycatcher in Africa. Extreme temperatures kill the developing embryos, but Baldwin and Kendeigh (1932: 142) found that House Wren eggs show a much greater resistance to low than to high temperatures. The embryos can survive moderately lowered temperatures for short intervals, although the time of hatching may be delayed up to 36 hours. Neff (1944) described an interesting case in which a Mourning Dove's egg, unattended in its nest for 4 days, was transferred to a nest built by two captive male Ringed Turtle Doves (*Streptopelia risoria*). The egg hatched in 21 days after being incubated during the day but not at night, even though night temperatures ranged from 65 to 70°F.

Prolonged incubation behavior may result if the eggs fail to hatch. Jickling (1940) reported that a male Bobwhite sat on a nest with 13 eggs for a minimum period extending from July 18 to October 7. Other nonpasserine birds may continue to incubate for a very long time (two or three times the normal period) and a small amount of information suggests that passerine birds tend to incubate about twice the normal period before they desert the eggs (Emlen, 1941, 1942; Nice, 1943: 222; Berger, 1953; Sowls, 1955: 97).

The Young

Based on the relative development at the time of hatching, birds are said to be either precocial or altricial. The young of precocial species are fully covered with down at hatching and are able to run about a short time after breaking out of the egg. The young of altricial species are helpless when hatched; they may be downy, have a scant covering of hairlike down on the crown and back, or they may be naked (without any down). The general condition of the young at hatching is given for each family in Chapter 13.

The fully developed embryo cuts the eggshell with the egg-tooth (or egg-breaker), which is located on the upper mandible; during this activity the egg is said to be "pipped." The time required for the young bird to break its way out of the egg—i.e., to hatch—varies among different birds. In the Ovenbird (*Seiurus*), for example, the eggs are "pipped from fifteen to twenty hours before hatching" (Hann, 1937). In the American Coot "pipping begins from 12 to 76 hours before the chick . . . is hatched" (Gullion, 1954). The time required for Royal Albatross chicks to hatch varies from "1 day 8½ hours to 4 days 10 hours" (Richdale, 1952). One should attempt to determine both the time required for the hatching of individual eggs and the time span for the entire clutch (see Williamson, 1945; Gibb, 1950).

The young of many birds have special mouth markings (directive marks or "targets"), which are presumed to aid in co-ordinating the gaping of the young with the feeding response of the adults. The simplest type of directive mark is seen in the light-colored and swollen corners of the mouth, which are typical of many young birds. The color of the mouth and tongue differs widely among nestling birds (black, brownish gray, yellow, orange, purplish red, crimson, etc.), and a wide variety in the pattern of the directive marks is found. In color these frequently are black, sometimes blue or white (Swynnerton, 1916; Neunzig, 1929b).

Van Tyne (1929: 30) stated that the "most striking feature of the nestling toucan is the presence of . . . well-formed heel-pads." These are thick, horny pads, studded with strong projecting tubercles, which cover the joint between the tibiotarsus and the tarsometatarsus. Structural details vary but heel-pads have also been described in the Quetzal (Trogonidae) and certain coraciiform (kingfishers, bee-eaters, hornbills) and piciform birds (jacamars, barbets, honeyguides, woodpeckers, and wrynecks).

Fig. 11. Nestlings of the Cutthroat Finch (*Amadina fasciata*) showing the directive marks in the roof of the mouth. (Courtesy of Desmond Morris.)

Little is known about the amount of food given to nestlings (see Chapter 9), but the growth of young passerine birds that leave the nest fully feathered less than 2 weeks after hatching is a remarkable phenomenon. Gibb (1950) presented excellent data on the increase in weight of two species of titmice in England. He tabulated the mean daily weight of nestling Great Tits for first broods in two consecutive years, the mean daily weight of first and second broods, and the percentage daily weight increase for Great and Blue tits. The Lacks (1951) compared daily changes in the weight of nestling Common Swifts with the amount of sunshine, temperature, rain, and wind each day. They found that the "maximum gain between one day's weighing and the next was 7.8 grams, in fine weather, and the maximum loss 6.6 grams, in bad weather." During the early part of the nestling period, bad weather (and concomitant low food supplies) often results in death of the young. At a later stage, inadequate quantities of food result in prolonging the nestling period by as much as 11 days over the average for broods raised during optimum weather conditions. In addition to weight increase and plumage development, the relative growth of the wings and legs during the nestling period also offers an intriguing problem for study. Interesting structural changes are seen in the bills of birds with specialized feeding habits, such as flamingos, hummingbirds, toucans, and crossbills.

Another change accompanying growth of nestlings is the development of temperature control. Birds are essentially "cold-blooded" (poikilothermic) at hatching, so that marked changes in air temperature result in a much greater fluctuation in body temperature than in the homoiothermic adults. Baldwin and Kendeigh (1932) analyzed certain factors concerned in the development of temperature control and concluded that the following are involved: development of feathers, functioning air sacs, and nervous and hormonal control; increase in total heat production; and decrease in proportion of body surface to bulk. These authors found (p. 111) that the most rapid development of temperature control in the House Wren (*Troglodytes aedon*) "begins when the nestling is 4 days old and continues until it is 9 days old." Temperature control in nestling Chipping Sparrows (*Spizella passerina*) appears to develop a day or two later than in Field Sparrows (*S. pusilla*), but both are essentially homoiothermic at 7 days of age (Dawson and Evans, 1957). During the first 2 days after hatching, the Field Sparrows were unable to maintain a body temperature more than 3°C. above experimental temperatures ranging from 15 to 30°C. Lack of temperature control in very young altricial birds is compensated for by an optimum nest temperature maintained by the adults' brooding behavior (see p. 305).

Much could be written about the behavior of nestling birds, but much needs to be learned. An altricial bird may be unable to raise its head and neck from the bottom of the nest for some time after hatching, and its chief need is not food but warmth, as indicated above. Its main activities during the first days are gaping, swallowing, digesting, and defecating. The young of many species void their excrement within a whitish fecal sac, often black-tipped. As soon as they are able to do so, the young of passerine species typically turn around (sometimes making a 360° turn) and elevate their cloacal regions when passing a fecal sac. This behavior tends eventually to result in deposition of the sac on or over the nest rim, or, in species making a domed nest, at the nest entrance. The same instinctive tendency is seen among certain nonpasserine birds (e.g., hawks, herons) in which the feces are not enclosed in a sac.

Nestlings exhibit a strong grasping reflex of the feet, so that young birds removed from the nest often bring part of the nest lining with them. Increased activities involving many body movements accompany the progressive weight increase and physical development of the nestlings: squirming, turning, standing, stretching the wings and legs, flapping the wings, preening, etc. The first sounds made by nestlings are usually faint and high-pitched, but distinctive hunger or food calls are emitted later. In some species these become so loud and persistent that they offer an easy clue to the location of the nest. Very young birds when hungry respond by gaping to "squeaking" or tapping the nest. A fear reaction develops later and the young crouch down in the bottom of the nest at the close approach of an observer; after a certain stage, the young will leave the nest prematurely if approached too closely.

There seem to be relatively few detailed descriptions of the behavior of young birds at nest-leaving time. The young of some hole-nesting species can fly expertly even though they have been unable to exercise their wings to any extent while in the nest cavity. The young of certain open-nest species (e.g., some tyrant-flycatchers, American Goldfinch) normally remain in the nest until they are able to fly 50 or more yards, but such birds often are unskilled in gaining a suitable perch. By contrast, many passerine species (larks, some bulbuls, wrens, thrushes, blackbirds, wood-warblers, finches) leave the nest several days before they are able to do anything more than flutter along the ground. There they hide in the vegetation, generally remaining quiet until hungry or until an adult appears. There is a paucity of information on the development of flight in such species and on the length of time the young remain dependent on the adults for food. Touracos, colies, and some cuckoos leave their nests and move about the nest tree for some time before they can fly (see Van Someren, 1956).

Length of Nestling Period

A young bird while still in the nest is a *nestling*. This statement, which appears to be a truism, is necessary because nestlings have been called fledglings by some writers, and, in order to reduce confusion, it seems advisable not to use the two words interchangeably. Use of both terms in reference to birds in the nest is explained by the dictionary definition of "fledge." To fledge is "to rear or care for (a bird) until its plumage is developed so that it can fly." A *fledgling* "is a young bird just fledged," i.e., a bird that can fly—but how well must it be able to fly? If we adopt this definition, when does a fledgling cease to be a fledgling?

As mentioned above, many birds leave the nest before they can fly; others fly strongly from the nest (the swift *Apus* is *independent* when it leaves the nest); and some can fly several days before they normally vacate the nest (see Skutch, 1945a: 11). Nevertheless, in the interest of standardization it seems advisable to refer to a young bird in the nest as a nestling. One may reserve the term "fledgling" for those young birds that can fly but which are dependent on the adults for food; for those birds which are capable of short flights but not of sustained flight when they leave the nest; or for all young out of the nest that are still dependent on the adults for food. We prefer the last of the three suggested possibilities. In any case, a writer should make clear what he means when he speaks of fledglings.

Little accurate information is available on the length of the nestling period for the majority of species, and on the normal range of variation for a particular species. Opinion among ornithologists differs on how much human interference affects the length of the normal nestling period. Some believe that the young should never be touched. Others feel that banding as soon as the young are large enough does not affect the time that the young remain in the nest. Most agree that daily weighing or banding in the latter part of the nestling period does shorten that period and that certain sorts of data obtained from such nests are not reliable; there is ample published information to indicate that this is true. In order to obtain the maximum information on a species, therefore, one must use different approaches in the study of a large number of nests.

In general, "the nestling periods of small altricial birds—except hole-nesters and long-winged species like swallows and swifts—are of about the same length as their incubation periods" (Skutch, 1945a: 34). Nestling periods shorter than the incubation periods characterize some genera of passerine families: e.g., antbirds, some wood-warblers and fringillids. Studies of certain barbets, toucans, and woodpeckers have revealed nestling periods two or more times longer than the incubation period. The young of precocial species remain in the nest for short periods, variously stated as a few hours to less than 2 days. Megapodes have no nestling period at all; the young are independent as soon as they hatch; there is no parental care. By comparison, a Royal Albatross chick may not be able to fly until it is 243 days old (Richdale, 1942). The nestling period of passerine birds varies from a minimum of about 8 days for the Ovenbird to 28 days for the Purple Martin and about

34 days for Wagler's Oropendola. More information is needed on the presumed "normal" 7-day nestling periods of passerine birds.

Sex Ratio

The expected sex ratio in vertebrate animals in general is 50 per cent males and 50 per cent females. There are many instances among birds, however, where such a ratio is not observed. Mayr (1939) pointed out the necessity for considering the sex ratio at different stages in the life cycle. Thus one may speak of a primary sex ratio at fertilization, a secondary sex ratio at hatching, and a tertiary sex ratio in adults. Obviously, the primary and secondary ratios are the same if all eggs hatch. The difficulties encountered in determining whether or not fertilization has occurred led McIlhenny (1940) to comment that a true sex ratio can be obtained only by examining nestlings when the full complement of eggs hatch. He studied nests of the Boat-tailed Grackle (*Cassidix mexicanus major*) and the Gulf Coast Redwinged Blackbird (*Agelaius phoeniceus littoralis*); in both species the normal clutch is three eggs and the sex can be distinguished before the young leave the nest. In a group of 412 nestling grackles, McIlhenny found 30.3 per cent males and 69.6 per cent females, but in a group of 420 Redwings, he found that 76.9 per cent were males, 23.3 per cent females. He also reported sex ratios obtained by trapping adult birds throughout the year for a 5-year period. These sex determinations, especially for the Redwinged Blackbird, differed considerably from the sex ratios of the nestlings. McIlhenny explained the discrepancies on the basis of sex differences in trap behavior and flocking habits and on the influx of winter migrants. Van Tyne (1944) discussed other factors (especially the use of museum specimens and inadequate samples) that complicate the determination of a true sex ratio (see also Friedmann, 1927a; Lack and Emlen, 1939; Lack, 1954, Chapter 10).

Mortality

Data on the success of nests are of great interest to the student of bird populations. The final criterion of "success" is the number of birds which survive to breed in subsequent years, but it is instructive to determine mortality during the several stages of the nesting cycle. Thus, one may be interested in the number of nests that are successful in fledging at least one young bird. It is pertinent also to know what percentage of eggs hatch in nests that are not destroyed during the incubation period and what percentage of young survive to leave the nest. The percentage of young surviving to nest-leaving varies widely among different species; within the same species it varies geographically (and locally), seasonally, and annually. As is true for other numerical data, survival rates to be of much value must be based on large numbers of nests. Basing her analysis on 24 studies involving 7788 nests, Nice (1957) stated that the success rate of open nests of altricial birds in the North Temperate Zone ranged from "38 to 77 per cent, averaging 49," and that "in 29 studies involving 21,951 eggs, fledging success ranged from 22 to 70 per cent, averaging 46." The survival rate for hole-nesting species averages 66 per cent, but a wide variation from this average is seen for individual species: 25.7 per cent for Prothonotary Warblers and 93.7 per cent for Tree Swallows. Moreover, Walkinshaw (1941) reported the survival of young to be 25.7 per cent for 121 Prothonotary Warbler nests over an 11-year period in Michigan, but a 61.3 per cent survival rate for 36 nests over a 2-year period in Tennessee. The low success for the Michigan nests was attributed largely to competition for nest sites with the House Wren.

Starvation is the chief cause of death in nestling Common Swifts and "probably also in raptorial birds, storks, and other species with asynchronous hatching, in which it is particularly the younger nestlings that starve" (Lack, 1954). Eye-witness accounts are uncommon but destruction of eggs and young appears to be due largely to predation by various reptiles, birds, and mammals; Lack thought it likely that such predators account for three-quarters of all nest losses (see Nice, 1957). A host of other factors contribute to the loss of eggs and young: The death of some nestlings has been attributed to attack by certain external parasites or by fire ants (see George and Mitchell, 1948; Allen and Nice, 1952). Many nests are destroyed by storms and high winds. Elevation of water levels may destroy nests of marsh birds. The nest of the American Goldfinch is so compact that it will hold water for many hours; this not uncommonly leads to desertion during the egg-laying period. Redwinged Blackbirds sometimes use both dead and living cattails as supports for early nests; the new growth (or unequal growth) often raises one side of the nest so much that the contents are tipped out. Nestlings of species building in hawthorns sometimes become impaled on thorns, and in rare instances nestlings become entangled in the nest lining. Birds sometimes select unsuitable nest sites, which may result in loss of eggs or death of the young. Cowbirds and other parasitic birds cause a considerable loss of eggs and young of certain species.

Nickell (1951) commented on the partially unexplained abandonment of completed nests before any eggs are laid and the abandonment of young in the nest, phenomena which have been observed by other workers. It seems certain that not all of these nests are deserted because of animal interference or the death of the female. In the case of Cedar Waxwings, American Goldfinches, and other late nesters (i.e., in September or October) it seems possible that physiological changes may occur that result in cessation of broodiness behavior part way through the nesting cycle.

Adult Behavior at Nests with Young

The first change in the activities of adults as the eggs begin to hatch concerns the disposal of the eggshells. A few birds (e.g.,

Fig. 12. Malayan Racket-tailed Drongo (*Dicrurus paradiseus platurus*) at nest. (Courtesy of Loke Wan Tho.)

most gallinaceous birds, some owls, some cuckoos, hoopoes, wood-hoopoes) leave the shells in the nest, where they may become trampled into the lining, but most birds eat the shells or carry them some distance from the nest. The adults' reactions to eggshells also vary within a species, so that one or both sexes may eat or remove the shells. The Nethersole-Thompsons (1942) gave an excellent summary of this behavior among British birds. Unhatched eggs are as a rule left in the nest.

Eggs are incubated; the nestlings are brooded. In view of the usual time span for the hatching of a clutch, an adult incubates and broods at the same time until all eggs (with living embryos) hatch. The ratio of attentive to inattentive periods of brooding varies with time of day, stage of the nestling period, weather, sex, and species. The young often are brooded at night after daytime brooding has ceased. The attentive periods decrease as the nestlings grow older, until they are not brooded at all, although the adults usually brood or cover the young in open nests during heavy rainstorms, and they sometimes shield the young from the sun. Most authors report that the rhythm for brooding (a continuation of incubation behavior) during the the first day or two after the eggs hatch is much the same as the incubation rhythm. Consequently, the young may be brooded from 66 to nearly 100 per cent of the time. Examples of variation in brooding behavior among different species and individuals of the same species may be found in the papers by Hann (1937), Nice (1943), Moreau (1949), and Putnam (1949).

The frequency with which the adults feed the young varies greatly among the genera and families of birds. An albatross chick is fed daily to the age of 22 days but after that it may be fed only twice a week (Richdale, 1942). A passerine bird, on the other hand, may be fed every 12 minutes, but there is much variation in feeding rates among passerine species as well. In a given species the rate of feeding varies with the age of the young, the number of young, length of the nestling period, number of adults feeding (sometimes), and with weather conditions. Few reports are based on continual observations throughout the nestling period, but Nice (1943: 235) tabulated data on ten passerine species, showing that the number of feedings per nestling per hour ranged from 0.8 to 8.4, the average being about 4 feedings per hour (see also Hann, 1937; Gibb, 1950; D. and E. Lack, 1951). The male, female, or both may feed the young, and Australian nuthatches may be assisted by other adults in feeding the young. In those species in

Fig. 13. Yellowvented Bulbul (*Pycnonotus goiavier personatus*) at nest; Singapore Island. (Courtesy of Loke Wan Tho.)

which both sexes bring food, one is usually more attentive than the other and there is much variation among the individuals of a species (see Putnam, 1949; Kendeigh, 1952).

Nest Sanitation

Although a few birds (e.g., motmots, hoopoes, many woodpeckers) apparently do not remove fecal sacs, the majority of passerine species do dispose of them, at least until the latter part of the nestling period. Many species of weaverbirds, especially in the subfamilies Carduelinae and Estrildinae, remove a decreasing number of fecal sacs as the young grow older, so that the nest rim becomes covered with them before the young vacate the nest. Some African and Australian ploceids are said not to remove the feces at all (D. F. Thomson, 1934; Bannerman, 1949; Chisholm, 1952). The adults may eat the fecal sacs or carry them away, dropping them while in flight or depositing them on a branch. Feeding stimulates voiding but the nestling does not void after each meal, and the number of sacs voided per day probably decreases as the young grow older (Nice, 1943: 237). Rand (1942) conducted experiments with artificial fecal sacs (clay and "white paper-pulp pellets") at nests of the Catbird and Song Sparrow; he concluded that "the voiding of the young provides no special stimuli to the nest-sanitation behavior of the adult, but the presence of the young is necessary for nest-sanitation to be carried out," and that "nest-sanitation behavior, the removal of material from the nest, appears to be complementary to the action of bringing food to the nest." Smith (1943) experimented with artificial fecal sacs made from white plasticene moulded to the proper size and shape. He found that a pair of Meadow-Pipits (*Anthus pratensis*) removed the artificial sacs from the nest rim unless the young made "any of the movements associated with defecation," in which case the adults waited for the appearance of the nestling's sac. Smith also reported that the pipits continued to carry away fecal sacs on the day that the young left the nest and were "huddled together on the ground about a yard from the nest."

Helpers at the Nest

In spite of the fact that nearly all birds exhibit territorial behavior at the nest, a number of instances have been reported where a pair is assisted by other birds in caring for the young (see Nice, 1943: 79, 242). Skutch (1935) classified these assistants as follows:

1. *Juvenile helpers* are found in some multibrooded species, in which the young of one brood help feed the young of a subsequent brood (in rare cases, a younger nest mate). Examples: some rails and gallinules, Barn Swallow, Long-tailed Tit, Wheatear, Eastern Bluebird.
2. *Unmated helpers* are assistants hatched "during the previous nesting season." These helpers may be sexually immature, sexually mature but unmated, or they may have young of their own. Examples: European Barn Swallow, Australian nuthatches, Brown Jay, Black-eared Bushtit (*Psaltriparus melanotis*), Eastern Bluebird, the wood-shrikes (*Prionops*), Scarlet Tanager.
3. *Mutual helpers* are "breeding birds which coöperate and assist each other in the care of their respective families. Among them we find all degrees of coöperation from casual assistance in repel-

ling a common enemy to the complete sharing of all duties of the nest" (Skutch, 1935: 259). In some respects, however, it seems better to subdivide this category.

a. *Communal nesting* is exemplified by the cuculine genera *Crotophaga* and *Guira* in which several adults build a communal nest, two or more females lay their eggs in the nest, and all the adults may share in incubation and in feeding the nestlings (D. E. Davis, 1942b). This rare type of social nesting has also been reported for the timaliid *Yuhina brunneiceps* (Yamashina, 1938), and possibly for the Acorn Woodpecker, *Melanerpes formicivorus* (Ritter, 1938).

b. *Co-operative nesting* differs from the above in that each pair takes care of its own young. Friedmann (1950) described co-operative nests of the Sociable Weaver (*Phile-*

Fig. 14. Co-operative nest of the Sociable Weaver (*Philetairus socius*); South Africa. (Courtesy of Herbert Friedmann and the Smithsonian Institution.)

tairus socius) which may be "as much as 25 feet long and 15 feet wide at the base and from 5 to 10 feet in height!" Such nests may be built by flocks of 75 or 80 pairs but, so far as is known, each pair has its own nest chamber, and a typical monogamous relationship. A similar nesting behavior is found in the African Buffalo-Weaver (*Bubalornis albirostris*). Friedmann (1927b: 177) described the nests of the parakeet *Myiopsitta monachus* as follows:

> The nests, unusual for parrots, are huge colonial structures of twigs, looking much like gigantic synallaxine nests. Each pair of parakeets has its own private compartment, but the entire flock seem to be on intimate terms. Not infrequently other species, including the tree-ducks (*Dendrocygna*), occupy one or more of the nest-holes in these structures; and occasionally even some mammals such as the opossum take possession. The nest is used as sleeping quarters all the year round and is added to from year to year until at times it breaks the supporting branches by its weight.

c. *Colonial nesting* species may be added here in order to distinguish them from communal and co-operative nesting species. Typically the members of colonial species do not assist other pairs with their nesting activities, but the individuals may profit by "mutual warning and defence against predators" (Lack, 1954: 257). In addition to most seabirds, herons, swifts, many swallows, and weaverbirds, colonial nesting is also found among some pigeons, oilbirds, bee-eaters, the woodpecker *Colaptes rupicola,* some corvids, timaliids, thrushes, the palmchat, wood-swallows, some wood-shrikes, starlings, and icterids.

Care of Fledglings

In those species in which both adults feed the nestlings, each adult may take charge of part of the brood after the young leave the nest, or the brood may be kept together and both adults feed all of the young. When the interval between nestings is short, the male may take charge of the young while the female is incubating the second set of eggs. Skutch (1935) reported that a female White-eared Hummingbird (*Hylocharis leucotis*) fed her one fledgling during inattentive periods from the second nest. The males of many passerine species (e.g., wrens, wood-warblers, finches) sing during the incubation and nestling periods, and some continue to sing while feeding young out of the nest.

Fig. 15. A nesting colony of the Black Weaver (*Ploceus nigerrimus*); Africa. (Courtesy of Herbert Friedmann and the Smithsonian Institution.)

The Breeding Season

Length of Breeding Season

The phrase "length of breeding season" means several things. It is the number of months in a year during which one may find the nest of an *individual bird,* or of a *particular species,* or of any of a host of species in a *given locality.* In southern Michigan, for example, active nests may be found in each of 9 months (February–October) but no one species is known to breed throughout that period, although the Mourning Dove, as a species, nests from late March to late October. In some tropical areas nests may be found in every month of the year. This raises the important question of single- versus multiple-brooded species. A *single-brooded* species is one that raises only one brood during each breeding season. A *multiple-brooded* species is one that raises *to an independent stage* more than one brood in a season. The obvious point, disregarded by some writers, is that renestings after the destruction of a nest with eggs or young should not be referred to as multiple broods. Most single-brooded as well as multiple-brooded species try again repeatedly if the first nest is destroyed.

The long breeding seasons of some species led many American ornithologists to assume that two, three, or four broods were raised each year, but for the majority of species we are still awaiting proof that this is so. Song Sparrows sometimes are successful in raising three broods in a season but this appears to be exceptional, and a pair may have a long nesting period without raising any young (Nice, 1937). The nesting season of a color-banded female Song Sparrow in Michigan was known to extend from April 24 to August 4; during this period, five nests were built but only two were successful in fledging young (Berger, 1951). It has been shown, especially for the House Sparrow, that a particular site may be used throughout the nesting season but not by the same pair of birds (Weaver, 1939; Berger, 1957). By studying color-marked Robins, Young (1951) found that 23 out of 39 pairs moved to new territories for raising a second brood.

Fig. 16. Part of a nesting colony of Great Blue Herons (*Ardea herodias*); Jackson County, Michigan. (Courtesy of L. H. Walkinshaw.)

The number of broods raised by a species (or closely related species) may vary geographically, as in swifts, some thrushes, the Prothonotary Warbler (Walkinshaw, 1941; Lack, 1954: 53). Some typically single-brooded species may raise two broods during certain seasons, but for American species little is known about the percentage of individuals that do so (see Stokes, 1950). Lack (1954) reported that the proportion of Great Tits raising second broods is higher in coniferous than in broad-leaved woods, and that there is an annual variation in the proportion raising second broods. The number of broods per year may also be influenced by food supply, age of the bird, and population density.

The total span of the breeding season for a species depends in part on the time required to raise a brood, the interval between the destruction of a nest and a renesting, and the interval between the fledging of one brood and the start of another nest. The Cedar Waxwing, for example, may begin to lay in the second nest the day before the young leave the first nest, and two broods may be raised in an average period of about 65 days (Putnam, 1949). The interval between nest-leaving and the laying of the first egg in the second nest varies from 3 to 10 days in the American Goldfinch and from 6 to 19 days in the Song Sparrow (Stokes, 1950; Nice, 1937). The interval between nest destruction and the first egg in the new

Fig. 17. Palm Warbler (*Dendroica palmarum*) with young; Schoolcraft County, Michigan. (Courtesy of L. H. Walkinshaw.)

nest varies from 4 to 7 days (average 5) for the Prothonotary Warbler, 5 to 7 for the Song Sparrow, 5 to 15 for the House Sparrow, and from 4 to 21 for the American Goldfinch.

It has been pointed out above that although a particular nest site may be used continuously throughout the season, one cannot assume that it is being used by the same pair of birds. Banding studies have revealed not only that some species (e.g., Catbirds, House Wrens, Bluebirds) tend to change mates for successive broods but also that there is considerable individual variation in this behavior within a species. Most Song Sparrows, for example, appear to keep the same mate throughout one breeding season, sometimes even longer, but some Song Sparrows do change mates.

Two notable exceptions are known of birds that do not have an annual breeding cycle. The Sooty Terns (*Sterna fuscata*) of Ascension Island return to breed approximately every 9½ months, so that the birds begin to nest "five times in every four-year period" (Chapin, 1954). The nestling period of the Royal Albatross (and perhaps other species) is so long that the female normally lays a single egg every other year unless a nesting is unsuccessful, in which case nesting may be resumed the following year (Richdale, 1952).

Initiation of Breeding Season

The discussion of recent ideas on the stimuli responsible for migration behavior (Chapter 7) pointed out complications encountered when one considers conditions in all parts of the world and not just those in the Temperate Zone. Similar problems arise when one attempts to analyze the factors that initiate breeding activity. Some writers have thought that both migration and reproduction are controlled by physiological activities of the gonads; others have suggested that these two types of behavior are "separate entities" in the life cycle.

Annual differences in the start of laying have been shown to exist for a number of species and many agents have been proposed as the controlling factors: temperature, precipitation, amount of sunshine, available food, and condition of the habitat. In the Temperate Zone, most migratory birds establish territory and begin to nest shortly after their return in the spring. The picture is quite different in tropical regions, where the majority of species may be nonmigratory and where some species nest during every month of the year. Even here, however, there is a pattern, but it cannot be explained by reference to any single stimulus. After many years of study of Central American birds, Skutch (1950a: 212) concluded that "if any single astronomic or climatic cycle tends directly to stimulate the reproductive activities of birds, its action is so weak that any species which finds conditions peculiarly favourable for reproduction at some divergent season of the year may escape its control."

Let us examine some of the observations which led Skutch to reach this conclusion. It has not been shown that the slight annual fluctuations in day-length within 10 or 15° of the Equator are great enough "to serve as a control of the reproductive processes of birds." A correlation between rising temperatures and egg-laying has been shown for some Temperate Zone species (Nice, 1937; Kluijver, 1951), whereas in Central America some species breed when temperatures are rising, others when they are falling. Physiological changes in certain endocrine glands accompany changes (either an increase or decrease) in day-length in higher latitudes and breeding is correlated with an enlargement of the gonads, which occurs when the days are becoming longer. Hummingbirds in the western highlands of Guatemala, however, begin to nest when the days are growing shorter. In desert areas of Africa and Australia precipitation is often the stimulus for reproduction (Moreau, 1950; Keast and Marshall, 1954). Skutch noted that in Costa Rica many birds appear to be stimulated "by the return of the rains," but that in western Guatemala "the great majority of the birds [were] nesting when the dry season was at its height, and there was still no indication of an approaching change in the weather" (see also Friedmann and Smith, 1955).

What, then, is the pattern in the breeding season of Central American birds? In his analysis of 1357 nests of 140 species, Skutch showed that some nests were found in each month of the year but that nearly 80 per cent of the nests were found during a period of 5 months (March–July) and that the greatest reproductive activity occurred during April, May, and June. This is the period when food appears to be most abundant for the majority of species. Annual differences in the start of the nesting season for some of these species are correlated with annual fluctuations in rainfall but others appear to be independent of this factor. Dependency on a particular food supply accounts, in part, for the nesting of certain species at other times of the year. Thus, the nectar-drinkers (hummingbirds, and the "honeycreepers" *Diglossa* and *Coereba*) "nest chiefly at the beginning of the dry season—from November to February, according to the locality—when flowers are most abundant" (Skutch, 1950a: 221). Grass-seed-eaters (*Tiaris olivacea, Sporophila aurita,* etc.) nest later than most birds "waiting for the seeds of the grasses which spring up with the rains"; annual variations in the onset of nesting may amount to 6 weeks or more.

Moreau (1950: 262–265) discussed similar problems encountered in the study of African birds, and A. L. Thomson (1950) gave a general review of the factors that have been thought to be responsible for initiating breeding activities. Other problems arise in dealing with Arctic species, some of which suspend nesting activities during unfavorable conditions. Bertram *et al.* (1934) offered the tentative conclusion that scarcity of the main food supply (lemmings) might account for the nonbreeding of carnivorous species (Long-tailed Skua, Snowy Owl) and that ice conditions might be the determining factor for ducks and geese. They noted that shorebirds and passerines "were clearly unaffected" by these conditions, but later workers found that passerine species, too, failed to nest in some years and in some regions of the vast Arctic area (Bird and Bird, 1940). Marshall (1952) worked on Jan Mayen where "such factors as lemmings, extremes of temperature, sea and bay ice, late snow-cover and resultant limitations of food and nest-site availability do not occur." Nevertheless, he found that nonbreeding does occur and that the causes differ from species to species.

Richdale commented that variable weather appears not to influence the onset of the breeding cycle of the Royal Albatross and other seabirds in New Zealand. He also pointed out that the Emperor Penguin lays its egg "in July in total darkness" and that four species of albatrosses and six species of smaller petrels lay "when the days are shortening" (Richdale, 1952: 67).

Nest Parasitism

Representatives of five different families (Anatidae, Cuculidae, Indicatoridae, Icteridae, Ploceidae) have dispensed with nest construction and rearing young by the simple expedient of laying their eggs in the nests of other species (the hosts or fosterers). Since the parasitic genera do not build nests, they differ from other birds (e.g., some ducks, North American cuckoos) which build nests but occasionally lay one or more eggs in the nest of another bird, either the same or a different species.

Among the Anatidae, the Black-headed Duck (*Heteronetta atricapilla*) of South America is entirely parasitic, laying its eggs in the nests of rails, coots, ibises, limpkins, gulls, etc. Semiparasitic habits are exhibited by the stiff-tailed ducks (Friedmann, 1932).

Several genera of cuckoos (e.g., *Cacomantis, Cercococcyx, Chrysococcyx, Clamator, Cuculus, Eudynamis, Dromococcyx, Pachycoccyx, Surniculus, Tapera*) are parasitic on other birds. More appears to be known about the egg-laying behavior of the European Cuckoo (*Cuculus canorus*) than of any other parasitic bird. The outstanding observations made by Chance (1940) in England should be an inspiration to anyone interested in life history studies. He established after years of the most intensive field work that the cuckoo lays its eggs almost invariably in the afternoon and on alternate days; that the egg might be laid in as short a time as 8 seconds; and that the cuckoo removes at least one egg of the host at the time of laying. Chance became so familiar with the behavior of female cuckoos that not only could he find nests of host species by watching the cuckoo but he could also predict with reasonable accuracy the nest in which she would lay her next egg. The eggs of *Cuculus* (and of many other parasitic genera) are noteworthy for their extreme variation in marking and color (various shades of reds and browns, "greyish" blue, white), and in many cases the birds lay in the nests of hosts whose eggs are similar in color and pattern. Largely on the basis of the different color types of eggs, it has been suggested that the European Cuckoo consists of "races or gentes, inherently parasitical upon particular species. Thus we have meadow-pipit cuckoos, reed-warbler cuckoos, wagtail cuckoos, etc., etc." (Chance, 1940: 108).

Beyond certain facts cited above, most of what is "known" about *Cuculus canorus* is based on assumption: the number of eggs laid by one bird in a season and in successive years; the inheritance of egg color; "that each individual Cuckoo is always parasitic on the same species" (Baker, 1942: 42–43); "that a female cuckoo tends to victimise the same species of fosterer by which she herself was reared" (Chance, 1940: 108); that cuckoos generally adopt a territory, selected by the female, "which they fight to retain against other Cuckoos of the same gens, parasitic on the same birds" (Baker, 1942: 178); etc. The one assumption upon which all of these statements rest is that "a female Cuckoo always lays the same type of egg all through the season and, indeed, all through her life" (Baker, 1942: 1). Baker added (pp. 107–108, 9): "I have a series of eggs laid by one female Cuckoo for eleven years and anyone looking at them would be able to identify them, after comparison with other Cuckoos' eggs, as all indisputably laid by one and the same Cuckoo." The series of eggs of this "same Cuckoo" were taken over the 11-year period by Baker's trained native men in India and sent to him! With the exception of one bird (Chance, 1940: 117), all of the "evidence" proposed by Baker and Chance is based on unmarked birds. It may well be that any or all of the statements cited above may prove to be true, but one should not accept them as facts until color-marked birds are studied.

The cuckoos appear to have evolved more specialized parasitic habits than the parasitic cowbirds. This is suggested by the greater variation in egg color within a species among the cuckoos (but see Friedmann, 1929: 83) and by the tendency for many parasitic cuckoos to lay smaller eggs, relative to body size, than nonparasitic cuckoos. Thus the Yellow-billed and Black-billed cuckoos (*Coccyzus americanus, C. erythropthalmus*) are considerably smaller than the European Cuckoo but they lay much larger eggs. The young of most parasitic cuckoos (not *Clamator*) forcibly eject from the nest the eggs or other nestlings (including other cuckoos usually) so that only one cuckoo is raised in a nest. For a detailed discussion of differences in behavior among African parasitic cuckoos see Friedmann's monograph (1948).

The honeyguides (Indicatoridae) are an Old World family (primarily African) known more for their habits of guiding man, honeybadgers (*Mellivora capensis*), and a few other mammals to bees' nests than for their parasitic habits. Friedmann (1955) has discussed the African species in detail. All but two of the African honeyguides (*Prodotiscus*) eat beeswax, but the guiding habit has been observed only in certain species of the subgenus Indicator. Friedmann (p. 39) found that in 23 guiding trips "the longest one covered 750 yards and lasted 28 minutes, several were from 250–350 yards and lasted from 9 to 16 minutes; and the shortest one involved a distance of 20 yards in 2 minutes."

Information is lacking on the egg-laying habits of 5 of the 11 species of honeyguides, but some of the other species differ from most parasitic birds in that they lay in the nests of hole-nesting species (bee-eaters, hoopoes, kingfishers). Friedmann summarized by saying that the "typical" honeyguides (*Indicator* and probably *Melichneutes*) "victimize picarian and coraciiform birds primarily, and only such passerine forms as utilize old nesting sites of these birds or other tunnels fairly similar to theirs" (p. 20). *Prodotiscus* is known to parasitize only small passerine birds. The nestlings of *Indicator* have well-developed "mandibular hooks" which may be used to kill the host young (p. 206).

Among the New World troupials or blackbirds (Icteridae), two genera of cowbirds (*Molothrus* and *Tangavius*) are entirely parasitic, whereas a third genus (*Agelaioides*) is nonparasitic. In addition, the Giant Cowbird (*Psomocolax oryzivorus*) is parasitic on other icterids: *Gymnostinops, Zarhynchus, Ostinops, Cacicus* (see Skutch, 1954: 316). The cowbirds are of special interest to the student of nest parasitism because habits of the several species suggest a way by which such parasitism may have evolved. The nonparasitic Bay-winged Cowbird (*Agelaioides badius*) sometimes builds its own nest but usually appropriates the nest of some other species in which to lay and incubate its eggs. The parasitic Shiny Cowbird (*Molothrus bonariensis*) exhibits what appears to be nest-building behavior at times (and rarely attempts to build) and it has "the parasitic habit very poorly developed, wasting large numbers of its eggs" (Friedmann, 1929: 351). This statement is based on the fact that many of the eggs are found on the ground and a large number of nests contain more than one cowbird egg—from 15 to 37 cowbird eggs have been found in a single nest of certain ovenbirds (Furnariidae). Such large numbers of eggs have not been found in any of the host nests parasitized by the Brown-headed Cowbird (*M. ater*) but very little is known about the percentage of "wasted" eggs laid by this species. Many eggs are "lost" due to nest desertion and the habit of some hosts either to remove or build over the cowbird eggs. The Screaming Cowbird (*M. rufo-axillaris*), so far as known, is parasitic almost exclusively on the Bay-winged Cowbird.

The Brown-headed Cowbird offers a stimulating challenge to American ornithologists. There is no proof that this species lays its eggs at daily intervals or in clutches throughout the season, although both seem likely possibilities. The three considered (and cautious) discussions of egg-laying were based on the assumption that an individual female can be identified because of similarity in color and length of her eggs (Friedmann, 1929: 182; Walkinshaw, 1949; Nice, 1949); this remains to be proved. Histological examination of the ovary in the attempt to determine clutch size in other species of *Molothrus* has yielded inconclusive results, only in part because of inadequate material (D. E. Davis, 1942a; 1958). Kabat *et al.* (1948) studied the ovaries of 38 Ring-necked Pheasants *whose egg-laying records were known.* "In twenty cases more structures were classified as ovulated follicles than there were eggs found, and in eighteen cases fewer structures were classified as ovulated follicles." Among other variations, they found that some ovulated follicles persisted into the following breeding season. In one instance a hen was sacrificed after laying three eggs in the second spring—"Her ovary contained 16 ovulated follicles." Nevertheless, they found "a highly significant correlation" between the number of ovulated follicles and number of eggs laid; the correlation decreased as the interval between cessation of egg-laying and examination of the ovaries increased. Similar information for the Cowbird is lacking, but these data suggest the use of caution in interpreting information obtained from a few ovaries, especially when the egg-laying history is not known.

The known hosts (including "accidental" hosts, such as the Mourning Dove) of the eastern race of the Brown-headed Cowbird now number about 160 species and subspecies of birds. There appears to be no compilation that shows which hosts have successfully fledged Cowbirds. Available evidence suggests, for example, that the Cowbird does not survive on the nestling food of the American Goldfinch. Space does not permit further discussion of the many interesting problems related to this Cowbird, but reference must be made to Laskey's (1950) excellent study of cowbird behavior, based on 29 color-banded individuals.

The large family of weaverbirds (Ploceidae) contains several parasitic genera, about which relatively little is known. Bannerman (1949: xxx, 368) placed the four genera known or thought to be parasitic (*Hypochera, Vidua, Steganura, Anomalospiza*) in the subfamily Viduinae, but Friedmann (1950) and others place *Anomalospiza* in the subfamily Ploceinae. *Anomalospiza* is known to parasitize two genera (*Cisticola* and *Prinia*) of Old-world warblers (Sylviidae). Members of the subfamily Estrildinae form the principal, but not exclusive, hosts for the several species of *Vidua*.

References

Ali, Salim A. 1931. The Nesting Habits of the Baya (*Ploceus philippinus*). A New Interpretation of Their Domestic Relations. *Jour. Bombay Nat. Hist. Soc.,* 34: 947–964.

Allen, Arthur A. 1914. The Red-winged Blackbird: A Study in the Ecology of a Cattail Marsh. *Proc. Linn. Soc., N. Y.,* 24–25: 43–128.

Allen, Robert W., and Margaret M. Nice. 1952. A study of the Breeding Biology of the Purple Martin (Progne subis). *Amer. Midl. Nat.,* 47: 606–665.

Amadon, Dean. 1943. Bird Weights and Egg Weights. *Auk,* 60: 221–234.

Averill, Charles K. 1924. Vigor, Distribution, and Pigmentation of the Egg. *Condor,* 26: 140–143.

——— 1933. Geographical Distribution in Relation to Number of Eggs. *Condor,* 35: 93–97.

Bailey, Robert E. 1952. The Incubation Patch of Passerine Birds. *Condor,* 54: 121–136.

——— 1953. Accessory Reproductive Organs of Male Fringillid Birds: Seasonal Variations and Response to Various Sex Hormones. *Anat. Rec.,* 115: 1–19.

Baker, E. C. Stuart. 1942. *Cuckoo Problems.* H. F. & G. Witherby, London.

Baldwin, S. Prentiss, and S. Charles Kendeigh. 1932. Physiology of the Temperature of Birds. Sci. Publ. Cleveland Mus. Nat. Hist., Vol. 3.

Bannerman, David Armitage. 1949. *The Birds of Tropical West Africa.* Vol. VII. Crown Agents for the Colonies, London.

Bartholomew, George A., Jr., William R. Dawson, and Edward J. O'Neill. 1953. A Field Study of Temperature Regulation in Young White Pelicans, *Pelecanus erythrorhynchos. Ecology,* 34: 554–560.

Baumgartner, A. M. 1938. Experiments in Feather Marking Eastern Tree Sparrows for Territory Studies. *Bird-Banding,* 9: 124–135.

Beer, James R., Louis D. Frenzel, and Norman Hansen. 1956. Minimum Space Requirements of Some Nesting Passerine Birds. *Wils. Bull.,* 68: 200–209.

Bendire, Charles. 1892–1895. Life Histories of North American Birds. *U. S. Natl. Mus. Special Bulletins, 1* and *3.*

Benoit, Jacques. 1950. Organes Uro-génitaux. In Grassé's *Traité de Zoologie,* Vol. 15, Oiseaux. Masson et Cie, Paris, pp. 341–377.

Bent, Arthur C. 1919, 1921, 1953. Life Histories of North American Birds . . . . *U. S. Natl. Mus. Bulletins 107, 113,* and *203.*

Berger, Andrew J. 1951. Ten Consecutive Nests of a Song Sparrow. *Wils. Bull.,* 63: 186–188.

——— 1953. Protracted Incubation Behavior of a Female American Goldfinch. *Condor,* 55: 151.

——— 1954. Association and Seasonal Succession in the Use of Nest Sites. *Condor,* 56: 164–165.

——— 1957. Nesting Behavior of the House Sparrow. *Jack-Pine Warbler,* 35: 86–92.

Bergtold, W. H. 1913. A Study of the House Finch. *Auk,* 30: 40–73.

Bertram, G. C. L., David Lack, and B. B. Roberts. 1934. Notes on East Greenland Birds, with a Discussion of the Periodic Non-breeding among Arctic Birds. *Ibis,* 1934: 816–831.

Bird, C. G., and E. G. Bird. 1940. Some Remarks on Non-breeding in the Arctic, especially in North-east Greenland. *Ibis,* 1940: 671–678.

Chance, Edgar P. 1940. *The Truth About the Cuckoo.* Country Life, London.

——— and Harry W. Hann. 1942. The European Cuckoo and the Cowbird. *Bird-Banding,* 13: 99–103.

Chapin, James P. 1954. The Calendar of Wideawake Fair. *Auk,* 71: 1–15.

Chapman, Frank M. 1928. The Nesting Habits of Wagler's Oropendola (*Zarhynchus Wagleri*) on Barro Colorado Island. *Bull. Amer. Mus. Nat. Hist.,* 58: 123–166.

Chappell, Bertram. 1948. The Dissimilar Egg and Other Problems. Part IV. *Ool. Rec.,* 22 (2): 17–20.

Chisholm, A. H. 1937. Bird-Insect Nesting Associations. *Ibis,* 1937: 411–413.

——— 1952. Bird-Insect Nesting Associations in Australia. *Ibis,* 94: 395–405.

Creutz, Gerhard. 1956. Die Sitzordnung junger Singvögel im Nest. *Beiträge zur Vogelkunde,* 5: 6–16.

Davis, David E. 1942a. The Number of Eggs Laid by Cowbirds. *Condor,* 44: 10–12.

——— 1942b. The Phylogeny of Social Nesting Habits in the Crotophaginae. *Quart. Rev. Biol.,* 17: 115–134.

——— 1942c. Number of Eggs Laid by Herring Gulls. *Auk,* 59: 549–554.

——— 1952. Definitions for the Analysis of Survival of Nestlings. *Auk,* 69: 316–320.

——— 1955. Breeding Biology of Birds. In *Recent Studies in Avian Biology,* Univ. Illinois Press, Urbana, pp. 264–308.

——— 1958. Relation of "Clutch-size" to Number of Ova Ovulated by Starlings. *Auk,* 75: 60–66.

Davis, Malcolm. 1938. Partial Nidification of the Flightless Cormorant. *Auk,* 55: 596–597.

Dawson, William R., and Francis C. Evans. 1957. Relation of Growth and Development to Temperature Regulation in Nestling Field and Chipping Sparrows. *Physiol. Zoöl.,* 30: 315–327.

Durango, S. 1949. The Nesting Associations of Birds with Social Insects and with Birds of Different Species. *Ibis,* 91: 140–143.

Elder, William H., and Milton W. Weller. 1954. Duration of Fertility in the Domestic Mallard Hen after Isolation from the Drake. *Jour. Wildl. Manag.,* 18: 495–502.

Emlen, John T., Jr. 1941. An Experimental Analysis of the Breeding Cycle of the Tricolored Red-wing. *Condor,* 43: 209–219.

——— 1942. Notes on a Nesting Colony of Western Crows. *Bird-Banding,* 13: 143–154.

——— 1954. Territory, Nest Building, and Pair Formation in the Cliff Swallow. *Auk,* 71: 16–35.

Evans, Charles D. 1951. A Method of Color Marking Young Waterfowl. *Jour. Wildl. Manag.,* 15: 101–103.

Friedmann, Herbert. 1922. The Weaving of the Red-billed Weaver Bird in Captivity. *Zoologica,* 2: 355–372.

——— 1927a. Testicular Asymmetry and Sex Ratio in Birds. *Biol. Bull.,* 52: 197–207.

——— 1927b. Notes on Some Argentina Birds. *Bull. Mus. Comp. Zoöl.,* 68, no. 4.

——— 1929. The Cowbirds. *A Study in the Biology of Social Parasitism.* Charles C. Thomas, Springfield, Ill.

——— 1932. The Parasitic Habit in the Ducks, a Theoretical Consideration. *Proc. U.S. Natl. Mus.,* 80: 1–7.

——— 1948. The Parasitic Cuckoos of Africa. Monograph No. 1, Washington Acad. Sci., Washington, D. C.

——— 1950. The Breeding Habits of the Weaverbirds: A Study in the Biology of Behavior Patterns. *Smiths. Rept. for 1949,* 1950: 293–316.

——— 1955. The Honey-guides. *U. S. Natl. Mus. Bull. 208.*

——— 1956. Further Data on African Parasitic Cuckoos. *Proc. U. S. Natl. Mus.,* 106: 377–408.

——— and Foster D. Smith, Jr. 1955. A Further Contribution to the Ornithology of Northeastern Venezuela. *Proc. U. S. Natl. Mus.,* 104: 463–524.

George, John L., and Robert T. Mitchell. 1948. Notes on Two Species of Calliphoridae (Diptera) Parasitizing Nestling Birds. *Auk,* 65: 549–552.

Gibb, John. 1950. The Breeding Biology of the Great and Blue Titmice. *Ibis,* 92: 507–539.
Gilbert, P. A. 1936. Some Notes on *Hypotaenidia philippensis.* *Emu,* 36: 10–13.
Gross, William A. O. 1935. The Life History Cycle of Leach's Petrel (Oceanodroma leucorhoa leucorhoa) on the Outer Sea Islands of the Bay of Fundy. *Auk,* 52: 382–399.
Gullion, Gordon W. 1954. The Reproductive Cycle of American Coots in California. *Auk,* 71: 366–412.
Haartman, Lars von. 1951. Successive Polygamy. *Behaviour,* 3: 256–274.
——— 1957. Adaptation in Hole-nesting Birds. *Evolution,* 11: 339–347.
Hale, W. G. 1956. The Lack of Territory in the Redshank, *Tringa totanus.* *Ibis,* 98: 398–400.
Hann, Harry W. 1937. Life History of the Oven-bird in Southern Michigan. *Wils. Bull.,* 49: 145–237.
——— 1940. Polyandry in the Oven-bird. *Wils. Bull.,* 52: 69–72.
——— 1941. The Cowbird at the Nest. *Wils. Bull.,* 53: 209–221.
Heinroth, O. 1928. Ehigkeit oder Keinehigkeit. *Beitr. Fortpfl.-biol. Vögel,* 4: 1–3.
Helm, Lewis G. 1955. Plastic Collars for Marking Geese. *Jour. Wildl. Manag.,* 19: 316–317.
Herrick, Francis H. 1911. Nests and Nest-building in Birds. *Jour. Animal Behavior,* 1: 159–192; 244–277; 336–373.
Hinde, R. A. 1954. The Courtship and Copulation of the Greenfinch (*Chloris chloris*). *Behaviour,* 7: 207–232.
——— 1956. The Biological Significance of the Territories of Birds. *Ibis,* 98: 340–369.
Hollom, P. A. D. 1952. *The Popular Handbook of British Birds.* H. F. & G. Witherby, London.
Hoyt, J. Southgate Y. 1948. Observations on Nesting Associates. *Auk,* 65: 188–196.
Jickling, Lee. 1940. Mr. Bob-white Sticks it Out. *Jack-Pine Warbler,* 18: 114–115.
Johnston, David W. 1956. The Annual Reproductive Cycle of the California Gull. I, II. *Condor,* 58: 134–162; 206–221.
Joubert, H. J. 1932. Commensalism Among Birds. *Ostrich,* 3: 59–60.
Kabat, Cyril, Irven O. Buss, and Roland K. Meyer. 1948. The Use of Ovulated Follicles in Determining Eggs Laid by the Ring-necked Pheasant. *Jour. Wildl. Manag.,* 12: 399–416.
Keast, J. A., and A. J. Marshall. 1954. The Influence of Drought and Rainfall on Reproduction in Australian Desert Birds. *Proc. Zool. Soc. London,* 124: 493–499.
Kendeigh, S. Charles. 1940. Factors Affecting Length of Incubation. *Auk,* 57: 499–513.
——— 1952. Parental Care and Its Evolution in Birds. *Illinois Biol. Monog., 22,* Univ. Illinois Press, Urbana.
———, Theodore C. Kramer, and Frances Hamerstrom. 1956. Variations in Egg Characteristics of the House Wren. *Auk,* 73: 42–65.
Kluijver, H. N. 1951. The Population Ecology of the Great Tit, *Parus m. major* L. *Ardea,* 39: 1–135.
Kobayashi, Hideshi. 1952. Effects of Hormonic Steroids on Molting and Broodiness in the Canary. *Annot. Zool. Japonenses,* 25: 128–134.
Lack, David. 1935. Territory and Polygamy in a Bishop-bird, *Euplectes hordeacea hordeacea* (Linn.). *Ibis,* 1935: 817–836.
——— 1940. Pair-formation in Birds. *Condor,* 42: 269–286.

Lack, David. 1947–1948. The Significance of Clutch-size. *Ibis,* 89: 302–352; 90: 25–45.

——— 1954. *The Natural Regulation of Animal Numbers.* Oxford Univ. Press, London.

———, and John T. Emlen, Jr. 1939. Observations on Breeding Behavior in Tricolored Red-wings. *Condor,* 41: 225–230.

Lack, David, and Elizabeth Lack. 1951. The Breeding Biology of the Swift Apus Apus. *Ibis,* 93: 501–546.

Lack, David, and E. T. Silva. 1949. The Weight of Nestling Robins. *Ibis,* 91: 64–78.

Laskey, Amelia R. 1943. The Nesting of Bluebirds Banded as Nestlings. *Bird-Banding,* 14: 39–43.

——— 1947. Evidence of Polyandry at a Bluebird Nest. *Auk,* 64: 314–315.

——— 1950. Cowbird Behavior. *Wils. Bull.,* 62: 157–174.

Lawrence, Louise de Kiriline. 1953. Nesting Life and Behaviour of the Red-eyed Vireo. *Canad. Field-Nat.,* 67: 47–77.

McIlhenny, E. A. 1940. Sex Ratio in Wild Birds. *Auk,* 57: 85–93.

Maclaren, P. I. R. 1950. Bird—Ant Nesting Associations. *Ibis,* 92: 564–566.

MacQueen, Peggy Muirhead. 1950. Territory and Song in the Least Flycatcher. *Wils. Bull.,* 62: 194–205.

Marshall, A. J. 1952. Non-breeding Among Arctic Birds. *Ibis,* 94: 310–333.

Mayaud, Noël. 1950. Biologie de la Reproduction. In Grassé's *Traité de Zoologie.* Vol. 15, Oiseaux. Masson et Cie, Paris, pp. 539–653.

Mayr, Ernst. 1935. Bernard Altum and the Territory Theory. *Proc. Linn. Soc. N. Y.,* 45–46: 24–38.

——— 1939. The Sex Ratio in Wild Birds. *Amer. Nat.,* 73: 156–179.

Middleton, Douglas S., and Bette J. Johnston. 1956. A Study of the Phoebe in Macomb County. *Jack-Pine Warbler,* 34: 63–66.

Moreau, R. E. 1940. Numerical Data on African Birds' Behaviour at the Nest .... *Ibis,* 1940: 234–248.

——— 1941. A Contribution to the Breeding Biology of the Palm-Swift, *Cypselus Parvus. Jour. East Africa & Uganda Nat. Hist. Soc.,* 15: 154–170.

——— 1944. Clutch-size: A Comparative Study, with Special Reference to African Birds. *Ibis,* 86: 286–347.

——— 1949. The Breeding of a Paradise Flycatcher. *Ibis,* 91: 256–279.

——— 1950. The Breeding Seasons of African Birds—1. Land Birds. *Ibis,* 92: 223–267.

——— and W. M. Moreau. 1940. Incubation and Fledging Periods of African Birds. *Auk,* 57: 313–325.

Neff, Johnson A. 1944. A Protracted Incubation Period in the Mourning Dove. *Condor,* 46: 243.

Nero, Robert W., and John T. Emlen, Jr. 1951. An Experimental Study of Territorial Behavior in Breeding Red-winged Blackbirds. *Condor,* 53: 105–116.

Nethersole-Thompson, Caroline, and Desmond Nethersole-Thompson. 1942. Egg-shell Disposal by Birds. *Brit. Birds,* 35: 162–169; 190–200; 214–223; 241–250.

——— 1943. Nest-site Selection by Birds. *Brit. Birds,* 37: 70–74; 88–94; 108–113.

Neunzig, Rudolf. 1929a. Zum Brutparasitismus der Viduinen. *Jour. f. Ornith.,* 77: 1–21.

——— 1929b. Beiträge zur Kenntnis der Ploceiden I. *Beitr. Fortpfl.-biol. Vögel,* 5: 7–17.

Newton, Alfred. 1896. Eggs. In A. Newton and Hans Gadow, *A Dictionary of Birds.* Adam and Charles Black, London, pp. 182–192.

Nice, Margaret Morse. 1937–1943. Studies in the Life History of the Song Sparrow. I, II. *Trans. Linn. Soc. N. Y.,* 4, 1937: vi + 247 pp.; 6, 1943: viii + 329 pp.

——— 1938. Notes on Two Nests of the Eastern Mourning Dove. *Auk,* 55: 95–97.

——— 1941. The Role of Territory in Bird Life. *Amer. Midl. Nat.,* 26: 441–487.

——— 1949. The Laying Rhythm of Cowbirds. *Wils. Bull.,* 61: 231–234.

——— 1953. The Question of Ten-Day Incubation Periods. *Wils. Bull.,* 65: 81–93.

——— 1954a. Problems of Incubation Periods in North American Birds. *Condor,* 56: 173–197.

——— 1954b. Incubation Periods Throughout the Ages. *Centaurus,* 3: 311–359.

——— 1957. Nesting Success in Altricial Birds. *Auk,* 74: 305–321.

Nickell, Walter P. 1951. Studies of Habitats, Territory, and Nests of the Eastern Goldfinch. *Auk,* 68: 447–470.

Noble, G. K., and D. S. Lehrman. 1940. Egg Recognition by the Laughing Gull. *Auk,* 57: 22–43.

Nolan, Val, Jr. 1955. Invertebrate Nest Associates of the Prairie Warbler. *Auk,* 72: 55–61.

Odum, Eugene P. 1941. Annual Cycle of the Black-capped Chickadee—1. *Auk,* 58: 314–333.

——— 1944. Circulatory Congestion as a Possible Factor Regulating Incubation Behavior. *Wils. Bull.,* 56: 48–49.

——— and Frank A. Pitelka. 1939. Storm Mortality in a Winter Starling Roost. *Auk,* 56: 451–455.

Pettingill, Olin Sewall, Jr. 1956. *A Laboratory and Field Manual of Ornithology.* 3rd ed. Burgess Publ. Co., Minneapolis.

Phillips, Charles L. 1887. Egg-laying extraordinary in Colaptes auratus. *Auk,* 4: 346.

Pohlman, A. G. 1919. Concerning the Causal Factor in the Hatching of the Chick, with Particular Reference to the Musculus Complexus. *Anat. Rec.,* 17: 89–104.

Preston, F. W. 1946. Nesting Heights of Birds Building in Shrubs. *Ecology,* 27: 87–91.

——— 1953. The Shapes of Birds' Eggs. *Auk,* 70: 160–182.

——— 1957. Pigmentation of Eggs: Variation in the Clutch Sequence. *Auk,* 74: 28–41.

——— and R. T. Norris. 1947. Nesting Heights of Breeding Birds. *Ecology,* 28: 241–273.

Preston, F. W., and E. J. Preston. 1953. Variation of the Shapes of Birds' Eggs within the Clutch. *Ann. Carnegie Mus.,* 33: 129–139.

Putnam, Loren S. 1949. The Life History of the Cedar Waxwing. *Wils. Bull.,* 61: 141–182.

Rand, A. L. 1942. Nest Sanitation and an Alleged Releaser. *Auk,* 59: 404–409.

Reed, Chester A. 1904. *North American Birds Eggs.* Doubleday, Page and Co., New York.

Richdale, L. E. 1942. The Royal Albatross, *Diomedea epomophora sandfordi.* Dunedin, New Zealand, 23 pp. (Published privately.)

——— 1949. The Effect of Age on Laying Dates, Size of Eggs, and Size of Clutch in the Yellow-eyed Penguin. *Wils. Bull.,* 61: 91–98.

——— 1950. The Pre-egg Stage in the Albatross Family. Dunedin, New Zealand, 92 pp. (Published privately.)

——— 1952. Post-egg Period in Albatrosses. Dunedin, New Zealand, 166 pp. (Published privately.)

Richdale, L. E. 1954. The Starvation Theory in Albatrosses. *Auk,* 71: 239–252.

Ritter, William Emerson. 1938. *The California Woodpecker and I.* Univ. California Press, Berkeley.

Robinson, Angus. 1945. The Application of "Territory and the Breeding Cycle" to some Australian Birds. *Emu,* 45: 100–109.

———— 1949. The Biological Significance of Bird Song in Australia. *Emu,* 48: 291–315.

Romanoff, Alexis L., and Anastasia J. Romanoff. 1949. *The Avian Egg.* John Wiley & Sons, New York.

Ryves, B. H. 1944. Nest-construction by Birds. *Brit. Birds,* 37: 182–188; 207–209.

Schaefer, Ernst. 1953. Contribution to the Life History of the Swallow-tanager. *Auk,* 70: 403–460.

Skead, C. J. 1947. A Study of the Cape Weaver. (*Hyphantornis capensis olivaceus.*) *Ostrich,* 18: 1–42.

———— 1950. A Study of the African Hoopoe. *Ibis,* 92: 434–461.

Skutch, Alexander F. 1935. Helpers at the Nest. *Auk,* 52: 257–273.

———— 1945a. Incubation and Nestling Periods of Central American Birds. *Auk,* 62: 8–37.

———— 1945b. Life History of the Blue-throated Green Motmot. *Auk,* 62: 489–517.

———— 1945c. Studies of Central American Redstarts. *Wils. Bull.,* 57: 217–242.

———— 1947. Life History of the Turquoise-browed Motmot. *Auk,* 64: 201–217.

———— 1949. Do Tropical Birds Rear as Many Young as They Can Nourish? *Ibis,* 91:430–458.

———— 1950a. The Nesting Seasons of Central American Birds in Relation to Climate and Food Supply. *Ibis,* 92: 185–222.

———— 1950b. Outline for an Ecological Life History of a Bird, Based upon the Song Tanager *Ramphocelus passerinii costaricensis. Ecology,* 31: 464–469.

———— 1951. Congeneric Species of Birds Nesting Together in Central America. *Condor,* 53: 3–15.

———— 1952. On the Hour of Laying and Hatching of Birds' Eggs. *Ibis,* 94: 49–61.

———— 1954. Life Histories of Central American Birds. *Pacific Coast Avifauna,* No. 31.

———— 1957. The Incubation Patterns of Birds. *Ibis,* 99: 69–93.

Smith, Stuart. 1943. The Instinctive Nature of Nest Sanitation. Part II. *Brit. Birds,* 36: 186–188.

Southern, H. N. 1954. Mimicry in Cuckoos' Eggs. In *Evolution as a Process,* ed. by J. Huxley *et al.* George Allen & Unwin, London.

Sowls, Lyle L. 1955. Prairie Ducks. A Study of Their Behavior, Ecology and Management. Wildlife Management Inst., Washington, D. C.

Stoddard, Herbert L. 1931. *The Bobwhite Quail.* Charles Scribner's Sons, New York.

Stokes, Allen W. 1950. Breeding Behavior of the Goldfinch. *Wils. Bull.,* 62: 107–127.

Summers-Smith, D. 1955. Display of the House Sparrow *Passer domesticus. Ibis,* 97: 296–305.

Sutton, George Miksch. 1932. Deposition of Eggs in Time of Snow-storm. *Auk,* 49: 366–367.

Swynnerton, C. F. M. 1916. On the Coloration of the Mouths and Eggs of Birds—1. The Mouths of Birds. *Ibis,* 1916: 264–294.

Thomson, A. Landsborough. 1950. Factors Determining the Breeding Seasons of Birds: An Introductory Review. *Ibis,* 92: 173–184 (and see p. 650).

Thomson, Donald F. 1934. Some Adaptations for the Disposal of Faeces. The Hygiene of the Nest in Australian Birds. *Proc. Zool. Soc. London,* 1934: 701–707.

Thomson, J. Arthur. 1923. *The Biology of Birds.* Macmillan Co., New York.

Tucker, B. W. 1943. Brood-Patches and the Physiology of Incubation. *Brit. Birds,* 37: 22–28.

Van Someren, V. G. L. 1956. Days with Birds: Studies of Habits of Some East African Birds. *Fieldiana: Zoology,* 38.

Van Tyne, Josselyn. 1929. The Life History of the Toucan *Ramphastos brevicarinatus. Univ. Mich. Mus. Zool. Misc. Publ., No. 19.*

———— 1944. The Sex Ratio in Wilson's Snipe. *Wils. Bull.,* 56: 170–171.

Wadkins, L. A. 1948. Dyeing Birds for Identification. *Jour. Wildl. Manag.,* 12: 388–391.

Wagner, H. O. 1957. Variation in Clutch Size at Different Latitudes. *Auk,* 74: 243–250.

Walkinshaw, Lawrence H. 1938. Life History Studies of the Eastern Goldfinch. *Jack-Pine Warbler,* 16: 3–11.

———— 1941. The Prothonotary Warbler, A Comparison of Nesting Conditions in Tennessee and Michigan. *Wils. Bull.,* 53: 3–21.

———— 1949. Twenty-five Eggs Apparently Laid by a Cowbird. *Wils. Bull.,* 61: 82–85.

———— 1953. Life-History of the Prothonotary Warbler. *Wils. Bull.,* 65: 152–168.

Weaver, Richard Lee. 1939. Winter Observations and a Study of the Nesting of English Sparrows. *Bird-Banding,* 10: 73–79.

Williamson, Kenneth, 1945. The Relation between the Duration of Hatching and the Incubation Period. *Ibis,* 87: 280–282.

Wright, Philip L., and Margaret H. Wright. 1944. The Reproductive Cycle of the Male Red-winged Blackbird. *Condor,* 46: 46–59.

Yamashina, Marquis. 1938. A Sociable Breeding Habit Among Timaliine Birds. *IX Congr. Ornith. Internatl., 1938:* 453–456.

Young, Howard. 1951. Territorial Behavior in the Eastern Robin. *Proc. Linn. Soc. N. Y.,* 62: 1–37.

11. Social relations

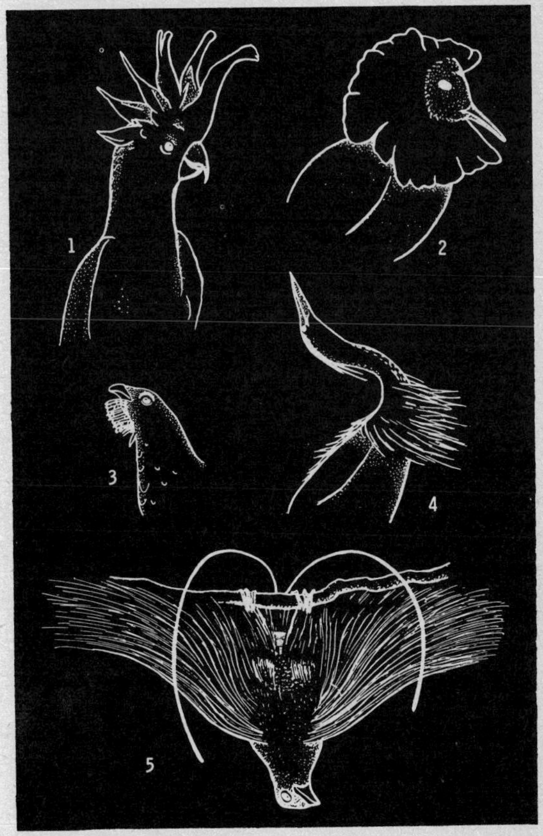

Fig. 1. Various specialized forms of feather signals: (1) crest, (2) ruff, (3) chin-growth, (4) throat-plumes, (5) flank-plumes. (Courtesy of Desmond Morris and the Editor of *Behaviour.*)

SO UNIVERSAL is sociality among birds that it may attend nearly all of a bird's activities. Several phases of social behavior have been discussed already in relation to singing, feeding, and breeding. In reading this chapter, as well as other works on the social relations of birds, the student would do well to bear in mind the following statement made by James Fisher (1954): "Sociality, territory, aggressiveness, courtship, concealment, exhibitionism, submissiveness, threat—all are dogged by their own contradictions and opposites; and the art of understanding bird behaviour . . . is the art of understanding the compromise or balance between different drives."

Dominance

Schjelderup-Ebbe (1935) first used the word *dominance* in describing his observations on social hierarchies in birds. He concluded that within a flock composed of a single species there exists a definite order of social distinction, and that between any two birds one invariably has precedence over the other. Noble (1939) later commented that "no two hens, or roosters, can remain very long together in the barnyard without establishing which is superior or inferior to the other. In a flock, a dominant hen may peck a subordinate without fear of retaliation. The latter may be dominant over a third, and the third over a fourth." Allee (1936) reported that this social despotism, or dominance, is "relatively firmly fixed" in chickens, but that in other species (e.g., pigeons, canaries) the social order is less firmly fixed and "subordinate individuals normally 'win' a minority of their pair contacts." Shoemaker (1939) found that the position of canaries in the social hierarchy fluctuated with breeding activity and that birds "subordinate in neutral territory become dominant in their nesting territory." Many later workers have published findings on the "peck-order" or "peck-right" within flocks of other species and among different species in mixed flocks.

Noble (1939) pointed out that it is necessary to distinguish between social dominance and sexual dominance: the social dominance drive is continuous, whereas the sex drive has a hormonal basis and is cyclic. He contrasted the two by stating: "Social dominance is directed toward objects with an uncanny eye for detail. The social position of the newcomer is learned by experience and a bird second or third in a pecking order is distinguished at once even though we can see no difference between them. In striking contrast, the more emotional behavior, namely, that activated by the sex drive, tends to ignore detail although sex differences in color may be recognized." This sexual dominance theory "postulates that at pair-formation the male in some sense impresses or overpowers the female, sometimes through aggressive display" (Lack, 1940b: 278). Lack added that the aggressive behavior shown by English Robins at pair formation "is not related to dominance in any way; it is sporadic, soon dies away and probably results from the maladjustment of the formerly isolated individuals to the new situation in which a second individual is tolerated." Moreover, contradictory evidence on the nature of sexual dominance has been presented by different authors studying the same species, and many ornithologists now feel that the "aggressive" nature of bird behavior has been overemphasized and misunderstood. Lack suggested that the male Song Sparrow dominates the female "in the sexual sense" but that she dominates him "in the social sense." However, Nice (1943: 198) commented that she did "not see any meaning in 'sexual domination' in regard to the Song Sparrow; during the preliminary, building and laying periods the female is as eager for copulation as her mate, and often more eager." She added: "If the male drives or pecks or pounces on the female, these activities are his signals that he is ready for pair formation or copulation. The female signals by posturing, trilling, etc. We do not have to say that one set of actions expresses dominance and the other submission."

It has now been demonstrated for a number of species that injecting male sex hormone will induce male sexual behavior (dominance, display, song, etc.) in adult females or in immature birds of either sex. Thus the different roles assumed by male and female during pair formation and courtship appear to be determined largely by the relative balance between androgens and estrogens in the two sexes. The resultant behavior patterns effect a mutual stimulation which serves to co-ordinate the reproductive activities. This interaction between individuals led Darling (1952) to state that "the basic element of *stimulation* in avian sociality seems to be psychological and psycho-physiological."

Relations Between Parents and Young

Parent–young recognition is a reciprocal social relationship that has been studied by several workers. Collias (1952) presented data on the domestic chicken in which "social responsiveness in the newly-hatched chick requires the presence of the basal portions of the cerebral hemispheres." The chick, as well as other precocial and some altricial species, gives distress calls when isolated from the parent or the rest of the brood, or when cold, hungry, or restrained. Pleasure notes are given in response to contact and to an optimum air temperature. Recently hatched incubator chicks paid "no apparent attention to mounted specimens of hens," and, in fact, a chick placed "beneath a mounted hen may desert this foster mother for a warm heating pad placed a few inches away." At the same time, distress calls of the chicks stimulate clucking by the hen and the chicks respond to the clucking by giving pleasure notes. This positive reaction to clucking may occur within 5 to 10 minutes after hatching, but Collias also found that the frequency of distress calls was decreased 85 per cent simply by clinking two glass bowls together. Such initial responses to normal or experimental stimuli are strengthened or modified by social experience. Reminiscent of the discussion of imprinting (Chapter 4), Collias discovered that the usual response of a chick to a moving object during the first few days of life is to follow the object (see also Ramsay, 1951). Chicks hand-reared for 10 days responded slowly or not at all to normal food calls after being placed with a hen.

Ramsay (1951) studied familial recognition by means of a series of experiments involving Muscovy and Mallard ducks, domestic chickens, turkeys, and several species of game birds. He found that the factors determining specific recognition were largely acquired rather than being "innate." Thus a 5-year-old Muscovy Duck that had hatched 13 White Rock chicks would not then accept a brood of Muscovy ducklings, even though in previous years she had "mothered several broods of Muscovy ducklings, Mallard ducklings, chicks, and a mixed brood of chicks and ducklings." Ramsay's observations of the reactions of a variety of incubator-hatched birds to hens and Muscovy and Mallard ducks also indicated, especially for ducklings, that the "innate perceptory pattern of the parent companion is non-specific or indeterminate." In general, the domestic chicks exhibited an innate ability to respond to the "biologically correct object," but their acquired bond was stronger than the inherent one. Parent-young recognition among the birds studied by Ramsay in all probability involves auditory cues, color, size, and form; variation in any one of these "upsets the recognition behavior of adults and young."

A red spot on the mandible of adult Herring Gulls apparently aids in stimulating the feeding response in newly hatched gull chicks. Tinbergen and Perdeck (1950) employed a series of cardboard models of heads of adult gulls in studying the role of the red spot as a signal or releaser. They found that positive pecking responses were reduced about 75 per cent when the red spot was absent or when it was displaced from the bill to the forehead, but that movement and degree of contrast between bill color and the spot (whether red or some other color) were also of considerable importance in eliciting positive responses. The adults will feed strange young the same age as their own for a couple of days after hatching, but after that the adults attack, and even kill, any strange young that come into their territory. A similar pattern has been found in the behavior of coots, in which the first-hatched bird in a brood may be a week older than the youngest bird. The downy young of the American Coot (*Fulica americana*) undergo several abrupt plumage changes. Gullion (1954) stated that the parent coots seem to recognize their own brood by the color pattern of the majority of the young. The oldest birds become subject to occasional attacks when their down begins to bleach, and "as more young progressively turn light, the parents accept the light-fronted birds as theirs, and the attacks are directed at the younger birds, still in their natal down." Alley and Boyd (1950) found that parent European Coots (*F. atra*) will feed and brood foreign young similar in age to their own young until they are about 12 days old. After that time, the parents attack all strange young coots. It would appear that young coots and some gulls and terns, for their own safety, "must" be able to learn to recognize their own parents, or, at least, any hostile signs displayed by adult birds; and Alley and Boyd found that young European Coots do learn to avoid adults in an attack posture, and later beg only from their parents.

Aside from bodily contact with nest mates, the first "social" activity (in the very broadest sense) of altricial birds is the act of gaping for food. The gaping response may be elicited by a variety of nonvisual stimuli: an adult alighting on the nest, adult call notes, "squeaking" or nest-tapping by an observer, etc. Gaping may also occur spontaneously in birds hatched in isolation. The gaping of newly hatched altricial birds is in the vertical direction, without reference to the position of the adult. Tinbergen (1939a) conducted experiments with nestling European Blackbirds in order to learn something about the recognition marks that serve to direct the gaping response toward the bill of the adult. This directive response is not seen until the nestlings are about 10 or 11 days old. Tinbergen concluded that the young recognize the head of the adult by the following features: the head changes the torso's outline, it is situated higher than any other part of the body, it comes closer to the young, it has a diameter of about one-third of the torso, and it is marked off from the torso by an indentation. When and how the young actually learn to recognize their own parents remains unknown. We have observed that nestling cuckoos (*Coccyzus*), *Empidonax* flycatchers, some wood-warblers, and some finches taken from the nest for hand-rearing often beg for food from other nestlings or fledglings, either of the same or another species. The primary stimulus for begging in such instances seems to be the movement of another bird at a slightly higher elevation.

Most of the available evidence also suggests that the adults of many altricial species (e.g., doves, hawks, herons, passerines) do not recognize their own nestlings (Nice, 1943: 239). This has been demonstrated by a number of workers who have transferred nestlings from one nest to another. The new nestlings, either of the same or a different species, are generally accepted and fed. It is well known that many New World passerines accept and rear young cowbirds and that Old World species accept young cuckoos. A different type of evidence is obtained from observations on the reaction of adult Horned Larks (*Eremophila alpestris*), Song Sparrows, and other passerine species to their own banded young. The adults apparently see the aluminum or colored band as extraneous material in the nest and attempt to remove it. If the young are small enough, the adult may be successful in carrying the banded young away from the nest.

A different type of parent–young relationship is found among certain colonial nesting birds (e.g., some penguins, Shelduck, Sandwich Tern, flamingos) in which the adults feed their own young for only a few days, after which the young herd together and are fed by many adults. Such an aggregation of young birds is called a crèche. Young flamingo chicks leave their nests when 3 or 4 days old and join a crèche in which all of the young are approximately the same age. The adult flamingos "seem to respond to the begging signals of any and all chicks within reach" (Allen, 1956). Allen also reported a "curious form of cooperative reaction in a flamingo *crèche*," in which there is a simultaneous movement of each chick away from any source of danger.

Leadership–followership relationships play a role in the learning of young birds. The downy young of gallinaceous species, for example, run to the hen in response either to auditory or visual stimuli when she pecks at food on the ground. (For other examples, see Collias, 1952.)

Relationships Between the Pair

The types of bonds formed between breeding birds were discussed in Chapter 10, but certain associated phenomena were left for treatment here.

Successful pair formation would appear to require the ability for species recognition and for sex recognition. Tinbergen (1939b) defined three groups based on recognition marks and behavior patterns which lead to pair formation. Nice (1943: 204) summarized these as follows: (1) species with marked sexual dimorphism that discriminate the sexes at the first reaction; (2) species with little or no dimorphism where the more active sex proclaims its sex and induces the other to do the same; (3) species where the process of sex recognition may be prolonged. The fundamental pattern concerns a difference in behavior of the two sexes. Usually both a first and a second reaction are involved, and there may be a more elaborate chain reaction as the sexes respond to each other's "signals." Nice has put it this way: "One animal—usually the male—*proclaims its sex and status;* according to the response to its display, it then reacts to the newcomer as a rival, an indifferent object or a potential mate." Thus the first reaction of a male Song Sparrow (the actor) in breeding condition is to fly at any intruder. If the intruder (the reactor) is another male Song Sparrow in breeding condition, the reactor displays and the actor then exhibits its second reaction by fighting the intruder. If, however, the intruder is a female Song Sparrow in breeding condition, she remains and gives special call notes, in which case the second reaction of the male is to court her. "The actor's signals are his display: his evident possession of a territory in many cases, his song, bright colors, and special gestures. These serve as a warning to other members of the same sex and an invitation to a mate. The reactor, according to its sex or condition, shows its signals—challenge, avoidance, or approach."

Experiments conducted with certain dimorphic species suggest that sex recognition occurs at the first reaction: e.g., some ducks, pheasants, Gould's manakin, Yellowthroat, Redwinged Blackbird. Noble and Vogt (1935), for example, placed mounted birds within the territories (and cages) of male Yellowthroats and Redwinged Blackbirds, and found that fully adult males usually attacked male mounts of their own species but copulated with female mounts. Yearling blackbirds, however, copulated with "nearly every species presented," including Blue Jay, Wood Thrush, Meadowlark, and male Cardinal. In some species (e.g., Northern Phalarope, Snow Bunting), recognition occurs not at the first reaction but shortly thereafter when the birds meet at close range. In still a third group (e.g., gannets, Ruffed Grouse, Common Tern, British Robin), in which both sexes display in the same way, there is a "much longer undifferentiated reaction of the sexes." In writing of the Common Tern, Tinbergen (1939b) said that "males and females both show exactly the same display during the first phase of their courtship, which may last for days, and this absence of a difference in behavior, together with the absence of morphological differences, probably makes it impossible for the birds to distinguish between the sexes."

Lack (1940b) doubted that "sex recognition" was involved at all at the time of pair formation because a bird's recognition of its own species is related to different external signs or releasers depending upon the particular phase of behavior concerned. He said: "The external situation leading to pair-formation is markedly different from that leading to copulation," and that "after the pair has formed, 'sex recognition' is a quite different problem; it is that of distinguishing the mate individually from all others of her species." Individual recognition of the mate by sight or sound has now been shown for several species. Noble (1936), for example, attached a black "moustache" to a female Yellow-shafted Flicker and found that the male no longer recognized her, but attacked her as he would another male. Lack thought that the major stimulus for copulation in most species is that "the female keeps still." However, various postural and other signals precede or accompany copulation in many species: the head may be lowered; the beak may be pointed upward; the wings may be drooped; the tail may be depressed, raised, or spread. In some species (e.g., Flicker, Song Sparrow) the female may give special call notes as an invitation to copulate.

Bird Display

Four general types of display have been described as being associated with secondary sexual differentiation in birds. According to Lack (1940b), the first three types have "all doubtless contributed to the evolution of brightly colored areas in male, and less commonly, female, birds, since one can find species in which a colored area is used exclusively in one or the other of these types of display." This is a classification of display behavior based on function, and the same display or ceremony may be used during several different parts of the breeding cycle. Moreover, these display types or behavior patterns are based on Huxley's (1938) stimulating discussion of the functions of color in birds and other animals. Few authors have had occasion to employ all of Huxley's detailed classification of color characters, and some of his terms have been used by others in a wider, or narrower, sense than originally defined.

Antaposematic Display

This is threat display between rivals, especially males. Armstrong (1947: 124) and others have used Huxley's more general term *aposematic* in place of the longer term used here. Aposematic coloration (and display) is that which serves *any* function involving "warning or threat"; antaposematic refers specifically to such coloration used in threat or dominance *against rivals.* The immediate object of fighting and antaposematic display between rival males is the acquisition and maintenance of a territory; secondarily, the male acquires a mate. Display often serves to reduce the instances of actual fighting and bodily contact during territorial disputes. In his discussion of the American Coot, Gullion (1952) described a type of display which he called *charging:* "In this display the neck is extended forward on a horizontal plane, the tail and wings are held in the normal position, but the ruff is erected and the frontal shield is prominent." He found that all species of ducks and small geese in the area react to the display and that other coots "often take evasive action while still 100 feet from the charging bird." The *song-spread* of the male Redwinged Blackbird, which appears "to be directed mainly toward other males," involves both song and postural elements: "Usually the head is lifted or thrust forward, the tail is spread and lowered, the wings are spread, and the epaulets are raised" (Nero, 1956). Nice (1937: 57) described display of male Song Sparrows during territory establishment as follows: "The invader—puffed out into the shape of a ball, and often holding one wing straight up in the air and fluttering it—sings constantly but rather softly, the songs being given in rapid succession and often being incomplete. The defender, silent and with shoulders hunched in menacing attitude, closely follows every move of the other bird." At the approach of another male, a male Snow Bunting on territory "turns his whole body, head foremost, in the direction of the newcomer, lowers his head between the shoulders" and gives a special call note. Many icterids (e.g., grackles, cowbirds, Redwinged and Brewer's blackbirds) engage in *bill-pointing* (also called *bill-tilting*), in which the bill is pointed nearly straight upward and the body plumage is compressed. Bill-pointing, like many other types of display, may also be used to intimidate males and females of other species. Flight songs are a type of antaposematic display in many passerines (see Chapter 5) and some nonpasserine species, such as the Redshank (*Totanus totanus*), Lapwing (*Vanellus vanellus*), Common Snipe (*Capella gallinago*), and Common Nighthawk (*Chordeiles minor*). Special flights with little or no vocal accompaniment may also serve as recognitional threats to trespassing males: "The oscillating flight of the male Ring Plover (*Charadrius hiaticula*), or the slow flapping 'butterfly flight' of the Oystercatcher (*Haematopus ostralegus*)" (Huxley, 1938).

Gamosematic Display

This assists the members of a pair to find each other. It "involves sexual selection in the narrower Darwinian sense, since gamosematic characters are those which influence the female in selection of a mate at pair-formation" (Lack, 1940b). The female may locate the male by means of visual or auditory clues: color, special behavior, song, or song flight. Noble *et al.* (1938) described the methods by which male Black-crowned Night Herons attract mates. Upon their return to the breeding grounds, the males first select territories, after which they perform two special types of display. In the *twig ceremony* the male stands near or over a crude nest platform, holds a stick in its bill, and loudly snaps the bill on the stick while the head is moved rhythmically up and down. The second display is the *snap-hiss ceremony,* in which the male, either while standing on the nest platform or while moving about the tree, "takes two or three steps forward, halts, arches the back, lowers the head until the bill is nearly as low as its feet and then while raising one foot produces a click or snapping sound in its throat, immediately followed by a prolonged hiss." This performance is repeated over and over. Two additional types of display are performed when a female approaches the male. Tinbergen (1939b) believed that the advertising song of the Snow Bunting served not only to warn rivals but also to "attract potential mates from afar." When a female entered the male's territory, his first reaction (the threatening attitude) was the same as when another male approached. If the female remained despite the male's threatening behavior, he responded with the second reaction: "He assumed an erect, strangely stretched attitude, spreading his tail widely and spreading the conspicuously colored wings backward and downward. In this attitude he directed the piebald surface of back and tail toward the female and then ran quickly away from her. Having run for some meters, he abruptly turned, came back without any display, and then repeated the performance."

Epigamic Display

Epigamic display, occurring between the members of a pair, synchronizes the sexes for copulation. It has also been called "sexual display," and, to add to the confusion, the term has been used to embrace all types of display which bring the sexes together and which lead to copulation, i.e., both gamosematic and epigamic display. To be sure, in some species practicing communal display (e.g., Ruff, Blackcock, Sage Grouse, some manakins, some birds-of-

Fig. 2. The Cutthroat Finch (*Amadina fasciata*). Left: male in normal posture. Center: male in courtship posture. Right: female. (Courtesy of Desmond Morris.)

paradise), essentially the same display or ceremony may bring the sexes together and promote copulation. In many species, however, entirely different behavior patterns are involved. Thus Tinbergen reported that on the first day that he saw a female Snow Bunting pick up nesting material, "she did not flee when the male, as on previous days, approached her, but adopted an attitude which was never seen before: she kept her back quite flat and horizontal, pointed her bill upward and lifted the tail." The male responded by mounting the female for copulation. American Coots build display platforms on which copulation often takes place. Gullion (1954) gave the following description: "After a moment of chasing, the female moved into the cat-tails with the male close behind. As she crossed the platform she remained silent but arched and slapped the platform with one foot. Still arched, she settled down on the platform, in a squat with her head under the water. The male mounted her and started giving a closely spaced *kurk, kurk, kurk*. . . . She now raised her head out of the water, he reared back, apparently hanging onto her back with his claws as copulation took place."

Morris (1954) described the "courtship dance" of the male Zebra Finch (*Poephila guttata*), which involves three different elements: auditory, static-visual, and dynamic-visual. A "rhythmic, pivoting dance" along a branch is accompanied by song and a characteristic courtship posture, in which the crown feathers are strongly depressed while the white belly feathers and the spotted flank feathers are fluffed out. The position of the feet is changed as the male swings his body from side to side and the tail is twisted out of its normal position so that the black and white bands of the upper tail coverts are displayed toward the female at any point in the dance. The female responds to this dance by bending her legs and lowering her body in the horizontal plane, followed by a rapid vibration of her tail in the vertical plane. Copulation then takes place.

It is pertinent here to discuss "courtship feeding" even though it is not always associated with copulation. Lack (1940a) and Armstrong (1947) have summarized information on those groups of birds in which the male offers food to the female during the courtship period, during incubation, or, less commonly, even when the pair has young in the nest. Inasmuch as the main function of courtship feeding is not the food that is exchanged, Lack suggested that it be classified as a type of "symbolic" display "in which an act normally playing some other part in bird behavior is introduced into display." Lack supposed that "feeding may have been introduced into the sexual cycle through an extension back into an earlier phase of the cycle of the habit of feeding the female during incubation," but Armstrong (1947: 44) felt that the "inference may be hazarded that courtship feeding did not arise from the habit of feeding the incubating mate but vice versa." Be that as it may, in nearly all known instances (exception: *Turnix*) it is the male that presents the food. In general, the female adopts both the posture and the call notes similar to those of young birds begging for food. Courtship feeding occurs in genera in which the female alone or both sexes incubate, but primarily only in those in which the sexes remain together throughout the breeding season. Courtship feeding immediately preceding (and perhaps as a necessary stimulus for) or during copulation has been recorded for such widely divergent species as the European Bittern, Laughing Gull, Herring Gull, Rock Dove, Yellow-billed Cuckoo, Roadrunner, British Nuthatch, Red-backed Shrike, and some Galápagos finches. In many species (see Lack, 1940a) courtship feeding is not specifically associated with copulation but primarily with the incubation period, in which case, of course, it falls within the category of postnuptial display.

The manner of presenting food varies among the different groups of birds: in passerine birds there is usually a simple transfer of food from the male to the female, but waxwings may pass the food back and forth, and in cardueline weaverbirds the male regurgitates the food to the female; the males of some birds of prey pass food to the female in mid-air; the male Herring Gull regurgitates the food on to the ground in front of the female. Some species engage in *mock feeding* (symbolic feeding), in which no food is exchanged but the elaborate behavior pattern resembles actual courtship feeding. Courtship feeding and its several modifications, then, may serve as a stimulus for copulation or it may function to maintain the pair-bond throughout the breeding season, perhaps even longer in some species. A few instances of courtship feeding in winter have been recorded.

Various forms of "billing," "fencing," and "bill-sparring," etc., have been referred to as incipient courtship feeding because there is "but a small step from the contact of bills to the transfer of food" (Armstrong, 1947: 43). Grebes, herons, puffins, guillemots, pigeons, kingfishers, woodpeckers, waxwings, thrushes, corvids, and fringillids may engage in some form of mutual bill stimulation either during the courtship period or even throughout the entire breeding season.

Symbolic nest-building is practiced by some birds (e.g., grebes, cormorants, lapwings, mockingbirds, Redwinged Blackbirds) during the courtship period. Either one or both sexes may pick up, manipulate, or carry nesting materials. The male Song Sparrow normally does not aid in building the nest but during the prenuptial and "preliminary" stages both the male and female often pick up pieces of bark or grass and fly "with them at random, soon dropping them" (Nice, 1943: 178).

Postnuptial Display

This is any display or ceremony that takes place between the sexes after copulation has ceased and incubation has begun. The display may have the same form or pattern as the epigamic display, and it often assumes the nature of courtship feeding, actual, symbolic, or incipient. Included in this category also are various forms of greeting and nest-relief ceremonies. Prolonged postnuptial display is characteristic of gannets, storks, and other birds which spend a long time in incubation and taking care of the young. Armstrong (1947) suggested that such birds have surplus energy "available for display activities." He observed, also, that postnuptial ceremonies at the nest often "recapitulate briefly the features of the pairing-up ceremony." Armstrong gave the following description of the postnuptial (or "connubial") display of gannets: "When a bird returns to its mate, or as the pair stand together on a ledge, they face each other, stretch up their heads with beaks pointing skywards, partially open their wings and waggle their heads energetically so that the beaks clatter as in a kind of fencing, or scrape together as if they were being whetted one upon the other . . . . At this point one of the birds may open its mouth capaciously showing the wide, black gape."

Aggregations

From an experimental point of view the study of bird aggregations is still in its infancy. One can in fact say little more than that bird aggregations do occur and that they can be observed to do certain things. Social organization implies communication among the members of the group. The regulation of behavior in groups of birds may depend on visual and/or auditory communication, as in species which engage in communal courtship displays or those in which call notes are important in maintaining the integrity of winter feeding flocks. Thus, Odum (1942) listed 16 different vocalizations given by the Black-capped Chickadee, many of which are used in flocking situations. Many other examples of voice signals have been cited in previous chapters. Probably both visual and auditory stimuli serve to co-ordinate the skilled maneuvering seen in the enormous flocks of swifts, swallows, and blackbirds during migration or in preroosting flights.

Breeding Colonies

In discussing the colonial nesting of such birds as auks, murres, and puffins, Friedmann (1935) remarked that "this formless gregariousness is the first step towards social growth." An increase in social organization is seen in the three types of gregarious nesting (colonial, co-operative, communal) mentioned in Chapter 10. There is a considerable difference of opinion concerning the possible influence of mutual stimulation on the breeding activities of colonial species. Based on his study of several species of gulls, Darling (1938, 1952) believed that social displays (both dual and communal) not only lead to synchronization of the sexual cycle between the members of a pair but also stimulate other pairs of the same species and of closely related species in the colony. Some support for this theory has come from the work of other authors. Allen and Mangels (1940) concluded that flock-stimulation "very likely is *essential* to reproduction" in the Black-crowned Night Heron. In their study of the influence of sex-hormone inplants on the behavior of California Quail (*Lophortyx californicus*), Emlen and Lorenz (1942) found that pairing behavior also appeared in eight of ten control (untreated) males between the tenth and sixteenth days of the experiment, and probably "was due to contagious behavior." Other authors, however, have denied Darling's thesis and have suggested that association in nesting colonies or in communal courtship areas serves simply to insure that the sexes meet at the appropriate time and to facilitate sex recognition (see Armstrong, 1947: 187).

James Fisher (1954) pointed out that although some of the most scholarly behavior studies have dealt with colonial species the emphasis has been largely on the role of the individual, primarily in an attempt to obtain information on the concept of releasers, fixed-action patterns, and the like. The enthusiasm accorded the concept of territoriality appears to have led to an overemphasis on the aggressive nature of bird behavior, and many papers exploiting this theme have been published. There is now a great need to reconsider and study aggressive display, and other forms of communication, in relation to the concept of sociality in birds. The phrase *a colonial species* can mean many different things according to the species concerned. Most authors in writing of the American Goldfinch, for example, refer to it as exhibiting semicolonial tendencies during the nesting season. Throughout a large and essentially uniform habitat goldfinch nests more often than not are concentrated in certain parts of the area, so that it appears that the birds "prefer" to nest in groups rather than singly. Similarly, the Kirtland's Warbler is found primarily in groups, and large areas of suitable habitat are not occupied at all; only rarely is a single bird or a pair encountered during the breeding season, and these instances seem to occur either when the habitat is just becoming suitable for the birds or at the time when the habitat has changed so much that it has "outgrown" them (Mayfield, 1953). In general, however, one tends to associate colonial nesting with seabirds and certain passerines, such as swallows and blackbirds. For seabirds in particular, it has been suggested that "their sociality is an inevitable consequence of the limitation of breeding-grounds." Nevertheless, Fisher (1954) stated that for most of the approximately 200 species belonging to five different orders of seabirds "there is plenty of unoccupied suitable cliff-, beach- or island-space, and only at a few remote oceanic islands is there apparent saturation, and a 'shift' system by which different species have different seasons, so that they occupy the breeding-ground in turns."

Although Fisher and others are convinced that social stimulation derives from colonial nesting and that it "confers a biological benefit," there is as yet little proof for the hypothesis. Nevertheless, both Fisher and Darling have proposed a more far-reaching hypothesis concerning sociality in birds. Thus Darling (1952) said: "so-called fighting, and singing, are in my opinion often a form of social stimulation and have indirect survival value as aids to development of reproductive condition. I should think the term 'aggressive behavior' could be dropped for a great deal of true display." He proposed, therefore, that "one of the important functions of territory in breeding birds is the provision of *periphery*—periphery being defined as that kind of edge where there is another bird of the same species occupying a territory." He added that if the hypothesis is correct, then *"territorial behavior as a whole is a social phenomenon, and it has survival value."* Fisher (1954: 73), also, developed the idea that sociality is the rule and not the exception among birds, based on the thesis that the most numerous—and therefore most successful—species are sociable during some period of the year. After discussing the 14 most successful species of England and Wales, Fisher stated: "The effect of the holding of territory by common passerines is to create 'neighbourhoods' of individuals which are masters of their own definite and limited property, but which are bound firmly, and *socially,* to their next door neighbours by what in human terms would be described as a dear enemy or rival friend situation, but which in bird terms should more safely be described as mutual stimulation." Viewed in this light, singing and other phenomena associated with strong territorial behavior may be as important for the mutual stimulation of adjacent pairs of a species as it may be in reducing interference between the pairs during the nesting season; the territories become units in the social network. If this be the case, one must reconsider such questions as whether birds nest together because of lack of suitable habitat and nest sites or because of the essentially gregarious nature of birds. The much-used terms "hostile" and "aggressive" behavior then take on a new meaning.

Darling (1938) also suggested that "there exist numerical thresholds in colonies of birds, below which the breeding cycle is not completed." And to be sure, there is evidence from studies of mammalian as well as avian species which seems to demonstrate this phenomenon. Although accepting this idea "as regards general reproductive efficiency under some conditions," Fisher did not think that the data presented by Darling proved the "threshold" theory. Based on his extensive study of the Fulmar (*Fulmarus glacialis*), Fisher suggested that the lower breeding efficiency of smaller colonies is due not to the small numbers of birds but to the higher percentage of young birds (the "young-pioneer" theory). He believed that the young birds return to the place where they were hatched, only to find older birds in possession of the nesting area. The young, having less "drive," then search for new nesting areas: "At these colonies the birds arrive late, breed inefficiently or not at all, and depart early."

Postreproductive Aggregations

This type of aggregation may be considered under several subheadings: roosting habits and various types of flock formation.

Fig. 3. Postbreeding flock of Tree Swallows (*Iridoprocne bicolor*), August 29, 1953, Muskegon County, Michigan. (Courtesy of L. H. Walkinshaw.)

Skutch (1940) described the sleeping habits of 14 species of Central American wrens, some of which build "dormitories" used for roosting. The dormitories may be indistinguishable from the nests or they may differ from them in structure, shape, or both. Some species of wrens sleep singly, others in pairs, while Cactus Wrens and Lawrence's Musician Wrens sleep in family groups. Skutch (1956) also mentioned once finding 16 Prong-billed Barbets (*Semnornis frantzii*) sleeping together in a small hole in a tree. Crested-swifts (Hemiprocnidae) and wood-swallows (Artamidae) are said to sleep in "clusters" of a dozen birds or so, and colies (Coliidae) sleep in "bunches of six or more clinging onto the topmost shoots of the tree or bush which is their communal roost" (Van Someren, 1956: 206).

Although many species roost alone, in pairs, or small groups, there are some notable exceptions in which hundreds or thousands of birds gather at common sleeping areas. Large numbers of a single species (e.g., Chimney Swifts, crows, rooks, Starlings) form homogeneous sleeping aggregations. Grackles, Redwinged Blackbirds, Cowbirds, and Robins or different species of swallows often gather in very large numbers to form heterogeneous roosting flocks.

In his discussion of the nature of flocking behavior in birds, Emlen (1952) defined a flock as "any aggregation of homogeneous individuals, regardless of size or density"; he excluded the "special heterogeneous groupings of sex and age categories occurring in the breeding pair and the parent–young family group." However, both homogeneous and heterogeneous flocks are formed by some birds during the postnuptial molting period, in preparation for migration, and in some types of winter feeding aggregations. There seems little reason to suppose that the formation of certain of these heterogeneous flocks results from the operation of factors that differ basically from those instrumental in the formation of the homogeneous flocks discussed by Emlen, but, as he pointed out, flocking or gregariousness "is little understood despite its conspicuousness and widespread occurrence." Emlen visualized flocking behavior as resulting from the operation of two opposing "forces" or "drives": a positive force of mutual attraction (*gregariousness*) and a negative force of mutual repulsion (*social intolerance*). Even in the most highly gregarious birds there is a negative reaction to overcrowding. The Cliff Swallows studied by Emlen, for example, exhibited gregariousness by perching on telephone wires in compact groups, but "no bird ever held a perch closer than about four inches from its nearest neighbor." The apparent negative social forces resulted in continual changes of position as new birds obtained a perch on the wire.

Little is known of the possible physiological factors affecting flocking behavior. Some species that demonstrate highly developed territorial behavior during the breeding season form rather close-knit postbreeding flocks. Social intolerance in these species, therefore, is high during the breeding season, low during the rest of the year. For these species the breakup of winter flocks may be correlated with the increased secretion of sex (or other) hormones as the breeding season approaches. Consequently, Emlen offered the tentative hypothesis that flocking responses appear to "have their physiological basis in stereotyped neural patterns and are influenced by hormonal factors only as these incite disruptive responses associated with sexual or parental activity." From this view, flocking "may be regarded as the neutral or 'resting' state, and any deviation from it toward a dispersed pattern, a state of tension effected by the introduction of negative social elements." It will be noted that this idea agrees in essence with that presented by Darling and Fisher that birds are fundamentally social animals. It hardly seems necessary to add that each of these authors has offered his theory of the innate social nature of birds in the full knowledge that there are many apparent exceptions, that experimental data are badly needed, and that "hormonal factors" are not a panacea for "explaining" all of a bird's activities.

References

Allee, W. C. 1936. Analytical Studies of Group Behavior in Birds. *Wils. Bull.,* 48: 145–151.

Allen, Robert Porter. 1956. The Flamingos: Their Life History and Survival. Natl. Audubon Soc. *Research Rept. No. 5.*

——— and Frederick P. Mangels. 1940. Studies of the Nesting Behavior of the Black-crowned Night Heron. *Proc. Linn. Soc. N. Y.,* 50–51: 1–28.

Alley, Ronald, and Hugh Boyd. 1950. Parent–Young Recognition in the Coot *Fulica atra. Ibis,* 92: 46–51.

Armstrong, Edward A. 1947. *Bird Display and Behaviour.* Lindsay Drummond, London.

Boyd, H. J., and Ronald Alley. 1948. The Function of the Head-coloration of the Nestling Coot and other Nestling Rallidae. *Ibis,* 90: 582–593.

Buss, Irven O. 1942. A Managed Cliff Swallow Colony in Southern Wisconsin. *Wils. Bull.,* 54: 153–161.

Collias, Elsie C., and Nicholas E. Collias. 1957. The Response of Chicks of the Franklin's Gull to Parental Bill-color. *Auk,* 74: 371–375.

Collias, N. E. 1950. Some Variations in Grouping and Dominance Patterns Among Birds and Mammals. *Zoologica,* 35: 97–119.

——— 1952. The Development of Social Behavior in Birds. *Auk,* 69: 127–159.

Darling, F. Fraser. 1938. *Bird Flocks and the Breeding Cycle.* Cambridge Univ. Press, London.

——— 1952. Social Behavior and Survival. *Auk,* 69: 183–191.

Davis, David E. 1952. Social Behavior and Reproduction. *Auk,* 69: 171–182.

Emlen, John T., Jr. 1950. Techniques for Observing Bird Behavior under Natural Conditions. *Annals N. Y. Acad. Sci.,* 51: 1103–1112.

——— 1952. Flocking Behavior in Birds. *Auk,* 69: 160–170.

——— 1954. Territory, Nest Building, and Pair Formation in the Cliff Swallow. *Auk,* 71: 16–35.

——— and F. W. Lorenz. 1942. Pairing Responses of Free-Living Valley Quail to Sex-Hormone Pellet Implants. *Auk,* 59: 369–378.

Fisher, James. 1954. Evolution and Bird Sociality. In *Evolution as a Process,* ed. by J. Huxley *et al.* George Allen & Unwin, London.

Friedmann, Herbert. 1935. Bird Societies. In Murchison's *A Handbook of Social Psychology.* Clark Univ. Press, Worcester, Mass., pp. 142–184.

Goethe, Friedrich. 1955. Beobachtungen bei der Aufzucht junger Silbermöwen. *Zeitschr. f. Tierpsychologie,* 12: 402–433.

Gullion, Gordon W. 1952. The Displays and Calls of the American Coot. *Wils. Bull.,* 64: 83–97.

——— 1954. The Reproductive Cycle of American Coots in California. *Auk,* 71: 366–412.

Hamerstrom, Frances. 1942. Dominance in Winter Flocks of Chickadees. *Wils. Bull.,* 54: 32–42.

Hanson, Harold C. 1953. Inter-family Dominance in Canada Geese. *Auk,* 70: 11–16.

Hinde, R. A. 1953. The Conflict between Drives in the Courtship and Copulation of the Chaffinch. *Behaviour,* 5: 1–31.

——— 1956. The Behaviour of Certain Cardueline F_1 Inter-species Hybrids. *Behaviour,* 9: 202–213.

———, W. H. Thorpe, and M. A. Vince. 1956. The Following Response of Young Coots and Moorhens. *Behaviour,* 9: 214–242.

Howard, Walter E., and John T. Emlen, Jr. 1942. Intercovey Social Relationships in the Valley Quail. *Wils. Bull.*, 54: 162–170.

Huxley, Julian S. 1938. Threat and Warning Coloration in Birds. *Proc. 8th Internatl. Ornith. Congr., 1934:* 430–455.

Jumber, Joseph F. 1956. Roosting Behavior of the Starling in Central Pennsylvania. *Auk,* 73: 411–426.

Lack, David. 1940a. Courtship Feeding in Birds. *Auk,* 57: 169–178.

——— 1940b. Pair-formation in Birds. *Condor,* 42: 269–286.

Lorenz, Konrad Z. 1937. The Companion in the Bird's World. *Auk,* 54: 245–273.

——— 1938. A Contribution to the Comparative Sociology of Colonial-nesting Birds. *Proc. 8th Internatl. Ornith. Congr., 1934:* 207–218.

Marler, P. 1957. Specific Distinctiveness in the Communication Signals of Birds. *Behaviour,* 11: 13–39.

Marshall, A. J. 1954. *Bower-Birds.* Oxford Univ. Press, London.

Mattingley, A. H. E. 1929. The Love-display of the Australian Bustard. *Emu,* 28: 198.

Mayfield, Harold. 1953. A Census of the Kirtland's Warbler. *Auk,* 70: 17–20.

Miller, Robert C. 1922. The Significance of the Gregarious Habit. *Ecology,* 3: 122–126.

Morris, Desmond. 1954. The Reproductive Behaviour of the Zebra Finch (*Poephila guttata*), with Special Reference to Pseudofemale Behaviour and Displacement Activities. *Behaviour,* 6: 271–322.

——— 1956. The Feather Postures of Birds and the Problem of the Origin of Social Signals. *Behaviour,* 9: 75–113.

Moynihan, M. 1955a. Remarks on the Original Sources of Displays. *Auk,* 72: 240–246.

——— 1955b. Types of Hostile Display. *Auk,* 72: 247–259.

Nero, Robert W. 1956. A Behavior Study of the Red-winged Blackbird. I, II. *Wils. Bull.,* 68: 5–37; 129–150.

Nice, Margaret Morse. 1937-1943. Studies in the Life History of the Song Sparrow. I, II. *Trans. Linn. Soc. N. Y.,* 4, 1937: vi + 247 pp.; 6, 1943: viii + 329 pp.

——— 1939. The Social Kumpan and the Song Sparrow. *Auk,* 56: 255–262.

Noble, G. K. 1936. Courtship and Sexual Selection of the Flicker (*Colaptes auratus luteus*). *Auk,* 53: 269–282.

——— 1939. The Rôle of Dominance in the Social Life of Birds. *Auk,* 56: 263–273.

——— and William Vogt. 1935. An Experimental Study of Sex Recognition in Birds. *Auk,* 52: 278–286.

Noble, G. K., and M. Wurm. 1940. The Effect of Testosterone Propionate on the Black-crowned Night Heron. *Endocrinology,* 26: 837–850.

——— and A. Schmidt. 1938. Social Behavior of the Black-crowned Night Heron. *Auk,* 55: 7–40.

Odum, Eugene P. 1942. Annual Cycle of the Black-capped Chickadee—3. *Auk,* 59: 499–531.

Ramsay, A. O. 1951. Familial Recognition in Domestic Birds. *Auk,* 68: 1–16.

——— 1956. Seasonal Patterns in the Epigamic Displays of Some Surface-feeding Ducks. *Wils. Bull.,* 68: 275–281.

Richdale, L. E. 1951. *Sexual Behavior in Penguins.* Univ. Kansas Press, Lawrence.

Sabine, Winifred S. 1949. Dominance in Winter Flocks of Juncos and Tree Sparrows. *Physiol. Zool.,* 22: 64–85.

Schjelderup-Ebbe, Thorleif. 1935. Social Behavior of Birds. In Murchison's *A Handbook of Social Psychology,* Clark Univ. Press, Worcester, Mass., pp. 947–972.

Shoemaker, Hurst Hugh. 1939. Social Hierarchy in Flocks of the Canary. *Auk,* 56: 381–406.

Skutch, Alexander F. 1940. Social and Sleeping Habits of Central American Wrens. *Auk,* 57: 293–312.

——— 1956. The Bird's Nest As a Dormitory. *Animal Kingdom,* 59: 50–55.

Slud, Paul. 1957. The Song and Dance of the Long-tailed Manakin, *Chiroxiphia linearis. Auk,* 74: 333–339.

Tinbergen, N. 1939a. On the Analysis of Social Organization Among Vertebrates, with Special Reference to Birds. *Amer. Midl. Nat.,* 21: 210–234.

——— 1939b. The Behavior of the Snow Bunting in Spring. *Trans. Linn. Soc., N. Y.,* 5: 1–95.

——— 1948. Social Releasers and the Experimental Method Required for their Study. *Wils. Bull.,* 60: 6–51.

——— 1953. *Social Behaviour in Animals.* John Wiley & Sons, New York.

——— 1954. The Origin and Evolution of Courtship and Threat Display. In *Evolution as a Process,* ed. by J. Huxley *et al.* George Allen & Unwin, London.

——— and A. C. Perdeck. 1950. On the Stimulus Situation Releasing the Begging Response in the Newly Hatched Herring Gull Chick (*Larus argentatus argentatus* Pont.). *Behaviour,* 3: 1–39.

Tucker, B. W. 1946. Courtship Feeding in Thrushes and Warblers. *Brit. Birds,* 39: 88–89.

Van Someren, V. G. L. 1956. Days with Birds: Studies of Habits of Some East African Birds. *Fieldiana: Zoology,* 38.

Wagner, Helmuth O. 1954. Versuch einer Analyse der Kolibribalz. *Zeitschr. f. Tierpsychologie,* 11: 182–212.

Wessel, John P., and W. Henry Leigh. 1941. Studies of the Flock Organization of the White-throated Sparrow. *Wils. Bull.,* 53: 222–230.

Winterbottom, J. M. 1929. Studies in Sexual Phenomena—VI, Communal Display in Birds. *Proc. Zool. Soc. London,* 1929: 189–195.

12. Taxonomy and nomenclature

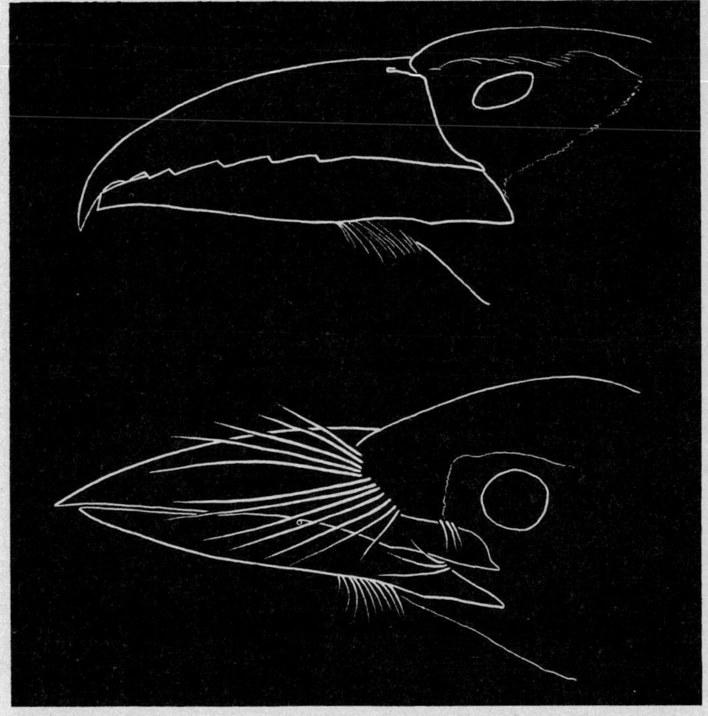

Fig. 1. The bills of the small toucan *Selenidera maculirostris* (above) and the large barbet *Megalaima chrysopogon,* drawn to the same scale. (Van Tyne, 1955.)

TAXONOMY, or systematics, is the science of arranging or classifying the forms of life. Nomenclature is a system of names. The need for naming and cataloguing animals is clear if one considers only the number of kinds of birds—about 8600 species. A system of classification provides different categories of names that permit the interchange of information among biologists, but it is more than that: it is a means of attacking the problem of the origin and evolution of life. Modern systems of classification, therefore, are based on phylogeny. It should be emphasized, however, that classification and phylogeny are not the same thing. Phylogeny is the actual evolutionary history of animals. Classification results from man's attempt to interpret information on extinct and living animals and to reconstruct their phylogeny. Insofar as man is successful in this attempt, his classification will be a natural one, i.e., will express the phylogenetic relationships of animals.

The need for classification was recognized very early. The Assyrians classified birds by habitat. Among the Greeks, Xenophon, Hippocrates, and Democritus proposed crude systems of classification; Aristotle (died 322 B.C.) knew over 170 species of birds, although not all are recognizable from his descriptions. Pliny the Elder (died 79 A.D.), in Book X of his *Historia Naturalis,* classified birds according to the structure of their feet. Gesner (1516–1565) used four or more Latin names, arranged alphabetically, in naming animals. John Ray (1627–1705) distinguished between superficial and fundamental similarities as a basis for classification, and recognized the distinction between the genus and the species.

The father of modern taxonomy, however, was the Swedish naturalist Linnaeus (1707–1778), who founded the binomial system of Latin names. It is the 10th edition (1758) of his *Systema Naturae Regnum Animale* that is considered the starting point for zoological nomenclature. In this work, Linnaeus adopted two Latin words (in place of many) for naming animals: one name to indicate the general kind (the *genus*) of animal; the other, the particular kind (the *species*). With the passing of years, confusion arose because there were no generally accepted rules for the naming of animals, and in 1842 the British Association for the Advancement of Science published the "Strickland Code." This code was modified in 1865, and still other codes were proposed by French, German, and American workers; the American Ornithologists' Union adopted the subspecies concept in its code of 1886. A permanent International Commission on Zoological Nomenclature was established in 1901. In addition to its responsibilities for amending and interpreting the International Code for Zoological Nomenclature, the Commission publishes the *Bulletin of Zoological Nomenclature;* the first issue appeared in 1943.

Some of the principal provisions of the International Code may be summarized as follows (for details see Mayr *et al.,* 1953; Schenk and McMasters, 1956):

1. Zoological nomenclature is independent of botanical nomenclature.
2. Family and subfamily names are formed by adding *idae* and *inae,* respectively, to the stem of the name of the type genus; they must be changed if the name of the type genus is changed or if, on the basis of priority, a new type genus is designated (e.g., the family name of the American wood-warblers has been, in turn, Mniotiltidae, Compsothlypidae, and Parulidae).
3. Names of subgenera and all higher categories are uninomial; names of species are binomial; of subspecies, trinomial. All names must be Latin or Latinized words. The generic name must be unique in zoology. The specific name must be unique in the genus; it may be a Latin adjective, noun, or patronym (though the last is not very desirable). Generic and subgeneric names are capitalized; specific and subspecific names are uncapitalized (formerly, names derived from personal names often were capitalized). The generic, specific, and subspecific names are underlined in manuscripts, italicized in published works.
4. The *Law of Priority* states that the generic and specific names of a particular animal shall be the name proposed by Linnaeus in 1758, or the name first proposed after that date. However, a recognizable description of the animal must be published together with a binomial or trinomial name (preferably but not necessarily appropriate). Although not essential, a wide distribution of the published description is desirable.
5. The author of a name is the one who first publishes it in conjunction with a suitable description of the animal. The author's name follows the trivial name without punctuation (and without being underlined or italicized) unless the species has been transferred to a genus other than that in which it was described, in which event the author's name is enclosed in parentheses.

The Taxonomic Hierarchy

The framework of classification is a hierarchy consisting of certain obligatory groups: kingdom, phylum, class, order, family, genus, and species. In order to express natural relationships clearly, however, other categories often are used. These are formed by adding the prefixes super-, sub-, and infra- to certain terms of the basic hierarchy; the cohort and tribe sometimes are used. The classification of the Kirtland's Warbler in hierarchic order is:

Kingdom	Animalia
Phylum	Chordata
Class	Aves
Subclass	Neornithes
Superorder	Neognathae
Order	Passeriformes[1]
Suborder	Passeres
Family	Parulidae
Genus	*Dendroica*
Species	*kirtlandii*

Such a system of classification is possible because there are discontinuities between the kinds of animals. These discontinuities, or different characteristics, among groups of birds, for example, enabled the Papuans of New Guinea to recognize and name 137 different kinds of birds, which ornithologists have recognized as 138 species.

Linnaeus and many later biologists assumed that all species had been created, that they were unchanging, and, therefore, that all individuals of a particular species had descended from the original pair. Some individual variation was recognized, but in collections the emphasis was placed on the "typical" specimen; the rest were merely "duplicates." The publication in 1859 of Charles Darwin's *On the Origin of Species by Means of Natural Selection* led in time to the overthrow of the doctrine of special creation and to the general acceptance of the doctrine of organic evolution. Even so, for nearly 50 years most biologists were concerned primarily with the history and results—and not the causes—of evolution, and they concentrated on the study of paleontology, morphology, and embryology. It was during this period especially that new information was interpreted in terms of the biogenetic "law": ontogeny recapitulates phylogeny. The structural unit of classification was, then as now, the species, but in the old systematics the species was "typologically conceived, morphologically defined, and essentially

[1] The ending "iformes" for ordinal names has been used for many years by British, French, and American ornithologists, but Mayr and Amadon (1951) used the older names, e.g., order Passeres; suborder Oscines.

non-dimensional." Huxley (1942) spoke of the new systematics as "the modern synthesis," resulting from the use of information obtained from the fields of systematics, genetics, cytology, physiology, ecology, and zoogeography. Consequently, the concept of the "type" species and genus also has changed. Modern ideas on this subject are discussed by Mayr *et al.* (1953: Chapter 12). Familiarity with certain terms (e.g., genotype, holotype) is necessary in order to understand the older taxonomic literature, especially; these are defined in the Glossary. Frizzell (1933) defined over 200 terms that have been used in taxonomic papers in the fields of botany and zoology.

Species and Subspecies

We have seen that the over-all objective of the systematic hierarchy is to indicate the identity and relationships of animals. When a systematist "creates" or conceives a genus, he does so in order to express the similarity among groups of birds—a similarity that he believes is due to a common ancestry. Thus the several kinds of crows are placed in the genus *Corvus* to indicate that they are more closely related to each other than to any other kinds of birds. The genus, then, is a concept. The species, on the other hand, is the structural unit of classification—the thing that actually exists. The species exhibit diversity within the genus.

The nature of the species, however, has been much debated. It was for many years, as indicated above, defined solely on external morphological characters, often very superficial ones, and many differences of opinion arose from the studies of different groups of animals, e.g., insects, snails, amphibians, birds. Mayr (1948) summarized the situation in this way:

> A species definition is merely the verbalization of a species concept. Species concepts, in turn, are based on the study of species. To many of the old fashioned museum taxonomists the "species" was an aggregate of museum specimens and it was easy for these workers to define the species in terms of the morphological characters of these specimens. They overlooked that in doing so they unconsciously made the species a human artifact. They did not say the species is a unit of nature, rather they said the species consists of specimens which conform to certain morphological criteria selected by me, the species is what I consider a species.

Such morphological definitions of the species have been replaced by biological definitions. Opinion still differs on the exact wording of such a definition, due, in part, to the nature of populations of animals and to a lack of information. As a starting point, most ornithologists would adopt a definition such as this: A species is a population of similar individuals occupying a definite (and usually continuous) geographical range and breeding among themselves but normally not breeding with individuals of other species. Although the wording of a reasonably short, workable definition of a species is open to argument, there is more or less general agreement among ornithologists on the factors that must be included in the concept of what a species is and how it can be recognized by the biologist. A species may be recognizable, i.e., distinguishable from another species, because of morphological, physiological, ecological, or behavioral attributes. Well-marked differences in size often are used to identify species and to assign them to the same genus: e.g., King and Virginia rails, Greater and Lesser yellowlegs, Hairy and Downy woodpeckers, the Central American kingfishers *Chloroceryle amazona* and *C. americana*. Differences in color pattern also are used to separate two closely related species: e.g., Audubon's and Myrtle warblers, the Central American tanagers *Ramphocelus passerinii* and *R. icteronotus*. A species may remain relatively stable (i.e., exhibit relatively little morphological variation) over long periods of time, but individual variation in the specific characters is the rule in natural populations of animals; thus a species consists, not only of individuals, but of populations of animals. The species concept also takes into consideration the mechanisms by which species remain distinct and those by which new species arise. If two groups of closely related animals are to remain distinct (i.e., retain their separate specific characters), they must in general—because of the nature of genes and their role in inheritance—not interbreed, i.e., they must be reproductively isolated: "species are groups of actually or potentially interbreeding natural populations, which are reproductively isolated from other such groups" (Mayr, 1942: 120). It is recognized also that within a species, especially one that occupies a large range, differences—due to gene changes—between the various populations may become so distinct that several populations may be recognized as geographical races or subspecies.

During one period, many ornithologists devoted a great deal of time to describing new subspecies, using, however, about the same philosophy that had been used earlier in the study of species. In extreme instances, subspecies were described on the basis of a single specimen or on a few specimens of one sex, and on one occasion one winter visitant was described as a new subspecies. It was not rare that, after examining essentially the same series of bird skins, two or more investigators proposed different series of subspecies, each of which possessed "obvious" morphological characters, even though they often were not recognizable by other workers. There can be little doubt that this approach to the subspecies led Mayr (1951) to comment that "instead of expending their energy on the describing and naming of trifling subspecies, bird taxonomists might well devote more attention to the evaluation of trends in variation."

Wilson and Brown (1953) questioned the very use of the subspecies as a taxonomic category. They stated:

> We are convinced that the subspecies concept is the most critical and disorderly area of modern systematic theory. . . . Particular confusion surrounds the drawing of the lower limits of the subspecies category within that spectrum of classes recognized by Mayr as extending from "the local population into the subspecies." The difficulties in this delimitation stem from four outstanding features of geographical variation: (1) the tendency for genetically independent characters to show independent geographical variation; (2) the capacity for characters to recur in more than one geographical area, yielding polytopic races; (3) the common occurrence of the microgeographical race; (4) the necessary arbitrariness of any degree of population divergence chosen as the lowest formal racial level.

They criticized avian taxonomic studies in particular because, in general, they are based on a "very limited number of characters" (usually variation in size, external proportions, and color). They suggested that, for the study of geographical variation, "the use of the simple vernacular locality citation or a brief statement of the range involved is adequate and to be preferred to the formal Latinized trinomial."

Mayr (1942) had pointed out the subjective nature of the subspecies, and he emphasized again (1954) that "the subspecies is not at all like the species. It is in principle a purely subjective category, even though there are many cases in which there is no difficulty about defining a given subspecies. The subspecies is merely a strictly utilitarian classificatory device for the pigeonholing of population samples." Mayr *et al.* (1953) gave this definition: *"Subspecies are geographically defined aggregates of local populations which differ taxonomically from other such subdivisions of a species."*

The *wise* use of trinomials, therefore, may be advantageous for indicating the relationship among different populations. A conservative treatment of trinomials seems indicated: use those that serve a purpose; discard those that are poorly conceived. The student first should be more concerned with understanding living populations of animals than with the intricacies of a much misunderstood and misused taxonomic category.

Speciation

Whether or not geographical races are called subspecies and are identified by the use of trinomials, the genetic differences that exist among the various populations of a given species are believed generally to be the basis for the evolution of new species. The differences among the several populations of a species (and even among the species of some genera) are not confined to grossly observable morphological characters; in fact, these may be exceedingly slight. The populations may differ in physiological or cytological characters, in habitat preference, in behavior patterns, etc. Whatever the differences, they are ultimately the result of the physicochemical processes produced by the particular combination of genes in the chromosomes. The chief source[2] of inherited variation in vertebrate animals is the result of changes (mutations) in one or more genes to produce alleles of those genes. A single gene, or point, mutation may or may not produce a visible change in the appearance of the animal; in fact, a very large number of small gene changes are necessary in most instances.[3] Available evidence indicates that gene mutation does not take place indiscriminately, i.e., at random. The same mutation tends to occur over and over again—e.g., gene A to its allele a; reverse mutations also occur—a to A. The relative frequency with which these mutations occur determines, in part, the nature of the population (for a discussion of the influence of size of population, see Miller, 1947; Wright, 1948). However, mutation of genes in itself does not create new species. The individual in which the mutation has taken place must live to reproduce and leave viable offspring that carry the allele. Even this is not enough. The origin of hereditary variation

---

[2] A few presumed examples of cytoplasmic inheritance have been reported for some invertebrate animals.

[3] Mechanical changes (deficiencies in chromosomes, duplications, polyploidy, etc.) occur in lower animals and plants; evolution by the process of macromutation was proposed by Goldschmidt; for a discussion of these phenomena, see Dobzhansky (1941) and Mayr (1942).

is only part of the mechanism of evolution: "the molding of the hereditary variation into racial, specific, generic, and other complexes, is due to action of the environment through natural selection and other channels" (Dobzhansky, 1941: 153).

Briefly, the theory of natural selection assumes that genetic variability exists in populations of animals (and plants) and that natural selective agents in the environment either favor or hinder the continuing expression of each variation. It is important to note that not all mutations are beneficial to the animal. The phenotypic expression of the various alleles present in a population may confer an advantage, be neutral, or be deleterious to the animals. The selection pressure of the environment will be proportional to the amount of advantage or disadvantage conferred by the total genetic pattern of the animal. Selective pressure may be exerted through many agents: e.g., physiology of the animal, temperature, humidity, rainfall, chemical composition of the soil, predation. Animals (or populations) that possess alleles which enable them to adapt to conditions as they are, or to changing conditions, will survive to reproduce; those that possess alleles that prevent (or reduce the effectiveness for) such adaptation will perish or reproduce less effectively.

Let us return now to the role of the geographical race in the formation of new species. Mayr (1948) summarized the process of geographic speciation as follows:

> Wherever extrinsic factors cause a retardation or interruption of gene flow between portions of a species (geographical or spatial isolation), these subdivisions of the species tend to drift apart genetically. The rate of this change is different in different species.
>
> If the isolation is sufficiently complete and lasts sufficiently long, it will permit the evolution of isolating mechanisms, which will inhibit the interbreeding of the two daughter species after the elimination of the extrinsic isolating factors.

If two populations of animals inhabit the same area and do not interbreed, one may assume that reproductive isolating mechanisms have developed and, therefore, that there are two (sympatric) species. When, however, two similar populations are geographically isolated so that interbreeding is a physical impossibility, direct proof for the existence of isolating mechanisms usually is lacking. This situation has led to much of the controversy concerning species and subspecies. Should such geographically separated populations (either mainland or insular) be considered subspecies or allopatric species? Mayr (1948) believes that

> . . . it is preferable for practical as well as for scientific reasons to treat all doubtful allopatric populations as subspecies. The scientific reason is that the mere fact that a population was unable to overlap the range of its nearest relative implies that it has been unable so far to develop isolating mechanisms that would permit coexistence. There is no more formidable zoogeographical barrier for a subspecies than the range of another subspecies.

There are many examples of sympatric species. Mayr (1942, 1948) discussed two general groups of characteristics that permit such closely related species to coexist at the same locality: those that prevent or reduce competition and those that prevent or reduce the amount of interbreeding (reproductive isolating mechanisms). Competition between the species may be reduced because each occupies a different habitat or has different food habits. Reproductive isolation may be effected because of differences in habitat preference (ecological factors), in behavior (ethological factors), in time of breeding season (for a detailed discussion of these and other factors, see Mayr, 1942, 1948).

The theories of natural selection and of geographical speciation have been criticized for a variety of reasons by some biologists. For example, mutation rates for certain genes are known to be low, 1 in 100,000 or 1,000,000 individuals. Moreover, laboratory studies (particularly on *Drosophila*) have revealed that many mutations either are lethal, causing the death of the embryo, or decrease the viability of the offspring. Wilson and Brown (1953) believed that

> . . . it is not too much to say that the development of the entire theory of geographical speciation has been dominated in large part by ornithological leadership. Yet a survey of ornithological taxonomic literature . . . has convinced us that the morphological and distributional data on relevant bird populations leave much to be desired, and in fact offer very little definitive information on the two central topics, independent character variation and the subspecies-species evolutionary transition, as they apply to insular populations.

Nevertheless, despite the paucity of experimental evidence for the process of natural selection (and geographical speciation), most biologists see in it the mechanism whereby new species could evolve over long periods of time (for a discussion of ecological and genetic speciation, see Huxley, 1942).

Climatic Responses of Populations

In studies of species with extensive geographical ranges, biologists have found that certain morphological characters often exhibit a gradual change from one extremity of the range to the other. Huxley (1942: 206) explained these by stating that "natural selection will all the time be moulding life adaptively into its environment; and since gradients in environmental factors are a widespread feature of the environmental mould, we should expect organisms to show corresponding adaptive gradients in their characters." He coined the term *cline* to refer to such character gradients. For expressing the correlation between environment and structure, several "rules," and other, less formal, generalizations have been proposed, each covering one or several groups of animals. All have exceptions, but support for each "rule" is found among various subspecies (and, rarely, some species) of birds.

Bergmann's Rule

"Within a polytypic warm-blooded species, the body-size of a subspecies usually increases with decreasing mean temperature of its habitat" (Huxley, 1942: 211). In practice this "decreasing mean temperature" means increasing latitude or altitude. Examples are found among the subspecies of many well-known birds: Bald Eagle, Red-tailed Hawk, Sparrow Hawk, Bobwhite, Great-horned Owl, Screech Owl, Hairy Woodpecker, Horned Lark, Redwinged Blackbird, Song Sparrow. Exceptions to the rule include the Sandhill Cranes and the Phainopepla. In an extended study of many species of New Guinea birds, Rand (1936) found but one exception to this correlation.

Allen's Rule

"In warm-blooded species, the relative size of exposed portions of the body (limbs, tail, and ears) decreases with decrease of mean temperature" (Huxley, 1942: 213). The bills of birds seem to follow this rule and it has been reported to apply to nonmigratory birds' wings. Actually, the opposite is true of migratory birds and even some nonmigratory birds. Mayr and Vaurie (1948) found this correlation in the bills of some Asiatic drongos. Rensch (1929: 149–151) lists a series of 25 groups (in 5 families) of nonmigratory birds in which he claims that this rule holds (with exceptions, which he marks) for birds' wings, but his list contains many errors and does not inspire confidence. There is, of course, no reason for Allen's rule to apply to wing length when that measurement is based primarily on length of the primary feathers; long primaries do not increase heat loss as long mammal ears or tails do. The presumed "close correlation" between length of wing and body size has not been substantiated except in a few isolated instances (for a discussion of this problem, see Mayr, 1956).

Kelso's Rule

"The ears [i.e., ear-opening and dermal flap] of northern owls are relatively larger than in southern owls" (Kelso, 1940). Kelso spoke mainly about differences between species but there is some evidence that it applies to subspecies as well. This seems at first glance to be the reverse of the above. Actually, it probably is an unrelated phenomenon.

Gloger's Rule

"Intensity of melanin pigmentation tends to decrease with mean temperature; the amount of black pigment tends to increase with increase of humidity; yellowish or reddish-brown pigmentation is characteristic of regions of high temperature and aridity." These correlations are very general among birds. Examples: Bobwhite, Red-tailed Hawk, Screech Owl, Hairy Woodpecker, Horned Lark, Fox Sparrow, Song Sparrow.

Feathering of the Legs and Feet

"The amount of feathering on the legs and feet of certain nonmigratory birds, such as owls and grouse, decreases with increasing mean temperature." This has been discussed especially by Kelso and Kelso (1936) and Uttal (1941). In populations of the Ruffed Grouse, for example, the tarsus is feathered in North Dakota birds, and bare in Virginia birds.

Wing Length

"Wings of subspecies of birds that live in mountains or cold climates are relatively longer than those of subspecies of lowlands or warm climates" (see Mayr, 1942: 92). Rand (1936) gave examples of New Guinea birds, mainly nonmigratory forms. Chapman (1940: 424–425) pointed out that a high latitude southern form of *Zonotrichia capensis* (i.e., *sanborni* of Chile), though non-migratory, is very long-winged. Usually the long-winged, high-latitude forms are also the migratory (or *more* migratory) ones. Examples: Solitary Vireo, Fox Sparrow.

Clutch Size

In the cooler parts of the range of a species (even a monotypic one) the individuals lay more eggs per clutch than in the warmer parts of the range. This has been discussed in some detail on p. 287.

Confusing Factors

The ornithologist who is interested in the causes of variation, and not simply in the mechanics of taxonomy, finds many intriguing problems. Some of the problems faced by the avian systematist may be demonstrated by citing examples that illustrate the kinds of variation encountered in the study of birds.

Plasticity

Why do some (stable) species exhibit so little geographical variation, whereas closely related (plastic) species vary so much? The Swamp Sparrow (*Melospiza georgiana*) occupies an extensive breeding range, extending from northern Manitoba and Newfoundland to Missouri and Delaware, and yet ornithologists recognize but three slightly differentiated races. Similarly, the three races of Lincoln's Sparrow (*M. lincolnii*) occupy a breeding range extending from Alaska to the lower peninsula of Michigan. By contrast, so much differentiation in external characters has occurred in the Song Sparrow that 31 races, mostly well differentiated, have been recognized. Almost nothing is known about differences in physiology or breeding behavior of these many races, and, as Mayr (1951) has stated, "it is not necessarily the taxonomic character that is adaptive, but rather the underlying gene." Extreme geographical variation is demonstrated in the Golden-fronted Woodpecker (*Centurus aurifrons*) by the subspecies *C. a. aurifrons* and *C. a. dubius*.

Clines

In clinal species the populations at the extremes of the range may be markedly different in one or more morphological characters; when dealing with populations from the intermediate parts of the range, however, it may not be possible to assign with certainty a given specimen to one of several populations. Moreover, the response to climatic conditions may result in "parallelism of subspecific clines," leading to taxonomically indistinguishable forms "being evolved independently in several areas" (Huxley, 1942). Mayr (1942: 96) gave examples in which clinal features seem to be independent of environmental gradients; in some species, clinal gradients may occur in some characters but not in others. Finally, Mayr (1954) reported that "among Australian birds there is nearly always a south-north cline of diminishing size, obeying Bergmann's rule, and a concentric cline from the humid outer periphery of Australia toward the arid interior. The latter cline is one of diminishing intensity of coloration (paling) obeying Gloger's rule." Such situations add to the difficulty of deciding the true phylogenetic relationships of populations. It is in such instances that the experience and judgment of the systematist play such an important role. Lack of experience or poor judgment may lead to false and misleading conclusions.

Sibling Species

Sibling species are "sympatric forms which are morphologically very similar or indistinguishable, but which possess specific biological characteristics and are reproductively isolated" (Mayr, 1942: 200). Thus, not all "good" species exhibit well-marked morphological differences. The three small *Empidonax* flycatchers, *virescens, trailii,* and *minimus,* are virtually indistinguishable in the field during migration, and even with a skin in hand it may be very difficult to identify single specimens of the Least and Traill's flycatchers. And yet each species can be identified instantly on the basis of song or nest. The plumage differences between the Olive-backed or Swainson's Thrush (*Hylocichla ustulata*) and the Gray-cheeked Thrush (*H. minima*) are slight, but the two species differ clearly in song and nesting habits. Another example of sibling species is found in two European creepers, *Certhia familiaris* and *C. brachydactyla,* whose ranges overlap but which do not interbreed; *brachydactyla* has a longer bill, a shorter and more curved hind claw, and is darker in color than *familiaris.*

Individual Variation

The degree of variation within one or both sexes of some species often complicates field recognition, and, in the past, especially, often led to confusion when skins were received from remote areas. The drongo *Dicrurus hottentottus* is said to be one of the most variable of all birds (Fig. 2). Better known examples are male Rose-breasted Grosbeaks and many hawks, especially the Red-tailed and Swainson's hawks.

Seasonal Variation

Seasonal variation in plumage of the males occurs in such birds as the Bobolink, Scarlet Tanager, and American Goldfinch. At the time when birds were less well known, such extreme seasonal differences in plumage sometimes led to descriptions of separate species or genera for birds collected at different periods of the year. Inadequate information on the sequence of plumages still poses problems in the study of birds from certain parts of the world.

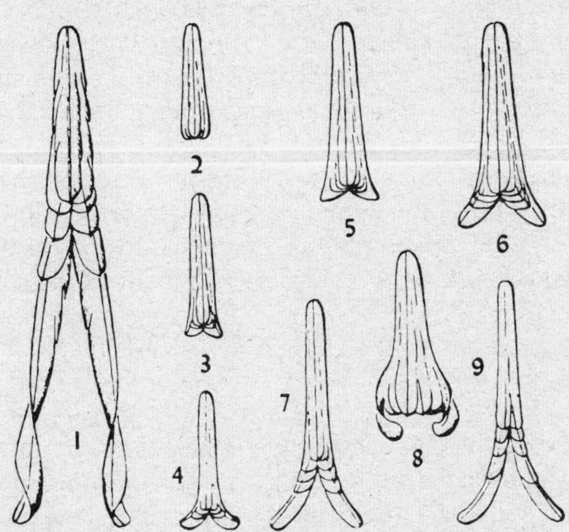

Fig. 2. Variation in the structure of the tail and the depth of its fork in the superspecies *hottentottus* (family *Dicruridae*). 1. *Dicrurus megarhynchus.* 2. *D. hottentottus samarensis.* 3. *D. h. sumatranus.* 4. *D. h. renschi.* 5. *D. h. longirostris.* 6. *D. h. atrocaeruleus* (the basic shape in *D. hottentottus*). 7. *D. h. densus.* 8. *D. h. hottentottus.* 9. *D. h. menagei.* (Courtesy of Charles Vaurie and the American Museum of Natural History.)

Age Variation

Age variation in plumage patterns is common among birds, and it is interesting to note that Mayr *et al.* (1953) commented that several hundred bird synonyms are based on juvenal plumages. One needs only to mention the "confusing fall warblers" to emphasize plumage differences between immature and adult birds. Such differences are especially interesting in relation to the Blackpoll and Bay-breasted warblers, two species in which the adult males are very different in plumage, whereas immature birds of the two species are almost indistinguishable. The males of many other species wear a femalelike first winter plumage and may not assume the fully adult nuptial plumage during their first breeding season: e.g., the manakin, *Pipra mentalis,* Redwinged Blackbird, Orchard Oriole, Indigo Bunting, Pine Grosbeak, Purple Finch. Some male birds-of-paradise are said not to attain their fully adult plumage until 7 years old.

Sexual Dimorphism

Sexual dimorphism (Fig. 3) is very widespread among birds. The male and female of the King Parrot (*Lorius roratus*) were considered to be separate species for 97 years; in this species the male is green, the female red. Sexual dimorphism in some species varies geographically. It is well developed in most races of the whistler *Pachycephala pectoralis,* but in two races the male and female have the same color pattern (Mayr, 1951). Among the phalaropes and a few other birds the female is more brightly colored than the male. Sexual dimorphism may be expressed in size, as in the Sharp-shinned Hawk (*Accipiter striatus*) in which the male is smaller than the female.

Polymorphism

Polymorphism "is the occurrence in the same population of two or more distinct forms of a species in such proportions that the rarest of them cannot be maintained by recurrent mutation" (Mayr, 1951: 111). This "pronounced type of individual variation" can be discussed in terms of color phases within a single population or in terms of differing frequencies of color phases between races of a species. One of the best-known examples of two color phases (dichromatism) is found in the red and gray plumages of the

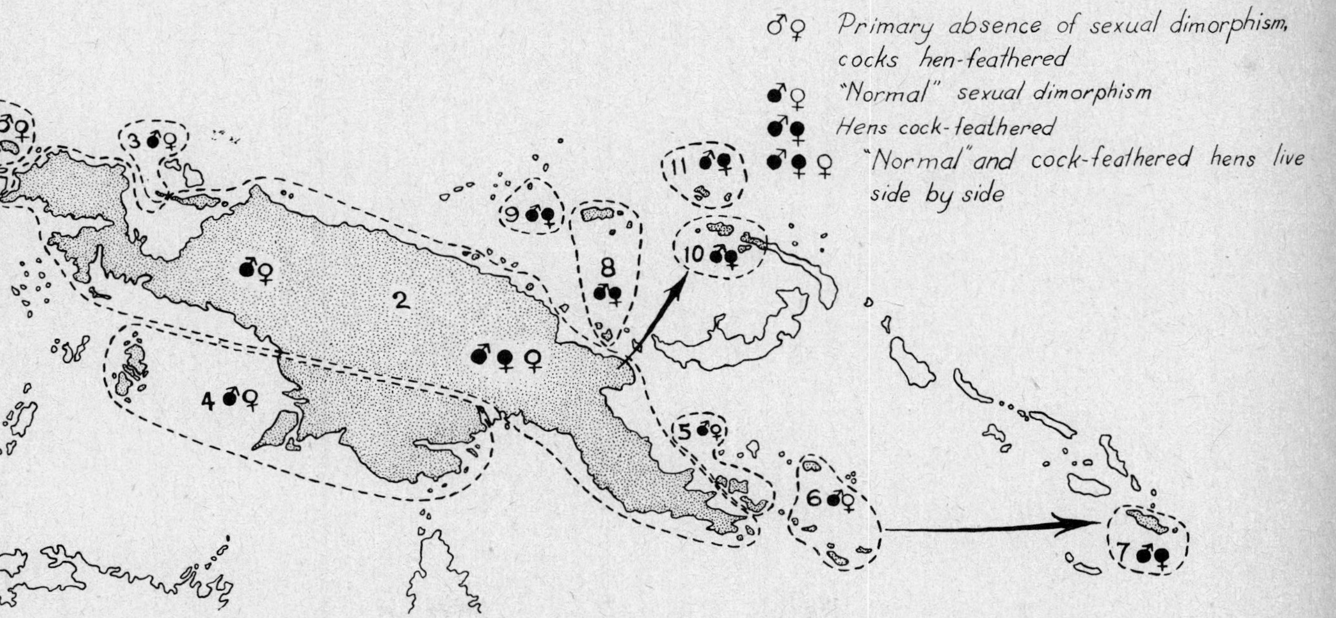

Fig. 3. Geographical distribution of the subspecies of *Myzomela nigrita* (Meliphagidae), showing the presence or absence of sexual dimorphism: 1. *steini*, 2. *meyeri*, 3. *pluto*, 4. *nigrita*, 5. *forbesi*, 6. *louisiadensis*, 7. *tristrami*, 8. *pammelaena*, 9. *ernstmayri*, 10. *ramsayi*, 11. *hades*. (Courtesy of Karl Koopman and the editor of *The Auk*.)

Screech Owl (*Otus asio*) in eastern North America. Polymorphism due to melanism and albinism is common in herons, egrets, the Long-tailed New Guinea Lory (*Charmosyna papou*), some paradise flycatchers (*Terpsiphone*), the honeycreeper *Coereba flaveola,* etc. (see Mayr, 1951). Mayr (1942: 83) presented a graphic illustration of polymorphism in the Asiatic bulbul *Microscelis leucocephalus,* in which varying combinations of white, gray, and black plumage characterize six subspecies.

Convergence

Convergence in form and color of unrelated species often makes it very difficult to determine the true relationship of the convergent species. The Derby Flycatcher (*Pitangus sulphuratus*) and the Boat-billed Flycatcher (*Megarhynchus pitangua*) are two distantly related tyrant-flycatchers that have secondarily become very similar in plumage. Convergence in color pattern is found also between certain races of the Pileated and Flint-billed woodpeckers (*Dryocopus* and *Phloeoceastes*). In these two examples the relationships seem well established, but there are large groups of passerine birds (e.g., Sylviidae, Muscicapidae) in which the interrelationships of the species and genera are poorly understood; how much of the difficulty is due to convergence is unknown. By means of natural selection, competition for food and other necessities leads to adaptations that enable various species to occupy most or all of the available ecological niches. Consequently, convergence in structure and habit may occur also among the species of totally unrelated families, as illustrated by the ground roller *Uratelornis* of Madagascar and the Roadrunner (*Geococcyx*) of the southwestern United States, or the woodpeckers, creepers, and woodcreepers (see Richardson, 1942). One of the most striking examples of convergence both in color and in habits is that demonstrated by the American meadowlarks (*Sturnella*) and the African pipits of the genus *Macronyx.* Both genera have streaked upper parts, yellowish under parts with a black pectoral band, white outer tail feathers, and they occupy the same type of habitat and build semidomed nests on the ground (for other examples, see Friedmann, 1946).

Divergence

Divergence or adaptive radiation is well illustrated by the Hawaiian honeycreepers (Drepaniidae) and the Galápagos finches

(Geospizinae). Among the honeycreepers, for example, are species which feed on nectar, insects, fruit, and seeds; the bill may be relatively small, pointed, and nearly straight, or long and markedly decurved, or very heavy and grosbeak-like. So striking are these differences in bill development that at one time the several species were assigned to different families: Meliphagidae, Dicaeidae, Fringillidae (Amadon, 1950; see also Chapter 9).

Hybridization

Hybridization occurs most often among species or genera that do not form a lengthy pair-bond: e.g., grouse, hummingbirds, manakins, birds-of-paradise. Interfamily hybrids are exceptional, but a few have been reported among gallinaceous birds (see Cockrum, 1952). Among most pair-forming species hybridization is rare. It should be noted that some species that apparently never interbreed in the wild do so in captivity and produce fertile hybrids. The parentage of most wild hybrids is inferred by analyzing the plumage characters of the hybrids. In some instances these (and other) characters are such that there seems to be little question about the identity of the parent species, but this is not always so. The successful mating of individuals belonging to different species, genera, or even families "indicates that some of the isolating mechanisms may break down occasionally" (Mayr, 1942: 260). Most often this appears to involve elimination of the mechanism of ecological isolation. Mayr (1951) reported that hybridization between *Passer domesticus* and *P. hispaniolensis* "occurs where the Willow Sparrow has shifted from river bottom into human settlements." Interspecific hybridization perhaps occurs most commonly between the Blue-winged (*Vermivora pinus*) and Golden-winged (*V. chrysoptera*) warblers. The two types of hybrids differ so much from either of the parent species that the hybrids were named as separate species (Brewster's Warbler, *V. leucobronchialis,* and Lawrence's Warbler, *V. lawrencei*), although as long ago as 1835 Audubon suggested (in an unpublished letter to Bachman) that the Blue-winged and Golden-winged warblers might be a single species. The situation presented by these two species of warblers is nearly unique in that actual breeding pairs have been observed at the nest numerous times; there are three incomplete records of nesting pairs of Brewster's Warbler. The frequency of hybridization where the ranges of the two parent species overlap may be suggested by pointing out that there are over 75 authentic records of Brewster's Warbler for Michigan alone. Nevertheless, very little is known about the life history of this group of warblers. In certain parts of their range the two species are said to occupy different habitats, but in southern Michigan the two species are usually found nesting in the same habitat.

Higher Taxonomic Categories

It would be very convenient if one could tabulate fixed sets of taxonomic characters that were applicable to orders, families, subfamilies, and genera of birds, but such a tabulation is not possible. Taxonomic characters fall into five main groups (morphological, physiological, ecological, ethological, and geographical), but "the taxonomic categories are not a consequence of the characters, but rather the opposite—the taxonomic characters are a consequence of the categories" (Mayr *et al.,* 1953: 121). The problem begins at the generic level, as indicated above (p. 353) with reference to the genus *Corvus.* The aim of the taxonomist in erecting or conceiving a genus is to include in it those species that have evolved from a common ancestor. The "characters of the genus," therefore, vary with the group of species involved. Inasmuch as subfamilies are composed of groups of genera, and families are composed of groups of subfamilies, the "diagnostic features" will vary among the families. *"A family may be defined as a systematic category including one genus or a group of genera of common phylogenetic origin, which is separated from other families by a decided gap"* (Mayr *et al.,* 1953: 51). It is clear, therefore, that there are no set characters or criteria that can be applied throughout the families or orders of birds. The taxonomist must find the characters by studying the birds.

"The use of taxonomic characters in classification is based on the simple fact that some characters change very rapidly in evolution, while others only change slowly. The rapidly changing characters are used to distinguish subspecies and species; the slowly changing ones are used to characterize the higher categories" (Mayr *et al.,* 1953: 123). By and large, however, the simplicity of the problem ends with that straightforward statement. Wetmore (1951) recognized 27 orders of recent birds; Stresemann (1927–1934) recognized 48 orders. There is less diversity of opinion on the families of nonpasserine birds, but there is considerable disagreement both on the number and arrangement of passerine families. A few passerine families are admittedly "taxonomic wastebaskets." The crux of

Fig. 4. Color patterns in the honey-eater genus *Myzomela* (black, solid; white, blank; red, vertical lines; yellow, stippled; gray or brown, closely hatched): A. *obscura fumata*, B. *eques*, C. *rosenbergii*, D. *nigrita forbesi*, E. *erythrocephala*, F. *erythromelas*, G. *vulnerata*, H. *dibapha wakaloensis*, I. *cardinalis lifuensis*, J. *cardinalis chermesina*, K. *cruentata cruentata*, L. *pulchella*, M. *sclateri*, N. *eichhorni atrata*, O. *lafargei*, P. *melanocephala*, Q. *malaitae*, R. *jugularis*. (Courtesy of Karl Koopman and the editor of *The Auk*.)

the problem, therefore, must be that of deciding which are plastic and which are relatively stable characters in an evolutionary sense. Let us reconsider some of the factors that tend to conceal phylogenetic relationships and which make it difficult to sort out meaningful taxonomic characters. If one assumes, with Mayr *et al.* (1953: 49–50), that "all the species of a genus occupy a more or less well-defined ecological niche," so that "it is probable that all generic characters are either adaptive or correlated with adaptive characters," one is confronted with all of the problems created by convergence in form and function among unrelated birds. The problem is increased immeasureably among passerine families, which, in general, differ less (morphologically) among themselves than do many nonpasserine genera.

With the exception of a few isolated instances, so little is known about physiological, ethological, and ecological differences, especially among the "problem" groups, that data from these fields of study must be collected and evaluated critically if the usual taxonomic pitfalls are to be avoided. In actual practice anatomical characters form the primary basis for current systems of classification. However, a given morphological feature may be of unequal importance in unrelated birds. The number of rectrices within different groups of birds, for example, may be a generic character, a subspecific character, or a matter of individual variation within a population. The adaptation of the forelimb for flight (and concomitant changes in other parts of the body) makes it extremely difficult to analyze the wing muscles and bones with respect to phylogenetic relationships and to correlation with type of flight and general locomotor pattern. Moreover, "a change of feeding habits in birds may result eventually in structural modifications of the bill, the tongue, the palate, the jaw muscles, the stomach, and perhaps other features. All these characters are a single adaptive complex and should not be treated and considered as a series of independent characters" (Mayr *et al.,* 1953: 123). There are few, if any, morphological features that can be considered to have been studied intensively throughout the families and orders of birds. The basic arrangement of the Passeriformes rests primarily on data (syringeal muscles) published during the last century, data which have been neither corroborated nor extended. Efforts to reconstruct the phylogeny of that order, or of the suborder Passeres, on the basis of a single character or a series of interdependent characters are not very rewarding. Such attempts reveal not only a lack of understanding of convergence and divergence among birds but also a naïve concept of basic morphology, including a failure to appreciate the dynamic interaction between developing bones and between bones and muscles. There are two well-considered schools of thought on which groups of passerines (fringillids or corvids) should be placed last in the classification, i.e., are the highest evolved birds. Not until the morphology of all of the genera in these families has been studied carefully can we begin to appreciate fully which are the relatively stable characters that will give clues to phylogeny in the Oscines.

References

Amadon, Dean. 1943. Specialization and Evolution. *Amer. Nat.*, 77: 133–141.

———— 1949. The Seventy-five Per Cent Rule for Subspecies. *Condor*, 51: 250–258.

———— 1950. The Hawaiian Honeycreepers (Aves, Drepaniidae). *Bull. Amer. Mus. Nat. Hist.*, 95: 151–262.

———— 1953. Migratory Birds of Relict Distribution: Some Inferences. *Auk*, 70: 461–469.

———— 1957. Remarks on the classification of the perching birds [order Passeriformes]. *Proc. Zool. Soc. Calcutta, Mookerjee Memor. Vol.*: 259–268.

American Ornithologists' Union. 1957. *Check-List of North American Birds.* 5th ed. Amer. Ornith. Union, Baltimore, Md.

Berger, Andrew J. 1958. The Golden-winged–Blue-winged Warbler Complex in Michigan and the Great Lakes Area. *Jack-Pine Warbler*, 36: 37–73.

Blackwelder, Richard E. 1941. The Gender of Scientific Names in Zoology. *Jour. Wash. Acad. Sci.*, 31: 135–140.

Chapin, James P. 1929. Eye-Color as a Subspecific Character in *Colius striatus*. *Jour. f. Ornith.*, 77: 174–183.

———— 1948. Variation and Hybridization Among the Paradise Flycatchers of Africa. *Evolution*, 2: 111–126.

Chapman, Frank M. 1920. Unusual Types of Apparent Geographic Variation in Color and Individual Variation in Size Exhibited by Ostinops decumanus. *Proc. Biol. Soc. Wash.*, 33: 25–32.

———— 1940. The Post-Glacial History of *Zonotrichia capensis*. *Bull. Amer. Mus. Nat. Hist.*, 77: 381–438.

Clay, Theresa. 1947. The Systematic Position of the Musophagi as indicated by their Mallophagan Parasites. *Ibis*, 89: 654–656.

Cockrum, E. Lendell. 1952. A Check-list and Bibliography of Hybrid Birds in North America North of Mexico. *Wils. Bull.*, 64: 140–159.

Cotter, William B., Jr. 1957. A Serological Analysis of Some Anatid Classifications. *Wils. Bull.*, 69: 291–300.

Cushing, John E., Jr. 1941. Non-Genetic Mating Preference as a Factor in Evolution. *Condor*, 43: 233–236.

Delacour, Jean, and Charles Vaurie. 1957. A Classification of the Oscines (Aves). *Contri. in Science, No. 16* (Los Angeles County Mus.).

Dementiev, G. P., and V. F. Larionov. 1945. The Development of Geographical Variations, with special reference to Birds. *Proc. Zool. Soc. London*, 115: 85–96.

Dice, Lee R. 1945. Measures of the Amount of Ecologic Association between Species. *Ecology*, 26: 297–302.

———— 1948. Application of Statistical Methods to the Analysis of Ecologic Association Between Species of Birds. *Amer. Midl. Nat.*, 39: 174–178.

Dilger, William C. 1956. Hostile Behavior and Reproductive Isolating Mechanisms in the Avian Genera *Catharus* and *Hylocichla*. *Auk*, 73: 313–353.

Dixon, Keith L. 1955. An Ecological Analysis of the Interbreeding of Crested Titmice in Texas. *Univ. Calif. Publ. Zool.*, 54: 125–206.

Dobzhansky, Theodosius. 1941. *Genetics and the Origin of Species.* Columbia Univ. Press, New York.

Friedmann, Herbert. 1946. Ecological Counterparts in Birds. *Sci. Monthly,* 63: 395–398.

——— 1955. Recent Revisions in Classification and Their Biological Significance. In *Recent Studies in Avian Biology.* Univ. Illinois Press, Urbana, pp. 23–43.

Frizzell, Donald Leslie. 1933. Terminology of Types. *Amer. Midl. Nat.,* 14: 637–668.

Griscom, Ludlow. 1950. Distribution and Origin of the Birds of Mexico. *Bull. Mus. Comp. Zoöl.,* 103: 341–382.

Gulick, Addison. 1932. Biological Peculiarities of Oceanic Islands. *Quart. Rev. Biol.,* 7: 405–427.

Hopkins, G. H. E. 1942. The Mallophaga as an Aid to the Classification of Birds. *Ibis,* 1942: 94–106.

Howard, Hildegarde. 1947. A Preliminary Survey of Trends in Avian Evolution from Pleistocene to Recent Time. *Condor,* 49: 10–13.

Huxley, Julian. 1942. *Evolution. The Modern Synthesis.* Harper & Brothers, New York.

Ihering, Herman v. 1915. The Classification of the Family Dendrocolaptidae. *Auk,* 32: 145–153.

Jourdain, F. C. R. 1915. The Bearing of Oology on Classification. *Bull. Brit. Ornith. Club,* 36: 11–28.

Kelso, Leon. 1940. Variation of the External Ear-opening in the Strigidae. *Wils. Bull.,* 52: 24–29.

——— and Estelle H. Kelso. 1936. The Relation of Feathering of Feet of American Owls to Humidity of Environment and to Life Zone. *Auk,* 53: 51–56.

Koopman, Karl F. 1957. Evolution in the Genus *Myzomela* (Aves: Meliphagidae). *Auk,* 74: 49–72.

Lack, David. 1940. Habitat Selection and Speciation in Birds. *Brit. Birds,* 34: 80–84.

——— 1944. Ecological Aspects of Species-formation in Passerine Birds. *Ibis,* 86: 260–286.

——— 1956. A Review of the Genera and Nesting Habits of Swifts. *Auk,* 73: 1–32.

Lanham, Urless N. 1947. Notes on the Phylogeny of the Pelecaniformes. *Auk,* 64: 65–70.

Lanyon, Wesley E. 1956. Ecological Aspects of the Sympatric Distribution of Meadowlarks in the North-central States. *Ecology,* 37: 98–108.

Lowe, Percy R. 1926. More Notes on the Quadrate as a Factor in Avian Classification. *Ibis,* 1926: 152–188.

——— 1939. On the Systematic Position of the Swifts (Suborder Cypseli) and Humming-birds (Suborder Trochili), with Special Reference to their Relation to the Order Passeriformes. *Trans. Zool. Soc. London,* 24: 307–348.

Mayr, Ernst. 1940. *Pericrocotus brevirostris* and its Double. *Ibis,* 1940: 712–722.

——— 1942. *Systematics and the Origin of Species.* Columbia Univ. Press, New York.

——— 1943. Criteria of Subspecies, Species and Genera in Ornithology. *Annals N. Y. Acad. Sci.,* 44: 133–140.

——— 1946a. The Number of Species of Birds. *Auk,* 63: 64–69.

——— 1946b. History of the North American Bird Fauna. *Wils. Bull.,* 58: 3–41.

——— 1948. The Bearing of the New Systematics on Genetical Problems. The

Nature of Species. In *Advances in Genetics,* Vol. II. Academic Press, New York, pp. 205–237.

——— 1951. Speciation in Birds. Progress Report on the Years 1938–1950. *Proc. 10th Internatl. Ornith. Congr. 1950:* 91–131.

——— 1954. Notes on Nomenclature and Classification. *Systematic Zool.,* 3: 86–89.

——— 1955. Comments on Some Recent Studies of Song Bird Phylogeny. *Wils. Bull.,* 67: 33–44.

——— 1956. Geographical Character Gradients and Climatic Adaptation. *Evolution,* 10: 105–108.

——— 1958. The Sequence of the Songbird Families. *Condor,* 60: 194–195.

——— and Dean Amadon. 1951. A Classification of Recent Birds. *Amer. Mus. Novitates, No. 1496.*

Mayr, Ernst, R. J. Andrew, and R. A. Hinde. 1956. Die systematische Stellung der Gattung *Fringilla. Jour. f. Ornith.,* 97: 258–273.

Mayr, Ernst, and James Bond. 1943. Notes on the Generic Classification of the Swallows, Hirundinidae. *Ibis,* 85: 334–341.

Mayr, Ernst, and J. C. Greenway, Jr. 1956. Sequence of Passerine Families (Aves). *Breviora* (Mus. Comp. Zool. Harvard), 58: 1–11.

Mayr, Ernst, E. Gorton Linsley, and Robert L. Usinger. 1953. *Methods and Principles of Systematic Zoology.* McGraw-Hill Book Co., New York.

Mayr, Ernst, and Charles Vaurie. 1948. Evolution in the Family Dicruridae (Birds). *Evolution,* 2: 238–265.

Mengel, Robert M. 1957. A Catalog of an Exhibition of Landmarks in the Development of Ornithology . . . . Univ. Kansas Libraries, Lawrence.

Miller, Alden H. 1941. A Review of Centers of Differentiation for Birds in the Western Great Basin Region. *Condor,* 43: 257–267.

——— 1942. Habitat Selection Among Higher Vertebrates and its Relation to Intraspecific Variation. *Amer. Nat.,* 76: 25–35.

——— 1947. Panmixia and Population Size with Reference to Birds. *Evolution,* 1: 186–190.

——— 1955. Concepts and Problems of Avian Systematics in Relation to Evolutionary Processes. In *Recent Studies in Avian Biology.* Univ. Illinois Press, Urbana, pp. 1–22.

Moreau, R. E. 1948. Some Recent Terms and Tendencies in Bird Taxonomy. *Ibis,* 90: 102–111.

Murphy, Robert Cushman. 1938. The Need of Insular Exploration as Illustrated by Birds. *Science,* 88: 533–539.

Neave, Sheffield Airey. 1939–1940. *Nomenclator Zoologicus.* A List of the Names of Genera and Subgenera in Zoology from the Tenth Edition of Linnaeus 1758 to the End of 1935. Zool. Soc., London.

Oliver, W. R. B. 1945. Avian Evolution in New Zealand and Australia. *Emu,* 45: 55–77; 119–152.

Parkes, Kenneth C. 1951. The Genetics of the Golden-winged × Blue-winged Warbler Complex. *Wils. Bull.,* 63: 5–15.

Peterle, Tony J. 1951. Intergeneric Galliform Hybrids: A Review. *Wils. Bull.,* 63: 219–224.

Plotnick, Ruben, and M. J. I. Pergolani de Costa. 1955. Clave de las familias de Passeriformes representadas en la Argentina. *Rev. Invest. Agric.,* 9: 65–88.

Rand, A. L. 1936. Altitudinal Variation in New Guinea Birds. *Amer. Mus. Novitates, No. 890.*
Rensch, Bernard. 1929. *Das Prinzip geographischer Rassenkreise und das Problem der Artbildung.* Gebrüder Borntraeger, Berlin.
Richardson, Frank. 1942. Adaptive Modifications for Tree-trunk Foraging in Birds. *Univ. Calif. Publ. Zool.,* 46: 317–368.
Schenk, Edward T., and John H. McMasters. 1956. *Procedure in Taxonomy.* 3rd ed. Stanford Univ. Press, California.
Schmitt, Waldo L. 1954. Applied Systematics: Usefulness of Scientific Names of Animals and Plants. *Ann. Rept. Smiths. Inst. for 1953:* 323–337.
Sibley, Charles G. 1954. Hybridization in the Red-eyed Towhees of Mexico. *Evolution,* 8: 252–290.
——— 1957. The Evolutionary and Taxonomic Significance of Sexual Dimorphism and Hybridization in Birds. *Condor,* 59: 166–191.
Simonetta, Alberto. 1957. Osservazioni sulla meccanica del cranio degli uccelli dromeognati. *Atti Soc. Toscana Sci. Nat. Pisa, Ser. B,* 64: 140–167.
Simpson, George G. 1953. *The Major Features of Evolution.* Columbia Univ. Press, New York.
Skutch, Alexander F. 1951. Congeneric Species of Birds Nesting Together in Central America. *Condor,* 53: 3–15.
Snow, D. W. 1954. Trends in Geographical Variation in Palaearctic Members of the Genus Parus. *Evolution,* 8: 19–28.
——— 1955. Geographical Variation of the Coal Tit, *Parus ater* L. *Ardea,* 43: 195–226.
Steiner, H. 1956. Die taxonomische und phylogenetische Bedeutung der Diastataxie des Vogelflügels. *Jour. f. Ornith.,* 97: 1–20.
Stimson, Louis A. 1956. The Cape Sable Seaside Sparrow: Its Former and Present Distribution. *Auk,* 73: 489–502.
Stresemann, Erwin. 1924. Scientific Nomenclature. *Auk,* 41: 507–512.
——— 1927–1934. Aves. Vol. 7, part 2, of *Handbuch der Zoologie,* W. Kükenthal and T. Krumbach. Walter de Gruyter, Berlin.
——— 1936. The Formenkreis-Theory. *Auk,* 53: 150–158.
——— 1950. The Development of Theories Which Affected the Taxonomy of Birds. *Ibis,* 92: 123–131.
Sutton, George Miksch, and David F. Parmelee. 1954. Survival Problems of the Water-pipit in Baffin Island. *Arctic,* 7: 81–92.
Tordoff, Harrison B. 1954. Relationships in the New World Nine-Primaried Oscines. *Auk,* 71: 273–284.
Traylor, Melvin A. 1950. Altitudinal Variation in Bolivian Birds. *Condor,* 52: 123–126.
Tucker, B. W. 1949. Species and Subspecies: A Review for General Ornithologists. *Brit. Birds,* 42: 129–134; 161–174; 193–205.
Uttal, Leonard J. 1941. Tarsal Feathering of Ruffed Grouse. *Auk,* 58: 74–79.
Van Tyne, Josselyn. 1952. Principles and Practices in Collecting and Taxonomic Work. *Auk,* 69: 27–33.
——— 1955. Evolution in the Toucan Genus *Ramphastos. Acta XI Congr. Internatl. Ornith., 1954:* 362–368.
Vaurie, Charles. 1949. A Revision of the Bird Family Dicruridae. *Bull. Amer. Mus. Nat. Hist.,* 93: 205–342.

Verheyen René. 1956. Analyse du Potential morphologique et Projet d'une nouvelle Classification des Psittaciformes. *Inst. Roy. Sci. Nat. Bel., Bull.,* 32: 1–54.

——— 1957. Contribution au demembrement de L'Ordo artificiel des Gruiformes (Peters 1934). I—Les Ralliformes. *Inst. Roy. Sci. Nat. Bel., Bull.,* 33: 1–44.

Wetherbee, David Kenneth. 1957. Natal Plumages and Downy Pteryloses of Passerine Birds of North America. *Bull. Amer. Mus. Nat. Hist.,* 113: 339–436.

Wetmore, Alexander. 1951. A Revised Classification for the Birds of the World. *Smiths. Misc. Coll.,* 117.

——— 1957. The Classification of the Oscine Passeriformes. *Condor,* 59: 207–209.

Wilson, E. O., and W. L. Brown, Jr. 1953. The Subspecies Concept and Its Taxonomic Application. *Systematic Zool.,* 2: 97-111.

Wright, Sewall. 1948. On the Roles of Directed and Random Changes in Gene Frequency in the Genetics of Populations. *Evolution,* 2: 279–294.

13. The classification of world birds by families

We now recognize about 8600 species of birds in the world (E. Mayr and D. Amadon, *Amer. Mus. Novitates, No. 1496,* 1951). No museum in the world contains specimens of all of them and no ornithologist can immediately recognize all of them, even as specimens in the hand. Only by grouping like species into larger categories, which we call "families," can we begin to deal with them with any success.

Most ornithologists agree on dividing world birds into about 170 families. These families contain from 1 to more than 300 species and any ornithologist who has had a little experience in a museum that has a general, world-wide collection of birds can promptly place *most* specimens in the proper family.

By definition, a family is a monophyletic group (i.e., it stems from some single ancestral species), and many families are so well marked that there is not the slightest disagreement among ornithologists about which species should be included in those families. Among such families are the parrots, the hummingbirds, and toucans. Other families (to be found mainly among the passerine birds) have not yet evolved far enough to be sharply demarked and there is considerable disagreement among ornithologists about where the boundary lines should be drawn.

As we pass from the more ancient types of birds (such as the struthious birds, the grebes, the tinamous, etc.) to what we may call the modern birds (i.e., the "Songbirds"), the differences between the family groups we have set up become less and less. In fact, this is really forced upon us by the great evolutionary proliferation of modern birds. They constitute much more than half of all the species now known. Yet if we rigidly maintained the same standards as we work through the birds of the world, setting up family groups from the ostriches and rheas down to the modern songbirds, we would probably place all passerine birds (or at least the songbirds—the suborder Passeres) in one family. Since this is obviously inexpedient, we have divided these songbirds into 44 to 48 families. Insofar as we have done this correctly, the birds in each family are related to each other more closely than to the species in any other group.

One interesting but unfortunate tendency evident of late has been the trend toward reducing the status of certain apparently closely related families to that of subfamilies of some single, all-inclusive family. For example, one worker suggests that we unite in one family the Waxwings (Bombycillidae), the Palmchats (Dulidae), and the Silky-flycatchers (Ptilogonatidae). It is true that these three groups seem to be more closely related to each other than they are to other families, but we fail to see what is to be gained by lumping them. It has been known for a very long time that there are many degrees of relationship between our family categories—*so* many that we cannot hope to express them all in our linear arrangement of families. Since that is the case, we prefer to maintain in this book the waxwings, the palmchats, and the silky-flycatchers—three units about each of which one can make some fairly clear generalizations, both in regard to external appearance and habits.

In this connection we may quote a very pertinent and well-expressed paragraph from the second volume of the great Witherby *Handbook of British Birds* (Vol. 2, 1938, p. 1):

> . . . we consider it preferable to recognize the *Muscicapidae, Sylviidae,* and *Turdidae* as distinct families rather than to merge them into one huge and unwieldy family [= 1109 spp.], as was done by Hartert. It may be repeated that the above three groups evidently do represent the main lines of divergence within this admittedly allied assemblage, and the several stocks are not less worthy of recognition because a small number of more generalized types tend to link them up and do not fit readily into simple definitions. In any case definition is not rendered any easier by lumping them together.

Family Descriptions

These statements of family attributes have been greatly condensed and a few explanatory remarks are probably needed.

Physical characteristics. Length is, of course, the distance from the tip of the bill to the tip of the tail. This is at best an inexact measurement because it depends a great deal on how much the curves in the bird's spinal column are straightened out when the measurement is made. For this reason collectors rarely even record it, and as a result we often have to use the even less accurate measurement taken from a museum specimen. Nevertheless, there seems to be no other measurement which will serve as well to tell the student the general size of a bird and therefore we have used "length" figures to describe the size range within each bird family and to give the scale for birds figured.

Range is the breeding range only. Also, man-made changes are ignored.

Habits. In many cases the data on habits, especially breeding habits, are necessarily based on very scanty information. As our knowledge increases, some of these statements will surely be greatly modified. However, for the sake of brevity we have not modified all of these statements with phrases like "as far as now known."

Breeding. Egg number is the normal number (as far as known), ignoring rare individual extremes.

Technical diagnosis. Instead of using the space that would be required for a recital of the technical characters of each family (facts which cannot possibly be remembered to any important extent) we have given a reference to a good published statement, again keeping in mind the general availability of publications.

References. For each family we give references to several of the best published studies on the habits, especially breeding habits. In choosing these we have for practical reasons tended to favor English language papers and particularly those most generally available in American libraries.

References to the most commonly cited works in the Technical diagnosis, Classification, and Reference items are given in brief in order to save space. Thus, for example, Murphy, 1: 329–471, means Vol. 1 of R. C. Murphy's *Oceanic Birds of South America,* published in 1936, pages 329–471.

Alexander, W. B., *Birds of the Ocean.* G. P. Putnam, New York. 1st ed., 1928; 2nd ed., 1954.

Baker, E. C. Stuart, *Fauna of British India: Birds.* Taylor & Francis, London. 8 vols. 1922–1930.

Baker, E. C. Stuart, *The Nidification of Birds of the Indian Empire.* Taylor & Francis, London. 4 vols. 1932–1935.

Bannerman, D. A., *The Birds of Tropical West Africa.* Crown Agents for the Colonies, London. 7 vols. 1930–1949.

Beddard, F. E., *The Structure and Classification of Birds.* Longmans, Green, New York. 1898.

Bent, A. C., Life Histories of North American Birds. *U. S. Natl. Mus. Bulletins.* 1919–1953.

Cory, C. B., B. Conover, and C. E. Hellmayr, Catalogue of Birds of the Americas. *Field Mus. Nat. Hist., Zool. Ser.,* vol. 13. Part 1, 1942–1949, is by C. E. Hellmayr and B. Conover. Part 2, 1918, is by C. B. Cory. Parts 3–5, 1924–1927, are by C. B. Cory and C. E. Hellmayr. Parts 6–11, 1929–1938, are by C. E. Hellmayr.

Mathews, G. M., *The Birds of Australia.* H. F. & G. Witherby, London. 12 vols. 1910–1927.

Murphy, R. C., *Oceanic Birds of South America.* The Macmillan Co. 2 vols. 1936.

Peters, J. L., *Check-list of Birds of the World.* Harvard Univ. Press, Cambridge, Mass. 7 vols. 1931–1951.

Ridgway, R., and H. Friedmann, Birds of North and Middle America. *U. S. Natl. Mus. Bull.,* vol. 50. Parts 1–8, 1901–1919, are by R. Ridgway. Parts 9 and 10, 1941 and 1946, are by R. Ridgway and H. Friedmann. Part 11, 1950, is by H. Friedmann.

Witherby, H. F., *et al., Handbook of British Birds.* H. F. & G. Witherby, London. 5 vols. 1938–1941.

Wytsman, P. [hilogène]. *Genera Avium.* V. Verteneuil & L. Desmet, Brussels. 26 parts. 1905–1914.

The drawings for this chapter are by George M. Sutton.

Orders and Families of Living Birds of the World

SPHENISCIFORMES
Spheniscidae—Penguin family

STRUTHIONIFORMES
Struthionidae—Ostrich family

RHEIFORMES

Rheidae—Rhea family

CASUARIIFORMES

Casuariidae—Cassowary family

Dromiceiidae—Emu family

APTERYGIFORMES

Apterygidae—Kiwi family

TINAMIFORMES

Tinamidae—Tinamou family

GAVIIFORMES

Gaviidae—Loon family

PODICIPEDIFORMES

Podicipedidae—Grebe family

PROCELLARIIFORMES

Diomedeidae—Albatross family

Procellariidae—Shearwater family

Hydrobatidae—Storm-petrel family

Pelecanoididae—Diving-petrel family

PELECANIFORMES

Phaëthontidae—Tropicbird family

Pelecanidae—Pelican family

Sulidae—Booby family

Phalacrocoracidae—Cormorant family

Anhingidae—Anhinga family

Fregatidae—Frigatebird family

CICONIIFORMES

Ardeidae—Heron family

Cochleariidae—Boat-billed Heron family

Balaenicipitidae—Whale-billed Stork family

Scopidae—Hammerhead family

Ciconiidae—Stork family

Threskiornithidae—Ibis family

Phoenicopteridae—Flamingo family

ANSERIFORMES

Anhimidae—Screamer family

Anatidae—Duck family

FALCONIFORMES

Cathartidae—American Vulture family

Sagittariidae—Secretarybird family
Accipitridae—Hawk family
Pandionidae—Osprey family
Falconidae—Falcon family

GALLIFORMES

Megapodiidae—Megapode family
Cracidae—Curassow family
Tetraonidae—Grouse family
Phasianidae—Pheasant family
Numididae—Guineafowl family
Meleagrididae—Turkey family

Opisthocomidae—Hoatzin family

GRUIFORMES

Mesoenatidae—Mesite family

Turnicidae—Hemipode-quail family
Pedionomidae—Collared-hemipode family

Gruidae—Crane family
Aramidae—Limpkin family
Psophiidae—Trumpeter family
Rallidae—Rail family

Heliornithidae—Finfoot family

Rhynochetidae—Kagu family

Eurypygidae—Sunbittern family

Cariamidae—Cariama family

Otididae—Bustard family

CHARADRIIFORMES

Jacanidae—Jaçana family
Rostratulidae—Painted-snipe family
Haematopodidae—Oystercatcher family
Charadriidae—Plover family
Scolopacidae—Sandpiper family
Recurvirostridae—Avocet family
Phalaropodidae—Phalarope family
Dromadidae—Crabplover family
Burhinidae—Thick-knee family
Glareolidae—Pratincole family
Thinocoridae—Seedsnipe family
Chionididae—Sheathbill family

Stercorariidae—Skua family
Laridae—Gull family
Rynchopidae—Skimmer family

Alcidae—Auk family

COLUMBIFORMES

Pteroclidae—Sandgrouse family

Columbidae—Pigeon family

PSITTACIFORMES

Psittacidae—Parrot family

MUSOPHAGIFORMES

Musophagidae—Touraco family

CUCULIFORMES

Cuculidae—Cuckoo family

STRIGIFORMES

Tytonidae—Barn-owl family

Strigidae—Typical-owl family

CAPRIMULGIFORMES

Steatornithidae—Oilbird family

Podargidae—Frogmouth family

Nyctibiidae—Potoo family

Aegothelidae—Owlet-frogmouth family

Caprimulgidae—Nightjar family

APODIFORMES

Apodidae—Swift family

Hemiprocnidae—Crested-swift family

Trochilidae—Hummingbird family

COLIIFORMES

Coliidae—Coly family

TROGONIFORMES

Trogonidae—Trogon family

CORACIIFORMES

Alcedinidae—Kingfisher family

Todidae—Tody family

Momotidae—Motmot family

Meropidae—Bee-eater family

Coraciidae—Roller family

Leptosomatidae—Cuckoo-roller family

Upupidae—Hoopoe family

Phoeniculidae—Woodhoopoe family

Bucerotidae—Hornbill family

PICIFORMES

Galbulidae—Jacamar family

Bucconidae—Puffbird family

Capitonidae—Barbet family
Indicatoridae—Honeyguide family
Ramphastidae—Toucan family
Picidae—Woodpecker family
Jyngidae—Wryneck family

PASSERIFORMES
Suborder EURYLAIMI
Eurylaimidae—Broadbill family
Suborder TYRANNI
Dendrocolaptidae—Woodcreeper family
Furnariidae—Ovenbird family
Formicariidae—Antbird family
Conopophagidae—Antpipit family
Rhinocryptidae—Tapaculo family
Cotingidae—Cotinga family
Pipridae—Manakin family
Tyrannidae—Tyrant-flycatcher family
Oxyruncidae—Sharpbill family
Phytotomidae—Plantcutter family
Pittidae—Pitta family
Acanthisittidae—New Zealand Wren family
Philepittidae—Asity family
Suborder MENURAE
Menuridae—Lyrebird family
Atrichornithidae—Scrub-bird family
Suborder PASSERES ("Oscines" of many authors)
Alaudidae—Lark family
Hirundinidae—Swallow family
Campephagidae—Cuckoo-shrike family
Dicruridae—Drongo family
Oriolidae—Oriole family
Corvidae—Crow family
Cracticidae—Bellmagpie family
Grallinidae—Mudnest-builder family
Ptilonorhynchidae—Bowerbird family
Paradisaeidae—Bird-of-paradise family
Paridae—Titmouse family
Sittidae—Common Nuthatch family
Neosittidae—Australian Nuthatch family
Hyposittidae—Coral-billed Nuthatch family
Certhiidae—Creeper family
Timaliidae—Babbler family
Pycnonotidae—Bulbul family
Irenidae—Leafbird family
Cinclidae—Dipper family

Troglodytidae—Wren family
Mimidae—Mockingbird family
Turdidae—Thrush family
Zeledoniidae—Wren-thrush family
Sylviidae—Old-world Warbler family
Muscicapidae—Old-world Flycatcher family
Prunellidae—Hedge-sparrow family
Motacillidae—Pipit family
Bombycillidae—Waxwing family
Ptilogonatidae—Silky-flycatcher family
Dulidae—Palmchat family
Artamidae—Wood-swallow family
Vangidae—Vanga-shrike family
Laniidae—Shrike family
Prionopidae—Wood-shrike family
Callaeidae—Wattlebird family
Sturnidae—Starling family
Meliphagidae—Honey-eater family
Nectariniidae—Sunbird family
Dicaeidae—Flowerpecker family
Zosteropidae—White-eye family
Cyclarhidae—Pepper-shrike family
Vireolaniidae—Shrike-vireo family
Vireonidae—Vireo family
Drepaniidae—Hawaiian Honeycreeper family
Parulidae—American Wood-warbler family
Icteridae—Troupial family
Tersinidae—Swallow-tanager family
Thraupidae—Tanager family
Catamblyrhynchidae—Plush-capped Finch family
Ploceidae—Weaverbird family
Fringillidae—Finch family

SPHENISCIDAE

Penguin family (17 species)

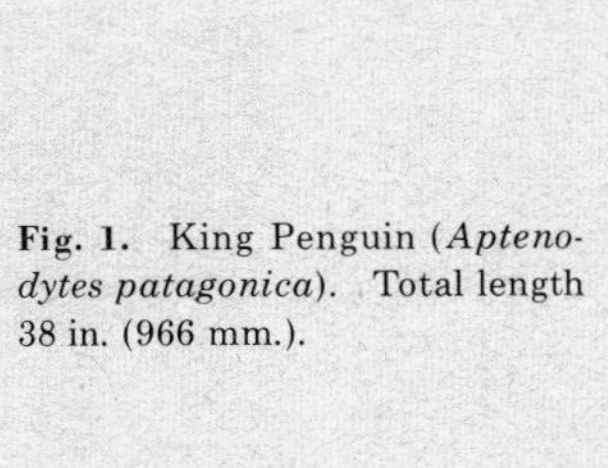

Fig. 1. King Penguin (*Aptenodytes patagonica*). Total length 38 in. (966 mm.).

Physical characteristics. Length—406 to 1219 mm. (16 to 48 in.). Plumage an extremely dense, compact coat of very small glossy feathers; gray or black above, white below; specific distinctions in pattern and color mainly confined to head and neck; in some, long superciliary crests, yellow on sides of head or neck, etc. No apteria. Bill short and stout to rather long and curved. Neck short; body stout. Wings are paddlelike, with scalelike remiges, and do not fold. Tail very short. Legs short and stout, set far back; feet webbed. Sexes alike.

Range. Coasts of Antarctica; subantarctic islands; s. coasts of Australia, Africa, and S. America; n. along w. coast of S. America to the Galápagos (on equator). Some spp. migratory.

Habits. Gregarious. Most completely marine of all birds. Flightless. Swim low in water, using wings alone, frequently leaping and diving porpoise-fashion. On land or ice walk upright, hop, or slide on belly. Voice—loud harsh brays, croaks, barks, or trumpeting calls.

Food. Fish, squid, crustacea.

Breeding. Nest on ground or ice (in some spp. the egg is held, sometimes carried, on top of the feet), or in burrows or caves—sometimes lined with grass or sticks.

Eggs. 1 or 2 (rarely 3); immaculate; white to pale olive-green. Incubated by ♂ and ♀.

Young. Nidicolous. Downy. Cared for by ♂ and ♀.

Technical diagnosis. Beddard, 396–402 ("Sphenisci").

Classification. Peters, 1, 1931: 29–33.

References. Murphy, 1: 329–471; Alexander, 1928: 214–233, pls. 51–57 (1954: 146–159, pls. 51–57).

E. A. Wilson, Vertebrata. Aves, in *Natl. Antarctic Exped. Nat. Hist.,* vol. 2, Zoology, London, 1907: 1–62, col. pls. 1–11, figs. 1–39.

B. Roberts, The Breeding Behaviour of Penguins with Special Reference to *Pygoscelis papua* (Forster). *Brit. Graham Land Exped. 1934–37, Sci. Repts.,* 1, 1940: 195–254, 4 pls.

G. G. Simpson, Fossil Penguins, *Bull. Amer. Mus. Nat. Hist.,* 87, 1946: 1–99, illus.

L. E. Richdale, Sexual Behavior in Penguins, Lawrence, Kans., 1951, 316 pp., 22 pls.

Synonym: Aptenodytidae.

STRUTHIONIDAE

Ostrich family (1 species)

Fig. 2. Ostrich (*Struthio camelus*). Total length 72 in. (1829 mm.).

Physical characteristics. Length—about 1829 mm. (72 in.). The largest extant bird, attaining 300 lb. (136 kilos) in weight, 8 ft. (2.44 m.) in height. Body plumage soft and loose-webbed (black in ♂, brownish gray in ♀), sparse on head and most of neck. Thighs bare. Remiges and rectrices (the "plumes" of commerce) very numerous, white in ♂, brownish gray in ♀. Bill short and flat; eyes very large; head small and neck long. Legs long and powerful; 2 toes (3rd and 4th). Sexes unlike.

Range. Africa (exc. c. West Africa), Arabia, and s. Syria. Habitat—open arid country. Nonmigratory.

Habits. Somewhat gregarious. Cursorial; run swiftly. Flightless. Crouch in presence of danger. Voice—a loud hiss; a booming roar (♂ in breeding season).

Food. Succulent plants, berries, seeds; some animal food.

Breeding. Polygamous? Nest a depression scraped in ground (by ♀).

Eggs. 10 to 20 or 25 (two or more ♀♀ often lay in one nest); with glossy, pitted surface; cream-colored. Incubated by ♂ (at night only) and ♀.

Young. Nidifugous. Downy. Cared for by ♂ and ♀.

Technical diagnosis. Beddard, 495–496.

Classification. Peters, 1, 1931: 3–4.

References. C. W. Beebe, The Ostriches and their Allies, *9th Ann. Rept. N. Y. Zool. Soc.,* 1905.

H. Poisson, L'Autruche, in *Encyclopédie Ornithologique,* Paris, vol. 2, 1926.

B. Laufer, Ostrich Egg-shell Cups of Mesopotamia and the Ostrich in Ancient and Modern Times, *Field Mus. Nat. Hist., Anthrop. Leaflet,* 23, 1926.

L. S. Crandall, The Struthious Birds. II. The Ostriches and Rheas, *Bull. N. Y. Zool. Soc.,* 32, no. 5, 1929: 193–212.

F. J. Jackson, *The Birds of Kenya Colony and the Uganda Protectorate,* London, vol. 1, 1938: 4–9.

K. M. Schneider, Vom Brutleben des Strausses (*Struthio*) in Gefangenschaft, in G. Creutz (ed.), *Beiträge zur Vogelkunde,* Leipzig, 1949, pp. 169–272, illus.

RHEIDAE

Rhea family (2 species)

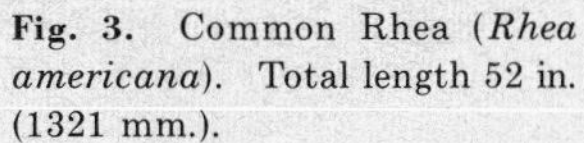

Fig. 3. Common Rhea (*Rhea americana*). Total length 52 in. (1321 mm.).

Physical characteristics. Length—914 to 1321 mm. (36 to 52 in.). The heaviest New World bird—weighs about 44 lb. (20 kilos). Plumage—loose-webbed; brownish gray, with some areas of paler, and some of darker, feathers on head, neck, and under parts; body and wing feathers white-tipped in one sp. Wide, flat bill. Neck long. Wings short, with long, soft remiges. No rectrices. Legs long and powerful; 3 toes (2nd, 3rd, and 4th). Sexes very similar—♂ slightly larger and darker.

Range. Eastern Brazil (Rio Grande do Norte), s. Bolivia, and s.e. Peru south to Straits of Magellan. Habitat—grassland and open-brush country. Nonmigratory.

Habits. Gregarious. Cursorial; run swiftly. Flightless. Swim well. Crouch in presence of danger. Voice—adult, a deep boom; young, a whistle.

Food. Grass, roots, and seeds; also insects, mollusca.

Breeding. Polygamous. Nest a large hollow scraped in ground (by ♂), thinly lined with grass.

Eggs. 20 to 30 (or even more), laid by several ♀♀ in one nest; golden yellow or deep green (fading rapidly). Incubated by ♂.

Young. Nidifugous. Downy. Cared for by ♂.

Technical diagnosis. T. Salvadori, Cat. of Birds of Brit. Mus., 27, 1895: 577.

Classification. Hellmayr and Conover, pt. 1, no. 1, 1942: 1–6.

References. Samuel Adams, Notes on the Rhea or South American Ostrich, *Condor,* 10, 1908: 69–71, 3 photos.

W. H. Hudson, *Birds of La Plata,* London, vol. 2, 1920: 230–236.

A. F. J. Portielje, Zur Ethologie bezw. Psychologie der *Rhea americana* L., *Ardea,* 14, 1925: 1–14, 5 photos.

A. Wetmore, Observations on the Birds of Argentina, Paraguay, Uruguay, and Chile, *U. S. Natl. Mus. Bull.,* 133, 1926: 23–27.

CASUARIIDAE

Cassowary family (3 species)

Fig. 4. One-wattled Cassowary (*Casuarius unappendiculatus*). Total length 65 in. (1651 mm.).

Physical characteristics. Length—1321 to 1651 mm. (52 to 65 in.). Plumage—harsh, hairlike, and drooping; black in adults, brown in immatures. Bill short, strong, and laterally compressed. Head and neck featherless, carunculated, particolored in brilliant shades, with heavy casque on forehead and crown, and wattles on lower neck. Wings extremely reduced, remiges represented by only a few bare shafts. No rectrices apparent. Legs long and robust; 3 toes (2nd, 3rd, and 4th). the 2nd with very long, sharp claw. Sexes alike, but ♀ larger.

Range. New Guinea and neighboring islands; Australia (n. Queensland). Habitat—forests. Nonmigratory.

Habits. Somewhat gregarious. Cursorial; run swiftly, even through dense brush. Flightless. Swim well. Pugnacious. Voice—harsh guttural croaks, or "snorting, grunting, and bellowing."

Food. Chiefly fruits and berries; also insects and spiders.

Breeding. Shallow nest on ground built of sticks and leaves.

Eggs. 3 to 8; light green, with coarsely granulated surface. Incubated by ♂.
Young. Nidifugous. Downy. Cared for by ♂ (and ♀?).

Technical diagnosis. T. Salvadori, Cat. of Birds of Brit. Mus., 27, 1895: 585, 590.

Classification. Peters, 1, 1931: 5–9.

References. Mathews, 1, pt. 1, 1910: 27–34, pl. 5.

W. Rothschild, A Monograph of the Genus *Casuarius, Trans. Zool. Soc. London,* 15, 1900: 109–148, pls. 22–41.

A. J. Campbell, *Nests and Eggs of Australian Birds,* Sheffield, England, pt. 2, 1901: 1069–1072, pl. 27.

L. Brasil, Fam. Casuariidae, Wytsman's *Genera Avium,* pt. 20, 1913.

Ernst Mayr, Notes on New Guinea Birds. VI. Notes on the Genus *Casuarius, Amer. Mus. Novitates, No. 1056,* 1940: 1–4.

DROMICEIIDAE

Emu family (2 species)

Fig. 5. Common Emu (*Dromiceius n. hollandiae*). Total length 78 in. (1981 mm.).

Physical characteristics. Length—1397 to 1981 mm. (55 to 78 in.). Plumage—rather coarse, hairlike, and drooping; blackish brown above, lighter brown below. Bill short, stout, and somewhat flattened. Sides of head and neck bare and bluish white. Wings much reduced, without real quills. No distinguishable rectrices. Legs long and robust; tarsus and tibiotarsal joint bare; 3 toes (2nd, 3rd, and 4th); claws short and strong. Sexes alike or nearly so.

Range. Australia and Tasmania. Habitat—open arid country. Nonmigratory.

Habits. Somewhat gregarious. Cursorial. Flightless. Swim well. Voice—hissing, grunting, or booming sounds.

Food. Vegetable matter, esp. fruits.

Breeding. Nest a hollow in ground, sometimes lined with leaves and twigs.

Eggs. 7 to 12; dark green. Incubated mainly by ♂.

Young. Nidifugous. Downy. Cared for by ♂ and ♀.

Technical diagnosis. L. Brasil, Fam. Dromaiidae, Wytsman's *Genera Avium,* pt. 25, 1914: 5 pp., col. pl.

Classification. Peters, 1, 1931: 9–10.

References. Mathews, 1, pt. 1, 1910: 1–26, col. pls. 1–4.

A. J. Campbell, *Nests and Eggs of Australian Birds,* Sheffield, England, vol. 2, 1901: 1058–1069.

D. W. Gaukrodger, The Emu at Home, *Emu,* 25, 1925: 53–57, pls. 12–18.

D. Fleay, Nesting of the Emu, *Emu,* 35, 1936: 202–210, pls. 17–20.

Synonyms: Dromaeidae, Dromaiidae.

APTERYGIDAE

Kiwi family (3 species)

Fig. 6. South Island Kiwi (*Apteryx australis*). Total length 27 in. (686 mm.).

Physical characteristics. Length—482 to 838 mm. (19 to 33 in.). Plumage—coarse and furlike; brown or grayish, streaked or barred, esp. above. Bill long, slender, and slightly curved; with nostrils near tip (lateral and somewhat ventral). Very long thin bristles about base of bill. Head small, neck rather long. Wings extremely reduced; no discernible rectrices. Legs rather short and very stout; tarsi bare. Four toes; hallux short, elevated; claws long and sharp. Sexes similar, but ♀ larger.

Range. New Zealand. Habitat—humid forest. Nonmigratory.

Habits. Somewhat gregarious. Pugnacious. Nocturnal or crepuscular. Cursorial. Flightless. Often feed by probing ground with bill. Voice—shrill whistle or scream.

Food. Worms, insects, berries, young shoots of plants.

Breeding. Nest in hole in ground, sometimes lined with leaves and grass.
Eggs. 1 or 2; white or slightly greenish; extremely large. Incubated by ♂.
Young. Nidicolous? Downy. Cared for by ♂?

Technical diagnosis. T. Salvadori, Cat. of Birds of Brit. Mus., 27, 1895: 603.

Classification. Peters, 1, 1931: 11–12.

References. W. L. Buller, *A History of the Birds of New Zealand* (2nd ed.), London, vol. 2, 1888: 308–332, 2 col. pls.; Suppl., vol. 1, 1905: 1–30, 1 col. pl., photos.
L. Brasil, Fam. Apterygidae, Wytsman's *Genera Avium*, pt. 22, 1913, col. pl.
W. R. B. Oliver, *New Zealand Birds*, Wellington, N. Z., 1930: 55–62, pl. 1.
H. R. Haeusler, Notes on the Habits of the North Island Kiwi (*Apteryx mantelli*), *Emu*, 22, 1923: 175–179, pl. 59.

TINAMIDAE

Tinamou family (45 species)

Fig. 7. Rufous-winged Tinamou (*Rhynchotus rufescens*). Total length 17 in. (432 mm.).

Physical characteristics. Length—203 to 534 mm. (8 to 21 in.). Plumage—tawny, brown, and gray, usually streaked, spotted, or barred in cryptic patterns. Erectile crest in some spp. Bill weak, somewhat elongated and curved. Body compact. Wings short and rounded. Tail very short (hidden by contour feathers in some spp.). Legs strong, short to moderately long; hallux elevated (or lacking). Sexes very similar in color; ♀ usually larger.

Range. Neotropical. Mainland from s. Mexico to s. Argentina. Habitat—forest or brushland; and (in S. America) grassland. Nonmigratory.

Habits. Solitary or (some spp.) gregarious. Many spp. crepuscular. Terrestrial; cursorial. Flight strong but not prolonged. Crouch in presence of danger. Voice—whistles and trills, often loud but very mellow in tone—flutelike.

Food. Mainly fruit and seeds; some insects.

Breeding. Polyandrous (at least some spp.). Nest on ground, unlined hollow to substantial structure of sticks.

Eggs. 1 to 10 (or more?); glossy; immaculate; green, blue, yellow, or purplish brown. Incubated by ♂.

Young. Nidifugous. Downy. Cared for by ♂.

Technical diagnosis. Beddard, 485–493.

Classification. Hellmayr and Conover, pt. 1, no. 1, 1942: 6–114.

References. C. Chubb, *The Birds of British Guiana,* London, vol. 1, 1916: 1–16, pls. 1–2.

W. H. Hudson, *Birds of La Plata,* London, vol. 2, 1920: 219–230, col. pl.

[C.] W. Beebe, The Variegated Tinamou, *Crypturus variegatus variegatus* (Gmelin), *Zoologica,* 6, 1925: 195–227.

A. Wetmore, Observations on the Birds of Argentina, Paraguay, Uruguay, and Chile, *U. S. Natl. Mus. Bull.,* 133, 1926: 27–42.

A. K. and O. P. Pearson, Natural History and Breeding Behavior of the Tinamou, *Nothoprocta ornata, Auk,* 72, 1955: 113–127.

Synonym: Crypturidae.

GAVIIDAE

Loon family (4 species)

Fig. 8. Arctic Loon (*Gavia arctica*). Total length 27 in. (686 mm.).

Physical characteristics. Length—661 to 953 mm. (26 to 37½ in.). Dense, compact body plumage; head, neck, and upper parts black or gray, streaked, barred, and spotted with white in bold patterns (in winter gray, unspotted, exc. *Gavia stellata*); under parts white (foreneck rich chestnut in *G. stellata*). Bill strong, tapering, acute. Wings relatively small; pointed. Tail well developed but short. Tarsi reticulate, laterally compressed. First 3 toes fully webbed. Sexes alike.

Range. Northern Eurasia and n. N. America. Habitat—lakes and ponds; mainly on sea in winter. Migratory.

Habits. Found singly or in pairs, occasionally (in winter) in small, loose flocks. Swim under water (foot-propelled). Go ashore only to nest. Flight strong, direct; large species require a long run along surface of water before rising. Voice—great variety of deep guttural notes and loud, quavering calls.

Food. Mainly fish; also crustacea, mollusca, insects.

Breeding. Nest a slight depression in ground to large heap of vegetable matter, at edge of water.

Eggs. 2 (rarely 1 or 3); olive-brown, irregularly spotted with darker brown. Incubated by ♂ and ♀.

Young. Nidifugous. Downy—uniform gray above, white below. Cared for by ♂ and ♀.

Technical diagnosis. Witherby, 4, 1940: 111.

Classification. Peters, 1, 1931: 34–35.

References. Bent, No. 107: 47–82; Witherby, 4, 1940: 111–129.

R. A. Johnson and H. S. Johnson, A Study of the Nesting and Family Life of the Red-throated Loon, *Wils. Bull.,* 47, 1935: 97–103, 5 photos.

H. Brandt, *Alaska Bird Trails,* Cleveland, Ohio, 1943: 216–222, col. pls. 319–323.

J. A. Munro, Observations of the Loon in the Cariboo Parklands, British Columbia, *Auk,* 62, 1945: 38–49, pls. 4–5.

S. T. Olson and W. H. Marshall, The Common Loon in Minnesota, *Minn. Mus. Nat. Hist. Occ. Paper No. 5,* 1952: vi + 77 pp.

Synonyms: Colymbidae of European ornithologists; Urinatoridae.

PODICIPEDIDAE

Grebe family (20 species)

Fig. 9. Pied-billed Grebe (*Podilymbus podiceps*). Total length 13 in. (330 mm.).

Physical characteristics. Length—222 to 603 mm. ($8\frac{3}{4}$ to $23\frac{3}{4}$ in.). Plumage—satiny; upper parts dark gray or black; under parts in some solidly reddish brown, but usually glistening white, immaculate or mottled with brown; throat and foreneck rich reddish brown in some; head usually with lateral tufts of feathers. Bill sharply pointed (exc. *Podilymbus*), relatively longer in the larger spp. Wings short; tail rudimentary. Tarsi laterally compressed; toes lobed; claws extremely flattened. Sexes alike.

Range. World-wide (exc. extreme n. and some oceanic islands). Habitat—lakes and ponds with much emergent vegetation (some to seacoast in winter). Northern species migratory.

Habits. Solitary or slightly gregarious. Swim under water (foot-propelled). Completely aquatic. Flight weak and infrequent (*Centropelma* flightless). Voice—great variety of clucks, croaks, whistling notes, and tremulous calls.

Food. Fish, crustacea,mollusca, insects, and some vegetable matter. Eat and even feed to small young many of their own body feathers.

Breeding. Nest a heap of wet, decaying vegetable matter in shallow water or floating in deep water.

Eggs. 3 to 9; dull white, unspotted. Incubated by ♂ and ♀.

Young. Nidifugous. Downy—head and neck boldly streaked and spotted (exc. *Aechmophorus occidentalis,* which is gray, unpatterned). Cared for by ♂ and ♀.

Technical diagnosis. Witherby, 4, 1940: 84–85.

Classification. Peters, 1, 1931: 35–41.

References. Bent, No. 107: 1–47; Witherby, 4, 1940: 84–111.

E. Coues, Birds of the Northwest, *U. S. Geol. Surv. Terr. Misc. Publ. No. 3,* 1874: 725–737.

J. S. Huxley, The Courtship-habits of the Great Crested Grebe . . . , *Proc. Zool. Soc. London,* 1914: 491–562, pls. 1–2.

A. Wetmore, Food and Economic Relations of North American Grebes, *U. S. Dept. Agric. Dept. Bull, No. 1196,* 1924.

J. A. Munro, Studies of Waterfowl in British Columbia: The Grebes. *B. C. Prov. Mus. Occ. Paper No. 3,* 1941.

N. Rankin, *Haunts of British Divers,* London, 1947: 17–46.

Synonyms: Colymbidae, Podicipitidae, Podicepidae, Podicipidae.

DIOMEDEIDAE

Albatross family (14 species)

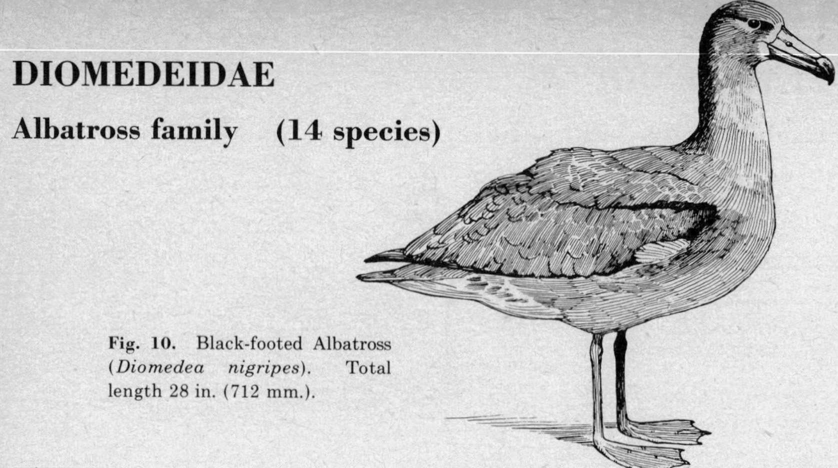

Fig. 10. Black-footed Albatross (*Diomedea nigripes*). Total length 28 in. (712 mm.).

Physical characteristics. Length—712 to 1346 mm. (28 to 53 in.). Plumage—mainly white or sooty brown; tip, edge, or whole of wing black or dark brown; tail and mid-back black in many spp. Bill very stout, hooked, covered with horny plates; nostrils tubular. Head large, body stout. Wings extremely long and narrow. Tail short or moderately long. Legs short; hallux absent or rudimentary; feet webbed. Sexes alike (exc. in *Diomedea exulans*).

Range. Southern oceans, from about 30° S. to Antarctica; n. in the Pacific to the Bering Sea. Most spp. migratory.

Habits. Often gregarious. Pelagic. Exceptional powers of gliding flight. Many spp. follow ships for long periods. Discharge oil from mouth and nostrils when disturbed. Remarkable communal displays or dances. Voice—loud screams, hoarse croaks, loud braying notes.

Food. Fish, squid, and other marine animals.

Breeding. Colonial (exc. *Phoebetria*). Nest a mere scrape in ground or a heap of grass, moss, and earth.

Eggs. 1; white, speckled with brown in some spp. Incubated by ♂ and ♀.

Young. Nidicolous. Downy. Fed by ♂ and ♀.

Technical diagnosis. E. Coues, *Key to North American Birds,* Boston, vol. 2, 1903: 1022–1023.

Classification. Peters, 1, 1931: 41–46.

References. Bent, No. 121: 1–25; Witherby, 4, 1940: 25, 81–84; Murphy, 1: 471–584; Alexander, 1928: 3–24, pls. 2–10 (1954: 1–15, pls. 2–10).

F. D. Godman, A Monograph of the Petrels (Order Tubinares), London, 1907–1910.

P. R. Lowe, On the Classification of the Tubinares or Petrels, *Proc. Zool. Soc. London* for 1925, 1926: 1433–1443.

L. E. Richdale, A Royal Albatross nesting on the Otago Peninsula, New Zealand, *Emu,* 38, 1939: 467–488, pls. 60–66 (see also vol. 41, 1942: 169–184, 253–264, pls. 26–28, 36).

Loye Miller, Observations on the Black-footed Albatross, *Condor,* 42, 1940: 229–238, figs. 65–67.

C. Yocom, Notes on Behavior and Abundance of the Black-footed Albatrosses in the Pacific Waters off the Continental North American Shores, *Auk,* 64, 1947: 507–523, pl. 17, 2 figs.

PROCELLARIIDAE

Shearwater family (56 species)

Fig. 11. Fulmar (*Fulmarus glacialis*). Total length 19 in. (482 mm.).

Physical characteristics. Length—280 to 914 mm. (11 to 36 in.). Plumage—white, gray, brown, or black, or combinations of these. Two color phases in some spp. Bill short and heavy to rather long and slender, hooked, covered with horny plates; nostrils tubular. Wings long and pointed; tail short. Legs short to medium; feet webbed. Sexes alike.

Range. Oceans of the world. Migratory.

Habits. Usually gregarious. Pelagic. Flight rapid and gliding, usually close above surface of water. Pick food from surface in passing flight, or swim about on the water to feed. Discharge oil from mouth and nostrils when disturbed. Voice—great variety of shrieks, wails, raucous calls, and cooing sounds.

Food. Fish, squid, crustacea, and other animal matter, including small birds; also carrion.

Breeding. Colonial. Nest in burrows or rock crevices, sometimes lined with vegetable matter. A few large spp. nest on open ground.

Eggs. 1; white. Incubated by ♂ and ♀.

Young. Nidicolous. Downy. Cared for by ♂ and ♀.

Technical diagnosis. E. Coues, *Key to North American Birds,* Boston, vol. 2, 1903: 1026–1027, 1031.

Classification. Peters, 1, 1931: 46–68.

References. Bent, No. 121: 26–123; Witherby, 4, 1940: 25, 41–80; Murphy, 1: 471–489, and 2: 584–726; Alexander, 1928: 25–73, pls. 11–18 (1954: 16–51, pls. 11–18).

F. D. Godman, A Monograph of the Petrels (Order Tubinares), London, 1907–1910.

R. M. Lockley, *Shearwaters,* London, 1942.

L. E. Richdale, The Sooty Shearwater in New Zealand, *Condor,* 46, 1944: 93–107. (See also vol. 47, 1945: 45–62.)

L. E. Richdale, The Parara or Broad-billed Prion, *Emu,* 43, 1944: 191–217, pls. 13–14.

J. Fisher, *The Fulmar,* London, 1952.

Synonyms: Fulmaridae, Puffinidae.

HYDROBATIDAE

Storm-petrel family (18 species)

Fig. 12. Wilson's Petrel (*Oceanites oceanicus*). Total length 7 in. (177 mm.).

Physical characteristics. Length 139 to 254 mm. (5½ to 10 in.). Plumage—brownish black or gray; with white on rump or under parts of many spp., on face and throat of 3. Bill and legs black (but webs of feet bright yellow in 2 spp.). Bill medium in length, slender, grooved, hooked; nostrils tubular. Neck short, wings long, tail medium to long. Legs slender, medium to long; feet webbed. Sexes alike.

Range. Oceans of the world, principally s. of Arctic Circle. Most spp. migratory.

Habits. Usually gregarious. Pelagic. Flight erratic and fluttering. Pick food from surface of sea as they flutter over it, often striking the water with the feet, or (rarely) dive for food. Discharge oil from mouth and nostrils when disturbed. Voice (rarely heard at sea)—great variety of chirping, squealing, and cooing notes used about nesting grounds.

Food. Crustacea, fish, and other small marine animals; also carrion, esp. fatty substances.

Breeding. Colonial. Nest in burrows or rock crevices, sometimes lined.

Eggs. 1; white, often with red or black spots on the larger end. Incubated by ♂ and ♀.

Young. Nidicolous. Downy. Cared for by ♂ and ♀.

Technical diagnosis. Witherby, 4, 1940: 25.

Classification. Peters, 1, 1931: 68–75.

References. Bent, No. 121: 123–181; Murphy, 1: 471–489, and 2: 726–771; Alexander, 1928: 74–92, pls. 19–21 (1954: 52–64, pls. 19–21).

A. O. Gross, The Life History Cycle of Leach's Petrel (*Oceanodroma leucorhoa leucorhoa*) on the Outer Sea Islands of the Bay of Fundy, *Auk,* 52, 1935: 382–399, pls. 18–21.

R. C. Murphy, The Ocean Birds, in G. Grosvenor and A. Wetmore, *The Book of Birds,* Washington, D. C., vol. 1, 1937: 35–58, illus.

B. Roberts, The life cycle of Wilson's Petrel, *Oceanites oceanicus* (Kuhl), *Brit. Graham Land Exped. 1934–37, Sci. Repts.,* 1, 1940: 141–194, 7 pls.

Synonyms: Procellariidae, Thalassidromidae.

PELECANOIDIDAE

Diving-petrel family (5 species)

Fig. 13. Peruvian Diving-petrel (*Pelecanoides garnotii*). Total length 10 in. (254 mm.).

Physical characteristics. Length—165 to 254 mm. ($6\frac{1}{2}$ to 10 in.). Plumage—black above and white below. Bill short and stout, hooked, covered with horny plates; nostrils tubular (opening upward). Neck, wings, and tail short. Legs short, laterally compressed; feet webbed. Sexes alike.

Range. Southern oceans (between about 35° and 60° S. lat.) and n. along the w. coast of S. America to n. Peru. Largely nonmigratory.

Habits. Somewhat gregarious. Pelagic. Fly with very rapid wing beats. Dive from the wing into the sea to obtain food and to escape enemies. Use wings to swim under water; often emerge flying. Voice—croaking and mewing sounds.

Food. Fish, crustacea, and other animal matter.

Breeding. Somewhat colonial. Nest in burrows or rock crevices with little or no lining.

Eggs. 1; white. Incubated by ♂ and ♀.

Young. Nidicolous. Downy. Cared for by ♂ and ♀.

Technical diagnosis. O. Salvin, Cat. of Birds of Brit. Mus., 25, 1896: 340–342.

Classification. Peters, 1, 1931: 75–77.

References. Murphy, 2: 771–792; Alexander, 1928: 93–100, pl. 22 (1954: 65–69, pl. 22).

R. C. Murphy and F. Harper, A Review of the Diving Petrels, *Amer. Mus. Nat. Hist. Bull.,* 44, 1921: 495–554, pls. 21-24.

L. E. Richdale, The Kuaka or Diving Petrel, *Emu,* 43, 1943: 24–48, 97–107, pls. 2–4.

L. E. Richdale, Supplementary Notes on the Diving Petrel, *Trans. Roy. Soc. N. Z.,* 75, 1945: 42–53, pl. 4.

Synonym: Pelecanoidae.

PHAËTHONTIDAE

Tropicbird family

(3 species)

Fig. 14. White-tailed Tropicbird (*Phaëthon lepturus*). Total length (without central tail feathers) 17 in. (432 mm.).

Physical characteristics. Length—406 to 482 mm. (16 to 19 in.), excluding the attenuate middle tail feathers, which may add as much as 535 mm. (21 in.) to length. Plumage—white, with varied amounts of black on side of head (as orbital line), on wing, and shafts of tail feathers. Webs of elongated tail feathers pink in *Phaëthon rubricauda.* Bill yellow or orange-red; rather long, stout, slightly decurved, and pointed. Head large, neck short. Wings long and pointed. Tail wedge-shaped and of moderate length, except for extremely long and narrow central feathers. Legs extremely short; feet webbed (including all 4 toes). Sexes alike.

Range. Tropical seas; n. in Atlantic to Bermuda and s. in Pacific to s. Australia. Migratory in part.

Habits. Somewhat gregarious. Range daily far out to sea (60 to 80 mi.). Fly with quick, steady wing beats high above water. Hover and plunge from height of 50 ft. or more for food. On ground can only shuffle along. Voice—shrill whistle, rasping calls.

Food. Fish, squid, crustacea.

Breeding. Somewhat colonial. Lay eggs on bare rock, in shallow caves, or on the ground under bushes.

Eggs. 1; buff, heavily marked with brown and black. Incubated by ♂ and ♀.
Young. Nidicolous. Downy. Cared for by ♂ and ♀.

Technical diagnosis. E. Coues, *Key to North American Birds,* Boston, vol. 2, 1903: 971.

Classification. Peters, 1, 1931: 77–79.

References. Bent, No. 121: 181–193; Murphy, 2: 796–807; Alexander, 1928: 321–325, pls. 84–85 (1954: 222–225, pls. 84–85).

F. E. Beddard, Notes upon the Anatomy of *Phaethon, Proc. Zool. Soc. London,* 1897: 288–295, figs. 1–4.

A. O. Gross, Observations on the Yellow-billed Tropic-bird (*Phaëthon americanus* Grant) at the Bermuda Islands, *Auk,* 29, 1912: 49–71, pls. 3–11.

K. Plath, With the Tropic-birds in Bermuda, *Ibis,* 1914: 552–559, pls. 21–24.

Synonym: Phaëtontidae.

PELECANIDAE

Pelican family (6 species)

Fig. 15. Brown Pelican (*Pelecanus occidentalis*). Total length 50 in. (1270 mm.).

Physical characteristics. Length—1270 to 1829 mm. (50 to 72 in.). Plumage—white (tinged with pink in some spp.), brown, or gray; primaries dark to black. Bill, face, and gular pouch brightly colored in some spp. Some spp. crested. Bill very long, straight, and hooked; nostrils obsolete; gular pouch very large. Neck long, body stout. Wings extremely large, tail short. Legs short and stout, feet large and fully webbed. Sexes alike.

Range. North America (from Great Slave Lake, s. Mackenzie) s. through Central America to the Galápagos; the w. coast (to about 40° S.) and part of the n.e. coast of S. America; Africa (exc. n.w. part), s.e. Europe, s. Asia, the East Indies, and Australia. Habitat—large lakes and the sea coast. Some spp. migratory.

Habits. Gregarious. Can fly strongly and even soar. Feed while swimming on surface, or (*P. occidentalis*) dive for food from the wing. Voice—adults usually silent, rarely uttering grunts and croaks; young grunt and chatter noisily.

Food. Fish; sometimes crustacea.

Breeding. Colonial. Nest of sticks in trees; or reeds, grass, or mud on the ground.

Eggs. 1 to 4; white. Incubated by ♂ and ♀.

Young. Nidicolous. Naked at hatching, downy later. Cared for by ♂ and ♀.

Technical diagnosis. E. Coues, *Key to North American Birds,* Boston, vol. 2, 1903: 956.

Classification. Peters, 1, 1931: 79–81.

References. Bent, No. 121: 282–306; Murphy, 2: 807–827; Baker, *Fauna,* 6, 1929: 270–275; Alexander, 1928: 267–277, pls. 1, 69–72 (1954: 184–191, pls. 1, 69–72).

D. G. Elliot, A Monograph of the Genus *Pelecanus, Proc. Zool. Soc. London,* 1869: 571–591, pl. 44.

F. M. Chapman, *Camps and Cruises of an Ornithologist,* New York, 1908: 83–112.

E. Raymond Hall, Pelicans versus Fishes in Pyramid Lake, *Condor,* 27, 1925: 147–160.

SULIDAE

Booby family (9 species)

Fig. 16. Blue-faced Booby (*Sula dactylatra*). Total length 30 in. (762 mm.).

Physical characteristics. Length—661 to 1029 mm. (26 to 40½ in.). Plumage of adult typically white, with primaries or whole wing brownish black. Tail of some spp. partly or wholly dark in color. Head and neck brown, streaked with white in *Sula nebouxii,* brownish black in *S. leucogaster.* Bill, bare skin about face and throat, and feet usually brightly colored. Bill stout, conical, pointed, and slightly curved toward the tip; nostrils obsolete. Neck moderate in length, body stout, wings long and pointed, tail rather long and wedge-shaped. Legs short, feet large and fully webbed. Sexes alike or nearly so.

Range. Tropical and temperate seas, exc. n. Pacific. Spp. of high latitudes are migratory.

Habits. Gregarious. Flight strong, with rapid, regular wing beats, interrupted by occasional glides. Feed by diving from the wing (from 30 to 100 ft. in air); pursue fish under water, even to considerable depths. Voice—silent at sea; soft guttural notes, loud grunts, croaks, and whistles used about nesting grounds.

Food. Fish, squid.

Breeding. Colonial. Nest variable, from slight hollow in ground to a structure of sticks in a tree.

Eggs. 1 to 3; pale blue, with chalky surface. Incubated by ♂ and ♀.

Young. Nidicolous. Naked at hatching, downy later. Cared for by ♂ and ♀.

Technical diagnosis. Witherby, 4, 1940: 14.

Classification. Peters, 1, 1931: 82–85.

References. Bent, No. 121: 193–229; Murphy, 2: 827–870; Mathews, 4, 1914–15: 199–235, col. pls. 225–228; Alexander, 1928: 278–288, pls. 73–77 (1954: 192–199, pls. 73–77).

J. H. Gurney, *The Gannet,* London 1913.

James Fisher and H. G. Vevers, The Breeding Distribution, History and Population of the North Atlantic Gannet (*Sula bassana*), *Jour. Animal Ecol.,* 12, 1943: 173–213; 13, 1944: 49–62.

K. A. Wodzicki and C. P. McMeekan, The Gannet on Cape Kidnappers, *Trans. and Proc. Roy. Soc. N. Z.,* 76, 1947: 429–452, 4 pls.

PHALACROCORACIDAE

Cormorant family (30 species)

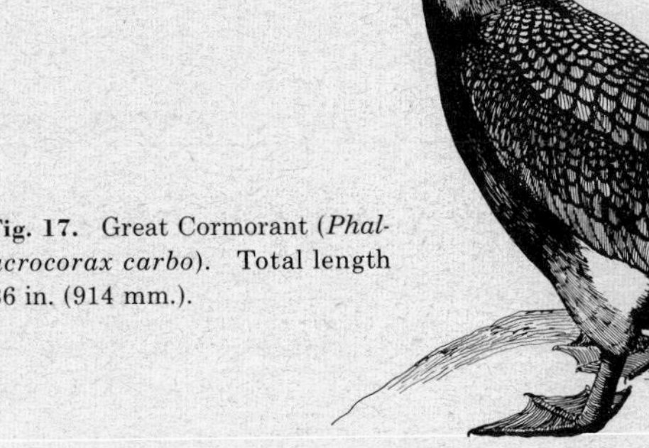

Fig. 17. Great Cormorant (*Phalacrocorax carbo*). Total length 36 in. (914 mm.).

Physical characteristics. Length—482 to 1016 mm. (19 to 40 in.). Plumage—largely black in most spp.; in spp. of S. Hemisphere the throat or whole under parts may be white, or the plumage largely gray and feet brightly colored. Eyes, bill, and skin of face usually brightly colored. In breeding plumage of many spp. there are light-colored plumes on head, neck, and flanks. Bill cylindrical, rather slender, hooked; nostrils obsolete. Neck and body long. Wings short or of moderate length; tail long and stiff. Legs short; feet large and fully webbed. Sexes very similar.

Range. Seacoasts and large lakes and rivers of the world, exc. n.c. Canada and n. Asia. Also absent from the islands of the s.w. Pacific. Spp. of higher latitudes migratory.

Habits. Gregarious. Littoral. Fly with steady wing beats, usually close to surface of the water. One species (*Nannopterum* of the Galápagos) flightless. Feed largely under water, diving (from surface) to considerable depths. Voice—rarely heard exc. at nest site, where a variety of grunts and guttural notes are used.

Food. Fish, crustacea, amphibia.

Breeding. Colonial (most spp.). Nest of seaweed, sticks, etc., on low rocks, on cliffs, or in trees.

Eggs. 2 to 4 (or 6); pale blue or pale green, with chalky surface (blotched with brown in *P. nigrogularis*). Incubated by ♂ and ♀.

Young. Nidicolous. Naked at hatching, downy later. Cared for by ♂ and ♀.

Technical diagnosis. Witherby, 4, 1940: 1–2.

Classification. Peters, 1, 1931: 85–94.

References. Bent, No. 121: 236–282; Murphy, 2: 870–919; Alexander, 1928: 289–320, pls. 69, 78–83 (1954: 200–221, pls. 69, 78–83).

H. F. Lewis, *The Natural History of the Double-crested Cormorant,* Ottawa, 1929.

H. L. Mendall, The Home-life and Economic Status of the Double-crested Cormorant, *Phalacrocorax auritus auritus* (Lesson), *Maine Bull.,* 39, no. 3, Oct. 1936.

Laidlaw Williams, Display and Sexual Behavior of the Brandt Cormorant, *Condor,* 44, 1942: 85–104, figs. 24–46.

Synonym: Graculidae (which has also been used as name for Sturnidae).

ANHINGIDAE

Anhinga family (2 species)

Fig. 18. Anhinga (*Anhinga anhinga*). Total length 35 in. (889 mm.).

Physical characteristics. Length—864 to 914 mm. (34 to 36 in.). Plumage—black, dotted and streaked with white on upper back, scapulars, and wing coverts; head and neck brown (black in ♂ *A. anhinga*). Heavy transverse fluting on central tail feathers and innermost tertials. Light-colored plumes on sides of head and neck of breeding ♂. Bill long, slender, sharply pointed, finely serrate; nostrils obsolete. Head small, neck very long and slender, body elongate. Wings long, pointed; tail long and stiff. Legs very short; feet large, fully webbed. Sexes unlike.

Range. Southeastern U. S.; Middle America; S. America (exc. s. third); Africa s. of Sahara; s. Asia; East Indies; Philippines; Australia and New Zealand. Habitat—lakes and rivers with wooded shores. Migratory in U. S.

Habits. Gregarious during migration and nesting. Fly well, soar with ease, but alight and take off with difficulty. Enter water only to feed; then perch in sun for long periods with wings spread. Feed by swimming under water and spearing fish with beak; at surface often swim with all but head and neck submerged (hence called "snake birds"). Voice (rarely heard)—utter harsh, grating calls and whistling notes when nesting.

Food. Fish, crustacea, amphibia, insects.

Breeding. Colonial. Bulky nests of sticks in trees or bushes near or over water.
Eggs. 3 to 6; bluish white, with chalky surface. Incubated by ♂ and ♀.
Young. Nidicolous. Naked at hatching, downy (exc. head) later. Cared for by ♂ and ♀.

Technical diagnosis. E. Coues, *Key to North American Birds,* Boston, vol. 2, 1903: 968.

Classification. Peters, 1, 1931: 94–95.

References. Bent, No. 121: 229–236.
A. Newton, Snake-bird, in *A Dictionary of Birds,* London, 1893–1896: 880–883.
F. J. Jackson, *The Birds of Kenya Colony and the Uganda Protectorate,* London, vol. 1, 1938: 23–25.
Helen G. Cruickshank, *Flight into Sunshine,* New York, 1948: 106-113, photos 99–101.
B. Meanley, Nesting of the Water-Turkey in Eastern Arkansas, *Wils. Bull.,* 66, 1954: 81–88.

Synonym: Plotidae.

FREGATIDAE

Frigatebird family

(5 species)

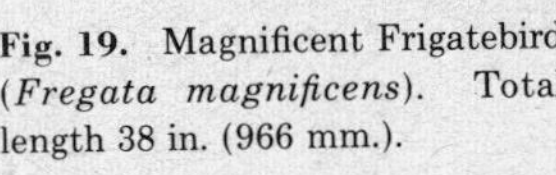

Fig. 19. Magnificent Frigatebird (*Fregata magnificens*). Total length 38 in. (966 mm.).

Physical characteristics. Length—787 to 1041 mm. (31 to 41 in.). Plumage—brownish black, with some iridescence. White areas on under parts of ♀ (and of ♂ in 2 spp.). Throat bare—that of breeding males greatly inflated at times, even in flight. Bill long and strongly hooked, rounded in cross section, the culmen convex; nostrils obsolete. Wings very long and pointed, with greatest area, relative to weight, of any bird. Tail long and deeply forked. Tarsi extremely short and feathered. Feet small; web includes all 4 toes but only basally. Claws strong; middle claw pectinate. ♀ larger than ♂. Head white in juvenal plumage.

Range. Pan-tropical. Oceanic islands and adjacent seas of all parts of the world. Nonmigratory.

Habits. Gregarious. Very light and graceful in flight—the most aerial of all waterbirds (apparently never voluntarily alight on water). Capture food from surface of sea while swooping or hovering; also rob boobies, terns, and other birds of food, especially during stress of feeding young. Voice (rarely heard)— a harsh croak; the young chatter.

Food. Fish, squid, crustacea, jellyfish, turtles, young birds.

Breeding. Nest of sticks, on trees, bushes, rocks, or ground; built by ♂ of material brought by ♀.

Eggs. 1 (rarely 2); white. Incubated by ♂ and ♀.

Young. Nidicolous. Naked at first, then downy (white). Fed by ♂ and ♀.

Technical diagnosis. Baker, *Fauna,* 6, 1929: 295.

Classification. Peters, 1, 1931: 95–97.

References. Bent, No. 121: 306–315; Murphy, 2: 919–940; Alexander, 1928: 259–266, pls. 66–68 (1954: 178–183, pls. 66–68).

H. R. Dill, The Mating and Nesting Habits of Fregata aquila, *Wils. Bull.,* 28, 1916: 153–157, 6 pls.

R. C. Murphy, Man-o-war, *Nat. Hist.,* 44, 1939: 133–143.

Synonym: Tachypetidae.

ARDEIDAE

Heron family (58 species)

Fig. 20. Great Blue Heron (*Ardea herodias*). Total length 41 in. (1041 mm.).

Physical characteristics. Length—280 to 1422 mm. (11 to 56 in.). Plumage—loose-textured; white, gray, blue, purple, or brown, usually in simple patterns. Some spp. all white; some speckled or barred above and/or streaked below. Many spp. have long filamentous plumes (esp. in breeding plumage) on back, lower foreneck, or head. Lores bare. Bill long and spearlike. Neck long. Wings large and broad; tail short. Legs and toes long and slender; tibiae partly bare. Claw of middle toe pectinate. Sexes alike or nearly so in most spp.

Range. World-wide exc. n. N. America and Asia and some oceanic islands. Habitat—shores and marshes. Migratory exc. in tropics.

Habits. Solitary, or (usually only while breeding) gregarious. Flight direct; neck carried in S-shape. Typically feed while standing or wading in shallows, darting at prey with the bill. Swallow prey whole, regurgitating undigested portions in pellets. Voice—varied squawks and raucous calls; a few rather musical notes.

Food. Fish; also amphibians, reptiles, crustacea, insects, mollusca, rodents, young birds.

Breeding. Colonial. Nest (in most spp.) shallow and made of sticks. In trees, bushes, or on ground.

Eggs. 3 to 6 or 7; blue, white, buff, or even yellow; typically unspeckled. Incubated by ♂ and ♀.

Young. Nidicolous. Downy. Cared for by ♂ and ♀.

Technical diagnosis. Witherby, 3, 1939: 125.

Classification. Peters, 1, 1931: 97–125.

References. Bent, No. 135: 72–219; Witherby, 3, 1939: 125–162; Baker, *Fauna,* 6, 1929: 335–371.

A. O. Gross, The Black-crowned Night Heron (Nycticorax nycticorax naevius) of Sandy Neck, *Auk,* 40, 1923: 1–30, 191–214, pls. 1–2, 5–14.

Robert P. Allen and F. P. Mangels, Studies of the Nesting Behavior of the Black-crowned Night Heron, *Proc. Linn. Soc. N. Y.,* No. 50–51, 1940: 1–28, 2 pls., 11 figs.

Richard F. Miller, The Great Blue Heron, *Cassinia* (for 1943), 1944: 1–23, 1 pl.

F. A. Lowe, *The Heron,* London, 1954.

COCHLEARIIDAE

Boat-billed Heron family

(1 species)

Fig. 21. Boat-billed Heron (*Cochlearius cochlearius*). Total length 21 in. (534 mm.).

Physical characteristics. Length—508 to 534 mm. (20 to 21 in.). Plumage—loose-textured. Crown, nuchal feathers (which are broad and elongated), anterior part of back, and flanks bluish black; rest of head and neck pale buff and gray; wings, tail, and back pale gray; ventral region brown. Lores bare. Eyes very large. Bill extremely broad, flat, and shovel-like; slightly hooked. Bare, somewhat distensible, gular pouch. Neck rather long. Wings large and broad; tail short. Legs and toes moderately long and slender; tibiae partly bare; claw of middle toe pectinate. Sexes nearly alike.

Range. Mexico (from Sinaloa and Tamaulipas) to Peru and s. Brazil. Habitat—shores and marshes. Nonmigratory.

Habits. Usually gregarious. Largely nocturnal. Terrestrial, but perch in trees. Flight direct, not strong. Voice—froglike calls, barking or squawking notes; also rattle or clap mandibles.

Food. Fish, crabs, amphibians, mice.

Breeding. Usually colonial. Nest a shallow structure of sticks placed in trees.

Eggs. 2 to 4; bluish white, slightly speckled with brown. Incubated by ♂ and ♀.

Young. Not recorded.

Technical diagnosis. R. Ridgway, Studies of the American Herodiones, *Bull. U. S. Geol. Geogr. Surv. Terr.,* 4, No. 1, 1878: 220.

Classification. Peters, 1, 1931: 125.

References. O. Salvin and F. D. Godman, *Biologia Centrali-Americana. Aves,* London, vol. 3, 1901: 185–186.

F. P. Penard and A. P. Penard, *De Vogels van Guyana,* Paramaribo, vol. 1, [1908]: 170–172.

D. R. Dickey and A. J. van Rossem, The Birds of El Salvador, *Field Mus. Nat. Hist., Zool. Ser.,* 23, 1938: 84–86.

Synonym: Cancromidae.

BALAENICIPITIDAE

Whale-billed Stork family (1 species)

Fig. 22. Whale-billed Stork (*Balaeniceps rex*). Total length 46 in. (1168 mm.).

Physical characteristics. Length—about 1168 mm. (46 in.). Plumage—gray, darker, with slight greenish gloss above. Remiges and rectrices grayish black. Short, bushy crest. Bill very large, broad, and flattened, with massive hook at tip of maxilla. Neck moderately long. Wings large and broad, tail short. Legs and toes long, tibiae partly bare. Sexes alike.

Range. Africa: from the valley of the White Nile in s. Sudan to n. Uganda and e. Belgian Congo. Habitat—marshes. Nonmigratory.

Habits. Sometimes gregarious. Largely nocturnal. Move with slow direct flight; sometimes soar. Voice—usually silent, but have a "shrill kitelike cry" and a laughing note; clatter bill.

Food. Fish, frogs, snakes, mollusca, carrion.

Breeding. Nest a large platform of rushes on the ground; lined with grass.

Eggs. 2; white, with slightly bluish tinge.

Young. Nidicolous. Downy.

Technical diagnosis. Beddard, 433–434.

Classification. Peters, 1, 1931: 125.

References. Bannerman, 1, 1930: lxviii-lxix, 86–89.

S. S. Flower, The Shoebill, *Balaeniceps rex, Avicultural Mag.,* 1908: 191–201, 1 pl.

P. Chalmers Mitchell, Observations on the Anatomy of the Shoe-bill (*Balaeniceps rex*) and allied Birds, *Proc. Zool. Soc. London,* 1913: 644–703, pls. 80–83.

J. P. Chapin, The Birds of the Belgian Congo, I, *Amer. Mus. Nat. Hist. Bull.*, 65, 1932: 447–449.

F. J. Jackson, *The Birds of Kenya Colony and the Uganda Protectorate,* London, vol. 1, 1938: 62–66.

SCOPIDAE

Hammerhead family (1 species)

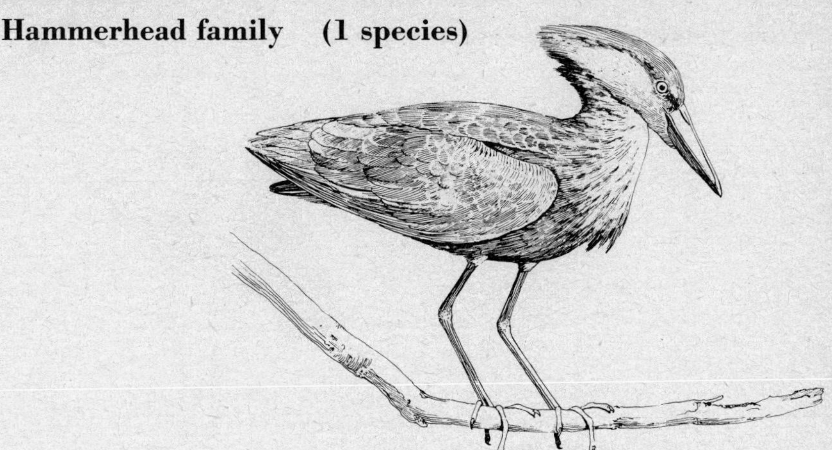

Fig. 23. Hammerhead (*Scopus umbretta*). Total length 19¾ in. (502 mm.).

Physical characteristics. Length—502 mm. (19¾ in.). Plumage—brown, with slight purplish iridescence on upper parts and flight feathers; throat faintly streaked with gray; tail faintly barred with dark brown. Bill long, straight, laterally compressed; maxilla slightly hooked. Head large; long crest carried horizontally. Neck short. Wings and tail rather long. Legs rather long, with tibiae partly bare. Feet slender; toes long. Sexes alike.

Range. Southwestern Arabia, Africa, and Madagascar. Habitat—tree-bordered streams, esp. in grassland. Nonmigratory.

Habits. Usually found in pairs. Slow flight, with neck only slightly curved (not drawn in on shoulders). Voice—harsh metallic croak; a call, *taket taket* . . . , given "continually in flight" (Rand).

Food. Amphibians, fish, insects, crustacea.

Breeding. Massive roofed nest of sticks and mud, placed in branches of large trees.

Eggs. 3 to 6; white. Incubated apparently by ♂ and ♀.

Young. Nidicolous. Downy. Cared for by ♂ and ♀.

Technical diagnosis. Beddard, 420–422; Bannerman, 1, 1930: 89–93.

Classification. A. L. Rand, *Amer. Mus. Novitates No. 827,* 1936.

References. R. B. Cowles, The Life History of Scopus umbretta bannermani C. Grant in Natal, South Africa, *Auk,* 47, 1930: 159–176, pls. 6–9.

J. P. Chapin, The Birds of the Belgian Congo, I, *Amer. Mus. Nat. Hist. Bull.,* 65, 1932: 449–452, fig. 180.

A. L. Rand, The Distribution and Habits of Madagascar Birds, *Amer. Mus. Nat. Hist. Bull.,* 72, art. 5, 1936: 339–340.

G. Archer and E. M. Godman, *The Birds of British Somaliland and the Gulf of Aden,* London, 1937: 65–67.

A. Roberts, *The Birds of South Africa,* London, 1940: 26, col. pl. 4.

CICONIIDAE

Stork family (17 species)

Fig. 24. White Stork (*Ciconia ciconia*). Total length 40 in. (1016 mm.).

Physical characteristics. Length—762 to 1524 mm. (30 to 60 in.). Plumage—in most spp. boldly black and white, or black (the black often with green, blue, or purple reflections). Remiges black (exc. in 3 spp.). Face or whole head and neck bare in some spp. Bill long, massive, ungrooved; and may be recurved or decurved (both in *Anastomus*), or straight. Neck long. Wings long and broad. Tail short; under tail coverts greatly developed in some spp. Legs very long; tibiae partly bare; toes of moderate length, webbed at base. Sexes alike.

Range. Southeastern U. S. and Mexico, Central and S. America, Africa, Eurasia (to about 60° N.), East Indies, Philippines, and Australia (exc. southern third). Northern spp. migratory.

Habits. Gregarious at times. Fly strongly and even soar. Most spp. fly with neck extended. Some spp. have a remarkable dance display. Nearly voiceless (rarely give low grunts or hisses), but rattle or snap mandibles.

Food. Mainly animal matter: fish, amphibia, insects, snails, carrion.

Breeding. Nest a platform of sticks in trees, on cliffs, or on buildings.

Eggs. 3 to 5, or even 6; white. Incubated by ♂ and ♀.

Young. Nidicolous. Naked at first, downy later. Cared for by ♂ and ♀.

Technical diagnosis. Witherby, 3, 1939: 112.

Classification. Peters, 1, 1931: 126–131.

References. Bent, No. 135: 57–72; Witherby, 3, 1939: 112–118; Baker, *Fauna,* 6, 1929: 320–334.

Lee S. Crandall, The Storks, [*N. Y.*] *Zool. Soc. Bull.,* 30, 1927: 149–168, photos, map.

H. Siewert, *Erlebnisse mit dem Schwarzen und Weissen Storch,* Berlin, 1932. (See also *Jour. f. Ornith.,* 80, 1932: 533–541, 2 pls.)

Fr. Haverschmidt, *The Life of the White Stork,* Leiden, 1949.

THRESKIORNITHIDAE

Ibis family (28 species)

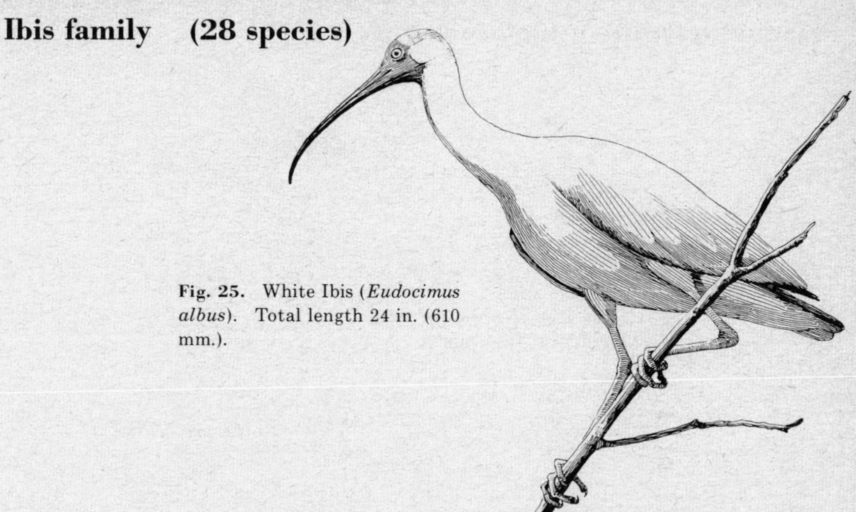

Fig. 25. White Ibis (*Eudocimus albus*). Total length 24 in. (610 mm.).

Physical characteristics. Length—482 to 1067 mm. (19 to 42 in.). Plumage—in most spp. white, grayish brown, or greenish black (one sp. pink, one scarlet); typically little pattern. Some spp. crested; neck feathers or inner secondaries ornamentally modified in some spp. Bill long, slender, grooved, and decurved; or extremely flattened and spatulate at tip. Face and throat, or whole head and neck, bare in some spp. Neck rather long. Wings long, tail short. Legs and toes moderately long; tibiae partly bare; toes webbed at base. Sexes alike or nearly so.

Range. Southern U. S., Middle and S. America, Africa (incl. Madagascar), Eurasia (exc. n. part), and Australia. Habitat—shores and marshes. Northern spp. migratory.

Habits. Usually gregarious. Fly strongly, with neck extended. Voice—harsh croaking or cackling.

Food. Fish, crustacea, reptiles, insects; some grain and other vegetable matter.

Breeding. Nest of sticks or of rushes and grass. In trees, on cliffs, on rocky islands, or on ground in marshes.

Eggs. 2 to 5; white or blue, immaculate or spotted. Incubated by ♂ and ♀.

Young. Nidicolous. Downy. Cared for by ♂ and ♀.

Technical diagnosis. Witherby, 3, 1939: 118.

Classification. Peters, 1, 1931: 131–139.

References. Bent, No. 135: 23–57; Witherby, 3, 1939: 118–125; Baker, *Fauna,* 6: 314–319.

C. A. Wood, The Cayenne or River Ibis in British Guiana, *Condor,* 25, 1923: 199–201, fig. 58.

O. E. Baynard, Home Life of the Glossy Ibis (*Plegadis autumnalis*), *Wils. Bull.,* 25, 1913: 103–117, 9 pls.

Robert P. Allen, The Roseate Spoonbill, *Natl. Aud. Soc. Res. Rept. No. 2,* 1942. (Or: *The Flame Birds,* New York, 1947.)

Synonyms: Ibidae, Ibididae, Plegadidae, Tantalidae. The Plataleidae are included.

PHOENICOPTERIDAE

Flamingo family (6 species)

Fig. 26. American Flamingo (*Phoenicopterus ruber*). Total length 45 in. (1143 mm.).

Physical characteristics. Length—914 to 1219 mm. (36 to 48 in.). Plumage—pinkish white or light vermilion, the color strongest on upper wing coverts. Remiges black. Bill thick, lamellate, bent sharply downward at the midpoint. Face bare. Neck extremely long. Wings large, tail short. Legs extremely long, tibiae largely bare, toes short and webbed. Sexes alike or nearly so.

Range. West Indies, Yucatán, S. America (n. of 40°), Africa, s. Europe, s.w. Asia to India. Habitat—shallow lagoons and lakes. Some spp. are migratory.

Habits. Gregarious. Fly with neck extended. Feed in shallow water with head immersed and bill in inverted position. Voice—a resonant honking and other gooselike notes.

Food. Mollusca, crustacea, insects, fish; also blue-green algae and diatoms.

Breeding. Colonial. Nest a truncated cone of mud built on a mud flat.

Eggs. 1 or 2; white. Incubated by ♂ and ♀.

Young. Nidifugous. Downy. Cared for by ♂ and ♀.

Technical diagnosis. Witherby, 3, 1939: 162–163.

Classification. Peters, 1, 1931: 140–142.

References. Bent, No. 135: 1–12; Witherby, 3, 1939: 162–166; Baker, *Fauna,* 6, 1929: 372–376.

F. M. Chapman, A Contribution to the Life History of the American Flamingo (*Phoenicopterus ruber*), with Remarks upon Specimens, *Bull. Amer. Mus. Nat. Hist.,* 21, 1905: 53–77, illus.

F. M. Chapman, *Camps and Cruises of an Ornithologist,* New York, 1908: 155–191, illus.

Charles McCann, The Flamingo (*Phoenicopterus ruber antiquorum* Temm.), *Jour. Bombay Nat. Hist. Soc.,* 41, 1939: 12-38, pls. 1–7.

E. Gallet, *The Flamingos of the Camargue,* Oxford, 1950.

Robert P. Allen, The Flamingos: Their Life History and Survival, *Natl. Aud. Soc. Res. Rept. No. 5,* 1956.

ANHIMIDAE

Screamer family
(3 species)

Fig. 27. Horned Screamer (*Anhima cornuta*). Total length 33 in. (838 mm.).

Physical characteristics. Length—712 to 914 mm. (28 to 36 in.). Plumage—black or gray above, light gray or white below; little pattern; head and neck feathers short and downy or sparse and attenuate; crest (2 spp.) or long horny frontal spike. Bill short, henlike. Head small and slender; neck rather short. Wings large and broad, with two long sharp spurs on forward edge of manus. Tail short and broad. Legs short and heavy; feet very large, slightly palmate; toes and claws long. Sexes alike or nearly so.

Range. South America s. to Uruguay and n. Argentina. Habitat—marshes and well-watered grassland. Nonmigratory.

Habits. Gregarious at times. Largely terrestrial and aquatic, but some perch in trees. Able to walk on mats of floating vegetation. Swim occasionally. Fly slowly; rise laboriously from the ground but soar for hours at great heights. Voice—adult, a loud trumpeting; young, a low piping.

Food. Vegetable matter.

Breeding. Shallow nest of rushes, etc., on marshy ground.

Eggs. 2 to 6; white. Incubated by ♂ and ♀.

Young. Nidifugous. Downy. Cared for by ♂ and ♀.

Technical diagnosis. Beddard, 451–456 ("Palamedeae").

Classification. Peters, 1, 1931: 142.

References. E. Gibson, Ornithological Notes from the Neighbourhood of Cape San Antonio, Buenos Ayres [Pt. 3], *Ibis,* 1880: 165–167.

W. H. Hudson, *Birds of La Plata,* London, vol. 2, 1920: 130–133.

A. Wetmore, Observations on the Birds of Argentina, Paraguay, Uruguay, and Chile, *U. S. Natl. Mus. Bull.,* 133, 1926: 67–69.

C. R. Stonor, Notes on the Breeding Habits of the Common Screamer (*Chauna torquata*), *Ibis,* 1939: 45–49, pl. 1.

Ida S. DeMay, A Study of the Pterylosis and Pneumaticity of the Screamer, *Condor,* 42, 1940: 112–118.

Synonym: Palamedeidae.

ANATIDAE

Duck family (145 species)

Fig. 28. Blue Goose (*Chen caerulescens*). Total length 28 in. (712 mm.).

Physical characteristics. Length—292 to 1524 mm. ($11\frac{1}{2}$ to 60 in.). Plumage—white, black, gray, brown, etc., often in pronounced patterns. Many spp. have colored "speculum" or a white area on the wing. Many spp. crested. Bill typically lamellate, broad, flat, and rounded at the tip. Neck medium to very long. In most spp. the wings are rather narrow and pointed, the tail short. Legs medium to very short, feet webbed. Sexes alike or unlike.

Range. World-wide. Most spp. migratory.

Habits. Many spp. gregarious exc. in nesting season. Typically aquatic. Most spp. fly well; some are flightless. Most spp. dive, regularly or occasionally, for food or to escape enemies. Voice—quack, croak, cackle, whistle, or hiss.

Food. Great variety of aquatic animals and plants; some spp. browse or eat grain on upland.

Breeding. Nest on ground; on rocky ledges, stumps, etc.; in holes in ground; in trees. Nest often lined with female's own down.

Eggs. 2 to 16; white, buff, or greenish; immaculate. Incubated by ♀, by ♂, or by both (*Heteronetta* is parasitic).

Young. Nidifugous. Downy. Cared for by ♀, by ♂, or by both.

Technical diagnosis. Witherby, 3, 1939: 167.

Classification. J. Delacour and E. Mayr, *Wils. Bull.,* 57, 1945: 3–55, pls. 1–7.

References. Bent, Nos. 126, 130; Baker, *Fauna,* 6, 1929: 377–475; Murphy, 2: 941–972.

J. G. Millais, *British Diving Ducks,* London, 2 vols., 1913.

John C. Phillips, *A Natural History of the Ducks,* Boston, 4 vols., 1922-26.

F. H. Kortright, *The Ducks, Geese and Swans of North America,* Washington, D. C., 1942.

H. Albert Hochbaum, *The Canvasback on a Prairie Marsh,* Washington, D. C., 1944.

Peter Scott, Key to the Wildfowl of the World, *Severn Wildfowl Trust 2nd Ann Rept.,* 1949: [p. 65], pls. 1–23, plus 23 unnumbered pls. with photos.

CATHARTIDAE

American Vulture family

(6 species)

Fig. 29. King Vulture (*Sarcoramphus papa*). Total length 31 in. (787 mm.).

Physical characteristics. Length—635 to 1118 mm. (25 to 44 in.). Plumage—typically brownish black, with a light area on the under surface of the wing. (Body plumage of *Sarcoramphus* white and cream.) Ruff of lanceolate or downy feathers about base of neck of larger spp. Head bare and carunculated; black, red, or yellow. (*Sarcoramphus* has the head elaborately patterned with black hairlike feathers.) Bill medium to very thick, rounded, hooked; nostrils perforate. Neck short. Wings very long and broad; tail medium to long. Legs medium or short; toes rather long; claws weakly hooked (not used for grasping). Sexes alike or nearly so.

Range. South America; N. America to s. Canada. Populations in high latitudes migratory.

Habits. Typically solitary; some spp. use colonial roosts. Have remarkable soaring flight, but larger spp. have difficulty getting off the ground. Disgorge food when disturbed on the ground. Voice (rarely heard)—low croaks or hissing sounds.

Food. Mainly carrion. Some spp. occasionally attack living animals, esp. new-born young.

Breeding. Nest in caves or hollow trees, usually without lining.

Eggs. 1 to 3; white or pale gray-green, immaculate or spotted with brown. Incubated by ♂ and ♀.

Young. Nidicolous. Downy. Cared for by ♂ and ♀.

Technical diagnosis. Friedmann, pt. 11, 1950: 3–6.

Classification. Hellmayr and Conover, pt. 1, No. 4, 1949: 1–14.

References. Bent, No. 167: 1–44.

W. L. Finley, Life History of the California Condor, *Condor,* 8, 1906: 135–142, 1 pl.; 10, 1908: 4–10, 58–65, 2 pls.; 12, 1910: 4–11, figs. 1–6.

H. Kirke Swann, *Monograph of the Birds of Prey,* London, pt. 1, 1924: 1–21, 1 pl.

J. B. May, *The Hawks of North America,* New York, 1935: 1–6, 2 pls.

C. B. Koford, The California Condor, *Natl. Aud. Soc. Res. Rept. No. 4,* 1953.

Synonym: Sarcoramphidae. The Cathartidae were formerly included in the "Vulturidae."

SAGITTARIIDAE

Secretarybird family

(1 species)

Fig. 30. Secretarybird (*Sagittarius serpentarius*). Total length 59 in. (1499 mm.).

Physical characteristics. Length—1270 to 1499 mm. (50 to 59 in.). Plumage—largely pale gray on body; remiges and thighs black; crest black and gray; rump black, barred with white; upper tail coverts white; tail gray, with white tip and black subterminal band. Conspicuous crest of long, paddle-shaped feathers on the nape. Bill short and hooked; face bare, the skin bright orange. Neck rather long. Wings large; tail long, with extremely long pair of central feathers. Legs extremely long and slender. Toes short and partly webbed; claws long. Sexes alike, but ♀ slightly larger.

Range. Africa: Senegambia; s. Sudan to the Cape (not Madagascar). Habitat—open plains. Some migration reported.

Habits. Solitary. Terrestrial; largely cursorial. Fly well but infrequently. Roost in trees. Voice (rarely heard)—loud, strident *doo-doo-dut,* "a deep raucous groan."

Food. Reptiles, small mammals, insects, young birds.

Breeding. Bulky nest of sticks and sod placed in a bush or tree.

Eggs. 2 or 3; bluish white. Incubated by ♀.

Young. Nidicolous. Downy. Cared for by ♂ and ♀.

Technical diagnosis. Friedmann, pt. 11, 1950: 60–61.

Classification. Peters, 1, 1931: 192.

References. Bannerman, 1, 1930: 165–169.

L. A. Fuertes, Album of Abyssinian Birds and Mammals, *Field Mus. Nat. Hist. Spec. Publ.,* 1930: col. pl. No. 3.

C. D. Priest, *The Birds of Southern Rhodesia,* London, vol. 1, 1933: 180–189, pl. 5.

F. J. Jackson, *The Birds of Kenya Colony and the Uganda Protectorate,* London, vol. 1, 1938: 123–127, fig. 25.

L. H. Brown, On the biology of the large birds of the Embu district, Kenya Colony, *Ibis,* 94, 1952: 592–595; see also *Ibis,* 97, 1955: 43–48.

Synonyms: Gypogeranidae, Serpentariidae.

ACCIPITRIDAE

Hawk family

(205 species)

Fig. 31. Crowned Hawk-eagle (*Stephanoaëtus coronatus*). Total length 39 in. (991 mm.).

Physical characteristics. Length—280 to 1143 mm. (11 to 45 in.). Plumage—typically of blended grays and browns. Lighter below. Many spp. have under parts barred or streaked and/or tail barred. Bill short and strongly hooked. Cere and orbital skin bare and usually brightly colored. Neck short. Wings large and, in most spp., rather rounded. Tail medium to long. Legs strong; medium to rather long. Claws stout and hooked. Sexes usually alike, but ♀ larger.

Range. Nearly world-wide (absent from Antarctic, the northern Arctic, and many oceanic islands). Most spp. migratory.

Habits. Usually solitary. Diurnal. Fly strongly; many soar. Capture prey with the feet. Voice—loud screams, whistles, cackling notes.

Food. Mammals, birds, reptiles, amphibians, fish, mollusca, various invertebrates, carrion.

Breeding. Nest of sticks, in trees, or on cliffs; or of grass and weed stalks, on ground.

Eggs. 1 to 6; white, immaculate or marked with brown. Incubated by ♀, or by ♂ and ♀.

Young. Nidicolous. Downy. Cared for by ♂ and ♀.

Technical diagnosis. Witherby, 3, 1939: 1, 38.

Classification. Peters, 1, 1931: 192–274 (not including the Pandioninae).

References. Bent, No. 167: 44–352; Baker, *Fauna,* 5, 1928: 6–29, 67–176; Witherby, 3, 1939: 38–106.

H. Kirke Swann, *Monograph of the Birds of Prey,* London, vol. 1, 1924–30: 22–62, 94–140, 154–487; vol. 2, 1933–36: 1–126, 131–316.

H. Siewert, Die Brutbiologie des Hühnerhabichts, *Jour. f. Ornith.,* 81, 1933: 44–94, pls. 1–12. (*Accipiter gentilis.*)

F. H. Herrick, *The American Eagle,* New York, 1934.

J. B. May, *The Hawks of North America,* New York, 1935: 7–91.

Vagn Holstein, Duehøgen, *Astur gentilis dubius* (Sparrman), *Biol. Stud. Danske Rovfugle,* 1, 1942: 1–155 (English summary, pp. 129–140), illus.

Synonyms: Aquilidae, Vulturidae (Cathartidae plus "Aegypiidae"). The Pandionidae are sometimes included in the Accipitridae. The Aegypiidae and Buteonidae are included here.

PANDIONIDAE

Osprey family

(1 species)

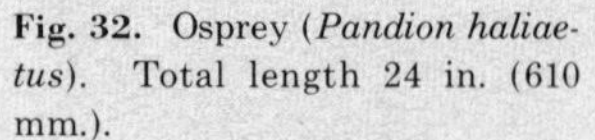

Fig. 32. Osprey (*Pandion haliaetus*). Total length 24 in. (610 mm.).

Physical characteristics. Length—559 to 610 mm. (22 to 24 in.). Plumage—brownish black above, with white edgings; head white, with black on crown and black line through eye and auricular region; under parts white, usually spotted across breast; tail barred. Bill short and strongly hooked. Wings long and pointed; tail medium and narrow. Tarsus reticulate; outer toe reversible; claws large; soles of feet studded with spines. Sexes alike.

Range. Europe and Asia s. to Spain, n. Africa, and s. China; East Indies, Australia, and some s.w. Pacific islands; N. America s. to Sinaloa and to Gulf Coast; also Bahamas, Yucatán, and British Honduras. Migrate in winter to S. Africa; India; s. S. America.

Habits. Always near water. Capture fish by hovering and then plunging, feet first, with half-closed wings, often submerging completely. Fish is carried head foremost by both feet (unless very small) to nest or perch. Voice—usually a series of short, shrill whistles, dropping in pitch at end.

Food. Fish. (When pressed by hunger: small mammals, wounded birds, or domestic fowl.)

Breeding. Sometimes loosely colonial. Nest of sticks and finer materials (as available) on rocks, trees, or on ground. Built by ♂ and ♀.

Eggs. 3 (rarely 2 or 4); white to fawn color, strongly marked with rich brown. Incubated mainly by ♀.

Young. Nidicolous. Downy. Food brought by ♂, fed to young by ♀.

Technical diagnosis. Witherby, 3, 1939: 106–107.

Classification. Peters, 1, 1931: 275 ("Pandioninae").

References. Bent, No. 167: 352–379; Witherby, 3, 1939: 106–111.

F. M. Chapman, *Camps and Cruises of an Ornithologist,* New York, 1908: 38–61.

C. G. Abbott, *The Home-life of the Osprey,* London, 1911.

J. B. May, *The Hawks of North America,* New York, 1935: 93–95, col. pl.

L. V. Compton, The Pterylosis of the Falconiformes with Special Attention to the Taxonomic Position of the Osprey, *Univ. Calif. Publ. Zool.,* 42, no. 3, 1938: 173–212.

H. Siewert, Zur Brutbiologie des Fischadlers (*Pandion h. haliaëtus*) (L.), *Jour. f. Ornith.,* Ergänzungsband 3, 1941: 145–193.

Synonymy: Sometimes included in Accipitridae.

FALCONIDAE

Falcon family (58 species)

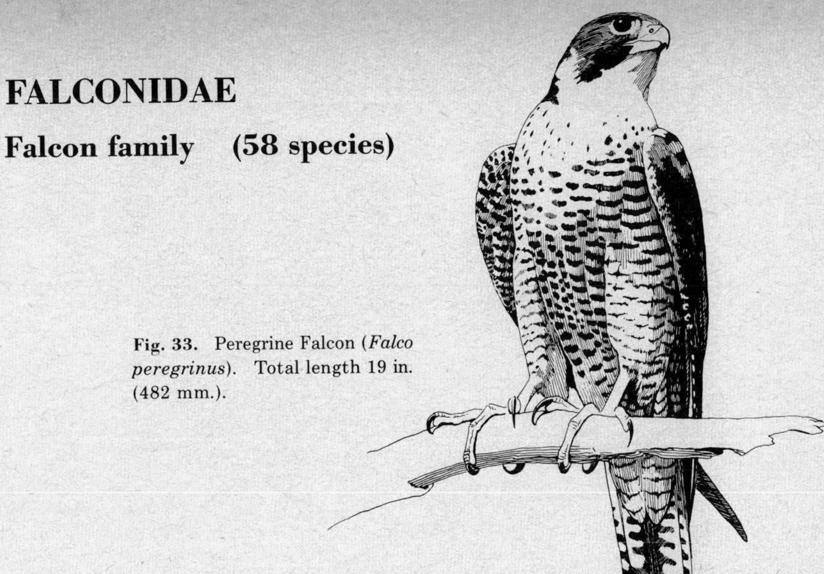

Fig. 33. Peregrine Falcon (*Falco peregrinus*). Total length 19 in. (482 mm.).

Physical characteristics. Length—152 to 635 mm. (6 to 25 in.). Plumage—gray or brown with white or buff, streaked and/or barred, especially below; or with solid contrast of black and white. Bill short, strongly hooked, and (in most spp.) toothed. Cere and orbital skin bare and usually brightly colored. Neck short. Wings of most spp. long and pointed. Tail medium to long. Legs strong, medium to rather long. Toes long, claws strong and hooked. Sexes usually alike, but ♀ larger.

Range. Nearly world-wide (absent from Antarctic and from oceanic islands). Many spp. migratory.

Habits. Usually solitary. Diurnal. Fly swiftly, soar infrequently. Capture prey with feet. Voice (little heard exc. at nest)—loud screams, squeals, and chattering notes.

Food. Mammals, birds, reptiles, amphibians, crustacea, insects, mollusca, carrion.

Breeding. Nest on cliffs, in old nests of other hawks, etc.; in holes in trees; or nest of sticks in a tree.

Eggs. 2 to 6; white, heavily blotched and spotted with brown. Incubated by ♂ and ♀.

Young. Nidicolous. Downy. Cared for by ♂ and ♀.

Technical diagnosis. Witherby, 3, 1939: 1–2.

Classification. Peters, 1, 1931: 276–306.

References. Bent, No. 170: 1–139; Baker, *Fauna,* 5, 1928: 29–67.

W. H. Hudson, *Birds of La Plata,* New York, vol. 2, 1920: 62–88. (Caracaras.)

H. Kirke Swann, *Monograph of the Birds of Prey,* London, vol. 1, 1925: 66–93, 140–153; vol. 2, 1933–36: 127–130, 317–477.

J. B. May, *The Hawks of North America,* New York, 1935: 97–129.

L. R. Wolfe, A Synopsis of North American Birds of Prey and Their Related Forms in Other Countries, *Bull. Chicago Acad. Sci.,* 5, no. 8, 1938: 167–208.

Synonymy: The Polyboridae are included.

MEGAPODIIDAE

Megapode family
(10 species)

Fig. 34. Mallee Fowl (*Leipoa ocellata*). Total length 24 in. (610 mm.).

Physical characteristics. Length—254 to 648 mm. (10 to 25½ in.). Plumage—solidly dark brown or slate (with white under parts in some spp.); or gray and brown, streaked and barred with buff or chestnut. One sp. crested, the others with head and neck partly or wholly bare (colored red and yellow or olive-drab). Some spp. have long wattles on nape and foreneck (*Aepypodius*) or a casque (*Macrocephalon*). Bill small and henlike to rather large and massive. Head small; neck medium. Wings large and rounded; tail medium to rather long, vaulted in several spp. Legs, feet, and claws very large and strong, esp. in *Megapodius*. Sexes alike or nearly so.

Range. Australia; Nicobars, islands off n. and e. Borneo, Philippines, Marianas; Celebes and eastward through New Guinea, Solomons, and New Hebrides to c. Polynesia. Habitat—forested areas, esp. near coast, and dry scrub. Nonmigratory.

Habits. Most spp. gregarious. Largely terrestrial. Some fly to offshore islands to roost. Voice—loud harsh calls and cackling notes.

Food. Insects, worms, snails, seeds, berries.

Breeding. Eggs buried in sand, in warm volcanic ash, or in mounds of decaying vegetation (usually mixed with soil).

Eggs. 6 to 24; buffy white, immaculate. Not incubated by parents (nests serve as natural incubators).

Young. Nidifugous. Downy. Extremely precocial—not cared for by parents.

Technical diagnosis. Ridgway and Friedmann, pt. 10, 1946: 5.

Classification. Peters, 2, 1934: 3–9.

References. Baker, *Fauna,* 5, 1928: 436–439.

A. J. Campbell, *Nests and Eggs of Australian Birds,* Sheffield, England, pt. 2, 1901: 698–721.

L. S. Crandall and C. Barrett, Avian Mound Builders and Their Mounds, *Bull. N. Y. Zool. Soc.,* 34, 1931: 106–127.

D. H. Fleay, Nesting Habits of the Brush-Turkey, *Emu,* 36, 1937: 153–163, pls. 23–27.

F. Lewis, Notes on the Breeding Habits of the Mallee-Fowl, *Emu,* 40, 1940: 97–110, pls. 22–27.

H. J. Frith, Breeding Habits in the Family Megapodiidae, *Ibis,* 1956: 620–640.

CRACIDAE

Curassow family

(38 species)

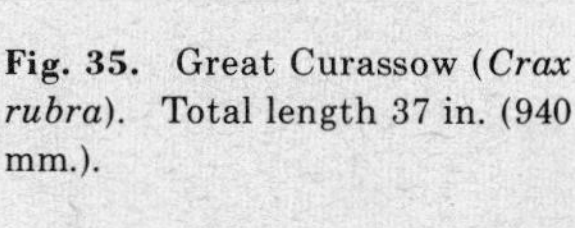

Fig. 35. Great Curassow (*Crax rubra*). Total length 37 in. (940 mm.).

Physical characteristics. Length—521 to 991 mm. ($20\frac{1}{2}$ to 39 in.). Plumage—glossy; black (or black and white), reddish brown, or olive-brown; with little pattern (exc. ♀ in some spp.). Many spp. crested, some casqued. Cere and lores bare in most spp., throat bare and/or wattled in some. Bill variable, usually rather small. Wings rounded; tail broad, long, and flat. Legs strong, moderately long to short; feet large; hind toe at same level as others. ♀ brown, with barred areas in some spp.; ♀ like ♂ in others.

Range. Neotropical. Mainland, s. Texas and Sonora to Paraguay. Habitat—forests. Nonmigratory.

Habits. Often gregarious. *Nothocrax urumutum* said to be nocturnal. Arboreal (may feed on ground but when alarmed take refuge in trees). Flight heavy and direct. ♂ in *Penelope* and *Penelopina* has a slow "drumming" display flight. Voice—loud and often harsh (trachea of ♂ in some spp. elongated and looped between pectoral muscles and skin).

Food. Fruits, leaves.

Breeding. Simple nest of sticks or leaves in branches of trees.

Eggs. 2 to 3 (or 5?); white. Incubated by ♀ only?

Young. Nidifugous. Downy (striped on head). Arboreal *ab ovo*.

Technical diagnosis. Ridgway and Friedmann, pt. 10, 1946: 5–8.

Classification. Hellmayr and Conover, pt. 1, no. 1, 1942: 114–197.

References. Bent, No. 162: 345–352.

O. Salvin and F. D. Godman, *Biologia Centrali-Americana. Aves,* London, vol. 3, 1901: 270–283.

P. R. Lowe, Some Notes and Observations on a Guan (*Ortalis vetula*) Suggested by an Examination of an Immature Specimen, *Ibis,* 1913: 283–301, pl. 7.

O. Heinroth, Beobachtungen bei der Aufzucht eines Knopfschnabel-Hokko's (*Crax globicera*) und eines Mitu's (*Mitua mitu*), *Jour. f. Ornith.,* 79, 1931: 278–283, pls. 17–19.

G. M. Sutton, and O. S. Pettingill, Jr., Birds of the Gomez Farias Region, Southwestern Tamaulipas, *Auk,* 59, 1942: 10–12, pl. 2.

E. Schäfer, Estudio bio-ecologico comparativo sobre algunos Cracidae del norte y centro de Venezuela, *Bol. Soc. venezol. Cienc. nat.,* 15 (No. 80): 30–63, illus.

TETRAONIDAE

Grouse family (18 species)

Fig. 36. Black Grouse (*Lyrurus tetrix*). Total length 20 in. (508 mm.).

Physical characteristics. Length—305 to 889 mm. (12 to 35 in.). Plumage—mainly brown, gray, or black, usually paler (or with white) below; most spp. barred, mottled, or scaled in cryptic patterns (3 spp. assume a white plumage in winter). Bill short and strong; nostrils feathered. Head entirely feathered (exc. bare orbital line in some spp.). Neck rather short, with (in some spp.) lateral inflatable air sacs and/or tufts of erectile feathers. Wings short and rounded; tail diverse in form, usually large. Legs short to medium (not spurred); tarsi (and, in some spp., toes) feathered; feet rather large. Sexes alike or unlike.

Range. North America, n. Europe and Asia. Most spp. nonmigratory.

Habits. Most spp. solitary. Terrestrial (some spp. somewhat arboreal). Flight strong but not prolonged. Males, alone or in groups, have (mainly in breeding season) various displays involving strutting, whirring the wings, and (sometimes) vocal accompaniment. Voice—whistling, cooing, cackling, and clucking notes.

Food. Buds, leaves, berries, and a variety of other vegetable matter; insects.

Breeding. Some spp. polygamous. Nests on the ground (exceptionally in a tree).

Eggs. 6 to 16; white, buffy, or brown; immaculate, speckled, or heavily blotched with brown and black. Incubated by ♀.

Young. Nidifugous. Downy. Cared for by ♀.

Technical diagnosis. Ridgway and Friedmann, pt. 10, 1946: 63–65.

Classification. Peters, 2, 1934: 24–42.

References. Bent, No. 162: 91–345; Witherby, 5, 1941: 209–233.

G. L. Girard, Life History, Habits, and Food of the Sage Grouse, *Centrocercus urophasianus* Bonaparte, *Univ. Wyoming Publ.,* 3, No. 1, 1937.

Charles W. Schwartz, The Ecology of the Prairie Chicken in Missouri, *Univ. Missouri Studies,* 20, no. 1, 1945.

G. Bump, R. W. Darrow, F. C. Edminster, and W. F. Crissey, *The Ruffed Grouse: Life History, Propagation, Management,* Albany, 1947.

PHASIANIDAE

Pheasant family

(165 species)

Fig. 37. Silver Pheasant (*Lophura nycthemera*). Total length 44 in. (1118 mm.).

Physical characteristics. Length—127 to 1981 mm. (5 to 78 in.). Plumage—ranging from brown and black in cryptic patterns to multicolored in conspicuous patterns (bright yellow, red, green, blue, white). Colored wattles or areas of bare skin on heads of some spp. Some spp. crested. Bill henlike, small or of moderate size. Neck short to fairly long. Wings strong, rounded; tail extremely short to extremely long. Legs strong, short to rather long; spurred in some spp. Sexes unlike in most spp.

Range. Mainland of: extreme s. Canada, s. through northern two-thirds of S. America; Old World, exc. n. Scandinavia and n. Asia. A few spp. migratory.

Habits. Gregarious or, in some spp., solitary. Terrestrial, but some roost in trees. Flight strong but not prolonged. Many spp. scratch or dig in ground with bill for food. Males of many spp. display plumage or whir wings in courtship. Voice—crowing, clucking, and cackling notes.

Food. Seeds, grains, berries, insects, worms, etc.

Breeding. Some spp. polygamous. Nest on ground, or (*Tragopan*) in trees.

Eggs. 2 to 22; white to buff or olive-green, speckled or immaculate. Incubated by ♀, or by ♂ and ♀.

Young. Nidifugous. Downy. Cared for by ♀, or by ♂ and ♀.

Technical diagnosis. Ridgway and Friedmann, pt. 10, 1946: 231.

Classification. Peters, 2, 1934: 42–133.

References. Bent, No 162: 1–90; Witherby, 5, 1941: 233–254; Baker, *Fauna,* 5, 1928: 281–435.

[C.] W. Beebe, *A Monograph of the Pheasants,* London, 4 vols., 1918–1922. (A 2-vol. edition, with new title, was issued in 1926.)

H. L. Stoddard, *The Bobwhite Quail: Its Habits, Preservation, and Increase,* New York, 1931.

W. L. McAtee (ed.), *The Ring-necked Pheasant and its Management in North America,* Washington, D. C., 1945.

A. F. Skutch, Life History of the Marbled Wood-Quail, *Condor,* 49, 1947: 217–232.

J. Delacour, *The Pheasants of the World,* London, 1951.

Synonymy: The Odontophoridae and Perdicidae are included.

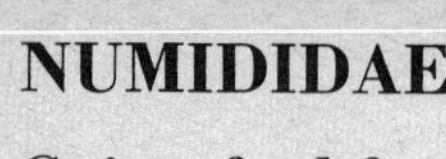

NUMIDIDAE

Guineafowl family (7 species)

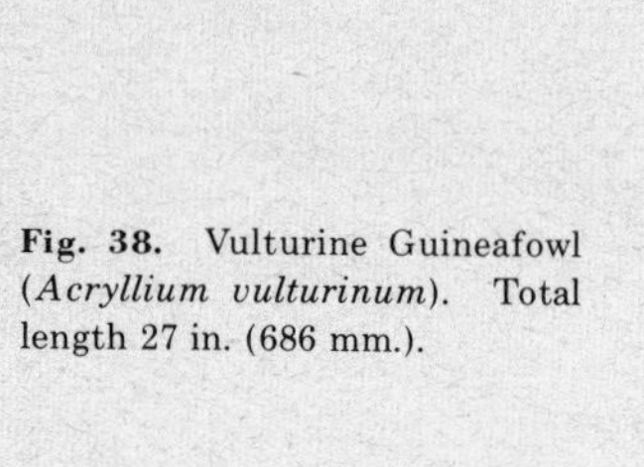

Fig. 38. Vulturine Guineafowl (*Acryllium vulturinum*). Total length 27 in. (686 mm.).

Physical characteristics. Length—432 to 750 mm. (17 to $29\frac{1}{2}$ in.). Plumage—black, uniformly spotted (exc. in *Phasidus*) with white, the spots becoming lines or bars on the remiges (*Acryllium* has the lower neck and breast bright blue, with long, pointed, black and white hackles; *Agelastes* has the forepart of body white). Head and neck largely bare (colored red, yellow, blue, or slate), marked with casque, a conspicuous vertical crest, or a band of short feathers, and (in most spp.) with wattles or loose folds of skin. Bill short and stout. Wings moderate and very rounded; tail medium (long and pointed in *Acryllium*), typically drooping and heavily overlain with coverts. Legs strong and feet large; spurs lacking exc. in *Phasidus* and *Agelastes*. Sexes alike or nearly so.

Range. Madagascar and Africa s. of the Sahara. Habitat—forest, brush, exceptionally grassland. Nonmigratory.

Habits. Most spp. gregarious. Largely terrestrial, but roost in trees. Flight strong but not prolonged. Notably wary. Voice—loud, harsh, and monotonously repetitive.

Food. Insects, snails, seeds, tubers, leaves.

Breeding. Nest, with little lining, placed on ground.

Eggs. 7 to 20; white to pale reddish brown, immaculate or lightly speckled. Incubated by ♀.

Young. Nidifugous. Downy. Cared for by ♂ and ♀.

Technical diagnosis. Ridgway and Friedmann, pt. 10, 1946: 430–431.

Classification. Peters, 2, 1934: 133–139.

References. A. Ghigi, Monografia delle Galline di Faraone (Numididae), *Pubbl. Staz. Sper. Pollicolt. Rovigo,* 2, 1927: 1–84, 1 pl.

J. P. Chapin, The Birds of the Belgian Congo, I, *Amer. Mus. Nat. Hist. Bull.,* 65, 1932: 656–683, pls. 8–10.

F. J. Jackson, *The Birds of Kenya Colony and the Uganda Protectorate,* London, vol. 1, 1938: 275–285, col pl. 7.

A. Roberts, *The Birds of South Africa,* London, 1940: 78–80, col. pl. 13.

A. R. Lee, The Guinea Fowl, *U. S. Dept. Agric. Farmers' Bull. No. 1391,* 1940.

MELEAGRIDIDAE

Turkey family (2 species)

Fig. 39. Ocellated Turkey (*Agriocharis ocellata*). Total length 41 in. (1041 mm.).

Physical characteristics. Length—838 to 1092 mm. (33 to 43 in.). Plumage—dark metallic brown or green, barred with black; wings barred with white; rectrices brown or gray, barred with black, tipped with a two-color band; upper tail coverts in *Agriocharis* broadly banded with copper, black, and metallic blue. Bill short. Skin of head and neck blue and red—bare and carunculated. Neck long; wings and tail broad and rounded; legs rather long, spurred (very slightly in ♀); feet large. Sexes similar, but ♀ smaller and duller.

Range. Eastern U. S. and s.w. to Arizona; Mexico, including the Yucatán peninsula; n. Guatemala; British Honduras. Habitat—wooded country. Nonmigratory.

Habits. Gregarious. Terrestrial, but roost in trees. Flight strong but not prolonged. Voice—many "gobbling" and clucking sounds.

Food. A great variety of vegetable material; some insects and other animal matter.

Breeding. Polygamous. Nest a hollow in the ground, with little lining.

Eggs. 8 to 18; buff, speckled with brown. Incubated by ♀.

Young. Nidifugous. Downy. Cared for by ♀.

Technical diagnosis. Ridgway and Friedmann, pt. 10, 1946: 436–437.

Classification. Ridgway and Friedmann, pt. 10, 1946: 436–463.

References. Bent, No. 162: 323–345.

G. F. Gaumer, Notes on Meleagris ocellata, Cuvier, *Trans. Kans. Acad. Sci.*, 8, 1883 (for 1881–82): 60-62.

E. A. McIlhenny, *The Wild Turkey and Its Hunting*, New York, 1914.

H. S. Mosby and C. O. Handley, *The Wild Turkey in Virginia*, Richmond, Va., 1943.

J. S. Ligon, History, and Management of Merriam's Wild Turkey, *Univ. N. Mex. Publ. Biol. No. 1*, 1946.

A. S. Leopold, The Wild Turkeys of Mexico, *Trans. 13th N. Amer. Wildl. Conf.*, 1948: 393–400.

OPISTHOCOMIDAE

Hoatzin family (1 species)

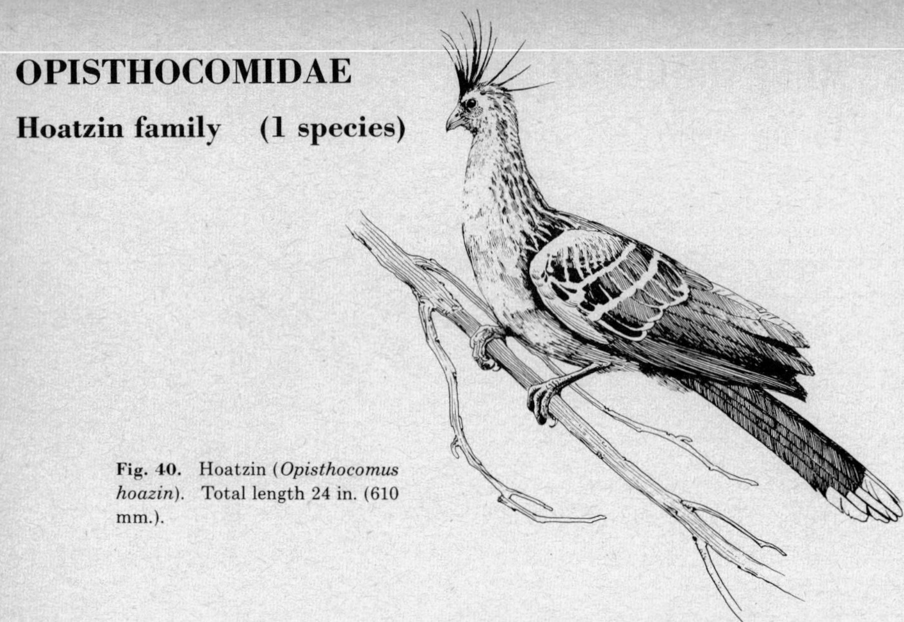

Fig. 40. Hoatzin (*Opisthocomus hoazin*). Total length 24 in. (610 mm.).

Physical characteristics. Length—about 610 mm. (24 in.). Plumage—loose-webbed; dark brown above, with olive reflections and conspicuous white streaks; top of head reddish brown; tail broadly tipped with pale buff; pale buff on throat and upper breast to rich chestnut on thighs and crissum. Bill short, stout, and laterally compressed. Long crest of stiff, narrow feathers; head otherwise scantily feathered. Neck long and slender. Wings and tail large and rounded. Legs short; feet rather large. Sexes alike.

Range. Northern S. America. (Distributed irregularly in Atlantic drainage from the Amazon system northward.) Habitat—wooded river banks. Nonmigratory.

Habits. Gregarious. Arboreal. Flight very weak. Voice—a harsh hissing screech; a harsh, monotonous *ca cherk, ca cherk.*

Food. Leaves and fruit, esp. of arum.

Breeding. Nest a platform of sticks 4 to 15 (rarely up to 50) ft. above water in trees.

Eggs. 2 to 3; white, speckled with brown. Incubated [by ♂ and ♀?].

Young. Semi-nidicolous. Almost naked at hatching. Cared for [by ♂ and ♀?].

Technical diagnosis. Ridgway and Friedmann, pt. 10, 1946: 2–4.

Classification. Peters, 2, 1934: 141.

References. J. J. Quelch, On the Habits of the Hoatzin (*Opisthocomus cristatus*), *Ibis,* 1890: 327–335.

C. W. Beebe, A Contribution to the Ecology of the Adult Hoatzin, *Zoologica,* 1, 1909: 45–66. (Reprinted in *Smiths. Rept. for 1910.*)

C. Chubb, *The Birds of British Guiana,* London, vol. 1, 1916: 51–64.

G. K. Cherrie, A Contribution to the Ornithology of the Orinoco Region, *Mus. Brooklyn Inst. Arts and Sci., Sci. Bull.,* 2, no. 6, 1916: 357–360.

[C.] W. Beebe, *Tropical Wildlife in British Guiana,* New York, 1917: 155–182.

MESOENATIDAE

Mesite family (3 species)

Fig. 41. Brown Mesite (*Mesoenas unicolor*). Total length 10 in. (254 mm.).

Physical characteristics. Length—254 to 266 mm. (10 to $10\frac{1}{2}$ in.). Plumage—chestnut-brown, or gray and olive-brown, above. One or more white streaks on side of head or neck. Throat and breast pale buff or white, spotted or barred (exc. in *Mesoenas unicolor*). Bill slender, moderate in length and straight to long (40 mm.) and sickle-shaped (*Monias*). Nostrils long, operculate slits. Wings short and rounded. Tail rather long and rounded. Legs slender or stout; moderate in length. ♀ unlike ♂ in *Monias*, like in others.

Range. Madagascar (in forests or brushy areas). Nonmigratory.

Habits. Usually found in pairs (*Monias* sometimes in flocks of 30 or more). Terrestrial. Run well; fly only when forced to do so (*Monias* apparently flightless). Voice (of *Monias*)—loud, explosive *nak nak nak* . . . ; a low *creeu*.

Food. Fruits, seeds, and insects.

Breeding. Some evidence of polyandry. Nest of sticks and leaves, 2 to 6 ft. above the ground, in low trees or brush.

Eggs. 1 to 3; white, greenish white, or buffy gray. Incubated by ♂ or by ♀ (or both?—recorded for ♂ in *Monias*, for ♀ in *Mesoenas*).

Young. Nidifugous. Downy. Apparently (in *Monias*) cared for by ♂.

Technical diagnosis. P. R. Lowe, *Proc. Zool. Soc. London,* 1924: 1131–1152.

Classification. Peters, 2, 1934: 141–142.

References. L. Brasil, Fam. Mesitidae, Wytsman's *Genera Avium,* pt. 26, 1914.

L. Levauden, Note preliminaire sur les oiseaux appartenant aux genres *Mesoenas* et *Monias, Alauda,* 3, 1931: 395–400, 2 pls.

J. Delacour, Les Oiseaux de la Mission Zoologique Franco-Anglo-Americaine à Madagascar, *L'Ois. et Rev. Franç. d'Ornith.,* 2, 1932: 30–31.

A. L. Rand, The Distribution and Habits of Madagascar Birds, *Bull. Amer. Mus. Nat. Hist.,* 72, art. 5, 1936: 364–368.

A. L. Rand, The Nests and Eggs of *Mesoenas unicolor* of Madagascar, *Auk,* 68, 1951: 23–26.

Synonyms: Mesitidae, Mesitornithidae, Mesoenidae.

TURNICIDAE

Hemipode-quail family

(15 species)

Fig. 42. Spotted Hemipode-quail (*Turnix ocellata*). Total length $7\frac{1}{2}$ in. (190 mm.).

Physical characteristics. Length—114 to 190 mm. ($4\frac{1}{2}$ to $7\frac{1}{2}$ in.). Plumage—brown, gray, and black; cryptically patterned above; plain (in most spp.) below; barred or spotted on sides. Bill short; stout to slender and pointed (*Ortyxelos*). Neck short; body compact. Wings short and rounded; tail feathers soft and extremely short (exc. in *Ortyxelos*). Legs strong but short; 3 toes (2nd, 3rd, and 4th). ♂ somewhat smaller and duller than ♀.

Range. Southern Spain and Portugal, Africa, India, Burma, Siam, Indo-China, s. and e. China, Malaysia, Papuan Region, Philippines, Solomon Ids., Australia. Habitat—grassland, scanty brush, or open forest. Nonmigratory (exc. in China).

Habits. Solitary. Terrestrial. Very secretive. Flight brief and infrequent. Pugnacious (esp. the ♀ during courtship). Voice—a booming note (♀); cooing or purring notes.

Food. Seeds, insects.

Breeding. Polyandrous. Nest of grass on the ground.

Eggs. Usually 4 (2 in *Ortyxelos*); white, gray, or olive, spotted with brown. Incubated by ♂.

Young. Nidifugous. Downy. Cared for by ♂.

Technical diagnosis. Ridgway and Friedmann, pt. 9, 1941: 2–4.

Classification. Peters, 2, 1934: 142–149.

References. Baker, *Fauna,* 5, 1928: 440–457; Mathews, pt. 1, 1910: 77–95, pls. 13–19; Bannerman, 2, 1931: xxvi-xxvii, 303–312, 2 figs, col. pl.

D. Seth-Smith, The Importance of Aviculture as an Aid to the Study of Ornithology, *Proc. 4th Internatl. Ornith. Congress* (London, 1905), 1907: 669–673.

P. R. Lowe, Notes on the Systematic Position of *Ortyxelus* . . . , *Ibis,* 1923: 276–299.

R. C. Pendleton, Field Observations on the Spotted Button-quail on Guadalcanal, *Auk,* 64, 1947: 417–421, pl. 14.

PEDIONOMIDAE

Collared-hemipode family (1 species)

Fig. 43. Collared-hemipode (*Pedionomus torquatus*). Total length 6½ in. (165 mm.).

Physical characteristics. Length—152 to 171 mm. (6 to 6¾ in.). Plumage (of ♀)—reddish brown, buff, and black in cryptic patterns above. A broad white collar, spotted with black. Upper breast (and nape) chestnut. Rest of under parts pale buff, marked along sides with dark brown and black. Bill medium; rather slender. Neck of moderate length; body compact. Wings short and rounded. Tail very short. Legs fairly long; tibiae partly bare; 4 toes. ♂ smaller and duller in coloration than ♀.

Range. Australia (New S. Wales, Victoria, s. Australia). Habitat—open plains. Migratory in part.

Habits. Solitary. Very secretive. Terrestrial. Flight weak. Often rise on toes and peer about. Voice—a hollow, "tapping" sound.

Food. Seeds, insects.

Breeding. Nest a hollow in the ground, lined with grass.

Eggs. Usually 4; yellowish or greenish white, spotted with olive and gray. Incubated by (♂?).

Young. Nidifugous (?). Downy (?). Cared for by (♂?).

Technical diagnosis. Mathews, 1, 1911: 96.

Classification. Peters, 2, 1934: 150.

References. Mathews, 1, pts. 1–2, 1910–11: 96–99, col. pl. 20.

W. V. Legge, Notes on the Habits of the Collared Plain Wanderer (*Pedionomus torquatus,* Gould), *Proc. Zool. Soc. London,* 1869: 236–238.

Hans Gadow, Notes on the Structure of *Pedionomus torquatus,* with Regard to its Systematic Position, *Records Australian Mus.,* 1, 1891: 205–211.

H. A. Purnell, Plain-Wanderer in Captivity, *Emu,* 15, 1915: 141–143, photo.

GRUIDAE

Crane family (14 species)

Fig. 44. Demoiselle Crane (*Anthropoïdes virgo*). Total length 35 in. (889 mm.).

Physical characteristics. Length—787 to 1524 mm. (31 to 60 in.). Plumage largely brown, gray, or white. Bare red areas or ornamental plumes on head. Bill straight and rather long. Wings large; secondaries (used in display) are usually modified—curled or elongated. Tail short. Legs long, with tibiae partly bare; hind toe elevated. Sexes alike or nearly so.

Range. North America s. to Cuba (to c. Mexico in winter) and the Old World exc. the Malayan Archipelago, Polynesia, and New Zealand. Most spp. migratory.

Habits. Gregarious (exc. in breeding season). Fly with neck extended; often soar. The elaborate "dance" characteristic of most cranes is apparently performed by some spp. at all seasons of the year. Voice—loud and resonant (trachea is elongated and coiled in sternum in most spp.).

Food. Omnivorous.

Breeding. Nest a sparse to bulky mass of vegetation on ground or in shallow water.

Eggs. 2 to 3; dull white to brown or olive-brown, spotted with darker shades (exc. those of *Balearica,* which are immaculate pale blue). Incubated by ♂ and ♀.

Young. Nidifugous. Downy. Cared for by ♂ and ♀.

Technical diagnosis. Ridgway and Friedmann, pt. 9, 1941: 1–6.

Classification. Peters, 2, 1934: 150–154.

References. Bent, No. 135: 219–259, pls. 65–71; Witherby, 4, 1940: 449–455.

F. E. Blaauw, A Monograph of the Cranes, Leiden, 1897.

L. Brasil, Fam. Gruidae, Wytsman's *Genera Avium,* pt. 19, 1913.

G. Hoffmann, *Rund um den Kranich,* Oehringen, 1936.

L. H. Walkinshaw, The Sandhill Cranes, *Cranbrook Inst. Sci. Bull. No. 29,* 1949.

R. P. Allen, The Whooping Crane, *Natl. Aud. Soc. Res. Rept. No. 3,* 1952.

Synonyms: Balearicidae; Megalornithidae; "Psophiidae" of Mathews (a name now used for the Trumpeters).

ARAMIDAE

Limpkin family (1 species)

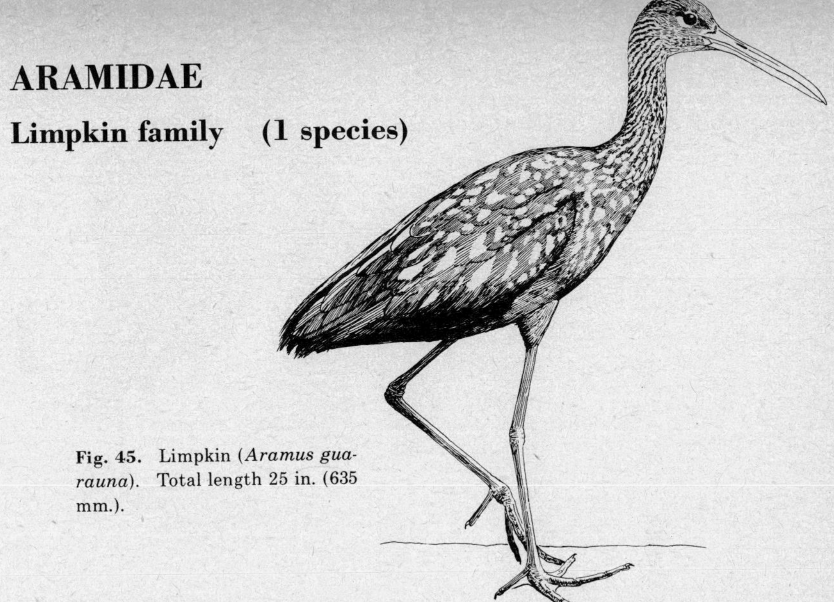

Fig. 45. Limpkin (*Aramus guarauna*). Total length 25 in. (635 mm.).

Physical characteristics. Length—584 to 712 mm. (23 to 28 in.). Plumage—dark olive-brown with greenish iridescence on upper part of body; feathers of head, neck, and under parts (also of back and wing coverts in some subspp.) broadly streaked with white. Bill long and laterally compressed (tip slightly decurved, usually somewhat twisted). Neck long and slender. Wings broad and rounded. Tail broad and of moderate length. Legs long, with tibiae partly bare. Toes long, claws long and sharp. Sexes alike.

Range. Southern Georgia, Florida, Greater Antilles, s. Mexico, tropical Central and S. America s. to c. Argentina (Buenos Aires Prov.). Habitat—swamps, wooded or open; or arid brush (West Indies). Nonmigratory.

Habits. Solitary or slightly gregarious. Somewhat crepuscular or nocturnal. Fly slowly and infrequently. Vociferous—loud wails and screams; a variety of clucking notes.

Food. Large snails (esp. *Ampullaria*); a few insects and seeds.

Breeding. Shallow nest of rushes or sticks, in marsh vegetation just above water, or in bushes or trees (as much as 17 ft. up).

Eggs. 4 to 8; pale buffy, blotched and speckled with light brown. Incubated by ♂ and ♀.

Young. Nidifugous. Downy—dark brown, unmarked. Cared for by ♂ and ♀.

Technical diagnosis. Ridgway and Friedmann, pt. 9, 1941: 28.

Classification. Hellmayr and Conover, pt. 1, no. 1, 1942: 301–308.

References. Bent, No. 135: 254–259.

A. H. Garrod, On the Anatomy of *Aramus scolopaceus, Proc. Zool. Soc. London,* 1876: 275–277.

W. H. Hudson, *Birds of La Plata,* London, vol. 2, 1920: 172–175.

D. J. Nicholson, Habits of the Limpkin in Florida, *Auk,* 45, 1928: 305–309, pl. 11.

A. H. Howell, *Florida Bird Life,* New York, 1932: 199–202.

C. Cottam, Food of the Limpkin, *Wils. Bull.,* 48, 1936: 11–13.

PSOPHIIDAE

Trumpeter family (3 species)

Fig. 46. White-winged Trumpeter (*Psophia leucoptera*). Total length 21 in. (534 mm.).

Physical characteristics. Length—432 to 534 mm. (17 to 21 in.). Feathers very soft and loose-webbed, velvetlike on head and neck; outer webs of tertials and secondaries modified to long, hairlike strands. Plumage largely black, with purple, green, or bronze reflections, esp. on lower neck and the wing coverts. Secondaries and tertials white, gray, or brown. Bill short, stout, and somewhat curved. Neck long. Wings very rounded. Tail short; tail coverts long and full. Legs long; tibiae partly bare; feet of moderate size. Sexes alike.

Range. South America: s.e. Venezuela, the Guianas, and the Amazon Valley. Habitat—humid forests. Nonmigratory.

Habits. Gregarious. Largely terrestrial, but roost in trees. Run swiftly; fly only when forced. Carriage "humped" like that of guineahen (*Numida*). Voice—a loud, deep-toned cry; a prolonged cackle.

Food. Vegetable material; insects.

Breeding. Nest in hole in tree or in the crown of a palm.

Eggs. 6 to 10; white or green, immaculate. Incubated by ♀.

Young. Probably nidifugous. Downy. Cared for by (♀?).

Technical diagnosis. Beddard, 374–377.

Classification. Hellmayr and Conover, pt. 1, no. 1, 1942: 308–314.

References. P. L. Sclater, On the *Psophia obscura* of Natterer and Pelzeln, *Ibis,* 1898: 520–524, pl. 11 (col.).

F. P. Penard and A. P. Penard, *De Vogels van Guyana,* Paramaribo, vol. 1, [1908]: 221–225.

C. Chubb, *The Birds of British Guiana,* London, vol. 1, 1916: 144–146.

[C.] W. Beebe, *Tropical Wild Life in British Guiana,* New York, 1917: 247–252, col. pl.

K. Plath, Trumpeters, *Aviculture,* 2 (ser. 2), 1930: 107–108, col. pl.

Note: The "Psophiidae" of Mathews = Gruidae.

RALLIDAE

Rail family

(132 species)

Fig. 47. King Rail (*Rallus elegans*). Total length 15½ in. (393 mm.).

Physical characteristics. Length—139 to 508 mm. (5½ to 20 in.). Plumage—black or soft shades of blue, gray, brown, or green; some spp. plain, others streaked above and/or barred below (esp. on sides and thighs). Bill strong; short and stout to long and curved. Some spp. have a bright-colored horny frontal shield. Neck medium to long. Body laterally compressed. Wings short and rounded; tail short and (usually) of soft feathers. Legs and toes long (toes lobed in *Fulica*). Tibiae partly bare. Sexes alike or nearly so in most spp.

Range. World-wide (exc. high latitudes). Habitat—marshes (typically), woods, or dry plains. Many spp. migratory.

Habits. Most spp. solitary. Secretive. Many spp. crepuscular. Terrestrial, but swim well. Flight appears weak, but some spp. make long migratory flights; many island spp. are flightless. Voice—great variety of screams, cackles, etc.; one note may be rapidly repeated in a long series.

Food. A great variety of animal and vegetable matter.

Breeding. Open nest on the ground or slightly above it in a bush; in a burrow; on piles of vegetation in the water; or globular nest of grass with side entrance.

Eggs. 2 to 16; nearly white to buff or olive, speckled. Incubated by ♂ and ♀.

Young. Nidifugous. Downy. Cared for by ♂ and ♀ (and sometimes by young of a previous brood).

Technical diagnosis. Witherby, 5, 1941: 173–174.

Classification. Peters, 2, 1934, 157–213.

References. Bent, No. 135: 260–371; Baker, *Fauna,* 6, 1929: 3–35; Witherby, 5, 1941: 173–208.

A. O. Gross and J. Van Tyne, The Purple Gallinule (*Ionornis martinicus*) of Barro Colorado Island, Canal Zone, *Auk,* 46, 1929: 431–446, pls. 20–24.

G. Steinbacher, Zur Brutbiologie des Grünfüssigen Teichhuhns (*Gallinula chloropus* L.), *Jour. f. Ornith.,* 87, 1939: 115–135, illus.

L. H. Walkinshaw, Summer Life of the Sora Rail, *Auk,* 57, 1940: 153–168, pl. 3.

John C. Jones, Food Habits of the American Coot, with Notes on Distribution, *U. S. Bur. Biol. Surv., Wildl. Res. Bull. 2,* 1940.

Paul H. Baldwin, The Life History of the Laysan Rail, *Condor,* 49, 1947: 14–21.

HELIORNITHIDAE

Finfoot family (3 species)

Fig. 48. African Finfoot (*Podica senegalensis*). Total length $24\frac{1}{2}$ in. (623 mm.).

Physical characteristics. Length—305 to 623 mm. (12 to $24\frac{1}{2}$ in.). Plumage—brown or greenish black above (spotted with white in *Podica*), buffy white below. Head and neck partly black, with white stripes (faint in *Podica*). Bill, legs, and feet green, yellow, or red. Bill strong, rather long and tapered. Neck fairly long. Wings short and rounded; tail rather long and broad. Legs very short; feet broadly lobed. Sexes alike or ♀ slightly smaller and duller.

Range. Central America and n. half of S. America; c. and s. Africa (exc. Madagascar); n.e. India, Burma, Siam, Malay Peninsula, Sumatra. Habitat—streams, lakes, and marshes. Nonmigratory.

Habits. Solitary. Very shy. Largely aquatic, but run rapidly on land (*Heliopais, Podica*). Perch on branches over water. Flight fairly strong but not prolonged. Fly along surface of water when alarmed. Swim with head-bobbing motion; dive well. Voice—a bark of one to three notes; a guttural growl or quack; a bubbling sound.

Food. Insects, crustacea, snails, fish, amphibia; seeds.

Breeding. Nest of reeds or sticks in brush or trees, one to 12 ft. above water.

Eggs. 2 to 7; cream-colored or greenish white, speckled and blotched. Incubated by ♂ and ♀.

Young. Nidifugous (?). Downy. Cared for by ?.

Technical diagnosis. Ridgway and Friedmann, pt. 9, 1941: 224–226.

Classification. Peters, 2, 1934: 213–214.

References. Baker, *Fauna,* 6, 1929: 36–38; Bannerman, 2, 1931: xvi-xvii, 36–40.

C. Hopwood, The Nidification of the Masked Finfoot (*Heliopais personata*), *Jour. Bombay Nat. Hist. Soc.,* 27, 1921: 634–637.

C. D. Priest, *The Birds of Southern Rhodesia,* London, vol. 2, 1934: 64–73.

J. P. Chapin, The Birds of the Belgian Congo (Pt. 2), *Bull. Amer. Mus. Nat. Hist.,* 75, 1939: 34–40, pls. 5–6.

W. Krienke, Podica senegalensis petersi; Peters' Finfoot, *Ostrich,* 14, 1943: 25–26.

RHYNOCHETIDAE

Kagu family (1 species)

Fig. 49. Kagu (*Rhinochetos jubatus*). Total length 22 in. (559 mm.).

Physical characteristics. Length—about 559 mm. (22 in.). Plumage—loose-webbed; pale gray, shaded with brown; wings and tail somewhat darker and narrowly barred with dark gray. Spread wing conspicuously barred with black and chestnut; marked with white. Long bushy crest. Bill rather long and sharp; slightly flattened and decurved. Neck medium. Wings broad and rounded; tail fairly long and rounded. Legs long; tibiae partly bare; hind toe elevated. Sexes nearly alike.

Range. New Caledonia (e. of Australia). Habitat—forests. Nonmigratory.

Habits. Solitary. Crepuscular. Terrestrial. Apparently flightless. Has remarkable dancelike displays. Voice—guttural, rattling notes, piercing cries.

Food. Worms, snails, insects, frogs.

Breeding. Nest of sticks and leaves on ground.

Eggs. 1; buff, speckled with brown and gray. Incubated by ♂ and ♀.

Young. Semi-nidicolous. Downy. Cared for by ♂ and ♀.

Technical diagnosis. Ridgway and Friedmann, pt. 9, 1941: 2–3, 4.

Classification. Peters, 2, 1934: 215.

References.

A. J. Campbell, The Kagu of New Caledonia, *Emu,* 4, 1905: 166–168, pl. 12.

A. J. Campbell, A Kagu Chick, *Emu,* 5, 1905: 32, pl. 4. (See also footnote, *Emu,* 5: 95.)

F. Sarasin, Die Vögel Neu-Caledoniens und der Loyalty-Inseln, in F. Sarasin and J. Roux, *Nova Caledonia, A. Zoologie* (vol. 1, Heft 1), Wiesbaden, 1913: 55–60, pl. 3.

L. Brasil, Fam. Rhinochetidae, Wytsman's *Genera Avium,* pt. 21, 1913 (col. pl.).

H. E. Finckh, Notes on Kagus (Rhinochetus jubatus), *Emu,* 14, 1915: 168–170.

D. W. Warner, The present status of the Kagu, *Rhynochetos jubatus,* on New Caledonia, *Auk,* 65, 1948: 287–288.

Synonym: Rhinochetidae.

EURYPYGIDAE

Sunbittern family (1 species)

Fig. 50. Sunbittern (*Eurypyga helias*). Total length 18 in. (457 mm.).

Physical characteristics. Length—457 mm. (18 in.). Plumage full and soft (but feathers of neck very short); mottled and barred: black, gray, brown, and white; with spread wing showing bold pattern of black, chestnut, pale olive, yellow, gray, and white; 2 broad bands of black and chestnut on tail. Bill long. Head large; neck long, slender. Wings broad. Tail long and broad. Legs long, with tibiae partly bare. Toes rather long. Sexes alike.

Range. Neotropical. Tabasco and Chiapas through Central America to e. Peru and Bolivia and to s.e. Brazil. Habitat—about streams and ponds in tropical forest. Nonmigratory.

Habits. Solitary. Wading, terrestrial birds, but take refuge in trees when alarmed. Flight light and graceful. "Dance" with wings and tail outspread. Voice—a soft, long-drawn whistle and plaintive piping. Rattle bill.

Food. Insects and crustacea.

Breeding. Bulky nest of sticks and mud in tree, 12 to 20 ft. above the ground, built by ♂ and ♀.

Eggs. 2 to 3; nearly oval; buff, spotted and blotched with brown and purplish gray. Incubated by ♂ and ♀.

Young. Nidicolous. Downy. Fed by ♂ and ♀.

Technical diagnosis. Ridgway and Friedmann, pt. 9, 1941: 232.

Classification. Peters, 2, 1934: 215–216.

References. A. Newton, Sun-bittern, in *A Dictionary of Birds,* London,1896: 923–925.

A. F. Skutch, A nest of the Sun-bittern in Costa Rica, *Wils. Bull.,* 59, 1947: 38.

C. D. Riggs, The Family Eurypygidae: A Review, *Wils. Bull.,* 60, 1948: 75–80, pl. 2.

CARIAMIDAE

Cariama family (2 species)

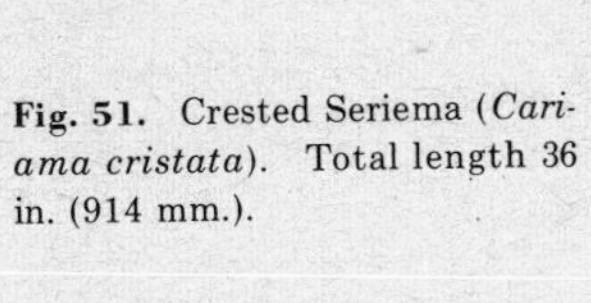

Fig. 51. Crested Seriema (*Cariama cristata*). Total length 36 in. (914 mm.).

Physical characteristics. Length—762 to 914 mm. (30 to 36 in.). Plumage soft and loose-webbed; rather light grayish brown, finely vermiculated with buff or white; under parts paler, becoming buffy white on belly and under tail coverts. Nuchal, as well as frontal, crest; long feathers on throat and lower neck. Remiges boldly barred with buff; tail tipped with gray or white. Bill short, broad, decurved. Wings short and rounded. Tail long. Legs very long; tibiae extensively bare. Feet small, semipalmate. Sexes alike or nearly so.

Range. East-central Brazil s. to n. Argentina. Habitat—grassland (*Cariama*) and forests (*Chunga*). Nonmigratory.

Habits. Occur in pairs or small groups. Largely cursorial. Run rapidly; fly weakly. Voice—barking and screaming cries, often given in chorus.

Food. Insects, reptiles, small mammals; also berries, seeds, leaves.

Breeding. Nest of sticks in trees or bushes.

Eggs. 2 to 3; white, sparsely spotted with brown. Incubated by ♂ and ♀.

Young. Nidicolous. Down with some pattern, very long and shaggy, especially on head. Cared for by ?

Technical diagnosis. Beddard, 373–374.

Classification. Hellmayr and Conover, pt. 1, no. 1, 1942: 427–430.

References.
F. E. Beddard, On the Anatomy of Burmeister's Cariama (*Chunga burmeisteri*), *Proc. Zool. Soc. London,* 1889: 594–602, figs. 1–6.

H. S. Boyle, Field Notes on the Seriema (*Chunga burmeisteri*), *Auk,* 34, 1917: 294–296.

O. Heinroth, Die Jugendentwicklung von *Cariama cristata, Jour f. Ornith.,* 72, 1924: 119–124, pls. 1–2.

Synonym: Dicholophidae.

OTIDIDAE

Bustard family (23 species)

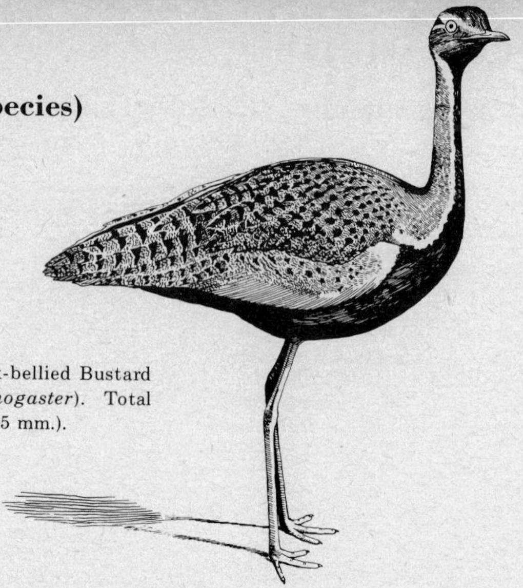

Fig. 52. Black-bellied Bustard (*Lissotis melanogaster*). Total length 25 in. (635 mm.).

Physical characteristics. Length—368 to 1321 mm. (14½ to 52 in.). Plumage—buff and gray above, barred and vermiculated with black in cryptic patterns; pale buff, white, or solid black below; bold black and white patterns on head and neck in a few spp.; some spp. have concealed white areas on the wing which become very conspicuous in flight. Some spp. crested, some with long, bristly feathers on sides of head or neck. Bill rather short, stout, and flattened. Neck long. Wings broad; tail short to medium. Legs strong and fairly long; tibiae extensively bare; 3 toes (2nd, 3rd, and 4th), short and broad. Sexes unlike.

Range. Southern Europe, Africa, s. Asia, Australia. Habitat—open plains. Some spp. migratory.

Habits. Rather gregarious. Terrestrial; cursorial. Flight strong but infrequent. Crouch in presence of danger. ♂ has remarkable courtship flight, posturing and strutting displays. Voice—a variety of booming, crowing, clucking, and other notes.

Food. Omnivorous.

Breeding. Nest a slight depression in ground, with little or no lining.

Eggs. 1 to 5; reddish brown to olive-green, speckled and blotched with brown. Incubated by ♀.

Young. Nidicolous. Downy. Cared for by ♀.

Technical diagnosis. Witherby, 4, 1940: 436.

Classification. Peters, 2, 1934: 217–225.

References. Baker, *Fauna,* 6, 1929: 59–73; Witherby, 4, 1940: 436–449, pl. 125; Bannerman, 2, 1931: xviii-xix, 49–67, col. pls. 4–6.

O. and M. Heinroth, *Die Vögel Mitteleuropas,* Berlin, vol. 3 [1928]: 114–131, pls. 227–228a, col. pl. 103.

F. L. Berney, The Bustard in Queensland, *Emu,* 36, 1936: 4–9.

A. Roberts, *The Birds of South Africa,* London, 1940: 89–95, col. pl. 16.

Synonym: Otidae.

JACANIDAE

Jaçana family (7 species)

Fig. 53. American Jaçana (*Jacana spinosa*). Total length 10 in. (254 mm.).

Physical characteristics. Length—165 to 534 mm. ($6\frac{1}{2}$ to 21 in.). Plumage—reddish or greenish brown and black above; greenish black, brown, or white below. One sp. with white crown, one with white rump; 5 spp. with yellow area on neck; 3 spp. with spread wing boldly marked with white or yellow. Bare forehead and crown, frontal wattle, or rictal lappets (exc. in *Microparra* and *Hydrophasianus*). Bill of moderate length and nearly straight. Wings broad, with metacarpal spur or knob. Tail short and weak (very long and narrow in *Hydrophasianus*). Legs long and tibiae extensively bare; toes and especially the claws extremely long. Sexes alike, but ♀ larger than ♂.

Range. Mexico, Central America, S. America (exc. s.w. quarter), Africa (s. of Sahara), s. Asia, Philippines, Malaysia, Papuan Region, n. Australia. Habitat—marshy shores of lakes and streams. Largely nonmigratory.

Habits. Some spp. gregarious in winter. Largely cursorial; walk habitually across water on floating lily pads. Swim readily and dive to escape danger. Flight slow and labored. Voice—loud harsh cries, mewing, chattering notes.

Food. Insects, snails, fish, seeds of water plants.

Breeding. Nest of water weeds, usually on floating vegetation.

Eggs. 3 to 6, usually 4; brown, immaculate or heavily marked with dark brown or black. Incubated by ♂ (or by ♂ and ♀?).

Young. Nidifugous. Downy. Cared for by ♂ (or by ♂ and ♀?).

Technical diagnosis. Ridgway, pt. 8, 1919: 1–6.

Classification. Peters, 2, 1934: 226–230.

References. Bent, No. 146: 324–327; Baker, *Fauna,* 6, 1929: 39–43.

A. H. Miller, Observations on the Incubation and the Care of the Young in the Jacana, *Condor,* 33, 1931: 32–33, illus.

D. R. Dickey and A. J. van Rossem, The Birds of El Salvador, *Field Mus. Nat. Hist., Zool. Ser.,* 23, 1938: 165–168.

K. A. Hindwood, Notes on the Distribution and Habits of the Jacana or Lotus-bird, *Emu,* 39, 1940: 261–267, pls. 34–37 (one colored).

Alfred Hoffmann, Über die Brutpflege des polyandrischen Wasserfasans, *Hydrophasianus chirurgus* (Scop.), *Zool. Jahrb.* (*Systematik*), 78, 1949: 367–403.

Synonym: Parridae.

ROSTRATULIDAE

Painted-snipe family (2 species)

Fig. 54. Painted-snipe (*Rostratula benghalensis*). Total length 9½ in. (241 mm.).

Physical characteristics. Length—190 to 241 mm. (7½ to 9½ in.). Plumage—brown, olive-brown, gray, black, and white; cryptically patterned above; throat and breast dark, belly buffy white. Bill long, somewhat curved, and slightly swollen at tip. Neck short. Wings broad; tail short and weak. Legs moderately long; tibiae partly bare. Toes long. ♂ smaller and duller than ♀.

Range. Southern S. America, Africa (s. of Sahara), Egypt, s. Asia, Japan, Malaysia, Australia, Philippines. Habitat—marshes. Nonmigratory (exc. for local movements).

Habits. Solitary. Crepuscular. Terrestrial. Flight strong but not prolonged. Voice—a booming call; whistling, purring, and hissing notes.

Food. Insects, mollusca, worms, grain.

Breeding. Apparently polyandrous. Nest of grass, placed on ground and usually concealed by surrounding vegetation.

Eggs. 2 to 5; buff, heavily marked with dark brown and black. Incubated by ♂.

Young. Nidifugous. Downy. Cared for by ♂.

Technical diagnosis. P. R. Lowe, *Ibis,* 1931: 507–530, 532; 1932: 390–391.

Classification. Peters, 2, 1934: 230.

References. Baker, *Fauna,* 6, 1929: 44–47.

J. O. Beven, Notes and Observations on the Painted Snipe (*Rostratula capensis*) in Ceylon, *Ibis,* 1913: 527–534.

W. H. Hudson, *Birds of La Plata,* London, vol. 2, 1920: 197–198.

A. Wetmore, Observations on the Birds of Argentina, Paraguay, Uruguay, and Chile, *U. S. Natl. Mus. Bull.,* 133, 1926: 163–164.

A. F. D'Ombrain, Behaviour of the Painted Snipe in Captivity, *Emu,* 43, 1944: 247–248, pls. 16–17.

HAEMATOPODIDAE

Oystercatcher family

(6 species)

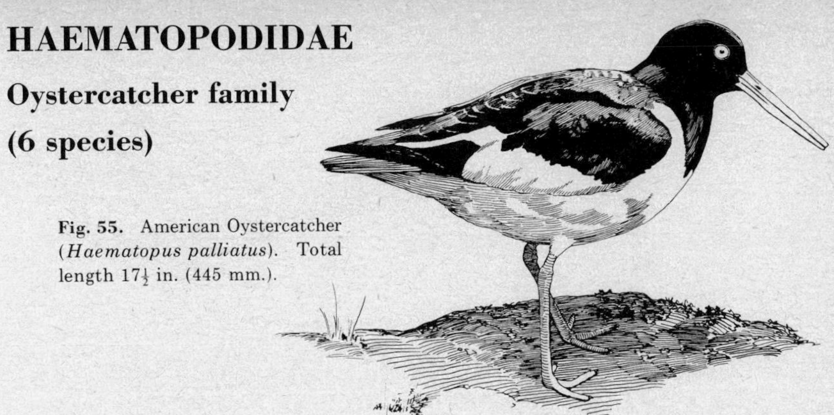

Fig. 55. American Oystercatcher (*Haematopus palliatus*). Total length 17½ in. (445 mm.).

Physical characteristics. Length—381 to 508 mm. (15 to 20 in). Plumage—dark brown or blackish brown exc. head and neck, which are black, and (in some spp.) the rest of under parts, rump, lower back, and large area on the wing, which are white. Bill bright red, legs pink. Bill long, stout, and much compressed laterally. Neck short. Wings long and pointed, tail short. Legs and feet very stout; feet slightly webbed; 3 toes (2nd, 3rd, and 4th). Sexes alike.

Range. Most temperate and tropical seacoasts; n. to Iceland and the Aleutians; s. to Cape Horn, Argentina, and to Tasmania. Also breed on some inland waters of Europe and Asia. Some forms migratory.

Habits. Gregarious. Flight strong and direct. Excitable, vociferous. Voice—a variety of loud, shrill notes; "song" a long series of monotonous piping notes, ending in a trill.

Food. Oysters, mussels, limpets, chitons, and other "shellfish"; sandworms (*Nereis*).

Breeding. Nest a hollow in the ground, usually lined (with grass, moss, or rock flakes).

Eggs. 2 or 3, sometimes 4; buff, blotched and speckled with black and brown. Incubated by ♂ and ♀.

Young. Nidifugous. Downy. Cared for by ♂ and ♀.

Technical diagnosis. Ridgway, pt. 8, 1919: 26–27.

Classification. Peters, 2, 1934: 231–234.

References. Bent, No. 146: 305–323; Baker, *Fauna,* 6, 1929: 164–167; Witherby, 4, 1940: 414–421; Murphy, 2: 973–993.

J. S. Huxley and F. A. Montague, Studies on the Courtship and Sexual Life of Birds. V. The Oyster-catcher (*Haematopus ostralegus* L.), *Ibis,* 1925: 868–897.

R. Dircksen, Die Biologie des Austernfischers, der Brandseeschwalbe und der Küstenseeschwalbe nach Beobachtungen und Untersuchungen auf Norderoog, *Jour. f. Ornith.,* 80, 1932: 427–521.

J. Dan Webster, The Breeding of the Black Oyster-catcher, *Wils. Bull.,* 53, 1941: 141–156.

I. R. Tompkins, Life History Notes on the American Oyster-catcher, *Oriole,* 19, 1954: 37–45.

G. F. Makkink, Contribution to the knowledge of the behaviour of the Oyster-Catcher (*Haematopus ostralegus* L.), *Ardea,* 31, 1942: 23–74.

CHARADRIIDAE

Plover family (63 species)

Fig. 56. Dotterel (*Eudromias morinellus*). Total length 9 in. (228 mm.).

Physical characteristics. Length—152 to 393 mm. (6 to $15\frac{1}{2}$ in.). Plumage—brown, olive, gray, or black, and white. Most spp. with back uniformly colored; many with broad collar and/or contrastingly marked tail or rump. Head and neck boldly marked in many spp. Below: white (or, rarely, solid black), marked in many spp. with one or two broad, contrasting bands. Spread wing with conspicuous pattern. Some (among Vanellinae) have long crest, wattles about face, and/or spurs on wing. Bill straight, of moderate length. Neck rather short. Wings long; tail short to medium. Legs short to long; tibiae partly bare. Toes moderately long; hallux vestigial or lacking. Sexes alike or nearly so.

Range. World-wide. Habitat—open, bare areas. Most spp. migratory.

Habits. Rather gregarious. Terrestrial. Run swiftly. Flight strong. Voice—shrill cries, melodious whistling notes.

Food. Variety of animal matter; some vegetable material.

Breeding. Nest on ground (with little or no lining).

Eggs. 2 to 5 (usually 4); buff or gray, heavily marked with black. Incubated by ♂ and ♀.

Young. Nidifugous. Downy. Cared for by ♂ and ♀.

Technical diagnosis. Ridgway, pt. 8, 1919: 61–62.

Classification. Peters, 2, 1934: 234–258.

References. Bent, No. 146: 144–305; Witherby, 4, 1940: 346–403; Baker, *Fauna,* 6, 1929: 152–164, 167–192; Baker, *Nidification,* 4, 1935: 387–403.

LeRoy Wilcox, Notes on the Life History of the Piping Plover, *Birds of Long Island No. 1,* 1939: 3–13, col. pl.

Hannes Laven, Beiträge zur Biologie des Sandregenpfeifers (*Charadrius hiaticula* L.), *Jour. f. Ornith.,* 88, 1940: 183–287.

G. L. Rinkel, Waarnemingen over het gedrag van de Kievit (*Vanellus vanellus* (L.)) gedurende de broedtijd, *Ardea,* 29, 1940: 108–147 (English summary, pp. 144–146), pls. 6–7.

SCOLOPACIDAE

Sandpiper family
(82 species)

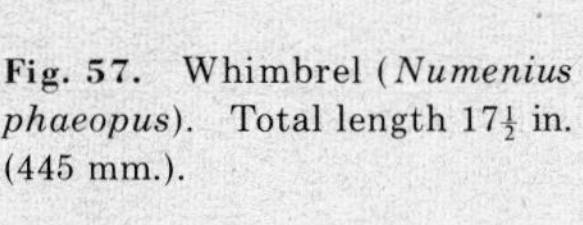

Fig. 57. Whimbrel (*Numenius phaeopus*). Total length 17½ in. (445 mm.).

Physical characteristics. Length—127 to 610 mm. (5 to 24 in.). Plumage—pale buff or gray to chestnut brown (black in a few spp.), and white; the back cryptically patterned in most spp., the under parts largely white in many, barred or spotted with black or brown in some; the winter plumage in many spp. paler, grayer, and less marked. Bill slender, moderately to extremely long; straight, decurved, or recurved. Neck medium to long. Wings long; tail short to medium. Legs short to long, tibiae partly bare in many spp. Toes rather long (hallux lacking in Sanderling). Sexes alike or nearly so in most spp.

Range. World-wide. Habitat—open, bare areas, usually near water. Most spp. migratory.

Habits. Rather gregarious. Terrestrial. Most spp. are waders. Flight strong. Many have elaborate courtship flights and displays, usually with vocal or instrumental (i.e., sounds made by flight feathers) accompaniment. Voice—a great variety of sharp, harsh call notes, musical trills, whistling, and other sounds.

Food. Variety of animal matter; some vegetable material.

Breeding. Nest on ground, or in vacant tree nests, or (*Coenocorypha*) ground burrows of other birds.

Eggs. 2 to 4; buff or olive, heavily marked with brown and black. Incubated by ♂ and ♀; by ♀ alone; or largely by ♂.

Young. Nidifugous. Downy. Cared for by ♂ and ♀; by ♀ alone; or by ♂ alone.

Technical diagnosis. Ridgway, pt. 8, 1919: 143–144; P. R. Lowe, *Ibis,* 1931: 747–750 (for subfamily Arenariinae).

Classification. Peters, 2, 1934: 258–288.

References. Bent, No. 142: 54–359; No. 146: 1–143, 269–305; Witherby, 4, 1940: 152–346; Baker, *Fauna,* 6, 1929: 153–156, 199–267.

O. S. Pettingill, Jr., The American Woodcock, *Philohela minor* (Gmelin), *Mem. Boston Soc. Nat. Hist.* 9, 1936: 169–391, pls. 12–21.

W. Vogt, Preliminary Notes on the Behavior and Ecology of the Eastern Willet, *Proc. Linn. Soc. N. Y.,* No. 49, 1938: 8–42, 2 pls.

G. Bergman, Der Steinwalzer, Arenaria i. interpres (L.), in seiner Beziehung zur Umwelt, *Acta Zool. Fennica,* 47, 1946: 1–151.

D. Nethersole-Thompson, *The Greenshank,* London, 1951.

Synonymy: The Aphrizidae are included.

RECURVIROSTRIDAE

Avocet family (7 species)

Fig. 58. Black-necked Stilt (*Himantopus mexicanus*). Total length 14 in. (355 mm.).

Physical characteristics. Length—292 to 482 mm. ($11\frac{1}{2}$ to 19 in.). Plumage—black (sometimes glossed with green), or brownish gray, and white above (uniform gray in *Ibidorhyncha*); mostly white below; chestnut pectoral shield in one sp., reddish brown head and neck in two. Bill long, very slender, straight or recurved (strongly decurved in *Ibidorhyncha*). Head small; neck moderately long. Wings rather long and pointed; tail rather short and square. Legs moderate to extremely long and slender; feet slightly to strongly webbed (slightly lobed in *Ibidorhyncha*); hallux vestigial or absent. Sexes alike or nearly so.

Range. Africa (including Madagascar), c. and s. Europe and Asia, Malaysia, Papuan Region, Australia, New Zealand, Philippines, Hawaiian Ids.; w. and s. U. S., West Indies, Central America, Galápagos Islands, and most of S. America. Habitat—usually near water. Northern forms migratory.

Habits. Gregarious. Terrestrial (waders). Swim readily. Flight strong. Voice—loud, harsh barks and calls; softer, more musical notes.

Food. Aquatic insects, mollusca, crustacea; fish, frogs, lizards; some vegetable matter.

Breeding. Colonial. Nest a scrape in sand or mud, bare or lined with pebbles or grass; sometimes a bulky platform (rarely floating) of sticks, etc.

Eggs. 2 to 5 (usually 4); pale stone color to olive, spotted, scrawled, or blotched with reddish brown to black. Incubated by ♂ and ♀.

Young. Nidifugous. Downy. Cared for by ♂ and ♀?

Technical diagnosis. Ridgway, pt. 8, 1919: 435 (does not include *Ibidorhyncha*).

Classification. Peters, 2, 1934: 288–291.

References. Bent, No. 142: 37–54; Baker, *Fauna,* 6, 1929: 192–198; Witherby, 4, 1940: 403–413; Mathews, 3, pt. 2, 1913: 144–164, col. pls. 141–143.

J. N. McGilp and A. M. Morgan, The Nesting of the Banded Stilt (*Cladorhynchus leucocephalus*), *S. Australian Ornith.,* 11, 1931: 37–52.

G. F. Makkink, An attempt at an ethogram of the European Avocet . . . , *Ardea,* 25, 1936: 1–74.

Jack Jones, The Banded Stilt, *Emu,* 45, 1945: 1–36, 110–118.

PHALAROPODIDAE

Phalarope family

(3 species)

Fig. 59. Northern Phalarope (*Lobipes lobatus*). Total length 8 in. (203 mm.).

Physical characteristics. Length—190 to 254 mm. ($7\frac{1}{2}$ to 10 in.). Plumage—soft and dense; the ♀ with bold patterns of black, white, gray, and rich brown on head and neck; back dark gray, streaked with buff or rich brown; white on rump area; under parts white or reddish brown. Winter plumage—black (or gray) and white. Bill moderate to very long and slender. Wings long and pointed; tail moderate. Tarsi rather long (exc. *Phalaropus*) and laterally compressed. Toes lobed, semipalmate. ♂ smaller and much duller in coloration than ♀.

Range. Arctic and subarctic regions; *Steganopus* s. in N. America to about 40° n. lat. Migratory; winter on ocean in restricted areas in tropics (*Steganopus* inland in s. S. America).

Habits. Aquatic. Float buoyantly; swim erratic course, bobbing head back and forth. Notably tame. Flight swift. Often feed by swimming rapidly and continuously in very small circle, snatching from water the small animal life thus stirred up. Voice—low, musical calls and whistles.

Food. Crustacea, insects, and some vegetable matter.

Breeding. Nest on open ground near water, often in small colonies. Substantial nest of grass or scantily lined hollow.

Eggs. 4 (rarely 3 or 5); olive-buff, heavily blotched and speckled with brown and black. Incubated typically by ♂ only.

Young. Nidifugous. Downy—light brown, streaked and spotted with light gray and black. Cared for by ♂ (sometimes assisted by ♀).

Technical diagnosis. Ridgway, pt. 8, 1919: 416–417.

Classification. Peters, 2, 1934: 292–293.

References. Bent, No. 142: 1–37; Witherby, 4, 1940: 213–222; Alexander, 1928: 326–333, pls. 86–88 (1954: 226–230, pls. 86–88).

A. Wetmore, Food of American Phalaropes, Avocets, and Stilts, *U. S. Dept. Agric. Dept. Bull. No. 1359,* 1925.

N. Tinbergen, Field Observations of East Greenland Birds. 1. The Behaviour of the Red-necked Phalarope (*Phalaropus lobatus* L.) in Spring, *Ardea,* 24, 1935: 1–42, pls. 1–4.

DROMADIDAE

Crabplover family (1 species)

Fig. 60. Crabplover (*Dromas ardeola*). Total length 15 in. (381 mm.).

Physical characteristics. Length—381 mm. (15 in.). Plumage—white, with a few orbital feathers, central feathers of back, and longer scapulars black; remiges and greater upper wing coverts brownish black (inner webs of remiges pale brown to white). Bill strong, laterally compressed. Wings long and pointed; tail short. Legs long and bare; middle claw pectinate. ♀ somewhat smaller, with black dorsal feathers shorter, than ♂.

Range. Coasts and island shores of Indian Ocean from Natal and Madagascar to Ceylon; also islands off Burma and the shores of s. portion of Red Sea. Migratory in part.

Habits. Gregarious. Noisy. Crepuscular. Fly well and run swiftly (in short, abrupt dashes). Voice—chatter; raucous cry somewhat like a crow's.

Food. Crabs and other crustacea; mollusca.

Breeding. Nest an unlined depression at the end of a burrow (4 to 8 ft. long, near surface of ground).

Eggs. 1; white; extremely large (65 × 46 mm.). Incubation unrecorded.

Young. Nidicolous. Downy. Cared for by ♂ and ♀?

Technical diagnosis. Baker, *Fauna,* 6, 1929: 94.

Classification. Peters, 2, 1934: 293.

References. Baker, *Fauna,* 6, 1929: 94–95; Baker, *Nidification,* 4, 1935: 353–355.

P. R. Lowe, Some Notes on the Crab-Plover (*Dromas ardeola* Paykull), *Ibis,* 1916: 317–337.

G. Archer and E. M. Godman, *The Birds of British Somaliland and the Gulf of Aden,* London, vol. 2, 1937: 495–497, col. pl. 2 (opp. p. 44).

R. Meinertzhagen, *Birds of Arabia,* London, 1954: 470–471.

BURHINIDAE

Thick-knee family

(9 species)

Fig. 61. Stonecurlew (*Burhinus oedicnemus*). Total length 16 in. (406 mm.).

Physical characteristics. Length—355 to 521 mm. (14 to $20\frac{1}{2}$ in.). Plumage—brown, gray-brown, or buff, mottled, barred, or streaked, with conspicuous wing pattern in some spp.; side of head patterned with broad stripes. Bill stout, short to moderately long. Head large and broad; eyes very large. Wings medium to long and pointed; tail moderately long, graduated. Legs rather long, tarsus bare, tibiotarsal joint thickened; feet partially webbed, with 3 toes (2nd, 3rd, and 4th). Sexes alike.

Range. Temperate and tropical Europe, Africa, Asia; Australia; tropical America (s. Mexico to n.w. Brazil and s. Peru; Hispaniola). Habitat—stony or sandy ground in semiopen country; some spp. littoral. Northern forms migratory.

Habits. Somewhat gregarious. Crepuscular and nocturnal. Run swiftly. Flight brief and infrequent but strong. Some spp. have remarkable communal display in autumn. Voice—clamorous; loud wailing and croaking cries; variety of shorter notes.

Food. Worms; land and water insects, crustacea, mollusca; mice, frogs, nestlings of other birds.

Breeding. Eggs laid directly on ground or in slight unlined depression—in open, or near grass or shrubs.

Eggs. 2 (rarely 3); white to pale buff, speckled and blotched. Incubated by ♀, assisted by ♂ in most spp.

Young. Nidicolous, or may leave nest in one day. Downy. Cared for by ♂ and ♀.

Technical diagnosis. Witherby, 4, 1940: 430.

Classification. Peters, 2, 1934: 293–298.

References. Baker, *Fauna,* 6, 1929: 76–82; Witherby, 4, 1940: 430–436; Mathews, 3, 1913–1914: 342–360, col. pls. 173–174; Baker, *Nidification,* 4, 1935: 340–345.

W. Banzhaf, Ein Beitrag zur Brutbiologie des Triels, *Burhinus oedicnemus oedicnemus* (L.), *Jour. f. Ornith.,* 81, 1933: 311–321.

Synonym: Oedicnemidae.

GLAREOLIDAE

Pratincole family (17 species)

Fig. 62. Pratincole (*Glareola pratincola*). Total length 9½ in. (241 mm.).

Physical characteristics. Length—152 to 254 mm. (6 to 10 in.). Plumage—olive, brown, gray, and chestnut; plain, with bold markings of black, white, and chestnut (a few spp. with metallic areas or with cryptic pattern). Pratincoles have short bills, long narrow pointed wings, forked tail, short legs, 4 toes. Coursers have rather long tapering bill, rather short and broad wings and tail, long legs, 3 toes. Middle toe elongate, with claw usually pectinate in both coursers and pratincoles; basal web between outer and middle toe in most spp. Sexes similar; may differ in size.

Range. Around Mediterranean, n. to British Isles and Germany; Africa, e. through India to Indo-China; Australia. Habitat—usually sandy or stony ground, often near water. More northern spp. migratory.

Habits. Usually gregarious. Some spp. crepuscular. Pratincoles aerial, their flight buoyant and erratic (hawk insects); coursers terrestrial, running swiftly, their flight direct and sometimes swift, but infrequent. Some spp. wade. Voice (most spp. vociferous)—a harsh *hark hark; zic zac; kik-kikki;* etc.

Food. Land and water insects, lizards, snails, seeds, and (?) fish.

Breeding. Usually colonial. Eggs laid directly on sand or rock, sometimes in shallow depression (rarely lined); sometimes buried in sand.

Eggs. 2 to 4 (rarely 5). Incubated by ♀, assisted by ♂ in some spp.

Young. Nidicolous (but may leave nest in one day?). Downy. Cared for by ♂ and ♀.

Technical diagnosis. Witherby, 4, 1940: 421.

Classification. Peters, 2, 1934: 298–306.

References. Baker, *Fauna,* 6, 1929: 84–93; Witherby, 4, 1940: 421–429; Bannerman, 2, 1931: xxiv, 191–220, pl. 8; Baker, *Nidification,* 4, 1935: 345–353.

W. MacGillivray, A Contribution on the Life-story of the Australian Pratincole, *Emu,* 24, 1924: 81–85, pls. 15–17.

Synonymy: The Cursoriidae are included.

THINOCORIDAE

Seedsnipe family (4 species)

Fig. 63. D'Orbigny Seedsnipe (*Thinocorus orbignyianus*). Total length 8¼ in. (210 mm.).

Physical characteristics. Length—171 to 280 mm. (6¾ to 11 in.). Plumage—cryptic pattern above, brown with pale buff edgings; below: pale buff, marked with darker brown; or white, with broad breast band of gray or mottled brown. Bill strong, short, pointed, rather sparrowlike. Nostrils long slits with protective operculum above. Wings long and pointed. Tail short. Legs very short. Sexes unlike.

Range. Southern half of Argentina and Chile, n. along the higher Andes to n. Ecuador. Habitat—open country. Some forms migratory.

Habits. Gregarious. Terrestrial. When disturbed creep away along ground or crouch, and suddenly, with snipelike calls, flush in zigzag flight. Run rapidly. *Thinocorus* has a soaring flight song. Voice—whistling or cooing calls, grating *chairp*.

Food. Largely vegetable; some insects.

Breeding. Nest on ground—a scantily lined depression or rough aggregate of plant material.

Eggs. 3 to 4 (or 6?); pointed; cream-white or clay-colored, heavily spotted with darker shades. Incubation not described.

Young. Nidifugous. Downy. Care of young not described.

Technical diagnosis. R. B. Sharpe, Cat. of Birds of Brit. Mus., 24, 1896: 714.

Classification. Peters, 2, 1934: 306–308.

References. G. R. Gray, *The Genera of Birds,* London, vol. 3, 1845: 520–521, col. pl. 135.

A. A. Lane, Field-Notes on the Birds of Chili, *Ibis,* 1897: 304–308.

W. E. D. Scott and R. B. Sharpe, Ornithology, *Repts. Princeton Univ. Exp. Patagonia,* 1896–1899, vol. 2, pt. 2, 1910: 239–253.

C. E. Hellmayr, The Birds of Chile, *Field Mus. Nat. Hist., Zool. Ser.,* 19, 1932: 398–402.

J. D. Goodall *et al., Las Aves de Chile,* Buenos Aires, vol. 2, 1951: 265–273.

Synonyms: Thinocorythidae, Attagidae.

CHIONIDIDAE

Sheathbill family (2 species)

Fig. 64. Sheathbill (*Chionis alba*). Total length 15½ in. (393 mm.).

Physical characteristics. Length—355 to 432 mm. (14 to 17 in.). Plumage—white. Bill black or yellow and black, with horny sheath on base of maxilla; legs and feet pale flesh or gray. Face partly bare and flesh-colored, more or less carunculated near base of bill. Eyes small. Bill short and stout. Neck short. Body compact. Wings rather long; tail short and somewhat rounded. Legs short and stout; tibiae partly bare; feet large and powerful, slightly webbed. Hallux elevated. Sexes alike or ♀ smaller than ♂.

Range. Islands of the extreme s. Atlantic and w. Indian oceans; tip of Graham Land and southernmost S. America. Habitat—seacoast. Locally migratory.

Habits. Gregarious. Largely terrestrial but make long sea flights. Swim well but infrequently. Flight strong. Pugnacious. Voice—"angry cries"; cooing sound (in courtship).

Food. Omnivorous. Small fish, mollusca and crustacea; birds' eggs and nestlings; algae and lichens; variety of offal.

Breeding. Nest a bulky collection of feathers, shells, algae, etc., in natural hole, old burrows, or rock crevices.

Eggs. 2 to 3; white, blotched and freckled with brown or black. Incubated by ♂ and ♀.

Young. Nidifugous? Downy. Cared for by ♂ and ♀.

Technical diagnosis. J. H. Kidder and E. Coues, *U. S. Natl. Mus. Bull.,* 3, 1876: 115 (Chionomorphae).

Classification. Peters, 2, 1934: 308–309.

References. Murphy, 2: 999–1006.

W. E. Clarke, Ornithological Results of the Scottish National Antarctic Expedition—II. On the Birds of the South Orkney Islands, *Ibis,* 1906: 182, pls. 3, 12, 13.

A. F. Cobb, *Birds of the Falkland Islands,* London, 1933: 62–63.

Synonym: Chionidae.

STERCORARIIDAE

Skua family (4 species)

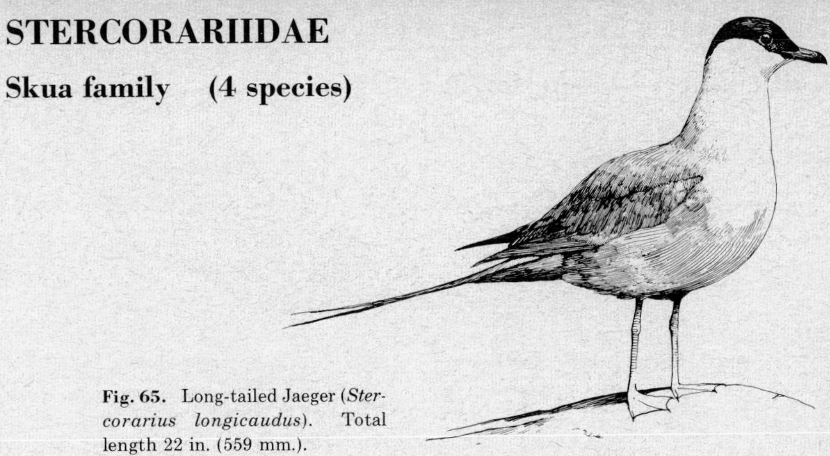

Fig. 65. Long-tailed Jaeger (*Stercorarius longicaudus*). Total length 22 in. (559 mm.).

Physical characteristics. Length—432 to 610 mm. (17 to 24 in.). Plumage (variable, with dark and light phases)—blackish brown above, with some light edgings or streaks; light brown to white below, plain or barred with brown; neck yellow or streaked with buff; white flash on spread wing. Bill strong, medium in length, rounded, and strongly hooked, with horny "cere." Body stout. Wings long, pointed; tail medium to long, wedge-shaped, the central rectrices elongated in *Stercorarius* (twisted in one sp.). Legs short; feet stout, fully webbed; hallux very small; claws strongly hooked. Sexes alike (or ♀ larger).

Range. High latitudes of both S. and N. Hemispheres. Habitat—oceans and their coasts; sometimes nest inland. Migratory.

Habits. Somewhat gregarious. Pelagic. Flight swift and powerful (some soar). Aggressive and predatory, robbing other birds of food. Sometimes eat own eggs and young. Some hawk insects. Striking flight display in one sp. Voice—quacking and chattering notes; wailing cries; shrieks and screams.

Food. Small mammals; large insects; eggs, young, and even adult birds; fish, crustacea, mollusca; carrion, offal; some vegetable matter.

Breeding. Loosely colonial (generally in or near colonies of other seabirds). Nest a depression in vegetation on tundra or pastures, lined or unlined.

Eggs. 2 to 4 (usually 2); pale green or blue to dark olive-brown, marked with reddish or blackish brown. Incubated by ♂ and ♀.

Young. Semi-nidifugous. Downy. Cared for by ♂ and ♀.

Technical diagnosis. Ridgway, pt. 8, 1919: 673.

Classification. Peters, 2, 1934: 309–312.

References. Bent, No. 113: 1–28; Witherby, 5, 1941: 122–142; Murphy, 2: 1006–1040; Alexander, 1928: 203–213, pls. 48–50 (1954: 140–145, pls. 48–50).

F. Pitt. The Great and Arctic Skuas in the Shetlands, *Brit. Birds,* 16, 1922: 174–181, 198–202.

Synonym: Catharactidae.

LARIDAE

Gull family (82 species)

Fig. 66. Great Black-backed Gull (*Larus marinus*). Total length 28 in. (712 mm.).

Physical characteristics. Length—203 to 762 mm. (8 to 30 in.). Plumage—typically gray and white, with black on wing tips (most gulls); some spp. are all white; others white, with black on upper parts, or largely dark gray or black; many spp. have black cap (terns) or hood (gulls) in breeding plumage. Some spp. (terns) are crested. Bill and feet brightly colored in many spp. Bill slender to rather heavy; medium to rather long; sharply pointed (terns) to rather blunt and slightly hooked. Wings long and pointed; tail medium to long, square (rarely graduated) to deeply forked. Legs very short to medium; feet webbed; hallux small (vestigial in some). Sexes alike.

Range. World-wide. Habitat—seacoasts, large rivers and lakes, or even ponds and marshes. Migratory exc. in low latitudes.

Habits. Gregarious. Aquatic. Flight strong (gulls soar). Many spp. dive for food from wing. Voice—harsh screams or squawks.

Food. Fish, crustacea, mollusca, insects, carrion; berries and other vegetable matter.

Breeding. Nest variable—from no material to bulky mass of vegetation; on ground, on cliffs, in trees, on floating vegetation, or even in burrows (*Larosterna*).

Eggs. 1 to 4; almost white to deep olive-buff, heavily spotted and speckled. Incubated by ♂ and ♀.

Young. Semi-nidicolous. Downy. Cared for by ♂ and ♀.

Technical diagnosis. Witherby, 5, 1941: 1.

Classification. Peters, 2, 1934: 312–349.

References. Bent, No. 113: 29–310; Witherby, 5, 1941: 1–122; Baker, *Fauna,* 6, 1929: 100–149; Murphy, 2: 1040–1169; Alexander, 1928: 101–197, pls. 23–46, 49 (1954: 70–136, pls. 23–46, 49).

J. Dwight, The Gulls (Laridae) of the World; Their Plumages . . . , *Bull. Amer. Mus. Nat. Hist.,* 52, 1925: 63–401, pls. 11–15.

G. Marples and A. Marples, *Sea Terns or Sea Swallows,* London, 1934.

R. S. Palmer, A Behavior Study of the Common Tern (*Sterna hirundo hirundo* L.), *Proc. Boston Soc. Nat. Hist.,* 42, 1941: 1–119, pls. 1–14.

Niko Tinbergen, *The Herring Gull's World,* London, 1953.

Synonymy: The Sternidae are included.

RYNCHOPIDAE

Skimmer family (3 species)

Fig. 67. Black Skimmer (*Rynchops nigra*). Total length 20 in. (508 mm.).

Physical characteristics. Length—368 to 508 mm. ($14\frac{1}{2}$ to 20 in.). Plumage—black, slate, or brownish above; white or whitish below. Bill red, orange, or yellow; feet black. Bill long, the mandibles laterally compressed to thin blades, the lower mandible much longer than upper. Wings very long, pointed; tail short, forked. Legs very short, feet small and slightly webbed, claws slender and sharp. Sexes alike, but ♀ smaller.

Range. Atlantic coast of N. America from Long Island southward; coasts and large rivers of Central America and most of S. America; tropical Africa; larger rivers of India, Burma, Indo-China. Habitat—ocean shores, large rivers and lakes. Migratory in part.

Habits. Gregarious. In part crepuscular and nocturnal. Flight dextrous and swift but not strong. Feed by flying over the water, ploughing the surface with knifelike lower mandible. Voice—loud raucous cries, a "bark"; softer courtship notes.

Food. Small fish, shrimps and other small crustacea.

Breeding. Colonial. Nest a shallow unlined depression in sand.

Eggs. 2 to 5 (sometimes 7?). Incubated by ♀ (assisted by ♂?).

Young. Nidicolous. Downy. Fed by ♂ and ♀.

Technical diagnosis. Ridgway, pt. 8, 1919: 449–457.

Classification. Peters, 2, 1934: 349–350.

References. Bent, No. 113: 310–318; Murphy, 2: 1169–1178; Baker, *Fauna*, 6, 1929: 150–151; Bannerman, 2, 1931: xxiv-xxv, 280–284, col. pl. 9; Alexander, 1928: 198–202, pl. 47 (1954: 137–139, pl. 47).

I. R. Tomkins, Ways of the Black Skimmer, *Wils. Bull.*, 45, 1933: 147–151, illus.

A. Koenig, Die Schwimmvögel (*Natatores*) Aegyptens, *Jour. f. Ornith.*, 80 (Supplt.), 1932: 34–44, pls. 2–4 (1 col.).

Witmer Stone, Bird Studies at Old Cape May, Philadelphia, vol. 2, 1937: 598–608, pls. 75–85.

I. T. [= I. R.] Tomkins, Method of Feeding of the Black Skimmer, *Rynchops nigra, Auk*, 68, 1951: 236–239, pl. 8.

Synonym: Rhynchopidae.

ALCIDAE

Auk family (22 species)

Fig. 68. Black Guillemot (*Cepphus grylle*). Total length 13 in. (330 mm.).

Physical characteristics. Length—165 to 762 mm. ($6\frac{1}{2}$ to 30 in.). Plumage—black, brownish black, or gray; patterned above with rusty or buff in 2 spp.; white below in most spp. (but chin and throat of breeding plumage black in many). A white wing patch, ornamental head plumes, and/or brightly colored bill, mouth, and feet in some spp. Bill short and stout to moderately long and slender, laterally compressed, elaborately sculptured in some spp. Head large; neck short; body heavy and compact. Wings small (with extremely short secondaries); tail short. Legs short and set far back; feet webbed; hallux absent or vestigial; claws strong. Sexes alike.

Range. Northern Pacific, n. Atlantic, and Arctic oceans and their coasts. Some spp. migratory.

Habits. Gregarious, esp. in breeding season. Pelagic. Flight direct and rapid but not usually sustained (Great Auk was flightless). Dive from surface for food. Use wings to swim under water. Voice—grunting, moaning, yelping, or sibilant notes.

Food. Fish, crustacea, mollusca, worms, algae.

Breeding. Colonial. Nest on rock ledges, in rock crevices, in burrows; no nest material (or but scanty lining).

Eggs. 1 or 2; white to deep buff or light green or blue; immaculate or lightly to heavily spotted and scrawled with brown and/or black. Incubated by ♂ and ♀, or by ♀.

Young. Semi-nidicolous. Downy. Cared for by ♂ and ♀.

Technical diagnosis. Witherby, 5, 1941: 141–142.

Classification. Peters, 2, 1934: 350–359.

References. Bent, No. 107: 82–224; Witherby, 5, 1941: 142–173; Alexander, 1928: 234–258, pls. 58–65 (1954: 160–177, pls. 58–65).

R. A. Johnson, Nesting Behavior of the Atlantic Murre, *Auk,* 58, 1941: 153–163, pls. 5–6.

R. W. Storer, A Comparison of Variation, Behavior, and Evolution in the Sea Bird Genera Uria and Cepphus, *Univ. Calif. Publ. Zool.,* 52, 1952: 121–222, pls. 1–2, 2 maps.

R. M. Lockley, *Puffins,* London, 1953.

Synonym: Uriidae.

PTEROCLIDAE

Sandgrouse family
(16 species)

Fig. 69. Tibetan Sandgrouse (*Syrrhaptes tibetanus*). Total length 16 in. (406 mm.).

Physical characteristics. Length—228 to 406 mm. (9 to 16 in.). Plumage—dense; sandy buff, reddish brown, or gray above, barred, spotted, or mottled in cryptic patterns; face and breast boldly marked with yellow, chestnut, vinaceous, or white and black; belly black or dark brown in some spp.; tail barred. Bill short and conical. Neck short. Wings long and pointed; tail medium and wedge-shaped to very long and acuminate, the tail coverts very long. Legs very short; tarsi (and toes in *Syrrhaptes*) feathered; toes medium to very short; claws short and thick. Sexes unlike (the ♀ smaller and more spotted and mottled).

Range. Portugal, Spain, s. France (erupting irregularly into n.w. Europe and Great Britain), Africa, s. Asia. Habitat—open sandy plains and deserts, thin brush, or (rarely) forest. Some spp. migratory.

Habits. Gregarious. Terrestrial. Flight very swift. Fly considerable distances in flocks daily at regular hours to drink; drink by immersing bill and sucking (also by sipping). Some spp. swim readily. Voice—whistles; clucking and croaking sounds.

Food. Seeds, berries, buds; small insects.

Breeding. Nest a scrape in ground, with little or no lining.

Eggs. 2 to 3; white, buff, or greenish, with brown, lavender, and/or gray markings. Incubated by ♂ and ♀.

Young. Nidifugous. Downy. Cared for by ♂ and ♀.

Technical diagnosis. Witherby, 4, 1940: 147.

Classification. Peters, 3, 1937: 3–10.

References. Witherby, 4, 1940: 147–151; Baker, *Fauna,* 5, 1928: 260–278; Bannerman, 2, 1931: xxvi-xxvii, 285–303, col. pls. 10–11.

E. C. Stuart Baker, *The Game-birds of India, Burma and Ceylon,* London, vol. 2, 1921: 235–323, col. pls. 12–19.

W. W. Bowen, Remarks on the Classification of the Pteroclidae, *Amer. Mus. Novitates, No. 273,* 1927: 1–12.

F. J. Jackson, *The Birds of Kenya Colony and the Uganda Protectorate,* London, vol. 1, 1938: 437–446.

Synonym: Eremialectoridae.

COLUMBIDAE

Pigeon family (289 species)

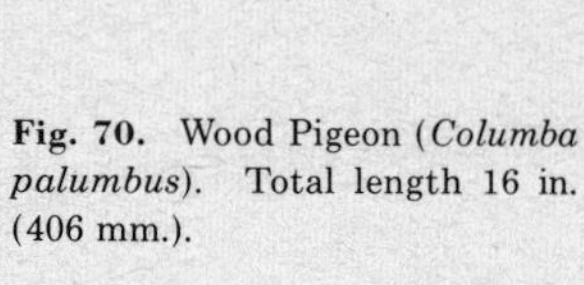

Fig. 70. Wood Pigeon (*Columba palumbus*). Total length 16 in. (406 mm.).

Physical characteristics. Length—152 to 838 mm. (6 to 33 in.). Plumage soft and very dense; with wide range of colors: pale shades of gray or brown; rich shades of reddish brown, green, yellow, purple, etc.; and, in many spp., metallic reflections, esp. on neck and wings. Scaled or barred patterns frequent. A few spp. crested. Bill slender to stout and of medium length, with bare cere (rarely with a fleshy knob). Head small; neck rather short; body compact. Wings short to long; tail medium to long, truncate to pointed. Legs very short to fairly long. Sexes alike in most spp.

Range. World-wide exc. n. N. America, n. Asia, s. S. America, and many oceanic islands. Many spp. migratory.

Habits. Solitary to highly gregarious. Arboreal or terrestrial. Flight strong in most spp. Drink by immersing bill and sucking. Young fed at first with "pigeon's milk," produced in crop of parents. Voice—variety of cooing or booming notes; also hissing, whistling, or guttural sounds. Occasionally make loud clapping with wings.

Food. Seeds, fruit, acorns, etc.; a few spp. also eat insects, worms, snails.

Breeding. Sometimes colonial. Nest usually a simple platform of sticks, placed on cliff (or building) ledges or in trees; or nest in tree cavities, in burrows, or on ground.

Eggs. 1 to 3 (usually 2); white or (rarely) buff. Incubated by ♂ and ♀.

Young. Nidicolous. With little or no down at hatching. Cared for by ♂ and ♀.

Technical diagnosis. Ridgway, pt. 7, 1916: 275–279.

Classification. Peters, 3, 1937: 11–141.

References. Bent, No. 162: 353–458; Witherby 4, 1940: 129–146; Baker, *Fauna,* 5, 1928: 177–259.

E. C. Stuart Baker, *Indian Pigeons and Doves,* London, 1913.

W. M. Levi, *The Pigeon,* Columbia, S. C., 1941.

E. W. Gifford, Taxonomy and Habits of Pigeons, *Auk,* 58, 1941: 239–245.

J. A. Neff, Habits, Food, and Economic Status of the Band-tailed Pigeon, *N. Amer. Fauna No. 58,* 1947.

Synonymy: The Didunculidae, Gouridae, Peristeridae, Turturidae, and Treronidae are included. [Closely related to the Columbidae are the Raphidae ("Dididae"), a family of 3 extinct spp. (the Dodos and the Solitaire) of the Mascarene Ids. e. of Madagascar.]

PSITTACIDAE

Parrot family (315 species)

Fig. 71. Pink Cockatoo (*Kakatoe leadbeateri*). Total length 15 in. (381 mm.).

Physical characteristics. Length—95 to 991 mm. ($3\frac{3}{4}$ to 39 in.). Plumage—sparse; hard and glossy; usually brightly colored, with green commonly predominant. Bill short, stout, and strongly hooked. Head and neck short. Body compact. Wings strong. Tail short to very long (racquet-shaped central feathers in *Prioniturus;* spine-tipped feathers in *Micropsitta*). Legs short, feet zygodactyl. Sexes usually alike.

Range. Southern Hemisphere (exc. remote oceanic islands and the s. tip of Africa) and tropical and subtropical parts of the N. Hemisphere (a few species originally ranged to about 40° N. lat. in N. America and 35° in s.e. Asia). Most species are nonmigratory.

Habits. Many species gregarious. Typically arboreal. Flight usually strong. Use beak in climbing. Manipulate food with feet. Voice—noisy; often remarkable mimics (in captivity only).

Food. Fruit, nuts, grains; nectar and other vegetable matter.

Breeding. Nest in unlined holes in trees, termite nests, rocks, or banks. Several Australasian species nest on the ground, and *Myiopsitta* of S. America builds colonial nests of twigs in branches of trees.

Eggs. 1 to 12; white. Incubated by ♂ and ♀, or by ♀ alone.

Young. Nidicolous. Naked at first, then downy. Cared for by ♂ and ♀.

Technical diagnosis. Ridgway, pt. 7, 1916: 103–106.

Classification. Peters, 3, 1937: 141–273.

References. Mathews, 6, 1916–1917; Baker, *Nidification,* 3, 1934: 373–386.

W. T. Greene, *Parrots in Captivity,* London, 3 vols., 1883–1887.

D. Seth-Smith, *Parrakeets. A Handbook to the Imported Species,* London, 1903.

T. Salvadori, Psittaci: Fam.—Stringopidae, Nestoridae, Cacatuidae, Loriidae, Cyclopsittacidae, Wytsman's *Genera Avium,* pts. 3–5, 11–12, 1905–1910.

Synonymy: See family names in T. Salvadori reference above.

MUSOPHAGIDAE

Touraco family

(20 species)

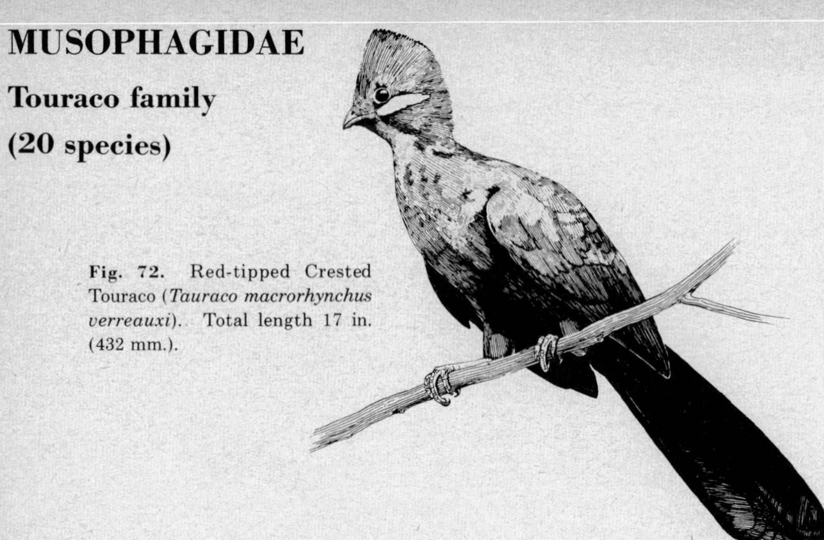

Fig. 72. Red-tipped Crested Touraco (*Tauraco macrorhynchus verreauxi*). Total length 17 in. (432 mm.).

Physical characteristics. Length—368 to 712 mm. (14½ to 28 in.). Plumage—glossy greens, blues, browns, with violet, crimson, and yellow (exc. *Crinifer,* which is ashy gray). Conspicuous patch of crimson (turacin pigment) on spread wing (exc. *Corythaeola* and *Crinifer*). Bill brightly colored in many spp. Typically crested. In many spp. skin around eye bare and (usually) red; face bare in one sp. Bill serrate; strong, stout, and broad; produced to form frontal shield in *Musophaga* and *Ruwenzorornis.* Nostrils placed near tip of bill in some spp. Wings short and rounded; tail long and broad. Feet semizygodactyl (4th toe capable of moving forward or backward). Sexes alike.

Range. Africa (s. of Sahara), exc. Madagascar. Habitat—dense forest and forest edges; woods near water. Nonmigratory, exc. for local movements.

Habits. Solitary or in small bands. Strictly arboreal. Flight direct, but labored, brief, and infrequent. Run along branches and jump across gaps. Climb with dexterity. Voice—loud raucous shrieks and croakings; explosive chatter; a soft coo.

Food. Fruits, seeds, and buds; insects and snails.

Breeding. Nest a rough bulky platform of sticks in a tree.

Eggs. 2 to 3; white or nearly so, immaculate. Incubated by ♂ and ♀.

Young. Nidicolous. Downy. Cared for by ♂ and ♀.

Technical diagnosis. G. E. Shelley, Cat. of Birds in Brit. Mus., 19, 1891: 435.

Classification. Peters, 4, 1940: 3–11.

References. Bannerman, 3, 1933: xviii-xix, 52–79, col. pls. 1–4.

A. Dubois, Fam. Musophagidae, Wytsman's *Genera Avium,* pt. 8, 1907 (2 col. pls.).

R. E. Moreau, A Contribution to the Biology of the Musophagiformes. . . . , *Ibis,* 1938: 639–671.

F. J. Jackson, *The Birds of Kenya Colony and the Uganda Protectorate,* London, vol. 1, 1938: 514–531, col. pl. 10.

CUCULIDAE

Cuckoo family (127 species)

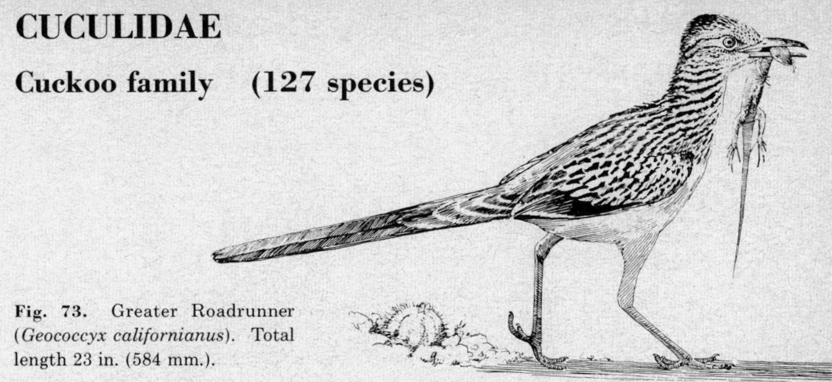

Fig. 73. Greater Roadrunner (*Geococcyx californianus*). Total length 23 in. (584 mm.).

Physical characteristics. Length—159 to 699 mm. ($6\frac{1}{4}$ to $27\frac{1}{2}$ in.). Plumage—loose-webbed (wiry in some spp.). Brown, olive, gray, or black (purple, blue, or bright iridescent green in a few spp.); uniform or in bold combinations; many spp. streaked or barred, esp. below; tail barred or tipped with white in many spp. A few spp. crested. Bill somewhat curved, rather stout to extremely heavy. Bare, colored orbital skin and/or conspicuous eyelashes in many spp. Wings medium to long; tail medium to extremely long, graduated (forked in *Surniculus*). Legs short (exc. in some terrestrial spp.); feet zygodactyl. Sexes alike in most spp.

Range. World-wide exc. some oceanic islands and high latitudes of Asia and the Americas. Many spp. migratory.

Habits. Solitary (exc. *Crotophaga*). Most spp. arboreal, a few terrestrial. Flight of some spp. strong; other spp. virtually flightless. Voice—typically loud, unmusical calls, monotonously repeated.

Food. Insects, snails, small vertebrates; fruit.

Breeding. Many spp. parasitic; *Crotophaga* builds communal nests; remaining spp. make nests of sticks or grass—shallow saucers to completely domed structures with entrance at side (*Centropus*).

Eggs. 2 to 6; white, blue, green, red, or brown; spotted or immaculate. In nonparasitic spp. incubated by ♂ and ♀.

Young. Nidicolous. Naked or "hairy" at hatching. In nonparasitic spp. cared for by ♂ and ♀.

Technical diagnosis. Witherby, 2, 1938: 296.

Classification. Peters, 4, 1940: 12–76.

References. Bent, No. 176: 19–105; Witherby, 2, 1938: 296–308; Baker, *Fauna,* 4, 1927: 133–195.

F. H. Herrick, Life and Behavior of the Cuckoo, *Jour. Exper. Zool.,* 9, 1910: 169–233, pls. 1–7.

D. E. Davis, Social Nesting Habits of the Smooth-billed Ani, *Auk,* 57, 1940: 179–218.

H. Friedmann, The Parasitic Cuckoos of Africa, *Wash. Acad. Sci., Monogr. No. 1,* 1948.

TYTONIDAE

Barn-owl family (11 species)

Fig. 74. Barn-owl (*Tyto alba*). Total length 15 in. (381 mm.).

Physical characteristics. Length—305 to 534 mm. (12 to 21 in.). Plumage—soft; variable in color, with light and dark phases frequent. Above: brown, spotted with white, or grayish brown or orange-buff, vermiculated with gray or brown; below: buff, grayish brown, or white, spotted, barred, or vermiculated with white, gray, or brown; wing and tail barred; face (long and heart-shaped) white or buff. Bill hooked and rather long, but mostly concealed by bristly radiating feathers of the facial discs; a cere at the base. Eyes comparatively small, directed forward. Wings long and rounded; tail short and slightly emarginate. Legs long, the flank feathers elongate, the tarsus completely feathered; toes strong, sparsely covered with bristles, the outer toe reversible; claws long, sharp, strongly hooked, the middle claw pectinate. Sexes alike or nearly so; ♀ sometimes larger.

Range. World-wide exc. extreme north and New Zealand, Hawaiian Ids., some islands of Malaysia. Largely nonmigratory.

Habits. Solitary. Nocturnal. Flight noiseless, buoyant but not swift. Prey swallowed whole, the bones, fur, etc., regurgitated later in pellets. Voice—varied; a shrill scream, a snoring sound, chirruping notes, hisses; also a clicking sound is made with the beak.

Food. Mammals, birds, insects, crustacea, frogs, fish.

Breeding. Nest in burrows, hollow trees, buildings, etc.; or on ground; little or no nest material.

Eggs. 3 to 11 (usually 4 to 7); white. Incubated by ♀.

Young. Nidicolous. Downy. Cared for by ♂ and ♀.

Technical diagnosis. Ridgway, pt. 6, 1914: 598–599 (excludes *Phodilus*—see p. 618, footnote).

Classification. Peters, 4, 1940: 77–86 (10 spp.).

References. Bent, No. 170: 140–153; Witherby, 2, 1938: 342–347; Baker, *Fauna,* 4, 1927: 384–392; Baker, *Nidification,* 3, 1934: 495–499.

G. Guérin, *L'Effraye commune en Vendée,* Paris, 1928.

E. L. Sumner. The Behavior of Some Young Raptorial Birds, *Univ. Calif. Publ. Zool.,* 40, No. 8, 1934: 352–358.

Synonyms: Aluconidae, Strigidae (the Typical-owls, now called Strigidae, were formerly called Bubonidae).

STRIGIDAE

Typical-owl family (123 species)

Fig. 75. Spectacled Owl (*Pulsatrix perspicillata*). Total length 20 in. (508 mm.).

Physical characteristics. Length—133 to 686 mm. ($5\frac{1}{4}$ to 27 in.). Plumage—long and soft; brownish black, gray, brown, or chestnut (one sp. white); barred, streaked, or vermiculated with white, buff, or brownish black (a few spp. nearly uniform above). Tail conspicuously barred in many spp. Some spp. have brown ("red") and gray phases. Earlike tufts ("horns") on many spp. Tarsus and (in many spp.) toes completely to slightly feathered. Bill short, strong, and hooked, with cere at base. Eyes very large and directed forward, surrounded by feathered discs. Head large, neck short. Wings broad and rounded, short to rather long; tail short to fairly long. Flank feathers greatly elongated. Legs short to medium; outer toe reversible; claws sharp, strongly hooked. Sexes in most spp. alike in color but ♀ larger.

Range. World-wide exc. some oceanic islands. Most spp. nonmigratory.

Habits. Solitary. Largely nocturnal or crepuscular. Most spp. arboreal. Flight noiseless, buoyant but not swift. Food swallowed whole, and bones, fur, etc., ejected later from the mouth in pellets. Voice— a variety of hooting, quavering, trilling, mewing, or barking sounds; also a loud snapping sound is made with the bill.

Food. Mammals, birds, reptiles, amphibians, fish, insects, crabs.

Breeding. Nest in tree cavities; in old nests of eagles, crows, etc.; on the ground; in burrows; and in buildings. Little or no nest material.

Eggs. 1 to 7, rarely up to 10; white. Incubated by ♀; or by ♂ and ♀.

Young. Nidicolous. Downy. Cared for by ♂ and ♀.

Technical diagnosis. Ridgway, pt. 6, 1914: 594–598, 617–618.

Classification. Peters, 4, 1940: 86–174.

References. Bent, No. 170: 153–444; Witherby, 2, 1938: 309–342; Baker, *Fauna*, 4, 1927: 392–458.

A. A. Allen, A Contribution to the Life History and Economic Status of the Screech Owl (*Otus asio*), *Auk*, 41, 1924: 1–16, pls. 1–5.

L. S. Crandall, The Owls, *Bull. N. Y. Zool. Soc.*, 33, 1930: 174–196.

Fr. Haverschmidt, Observations on the breeding habits of the Little Owl, *Ardea*, 34, 1946: 214–246. (*Athene noctua vidalli.*)

Synonyms: Asionidae, Bubonidae.

STEATORNITHIDAE

Oilbird family (1 species)

Fig. 76. Oilbird (*Steatornis caripensis*). Total length 18 in. (457 mm.).

Physical characteristics. Length—432 to 482 mm. (17 to 19 in.). Plumage—chestnut, bright above, paler below. Marked (exc. on back) with small, angular spots of white edged with black. Narrow dark bars on upper parts, exc. head. Bill short, rather wide-gaped, hooked. Very long rictal bristles. Wings pointed, tail rounded, both long. Legs extremely short; bare; not scaled. Toes long; claws sharp and curved. Sexes alike.

Range. Locally from c. Peru, through Ecuador, Colombia, and Venezuela, to French Guiana; also island of Trinidad. Nonmigratory.

Habits. Gregarious. Nocturnal. Flight strong, noiseless. Hover to feed, picking fruits from trees. Voice—loud squawks, croaks, and shrieks.

Food. Fruits, especially of palms.

Breeding. Colonial nesters (on ledges in caves). Nest a truncated cone of seeds and droppings, with shallow egg cavity.

Eggs. 2 to 4; white. Incubated by ♂ and ♀.

Young. Nidicolous. Said to be naked at hatching, but later acquire a sparse down. Become exceedingly fat (reaching twice the weight of adults) and are used as a source of oil by primitive peoples—hence name of family.

Technical diagnosis. Ridgway, pt. 6, 1914: 488–489.

Classification. Peters, 4, 1940: 174.

References. L.Taczanowski, *Ornithologie du Pérou,* Rennes, vol. 1, 1884: 199–203.

G. K. Cherrie, The Home of the Guacharo, *Brooklyn Inst. Arts and Sci., Mus. News,* 3, no. 1, 1907: 1–4.

W. L. McAtee, Notes on the Food of the Guacharo (*Steatornis caripensis*), *Auk,* 39, 1922: 108–109.

G. E. Hollister, The Guacharo or Oil Bird of the Arima Gorge, [N. Y.] *Zool. Soc. Bull.,* 29, 1926: 139–145, 160–161.

M. A. Carriker, Jr., The Cave Birds of Trinidad, *Auk,* 48, 1931: 186–194.

D. R. Griffin, Acoustic Orientation in the Oil Bird, *Steatornis, Proc. Natl. Acad. Sci.,* 39, 1953: 884–893 (or—less detailed—*Sci. Amer.,* 190, 1954: 78–93).

PODARGIDAE

Frogmouth family (12 species)

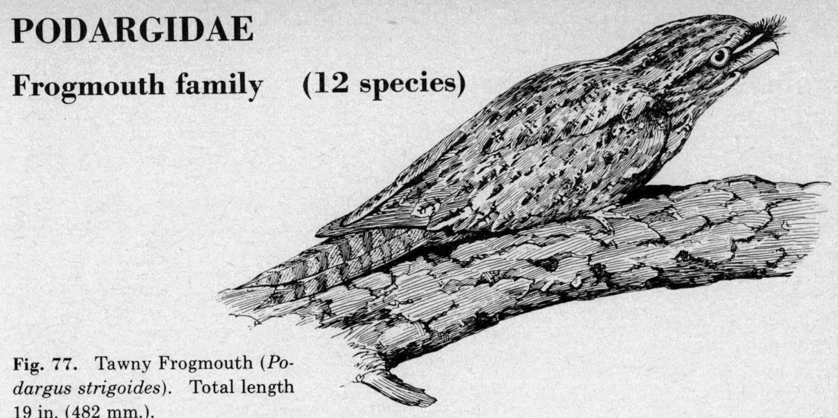

Fig. 77. Tawny Frogmouth (*Podargus strigoides*). Total length 19 in. (482 mm.).

Physical characteristics. Length—216 to 534 mm. ($8\frac{1}{2}$ to 21 in.). Plumage—soft, silky; brown, tawny, and gray; mottled, vermiculated, barred, or streaked with black and chocolate-brown in cryptic patterns; ear tufts in some spp. Bill broad, flat, and triangular, strongly hooked and extremely wide-gaped; long bristly feathers at base. Neck short and thick. Wings rounded, of moderate length; tail medium to long. Legs very short; feet small and weak; middle toe elongated. Sexes similar; ♀ more reddish or has red phase.

Range. Ceylon, s. and n.e. India, Burma, Siam, Malaysia, Papuan Region, Australia (incl. Tasmania), Solomons, Philippines. Habitat—forest. Migratory in part.

Habits. Usually in pairs. Nocturnal. Somewhat lethargic. Flight direct, not strong. Characteristically perch lengthwise on branches; when alarmed, assume rigid posture resembling broken branch. Voice—low, hoarse booming note, loud hiss; *oom-oom* repeated many times.

Food. Beetles, moths, other insects (usually picked from ground or branches); mice.

Breeding. Shallow nest of loosely interwoven sticks or flat pad of birds' own down overlaid with bark, lichen, and moss; placed at fork on horizontal branch.

Eggs. 1 or 2 (sometimes 3?); white. Incubated by ♂ and ♀.

Young. Nidicolous. Downy. Cared for by both ♂ and ♀.

Technical diagnosis. Baker, *Fauna,* 4, 1927 (2nd ed.): 377.

Classification. Peters, 4, 1940: 175–179.

References. Baker, *Fauna,* 4, 1927: 377–382, pl. 5; Baker, *Nidification,* 3, 1934: 492–495.

Hubert L. Clark, The Pterylosis of *Podargus:* with Notes on the Pterylography of the Caprimulgi, *Auk,* 18, 1901: 167–171.

F. Irby, The Curious Frogmouth, *Emu,* 27, 1927: 38–41, pl. 9.

D. L. Serventy, Feeding Methods of *Podargus, Emu,* 36, 1936: 74–90, pls. 12–13.

Max Bartels, Jr., Notizen über einige Batrachostomus-Arten, *Jour. f. Ornith.,* 86, 1938: 244–247, pls. 12–13.

NYCTIBIIDAE

Potoo family (5 species)

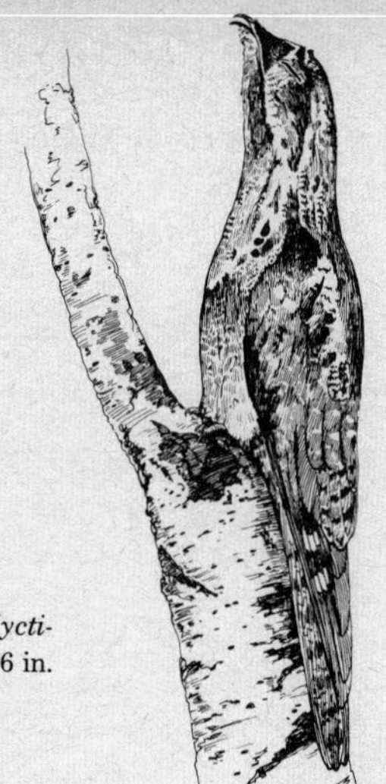

Fig. 78. Common Potoo (*Nyctibius griseus*). Total length 16 in. (406 mm.).

Physical characteristics. Length—406 to 495 mm. (16 to 19½ in.). Plumage—soft; cryptic pattern of gray, buff, blackish brown, and white. Juvenal plumage white, with narrow dark shaft-streaks. Bill small, narrow, and terminally decurved; projection, or "tooth," on maxillary tomium; mouth very large. No rictal bristles, but loral feathers have bristlelike tips, much elongated and decurved. Wings and tail long. Legs extremely short; toes strong and much flattened below; claws curved (middle claw not pectinate). Sexes alike or nearly so.

Range. Southern Sinaloa and Tamaulipas to s. Brazil and Paraguay; also Jamaica and Hispaniola. Habitat—forested or semiforested areas. Nonmigratory.

Habits. Solitary. Nocturnal. Perch in very upright position. Hawk insects. Voice—"clear, plaintive, far-carrying 'chant' of seven or eight whistled notes," starting high and running down scale (Butler); guttural *ch-r-r* (Scott); mews like cat (Goeldi); quacking notes.

Food. Insects.

Breeding. Lay egg on top of broken tree stub and incubate in stiffly erect posture.

Eggs. 1; oval; white, lightly and irregularly spotted with violet and brown. Incubated by ♂ and ♀.

Young. Nidicolous. Downy. Cared for by ?

Technical diagnosis. Ridgway, pt. 6, 1914: 583–584.

Classification. Peters, 4, 1940: 179–181.

References. E. A. Goeldi, On the Nesting of *Nyctibius jamaicensis* and *Sclerurus umbretta, Ibis,* 1896: 299–309.

A. Wetmore, On the Anatomy of Nyctibius with Notes on Allied Birds, *Proc. U. S. Natl. Mus.,* 54, 1918: 577–586.

A. Muir and A. L. Butler, The Nesting of *Nyctibius griseus* (Gmel.) in Trinidad. . . . , *Ibis,* 1925: 654–659, pls. 16–21.

Fr. Haverschmidt, Observations on *Nyctibius grandis* in Surinam, *Auk,* 65, 1948: 30–32, pl. 3.

H. Sick, The voice of the Grand Potoo, *Wils. Bull.,* 65, 1953: 203.

AEGOTHELIDAE

Owlet-frogmouth family (8 species)

Fig. 79. Owlet-frogmouth (*Aegotheles insignis*). Total length 12 in. (305 mm.).

Physical characteristics. Length—190 to 323 mm. ($7\frac{1}{2}$ to $12\frac{3}{4}$ in.). Plumage—soft; rufous cinnamon, gray, brown (to black) and buff, mottled, spotted, vermiculated, and barred with brown, gray, black, and white. Elongated, erect loral bristles with hairlike barbs. Flank feathers lengthened. Bill small, flat, with large gape; hooked (but not toothed). Wings long and rounded; tail long and wedge-shaped. Legs and feet small and weak; toes long and slender; claws long (middle claw not pectinate). Sexes alike or nearly so.

Range. Australia, Tasmania, New Guinea, New Caledonia; Moluccan, Fergusson, Goodenough, and Aru Ids. Habitat—dense brush and open wooded country. Nonmigratory.

Habits. Solitary. Nocturnal. Arboreal. Flight noiseless; direct and rapid, but not prolonged. Hawk insects; also feed on ground insects. Spend day in hollow tree or log. Voice—loud hissing; whistling call; churring notes; shrill squeak.

Food. Insects.

Breeding. Nest in hollow tree (sometimes in holes in banks), lined with leaves or without lining.

Eggs. 3 to 5; white, immaculate or striated. Incubation not described.

Young. Nidicolous. Downy. Care of young not described.

Technical diagnosis. Mathews, 7, 1918: 51.

Classification. Peters, 4, 1940: 181–184 (7 spp.).

References. Mathews, 7, 1918: 51–68, col. pl. 330.

H. Burrell, Owlet-Nightjar Nestlings, *Emu,* 13, 1914: 216–217, photo.

D. L. Serventy and H. M. Whittell, *A Handbook of the Birds of Western Australia,* Perth, 1948: 228.

CAPRIMULGIDAE

Nightjar family

(67 species)

Fig. 80. Pennant-winged Nightjar (*Semeïophorus vexillarius*). Total length 12 in. (305 mm.).

Physical characteristics. Length—190 to 292 mm. ($7\frac{1}{2}$ to $11\frac{1}{2}$ in.), excluding the extremely elongate tail feathers of 2 spp., which may add as much as 215 mm. ($8\frac{1}{2}$ in.). Plumage—soft; rufous, buff, gray, black, and white, mottled and finely vermiculated in cryptic patterns. Many spp. with barring below and/or with white throat; also areas of white on wings and/or tail (visible only when spread). Some spp. have extremely elongated rectrices or inner primaries; some have tufts of lengthened feathers on head. Bill small and weak, but with very wide gape. Long rictal bristles in many spp. Large eyes. Head large, neck appearing short. Wings and tail medium to long. Legs very short; tarsus feathered in some spp.; toes and claws small, but 3rd (middle) toe long, with pectinate claw. Sexes unlike in most spp.

Range. World-wide, exc. n. N. America, n. Asia, s. S. America, New Zealand, and most oceanic islands. Some spp. migratory.

Habits. Solitary (some spp. migrate in loose flocks). Largely nocturnal or crepuscular. Flight weak to strong. Hawk insects. Perch lengthwise on branches. Voice—purring, rasping, and whistling notes; loud, 2- to 4-syllable calls.

Food. Insects (rarely small birds).

Breeding. Eggs laid directly on ground (no nest material).

Eggs. 1 to 2 (very rarely 3); white to pinkish buff, with dark specks and blotches (immaculate in a few spp.). Incubated by ♂ and ♀.

Young. Nidicolous. Downy. Cared for by ♂ and ♀.

Technical diagnosis. Witherby, 2, 1938: 251.

Classification. Peters, 4, 1940: 184–220 (70–72 spp.).

References. Bent, No. 176: 147–254; Witherby, 2, 1938: 251–262; Baker, *Fauna*, 4, 1927: 358–376; Bannerman, 3, 1933: xxii-xxiii, 147–178.

D. Lack, Some Breeding-habits of the European Nightjar, *Ibis*, 1932: 266–284.

G. Pickwell and E. Smith, The Texas Nighthawk in Its Summer Home, *Condor*, 40, 1938: 193–215.

APODIDAE

Swift family (76 species)

Fig. 81. White-throated Swift (*Aëronautes saxatalis*). Total length $6\frac{1}{2}$ in. (165 mm.).

Physical characteristics. Length—89 to 228 mm. ($3\frac{1}{2}$ to 9 in.). Plumage—bluish or brownish black to grayish brown (one sp. with chestnut breast and collar). Some spp. have throat, collar, flanks, or rump white (or very pale brown). Bill very small, slightly decurved; gape large. Neck short; body compact. Wings very long and pointed. Tail short and truncate (with the feathers in some spp. spine-tipped) to very long and forked. Legs extremely short; many spp. have tarsi (or even toes) feathered. Feet very small but strong; hallux completely reversible; claws strong and curved. Sexes alike.

Range. World-wide, exc. n. N. America, n. Asia, s. S. America, and some oceanic islands. Many spp. migratory.

Habits. Usually gregarious. Flight very strong and swift—the most aerial of birds; rest only by clinging to cliffs or inner walls of caves, chimneys, hollow trees, etc. Capture all food on the wing. Voice—rasping, twittering notes.

Food. Insects.

Breeding. Sometimes colonial. Nest of a salivary secretion or (in most spp.) of plant fragments glued together with the secretion, ranging from slight bracket to long elaborate tube and placed in cave or cleft or hollow tree, under overhanging rock or tree limb, or on under surface of palm leaf; or a few grasses and feathers in swallow nest or in old burrow in earth bank.

Eggs. 1 to 6; white. Incubated by ♂ and ♀.

Young. Nidicolous. Naked at hatching. Cared for by ♂ and ♀.

Technical diagnosis. Ridgway, pt. 5, 1911: 683–684.

Classification. Peters, 4, 1940: 220–256 (73–81 spp.).

References. Bent, No. 176: 254–319; Witherby, 2, 1938: 242–251; Baker, *Fauna,* 4, 1927: 322–353.

C. G. Manuel, Beneficial Swiftlet and Edible Bird's Nest Industry in Bacuit, Palawan, *Phil. Jour. Sci.,* 62, 1937: 379–390, pls. 1–3.

H. Sick, The Nesting of *Reinarda squamata* (Cassin), *Auk,* 65, 1948: 169–174, pl. 6.

D. Lack and E. Lack, The Breeding Behaviour of the Swift, *Brit. Birds,* 45, 1952: 186–215. (See also: *Ibis,* 93, 1951: 501–546.)

D. Lack, A Review of the Genera and Nesting Habits of Swifts, *Auk,* 73, 1956: 1–32.

Synonyms: Micropodidae, Cypselidae, Triopidae.

HEMIPROCNIDAE

Crested-swift family

(3 species)

Fig. 82. Indian Crested-swift (*Hemiprocne coronata*). Total length 8½ in. (216 mm.).

Physical characteristics. Length—165 to 330 mm. (6½ to 13 in.). Plumage—soft; gray or bronze-brown above, with head, wings, and sometimes the back glossed with green or blue; under parts uniform gray or bronze-brown, or with white on abdomen and under tail coverts, white on chin, blue or green gloss on breast. In 2 spp. conspicuous white lines extend from base of bill over the eye and under the cheek, ending in tufts at nape and shoulder. All spp. have a crest and a patch of silky feathers on flanks; all have some chestnut on head (in ♂ only). Bill small, flat, and broadly triangular, the gape large. Eye very large. Neck short. Wings extremely long and pointed; tail long and deeply forked, the outer feathers much attenuated. Legs very short; feet weak; toes long and slender (the hallux not reversible). Sexes unlike.

Range. India and Ceylon, Burma, Siam, Indo-China, Philippine Ids.; Malaysia, Papuan Region, e. to the Solomon Ids. Habitat—open wooded hillsides and forest clearings. Nonmigratory.

Habits. Somewhat gregarious. Aerial, but perch regularly in trees. Flight strong, rapid, wheeling. Hawk insects. Voice—a loud screaming cry.

Food. Insects.

Breeding. Nest an extremely small and shallow cup of bark fragments and small feathers plastered with saliva, attached to branch of tree.

Eggs. 1; pale gray, tinged with blue. Incubated by ♂ and ♀.

Young. Nidicolous. Downy. Cared for by ♂ and ♀.

Technical diagnosis. Ridgway, pt. 5, 1911: 683 ("Dendrochelidonidae").

Classification. Peters, 4, 1940: 257–259.

References. Baker, *Fauna,* 4, 1927: 353–357; Baker, *Nidification,* 3, 1934: 475–477.
J. Delacour, *Birds of Malaysia,* New York, 1947: 144–145.
E. H. N. Lowther, *A Photographer in India,* London, 1949: 1–10, 5 pls.

Synonyms: Macropterygidae, Dendrochelidonidae.

TROCHILIDAE

Hummingbird family

(319 species)

Fig. 83. White-booted Rackettail (*Ocreatus underwoodii*). Total length 5 in. (127 mm.).

Physical characteristics. Length—63 to 216 mm. ($2\frac{1}{2}$ to $8\frac{1}{2}$ in.). Plumage—mainly green, brown, or black. Many spp. are gray or white below. Areas of brilliant iridescent green, red, blue, purple, or gold (on throat, crown, sides of head, back) in most spp. Some spp. crested. Bill slender and pointed, rather short to extremely long (7–100 mm.), straight to strongly decurved (recurved in a few spp.). Wings long and narrow; tail extremely varied—acuminate to deeply forked, the rectrices highly modified (racquet-tipped, etc.) in some spp. Legs very short (covered in some spp. with "muffs" of long downy feathers); feet very small and weak. Sexes unlike in most spp.

Range. South, Middle, and N. America (exc. extreme n.). Many spp. migratory.

Habits. Solitary. Pugnacious. Arboreal. Flight very swift and agile, with extremely rapid wing beat. Perch but do not walk or hop. Frequently hover, esp. when feeding. ♂ has elaborate display flight. Voice—squeaking or twittering notes; also various sounds are made by vibration of flight feathers during courtship display of ♂.

Food. Insects, arachnids; nectar.

Breeding. Some spp. polygamous? Deep, cup-shaped nest of plant down and spider web, saddled on branch, suspended in fork, or (in palms, etc.) fastened to under side of leaf tip.

Eggs. 2 (in some spp. only 1?); white, immaculate. Incubated by ♀ (assisted by ♂ in *Colubri coruscans*).

Young. Nidicolous. With trace of down. Cared for by ♀ (assisted by ♂ in *C. coruscans*).

Technical diagnosis. Ridgway, pt. 5, 1911: 300–301.

Classification. Peters, 5, 1945: 1–143 (327 spp).

References. Bent, No. 176: 319–472.

J. Gould, Monograph of the Trochilidae, London, 1849–61 and (supplement) 1880–87.

R. Ridgway, The Humming Birds, *Rept. Natl. Mus.* (for 1890), 1892: 253–383, pls. 1–46.

H. O. Wagner, Food and Feeding Habits of Mexican Hummingbirds, *Wils. Bull.*, 58, 1946: 69–93.

A. F. Skutch, Life History of Longuemare's Hermit Hummingbird, *Ibis,* 1951: 180–195.

E. Schäfer, Sobre la biologia de Colubri coruscans, *Bol. Soc. venezol. Cienc. nat.*, 15 (No. 82), 1954: 153–162.

COLIIDAE

Coly family (6 species)

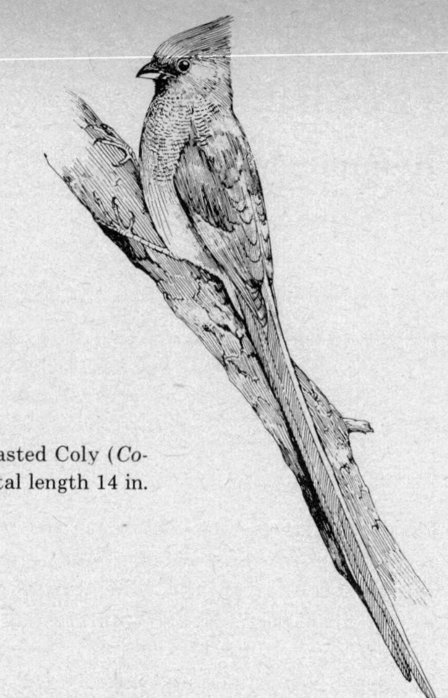

Fig. 84. Bar-breasted Coly (*Colius striatus*). Total length 14 in. (355 mm.).

Physical characteristics. Length—292 to 355 mm. ($11\frac{1}{2}$ to 14 in.), the tail more than twice the length of the body. Plumage—soft, the feathers of head and neck lax; somber brown (barred with dusky) or gray, marked with a blue patch on the nape, with black on the throat, or chestnut on the rump; under parts lighter. All spp. crested. Bill red or black and white in some spp.; feet red. Bare skin around eye red, blue, or gray. Bill short, stout, and curved, fleshy about the nostrils. Neck short; body slender. Wings short and rounded; tail extremely long and slender, sharply graduated, with stiff shafts. Legs short; feet strong; toes very long, the 1st toe reversible; claws long, sharp, and strong. Sexes alike.

Range. Africa s. of the Sahara, exc. Madagascar. Habitat—forest edge and brushland. Nonmigratory.

Habits. Gregarious (sleep hanging together in clusters). Arboreal. Flight rapid and direct but not sustained. Creep about trees, using bill and feet, the tarsus resting on the branches. Acrobatic; often hang head downward (even when sleeping). Preen each other. Voice—harsh calls, mewing cries, whistling notes.

Food. Fruit, new shoots, leaves, seeds; rarely insects.

Breeding. Nest an open shallow cup of sticks, bark, and roots, lined with wool, cotton, or leaves; placed in bush or tree.

Eggs. 2 to 7 (usually 2 to 4?); white or creamy white, immaculate or streaked with brown. Incubated by ♂ and ♀.

Young. Nidicolous. With sparse down. Cared for by ♂ and ♀?

Technical diagnosis. P. L. Sclater, Fam. Coliidae, Wytsman's *Genera Avium,* pt. 6, 1906: 1–2.

Classification. Peters, 5, 1945: 143–146.

References. Bannerman, 3, 1933: xx-xxi, 139–146.

J. P. Chapin, The Birds of the Belgian Congo, *Bull. Amer. Mus. Nat. Hist.,* 75, pt. 2, 1939: 469–479.

A. Roberts, *The Birds of South Africa,* London, 1940: 158–159, col. pl. 25.

TROGONIDAE

Trogon family (34 species)

Fig. 85. Mexican Trogon (*Trogon mexicanus*). Total length 12 in. (305 mm.).

Physical characteristics. Length—228 to 337 mm. (9 to $13\frac{1}{4}$ in.). Plumage—soft and dense. Back, tail coverts, and central rectrices brilliant metallic green (chestnut in a few spp.; coverts red in one sp.); head, neck, and chest varied, green, black, gray, blue, violet, chestnut, rose, red; wings and outer rectrices black with white markings; abdomen and lower tail coverts red, yellow, or orange. Upper tail coverts extremely elongate in the Quetzal. Crest or tufts behind eyes in some spp. Brightly colored bare orbital ring. Eyes large. Bill short, broad, usually brightly colored; serrate in some spp. Nostrils and base of bill covered with bristles. Neck short. Wings short, rounded; tail long, broad, and truncate. Legs and feet very small and weak; tarsus feathered; 1st and 2nd toes turned backward. Sexes unlike in most spp.

Range. Tropics. Southern half of Africa, India, and s.e. Asia; Malaysia and the Philippines; Arizona, extreme s. Texas, Mexico, Central America, West Indies, and n. three-quarters of S. America. Habitat—forest. Nonmigratory (exc. for local movements).

Habits. Usually solitary. Strictly arboreal. Flight undulating; rapid but not prolonged. Rarely walk or hop. Feed by darting from perch and snatching insects from air or from foliage, or small fruits from stem. Voice—a variety of simple call notes.

Food. Insects and small fruits; snails, small lizards, frogs.

Breeding. Nest a hollow in decayed stump or tree, termites' or wasps' nest. No lining.

Eggs. 2 to 4; white or buff to greenish blue; immaculate. Incubated by ♂ and ♀.

Young. Nidicolous. Naked at hatching. Cared for by ♂ and ♀.

Technical diagnosis. Ridgway, pt. 5, 1911: 729–731.

Classification. Peters, 5, 1945: 148–164.

References. Bent, No. 176: 106–110; Baker, *Fauna,* 4, 1927: 314–321; Bannerman, 3, 1933: xxxii-xxxiii, 355–360.

J. Gould, A Monograph of the Trogonidae . . . , London, 1858–75: 47 col. pls.

A. F. Skutch, Life History of the Mexican Trogon, *Auk,* 59, 1942: 341–363, pls. 10–11.

A. F. Skutch, Life History of the Quetzal, *Condor,* 46, 1944: 213–235. (Reprinted: *Smiths. Rept. for 1946:* 265–293, pls. 1–4.)

ALCEDINIDAE

Kingfisher family (87 species)

Fig. 86. Laughing Kookaburra (*Dacelo novaeguinae*). Total length 16 in. (406 mm.).

Physical characteristics. Length—102 to 457 mm. (4 to 18 in.). Plumage—green, blue, purple, reddish brown, white, usually in contrasting solid areas. Some spp. crested, and some barred (esp. on tail) and/or spotted; many with broad collar and/or pectoral band. Bill and feet of many spp. bright red or yellow. Bill massive, straight (but gonys typically upcurved), and pointed (hooked in one sp.). Head large; neck short; body compact. Wings generally short and rounded. Tail very short to very long, with central feathers much elongated (and even racquet-tipped). Legs very short; feet (4 or 3 toes) strongly syndactyl. Sexes alike or unlike.

Range. World-wide (exc. some oceanic islands and extreme n. parts of N. America and Eurasia). Spp. of higher latitudes migratory.

Habits. Solitary. Flight strong and direct but usually not sustained. Watch from exposed perch or hover over water, feeding by diving for fish, by catching insects in the air, or by pouncing on large insects or small vertebrates on the ground. Voice—sharp calls or rattling cries.

Food. Fish, crustacea, insects, amphibians, reptiles, or even small birds or mammals.

Breeding. Nest in burrows in banks, in termite nests, or in tree cavities. No nest lining.

Eggs. 2 to 7; white. Incubated by ♂ and ♀.

Young. Nidicolous. Naked or (*Dacelo*) with down on upper parts. Cared for by ♂ and ♀.

Technical diagnosis. Ridgway, pt. 6, 1914: 404–406.

Classification. Peters, 5, 1945: 165–219.

References. Bent, No. 176: 11–146; Witherby, 2, 1938: 272–276; Baker, *Fauna,* 4, 1927: 245–281.

R. B. Sharpe, A Monograph of the Alcedinidae . . . , London, 1868–1871, 120 col. pls.

B. B. Rivière, Some Nesting-Habits of the Kingfisher, *Brit. Birds,* 26, 1933: 262–270.

R. S. Miller, The Mangrove-Kingfisher, *Emu,* 36, 1937: 149–152, col. pl. 22.

J. C. Salyer, II, and K. F. Lagler, The Eastern Belted Kingfisher, *Megaceryle alcyon alcyon* (Linnaeus), in Relation to Fish Management, *Trans. Amer. Fisheries Soc.,* 76 (for 1946), 1949: 97–117.

P. O. Swanberg, Observations on feeding, brooding and bathing habits in a pair of Kingfishers (*Alcedo atthis*), *Vår Fågelvärld,* 11, 1952: 49–66, 10 photos (in Swedish, with two-page English summary).

Synonym: Halcyonidae. The Dacelonidae are included.

TODIDAE

Tody family (5 species)

Fig. 87. Cuban Tody (*Todus multicolor*). Total length 3¾ in. (95 mm.).

Physical characteristics. Length—89 to 114 mm. (3½ to 4½ in.). Plumage—uniform bright green above, with lores and forehead yellow in one sp.; subauricular region blue or gray; malar stripe and chin white; throat geranium-red; under parts mostly white or washed with green, yellow, pink, gray; flanks pink or (one sp.) yellow; bill brown and red; feet orange-red. Bill long, straight, flattened, obtusely pointed. Head large; neck short; body compact. Wings short and rounded; tail medium in length, slightly rounded. Legs slender; feet weak, syndactyl; toes long. Sexes alike.

Range. Greater Antilles. Habitat—thickets on hillsides and streambanks. Nonmigratory.

Habits. Usually in pairs. Strictly arboreal. Flight weak. Sedentary exc. for brief swift darts from perch to seize insects. Very tame. Voice—harsh chattering; chipping notes; a harsh *chreck; terp terp terp* (*Todus subulatus*). Wings make whirring rattle in flight.

Food. Insects; rarely minute lizards.

Breeding. Nest in unlined burrow which they excavate in earth bank or even in very slight vertical elevation, as in the side of a rut.

Eggs. 2 to 5; white. Incubated by ♂ and ♀.

Young. Nidicolous. Not otherwise described.

Technical diagnosis. Ridgway, pt. 6, 1914: 441.

Classification. Peters, 5, 1945: 220.

References.
J. W. Daniel, Jr., The Cuban Tody (*Todus multicolor*), *Wils. Bull.*, 14, 1902: 113–116.

P. Wytsman, Fam. Todidae, Wytsman's *Genera Avium*, pt. 2, 1905 (col. pl.).

A. Wetmore and B. H. Swales, The Birds of Haiti and the Dominican Republic, *U. S. Natl. Mus. Bull.*, 155, 1931: 283–290.

J. Bond, *Birds of the West Indies*, Philadelphia, 1936: 226–228.

J. Bond, Nesting of the Narrow-billed Tody, *Wils. Bull.*, 61, 1949: 188.

MOMOTIDAE

Motmot family (8 species)

Fig. 88. Blue-crowned Motmot (*Momotus momota*). Total length 17 in. (432 mm.).

Physical characteristics. Length—171 to 502 mm. ($6\frac{3}{4}$ to $19\frac{3}{4}$ in.). Plumage—loose-webbed; green, blue, and brown. Crown, face or throat boldly marked with black, blue, or brown. Usually a spot in center of breast. Bill large, broad, decurved; usually serrate. Wings short and rounded. Tail long (exc. *Hylomanes*); graduated; racquet-tipped (exc. *Hylomanes, Aspatha,* and two subspp. of *Baryphthengus*)—racquet shape develops after growth is complete but is not caused by deliberate action of bird. Legs very short; feet syndactyl. Sexes alike or nearly so.

Range. Neotropical. Forests of Mexico (s. Sonora and Tamaulipas) to Paraguay and n.e. Argentina; also Cozumel, Trinidad, and Tobago islands. Most spp. non-migratory.

Habits. Usually solitary. Perch long in one spot. Twitch tail from side to side in irregular mechanical manner. Flight undulating. Voice—low-pitched hooting or cooing notes, singly or in series.

Food. Insects, spiders, worms, snails, lizards, fruit.

Breeding. Nest in crevices in rocks or in a hollow at end of a burrow in a vertical bank or in the level ground; no lining.

Eggs. 3 to 4; white. Incubated by ♂ and ♀.

Young. Nidicolous. Naked. Cared for by ♂ and ♀. Nest not cleaned.

Technical diagnosis. Ridgway, pt. 6, 1914: 450–452.

Classification. Peters, 5, 1945: 221–228.

References. H. D. Astley, The Denudation of the Shaft in the Motmot's Tail, *Ibis,* 1916: 337–340.

F. M. Chapman, The Distribution of the Motmots of the Genus Momotus, *Amer. Mus. Nat. Hist. Bull.,* 48, art. 2, 1923: 27–59.

A. F. Skutch, Life History of the Blue-throated Green Motmot, *Auk,* 62, 1945: 489–517, pl. 22.

G. M. Sutton, Blue-crowned Motmot, *Wils. Bull.,* 58, 1946: frontispiece.

A. F. Skutch, Life History of the Turquoise-browed Motmot, *Auk,* 64, 1947: 201–217, pl. 9.

H. O. Wagner, Observations on the Racquet-tips of the Motmot's Tail, *Auk,* 67, 1950: 387–389.

MEROPIDAE

Bee-eater family (24 species)

Fig. 89. European Bee-eater (*Merops apiaster*). Total length 11 in. (280 mm.).

Physical characteristics. Length—152 to 355 mm. (6 to 14 in.). Plumage—soft and compact. Most spp. are green, with broad black line through eye, black wing tips, and bold areas (head, chin, throat, tail coverts) of bright yellow, vermilion, chestnut, blue; one sp. is black, with turquoise-blue streaks and a red throat; one slate-gray and red, with white markings; two spp. red, with green head and blue and black markings; two spp. largely blue and chestnut. *Nyctiornis* and *Meropogon* have the chin and throat feathers much elongated. Bill long, slender, laterally compressed, and decurved; both mandibles pointed. Wings long and pointed. Tail long; with the central pair of rectrices elongated, square (or slightly emarginate), or forked (1 sp.). Lower tibia bare or sparsely feathered; feet syndactyl, rather small and weak; toes slender, short to long; claws slender and acute. Sexes alike or nearly so.

Range. Temperate and tropical parts of Old World. Most spp. migratory, at least locally.

Habits. Most spp. gregarious. Graceful wheeling flight (spectacular evolutions in some spp.). Hawk insects or capture them in short sallies from a perch. Fearless. Voice—musical trills, chirps, and whistles; hoarse chuckling and croaking notes.

Food. Insects, especially bees and their allies.

Breeding. Colonial in most spp. Nest in burrows, excavated (by ♂ and ♀) very frequently in riverbanks, sometimes in level ground; no lining.

Eggs. 2 to 9; white, immaculate. Incubated by ♂ and ♀.

Young. Nidicolous. Naked at hatching. Cared for by ♂ and ♀.

Technical diagnosis. Witherby, 2, 1938: 262–263.

Classification. Peters, 5, 1945: 229–239.

References. Witherby, 2, 1938: 262–263; Baker, *Fauna,* 4, 1927: 232–244.

H. E. Dresser, A Monograph of the Meropidae, London, 1884 (34 col. pls.).

C. Parrot, Fam. Meropidae, Wytsman's *Genera Avium,* pt. 14, 1911 (col. pl.).

E. Comrie-Smith, Notes on the Rainbow-Bird, *Emu,* 30, 1930: 64–66 (*Merops ornatus*).

A. Rivoire, Contribution à l'étude du *Merops apiaster, L'Ois. et Rev. Franç. d'Ornith.,* 17, 1947: 23–43.

CORACIIDAE

Roller family (17 species)

Fig. 90. Indian Roller (*Coracias benghalensis*). Total length 13 in. (330 mm.).

Physical characteristics. Length—241 to 457 mm. (9½ to 18 in.). Plumage of typical rollers (Coraciinae) brightly colored in most spp.: blended shades of blue, bluish green, green, violet, reddish brown; usually unmarked, but streaked below in a few spp. Bill and feet yellow, red, or black. Bill wide, strong, decurved, slightly hooked. Neck short. Wings long. Tail rather long; truncate, emarginate, or deeply forked (with outer feathers lengthened and attenuate or even spatulate). Legs very short; feet strong, the 2nd and 3rd toes united basally. Sexes alike or nearly so. (The 5 spp. of Ground Rollers, the Brachypteraciinae of Madagascar, have mottled, cryptic plumage, longer legs, shorter wings, and more pointed—sometimes very long—tails.)

Range. Africa, Eurasia (exc. n. part), East Indies, Philippines, n. and e. Australia; e. to Solomon Ids. Some spp. migratory.

Habits. Usually solitary. Arboreal. Flight strong and skillful (tumble or roll over during display flight). Fly from perch to perch, but hop on ground. Sit motionless on high, exposed perches. Voice—harsh, loud cries, frequently uttered. (Ground Rollers are mainly terrestrial birds which frequent heavy forest or—*Uratelornis*—sandy brush country.)

Food. Small animals, esp. insects; fruit exceptionally.

Breeding. Nest in holes in trees, in banks, in rock crevices, or in abandoned nests of magpies (*Pica*). Little or no lining.

Eggs. 3 to 6; white. Incubated by ♂ and ♀ (or by ♀ only?).

Young. Nidicolous. Naked. Cared for by ♂ and ♀.

Technical diagnosis. Witherby, 2, 1938: 269.

Classification. Peters, 5, 1945: 240–247.

References. Witherby, 2, 1938: 269–272; Baker, *Fauna,* 4, 1927: 221–231.

H. E. Dresser, A Monograph of the Coraciidae . . . , Farnborough, England, 1893: 1–99, col. pls. 1–25.

H. von Boetticher, Rolliers et Eurystomes, *L'Ois. et Rev. Franç. d'Ornith.,* 6, 1936: 422–434.

A. L. Rand, The Distribution and Habits of Madagascar Birds, *Bull. Amer. Mus. Nat. Hist.,* 72, 1936: 416–421 (omit *Leptosomus*).

H. Wigsten, Blåkråkans (*Coracias garrulus*) levnadsvanor på Fårö, *Vår Fågelvärld,* 14, 1955: 21–45 (English summary, pp. 44–45).

Synonymy: The Brachypteraciidae are included.

LEPTOSOMATIDAE

Cuckoo-roller family

(1 species)

Fig. 91. Cuckoo-roller (*Leptosomus discolor*). Total length 18 in. (457 mm.).

Physical characteristics. Length—406 to 457 mm. (16 to 18 in.). Plumage of ♂ dark plumbeous gray above, with strong metallic green and coppery red reflections; face, throat, and complete collar ashy gray; rest of under parts grayish white. ♀ with gray largely replaced by rufous brown; head and hind neck barred, and whole under parts boldly spotted, with black. Short crest in both sexes. Bill stout, decurved, slightly hooked. Head large, neck short. Wings long and pointed; tail long and truncate. Legs extremely short; feet semizygodactyl; toes, exc. hallux, long. ♀ larger than ♂, as well as differently colored.

Range. Madagascar and the nearby Comores Ids. Habitat—forests and brushland. Nonmigratory.

Habits. Somewhat gregarious. Arboreal. Flight strong; perform spectacular aerial evolutions above the forest. Feed largely in treetops. Vociferous. Voice—loud, whistled *wheu,* or *wha-ha-ha-ha.*

Food. Large insects, lizards.

Breeding. Polyandrous? Nest in hollows in trees (and in holes in banks?).

Eggs. 3?; white. Incubation not described.

Young. Not described.

Technical diagnosis. R. B. Sharpe, Cat. of Birds in Brit. Mus., 17, 1892: 1.

Classification. Peters, 5, 1945: 239–240.

References. R. B. Sharpe, On the *Coraciidae* of the Ethiopian Region. Subfamily III. Leptosominae, *Ibis,* 1871: 285–289.

H. E. Dresser, A Monograph of the Coraciidae . . . , Farnborough, England, 1893: 101–108, pls. 26, 27.

A. L. Rand, The Distribution and Habits of Madagascar Birds, *Bull. Amer. Mus. Nat. Hist.,* 72, 1936: 417–418.

Synonymy: Sometimes included in the Coraciidae.

UPUPIDAE

Hoopoe family (1 species)

Fig. 92. Hoopoe (*Upupa epops*). Total length 11 in. (280 mm.).

Physical characteristics. Length—266 to 305 mm. ($10\frac{1}{2}$ to 12 in.). Plumage—pinkish cinnamon to rufous chestnut (paler below), with bands of black, white, and buff on back and wings; tail barred with white. Long, conspicuous, black-tipped crest (with white subterminal area in some races). Bill long and very slender; tongue short. Wings broad and rounded; tail square, moderate in length. Tarsi short, slender, and bare; toes long (3rd and 4th fused at base), claws short. Sexes similar (♀ duller and/or smaller in some).

Range. Central and s. Europe, Africa (except central region), Madagascar, and Asia (exc. northern third) to Japan. Habitat—semiopen country and cultivated clearings. Migratory in parts of range.

Habits. Solitary or in small bands. Terrestrial, but perch and roost in trees and occasionally hawk insects. Flight slow, undulating, and erratic, but efficient in danger. ♂ feeds ♀ in courtship and during breeding. Voice—typically *hoop-hoop* or *poup-poup;* hawing and mewing sounds.

Food. Insects, worms, spiders, etc.

Breeding. Nest a hole in tree, wall, earth bank, or termites' nest, sometimes a bulky structure of sticks, etc., but usually without lining.

Eggs. 4 to 12 (usually 4 to 6); pale blue to olive-brown, usually immaculate. Incubated by ♀.

Young. Nidicolous. With sparse down. Cared for by ♂ and ♀.

Technical diagnosis. Witherby, 2, 1938: 266.

Classification. Peters, 5, 1945: 617–620.

References. Witherby, 2, 1938: 266–269; Baker, *Fauna,* 4, 1927: 307–313; Bannerman, 3, 1933: xxvi–xxvii, 222–228; Baker, *Nidification,* 3, 1934: 442–447.

F. J. Jackson, *The Birds of Kenya Colony and the Uganda Protectorate,* London, vol. 2, 1938: 617–620.

C. J. Skead, A Study of the African Hoopoe, *Ibis,* 92, 1950: 434–463.

PHOENICULIDAE

Woodhoopoe family (6 species)

Fig. 93. Scimitarbill (*Rhinopomastus cyanomelas*). Total length 11 in. (280 mm.).

Physical characteristics. Length—222 to 381 mm. ($8\frac{3}{4}$ to 15 in.). Plumage—blackish-blue, -purple, and -green with metallic gloss, uniform in color exc. 2 spp., which have white or light brown heads; terminal and subterminal white spots on tail in some; bill brightly colored in some. Bill long, slender, and laterally compressed, almost straight to sickle-curved; tongue short. Wings rounded; tail long and steeply graduated. Tarsus very short, partly feathered in some spp.; toes rather long (esp. hallux), the 3rd and 4th fused basally; claws long and sharply curved. ♀ similar to ♂ but smaller and/or browner in some.

Range. Central and s. Africa, exc. Madagascar. Habitat—dense forest, forest edges, wooded grasslands. Nonmigratory (exc. for local movements).

Habits. Solitary or in small bands. Arboreal. Run along trunks and branches; climb (often head downward) with dexterity. Flight brief and infrequent, rather labored. Voice—loud chattering notes.

Food. Insects, spiders, small fruits, seeds.

Breeding. Nest a hole in tree.

Eggs. 3 to 5 (usually 3?); pale blue, green, or greenish blue. Incubated by ♀.

Young. Nidicolous. Downy. Cared for by ♂ and ♀.

Technical diagnosis. Bannerman, 3, 1933: xxvi–xxvii, 228.

Classification. Peters, 5, 1945: 250–253.

References. Bannerman, 3, 1933: 228–239.

W. Hoesch, Brutbiologische Beobachtungen am Sichelhopf (*Rhinopomastus cyanomelas*), *Ornith. Monats.*, 41, 1933: 33–37.

F. J. Jackson, *The Birds of Kenya Colony and the Uganda Protectorate,* London, vol. 2, 1938: 620–629.

J. P. Chapin, The Birds of the Belgian Congo, Part II, *Bull. Amer. Mus. Nat. Hist.,* 65, pt. 2, 1939: 323–332.

Synonym: Irrisoridae.

BUCEROTIDAE

Hornbill family

(45 species)

Fig. 94. Great Hornbill (*Buceros bicornis*). Total length 42 in. (1067 mm.).

Physical characteristics. Length—381 to 1600 mm. (15 to 63 in.). Plumage—loose-webbed and wiry; brown; black, white, and brown; or (typically) black and white. Bill typically red or yellow, very large, curved, variously sculptured, serrated in some spp.; usually with casque on culmen. Many spp. crested. Bare skin about eye and, sometimes, throat brightly colored. Conspicuous eyelashes. Wings strong. Tail long. Legs very short (exc. Ground Hornbill, *Bucorvus*); feet broad-soled and syndactyl. Sexes unlike in many spp., alike in others.

Range. Africa, s. of Sahara (exc. Madagascar), tropical Asia, Malaysia, Philippines, and east to the Solomons. Nonmigratory.

Habits. Usually in pairs or small flocks. Arboreal (exc. *Bucorvus*). Voice (most spp. vociferous)—harsh calls and loud whistles. Wings very noisy in flight.

Food. Omnivorous; some live principally on fruit.

Breeding. Nest in hollow trees, occasionally in caves. From before egg-laying until fledging of young, ♀ remains in nest and is fed by ♂; one or both members of pair wall up nest entrance with mud, etc., leaving small feeding aperture.

Eggs. 1 to 6; white. Incubated by ♀.

Young. Nidicolous. Naked. Heel-pads. Fed by ♀ with food brought by ♂; in some small spp. (*Tockus*), ♀ leaves nest when young are half-fledged and assists in gathering food.

Technical diagnosis. Baker, *Fauna,* 4, 1927: 282.

Classification. Peters, 5, 1945: 245–272.

References. D. G. Elliot, A Monograph of the Bucerotidae, London, 1877–1882.

A. Dubois, Fam. Bucerotidae, Wytsman's *Genera Avium,* pt. 13, 1911.

R. E. Moreau, The Comparative Breeding Biology of the African Hornbills (Bucerotidae), *Proc. Zool. Soc. London,* 107A, 1937: 331–346.

R. E. Moreau and W. M. Moreau, Breeding Biology of Silvery-cheeked Hornbill, *Auk,* 58, 1941: 13–27.

Gordon Ranger, Life of the Crowned Hornbill. *Lophoceros suahelicus australis. Ostrich,* 20, 1949: 54–65, 152–167; 21, 1950: 2–13; 22, 1951: 77–93; 23, 1952: 26–36.

GALBULIDAE

Jacamar family (15 species)

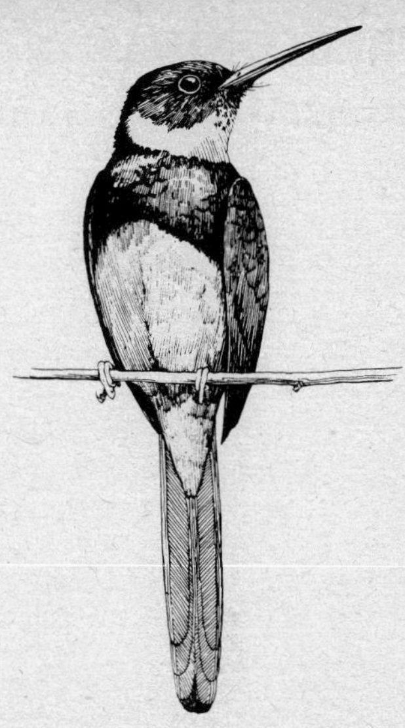

Fig. 95. Rufous-tailed Jacamar (*Galbula melanogenia*). Total length 9½ in. (241 mm.).

Physical characteristics. Length—127 to 299 mm. (5 to 11¾ in.). Plumage—soft and loose-webbed; usually metallic green or black above, tawny or black below; throat usually white in ♂, buff in ♀. Long, attenuate bill (nearly straight in most spp.), sharply ridged above and below. Wings short; tail usually long and graduated (or acuminate). Feet zygodactyl (3-toed in *Jacamaralcyon*). Sexes unlike.

Range. Mainland from s. Mexico (Veracruz) to s. Brazil, but chiefly Amazon Valley. Habitat—tropical forests. Nonmigratory.

Habits. Solitary. Perch quietly on tree branches for long periods and then make lengthy, elaborate sallies for flying insects. Voice—varied squeaks and trills; ♂ of at least one sp. (*Galbula melanogenia*) has a long, rather melodious song.

Food. Insects, especially butterflies and dragonflies.

Breeding. Nest in hole in bank, excavated by ♂ and ♀.

Eggs. 3 to 4; white; nearly round. Incubated by ♂ and ♀.

Young. Nidicolous. Long white down. Heel-pads. Fed by ♂ and ♀.

Technical diagnosis. Ridgway, pt. 6, 1914: 360.

Classification. Peters, 6, 1948: 3–9.

References. Cory, pt. 2, no. 2, 1919: 381–390.

P. L. Sclater, A Monograph of the Jacamars and Puff-birds, London, 1879–1882.

P. L. Sclater, Fam. Galbulidae, Wytsman's *Genera Avium,* pt. 10, 1909 (with col. pl.).

A F. Skutch, Life-history of the Black-chinned Jacamar, *Auk,* 54, 1937: 135–146, pls. 7–8.

BUCCONIDAE

Puffbird family (30 species)

Fig. 96. White-necked Puffbird (*Notharcus macrorhynchos*). Total length $9\frac{1}{2}$ in. (241 mm.).

Physical characteristics. Length—139 to 317 mm. ($5\frac{1}{2}$ to $12\frac{1}{2}$ in.). Plumage—thick and loose-webbed; brown (or black) and white, sometimes with chestnut or gray; often streaked and spotted; throat often white or pale buff; broad breast band in many spp. Bill (often red or yellow) large and strong, rounded, almost straight to markedly decurved and hooked, with tip of maxilla sometimes bifid. Conspicuous rictal bristles. Wings rounded (exc. *Chelidoptera*); tail medium to long. Legs short; feet zygodactyl. Sexes alike or nearly so.

Range. Mainland from s. Mexico (Oaxaca) to s. Brazil and Paraguay. Habitat—tropical forests. Nonmigratory.

Habits. Usually solitary. Arboreal. Very stolid and sedentary (exc. *Chelidoptera,* which has long pointed wings and flies strongly). Capture insects on the wing or pick them from ground or trees during brief sallies from a perch. Voice (rarely heard)—low peeps, thin whistles, a high-pitched *tzeeee tzeeee,* a twittering song.

Food. Insects.

Breeding. Nest (sometimes lined with grass or leaves) is excavated by ♂ and ♀—holes in arboreal termite nests or banks or tunnels (up to 1.5 m. long) in level ground, with leaves and sticks piled around entrance by some spp.

Eggs. 2 to 3; glossy white. Incubated by ♂ and ♀.

Young. Nidicolous. No down. Fed by ♂ and ♀ (?).

Technical diagnosis. Ridgway, pt. 6, 1914: 370–371.

Classification. Peters, 6, 1948: 10–23.

References.
P. L. Sclater, A Monograph of the Jacamars and Puff-birds, London, 1879–1882.

G. K. Cherrie, A Contribution to the Ornithology of the Orinoco Region, *Mus. Brooklyn Inst. Arts and Sci., Sci. Bull.,* 2, no. 6, 1916: 319–324.

G. Hollister and W. Beebe, The Secret Of The Swallow-winged Puff-bird, *N. Y. Zool. Soc. Bull.,* 30, 1927: 115–119.

A. F. Skutch, Life History Notes on Puff-birds, *Wils. Bull.,* 60, 1948: 81–97.

F. Haverschmidt, Notes on the Swallow-wing, *Chelidoptera tenebrosa* in Surinam, *Condor,* 52, 1950: 74–77.

CAPITONIDAE

Barbet family (72 species)

Fig. 97. Black-spotted Barbet (*Capito niger*). Total length 7 in. (177 mm.).

Physical characteristics. Length—89 to 317 mm. (3½ to 12½ in.). Plumage—bright green, olive, brown, or black, boldly marked (esp. on head and breast) with solid areas of bright yellow, red, blue, gray, white (many spp. brilliantly multicolored). Some spp. conspicuously spotted; some uniformly dull-colored. Most spp. have tufts of feathers over the nostrils and/or well-developed rictal and chin bristles. Bill large and heavy, somewhat curved, pointed. Head large; body heavy. Wings short to medium; rounded. Tail short to medium. Legs short and strong; feet large, zygodactyl. Sexes alike in most spp.

Range. Costa Rica, Panama, and n.w. S. America; Africa (s. of Sahara), India, Burma, Siam, Indo-China, Malaysia, and the Philippines. Nonmigratory.

Habits. Usually solitary. Arboreal. Perch long in one spot. Flight weak. Voice—typically harsh single notes indefinitely repeated; also low whistling calls.

Food. Fruit, insects.

Breeding. A few spp. somewhat colonial. Nest in holes which they excavate in trees, or in holes in banks (*Trachyphonus*); no nest lining.

Eggs. 2 to 4; white. Incubated by ♂ and ♀.

Young. Nidicolous. No down. Cared for by ♂ and ♀.

Technical diagnosis. Ridgway, pt. 6, 1914: 310–311. (See also P. R. Lowe, *Ibis,* 1946: 118.)

Classification. Peters, 6, 1948: 24–63 (78 spp.).

References. Baker, *Fauna,* 4, 1927: 102–130; Bannerman, 3, 1933: xxxiv–xxxv, 361–403, col. pl. 12.

C. H. T. and G. F. L. Marshall, A Monograph of the Capitonidae, London, 1870–1871.

A. F. Skutch, The Life-History of the Prong-billed Barbet, *Auk,* 61, 1944: 61–88.

S. Dillon Ripley, The Barbets, *Auk,* 62, 1945: 542–563. See also *Auk,* 63, 1946: 452–453 (Ripley); 384–388 (R. E. Moreau); 481 (C. M. N. White).

Synonym: Megalaemidae.

INDICATORIDAE

Honeyguide family (11 species)

Fig. 98. Greater Honeyguide (*Indicator indicator*). Total length $7\frac{1}{2}$ in. (190 mm.).

Physical characteristics. Length—108 to 203 mm. ($4\frac{1}{4}$ to 8 in.). Plumage—brown, olive, and gray above, lighter below; variously streaked, spotted; with small areas of yellow in some spp.; tail marked with white. Bill short; stout and blunt to slender and pointed; nostrils have raised rims. Wings long, pointed; tail somewhat graduated, the outermost rectrix always shorter than the next (*Melichneutes* has lyre-shaped tail). Tarsus rather short; feet zygodactyl; toes strong; claws long, strongly hooked. Sexes unlike in most spp.

Range. Africa s. of Sahara (exc. Madagascar), Himalayas, Burma, Siam, Malaya, Sumatra, and Borneo. Habitat—forest and brush country. Nonmigratory exc. for local movements.

Habits. Solitary. Arboreal. Flight rapid; direct or undulating. Some spp. lead man (and other mammals) to stores of wild honey. Some spp. hawk insects. Voice—harsh squeak, loud clear whistle, chattering and croaking notes.

Food. Insects (in some spp., largely bees and their larvae), honey, beeswax.

Breeding. Parasitic in all spp. for which data are available. Eggs usually laid in nests of hole- or burrow-nesting birds.

Eggs. Number unknown. White. Incubated by hosts.

Young. Nidicolous. No down. Both mandibles hooked in nestlings of some spp. Cared for by hosts.

Technical diagnosis. H. Friedmann, The Honey-guides, *U. S. Natl. Mus. Bull.,* 208, 1955: 6.

Classification. H. Friedmann, The Honey-guides, *U. S. Natl. Mus. Bull.,* 208, 1955: 6.

References. Baker, *Fauna,* 4, 1927: 131–132; Bannerman, 3, 1933: xxxiv–xxxv, 403–423.

J. P. Chapin, The Birds of the Belgian Congo, Part II, *Bull. Amer. Mus. Nat. Hist.,* 75, 1939: 535–556.

C. J. Skead, Notes on Honeyguides in Southeast Cape Province, South Africa, *Auk,* 68, 1951: 52–62.

RAMPHASTIDAE

Toucan family (37 species)

Fig. 99. Cuvier Toucan (*Ramphastos cuvieri*). Total length 23 in. (584 mm.).

Physical characteristics. Length—305 to 610 mm. (12 to 24 in.). Plumage—lax, usually brightly colored, with bold contrast (black and white, orange, red, yellow, green, blue). Bare skin around eye. Bill usually bright in color; very large (relatively larger in larger species); serrate; with nostrils at extreme base. Tongue very long, narrow, and fringed. Wings short and rounded. Tail usually rather long, rounded to extremely graduate. Legs strong, feet zygodactyl. Sexes alike in most spp.

Range. Vera Cruz s. to Brazil, Paraguay, and n. Argentina. Habitat—forests. Altitudinal migration in some spp.

Habits. Rather gregarious. Arboreal. Restless, active. Flight weak. "Mob" birds of prey. Voice (often noisy)—a variety of croaks, shrill calls, and harsh undiversified "songs."

Food. Fruit, large insects, nestlings of smaller birds, lizards, etc.

Breeding. Nest in unlined tree cavity, natural or made by other birds.

Eggs. 2 to 4; white, glossy. Incubated by ♂ and ♀.

Young. Nidicolous. Naked. With heel-pads. Cared for by ♂ and ♀.

Technical diagnosis. Ridgway, pt. 6, 1914: 327–329; P. R. Lowe, *Ibis,* 1946: 119.

Classification. Peters, 6, 1948: 70–85.

References. J. Gould, Monograph of the Ramphastidae, London, 1833–35; 2nd ed., 1852–54; Suppl., 1855.

J. Van Tyne, The Life History of the Toucan Ramphastos brevicarinatus, *Univ. Mich. Mus. Zool. Misc. Publ. No. 19,* 1929.

H. O. Wagner, Notes on the Life History of the Emerald Toucanet, *Wils. Bull.,* 56, 1944: 65–76.

A. F. Skutch, Life History of the Blue-throated Toucanet, *Wils. Bull.,* 56, 1944: 133–151.

Synonym: Rhamphastidae.

PICIDAE

Woodpecker family (208 species)

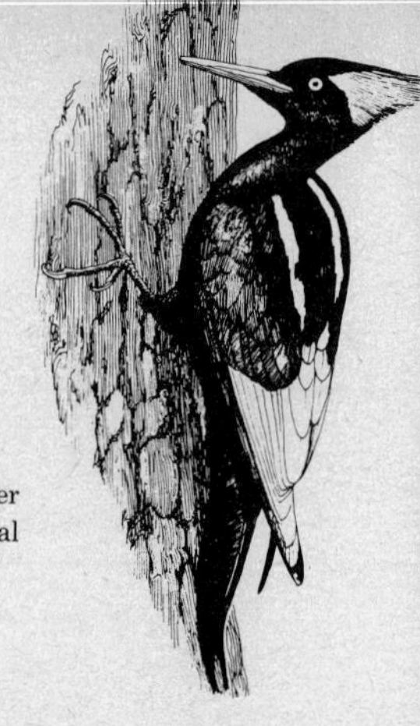

Fig. 100. Imperial Woodpecker (*Campephilus imperialis*). Total length 23 in. (584 mm.).

Physical characteristics. Length—89 to 559 mm. ($3\frac{1}{2}$ to 22 in.). Plumage—black, white, yellow, red, brown, green. Red or yellow on the head of many spp. Many are barred, spotted, or streaked, esp. below; some are crested. Bill strong; typically straight and chisel-like. Head large; neck slender but very strong. Wings strong, rather rounded; tail rounded or wedge-shaped, the rectrices stiff and pointed (exc. in Picumninae). Legs short; feet 3-toed, or 4-toed and zygodactyl. Sexes unlike in most spp.

Range. World-wide (exc. the extreme n., Madagascar, the Papuan Region, Australia, and most oceanic islands). Most spp. nonmigratory.

Habits. Solitary. Typically arboreal. Flight strong but not sustained; undulating except in largest spp. Bore into wood (or earth) for food. Cling to tree trunks, bracing with the tail (rarely perch). Voice—loud and harsh in most spp.; some have "laughing" or ringing cries. Drumming with the bill partly replaces voice.

Food. Insects; fruits, nuts; sap of trees.

Breeding. Nest (usually freshly excavated) a tree cavity or hole in bank, without lining. (*Colaptes rupicola* nests colonially.)

Eggs. 2 to 8; glossy, white. Incubated by ♂ and ♀.

Young. Nidicolous. Naked or (rarely) with sparse down. Cared for by ♂ and ♀.

Technical diagnosis. Ridgway, pt. 6, 1914: 5.

Classification. Peters, 6, 1948: 88–232.

References. Bent, No. 174; Witherby, 2, 1938: 276–292; Baker, *Fauna,* 4, 1927: 2–98.

A. Malherbe, Monographie des Picidées . . . , Metz, 4 vols., 1859–1862.

W. H. Burt, Adaptive modifications in the Woodpeckers, *Univ. Calif. Publ. Zool.,* 32, no. 8, 1930.

A. Pynnönen, Beiträge zur Kenntnis der Biologie Finnischer Spechte, *Ann. Zool. Soc. Zool.-Bot. Fenn. Vanamo,* 7, no. 2; 9, no. 4, 1939–43.

J. T. Tanner, The Ivory-billed Woodpecker, *Natl. Aud. Soc. Research Rept. No. 1,* 1942.

A. F. Skutch, Life History of the Olivaceous Piculet and related forms, *Ibis,* 90, 1948: 433–449.

J. Dorst, Notes sur la biologie des Colaptes, *Colaptes rupicola . . . , L'Ois. et Rev. Franç. d'Ornith.,* 26, 1956: 118–125.

JYNGIDAE

Wryneck family (2 species)

Fig. 101. Eurasian Wryneck (*Jynx torquilla*). Total length 6½ in. (165 mm.).

Physical characteristics. Length—165 to 177 mm. (6½ to 7 in.). Plumage—soft; brown, gray, and black in mottled, cryptic pattern. Under parts paler: throat, breast, and under tail coverts buff (barred with black) or chestnut (unmarked); belly white or pale buff, barred or streaked with black. Bill slender, pointed. Wings rounded; tail rather long, the feathers soft and rounded at tips. Legs short; feet 4-toed, zygodactyl. Sexes alike.

Range. Eurasia (exc. extreme n.) and Africa (exc. c. part). Northern forms migratory.

Habits. Solitary (but small groups form during migration and in winter). Arboreal. Flight slow and undulating. Twisting motions of the neck are responsible for the common name. Remain motionless when alarmed. Obtain food largely from surface of trees. Usually perch across branches in passerine fashion; sometimes also cling to tree trunks (but without bracing with tail). Voice—a shrill *quee-quee-quee* monotonously repeated; a harsh screaming cry; hissing notes.

Food. Insects; fruit rarely.

Breeding. Nest in natural cavity of tree or bank, or a crevice in wall; no nest lining.

Eggs. 2 to 12; white. Incubated chiefly by ♀.

Young. Nidicolous. Naked. Heel-pads. Cared for by ♂ and ♀.

Technical diagnosis. Ridgway, pt. 6, 1914: 4.

Classification. Peters, 6, 1948: 86–88.

References. Witherby, 2, 1938: 292–296; Bannerman, 3, 1933: 462–466.

H. Siewert, Beitrage zur Biologie des Wendehalses, *Beitr. Fortpfl. Vögel,* 4, 1928: 47–49, pls. 1–3.

J. Bussmann, Beitrage zur Kenntnis der Brutbiologie des Wendehalses (*Jynx torquilla torquilla*), *Arch. suisses d'Orn.,* 1, 1941: 467–480.

Synonym: Yungidae.

EURYLAIMIDAE

Broadbill family (14 species)

Fig. 102. Black and Yellow Broadbill (*Eurylaimus ochromalus*). Total length 6 in. (152 mm.).

Physical characteristics. Length—127 to 280 mm. (5 to 11 in.). Plumage—lax; bright green and blue (or black and pale vinous to crimson), marked with black, white, and yellow or orange; gray and chestnut, marked with blue; or brown and buff (plain or streaked), marked with black, white, and small areas of yellow. Most spp. have white dorsal patch, concealed exc. in flight. Bill (largely covered by short crest in some spp.) broad and flattened, with wide gape; moderate to extremely large and heavy; hooked. Eyes large; head broad; body stout. Wings short to long, rounded; tail very short and square to long, slender, and graduated. Legs short; feet strong, syndactyl; toes (incl. hallux) long; claws long, strongly hooked. Sexes unlike in most spp.

Range. Central and s. Africa; Himalayas of India through s. China, Indo-China, and the Malay Peninsula to Sumatra, Java, and Borneo; Philippines. Habitat—forest edges, open wooded country. Nonmigratory.

Habits. Solitary or gregarious. Some spp. crepuscular. Arboreal. Unsuspicious. Lethargic exc. for short flights to catch insects on the wing. Voice—churring notes; clear whistles.

Food. Insects; fruit; frogs and lizards.

Breeding. Nest a large pear-shaped pendent structure of grass, etc., decorated with streamers of moss, etc.; with a porched entrance at side; usually placed over water.

Eggs. 2 to 8 (usually 3 to 5); white to salmon, immaculate or spotted. Incubated by ♂ and ♀.

Young. Nidicolous. Naked at hatching. Cared for by ♂ and ♀?

Technical diagnosis. Baker, *Fauna,* 2nd ed., 3, 1926: 459–460.

Classification. Peters, 7, 1951: 3–13.

References. Baker, *Fauna,* 3, 1926: 459–476; Baker, *Nidification,* 3, 1934: 260–271; Bannerman, 4, 1936: xx–xxi, 5–12.

E. Hartert, Fam. Eurylaemidae, Wytsman's *Genera Avium,* pt. 1, 1905 (col. pl.).

DENDROCOLAPTIDAE

Woodcreeper family (48 species)

Fig. 103. Ivory-billed Woodcreeper (*Xiphorhynchus flavigaster*). Total length $10\frac{1}{2}$ in. (266 mm.).

Physical characteristics. Length—146 to 368 mm. ($5\frac{3}{4}$ to $14\frac{1}{2}$ in.). Plumage—olive-brown or grayish brown to cinnamon; most spp. streaked (sometimes also barred) or spotted with black, gray, buffy, white, esp. on head, shoulders, and under parts; wings and tail in most spp. rufous. Bill typically strong, laterally compressed, short and straight to very long and curved. Wings rather long, rounded. Tail long; rounded or graduated; the feathers with very strong, rigid, sharp-pointed shafts (the tips curved and abruptly attenuate in some spp.). Legs short; feet and claws strong; anterior toes adherent basally. Sexes alike or nearly so.

Range. Mexico, Central and S. America (exc. extreme s.). Habitat—forest or brushland. Largely nonmigratory.

Habits. Solitary, or in mixed flocks of other spp. Arboreal. Flight strong but not sustained. Climb tree trunks (bracing with tail) in search of food, then fly to base of another tree to repeat the process. Some spp. occasionally feed on ground. Voice—loud, ringing, repetitive songs; a musical trill; harsh alarm notes.

Food. Insects, spiders, amphibians.

Breeding. Nest in tree cavities, natural or made by other birds (lined with bark, leaves, etc.).

Eggs. 2 to 3; white or greenish white, immaculate. Incubated by ♂ and ♀.

Young. Nidicolous. Downy. Cared for by ♂ and ♀.

Technical diagnosis. Ridgway, pt. 5, 1911: 4, 224–226.

Classification. Peters, 7, 1951: 13–57.

References. H. von Ihering, The Classification of the Family Dendrocolaptidae, *Auk,* 32, 1915: 145–153.

A. Wetmore, Observations on the Birds of Argentina, Paraguay, Uruguay, and Chile, *U. S. Natl. Mus. Bull.,* 133, 1926: 234–242.

D. R. Dickey and A. J. van Rossem, The Birds of El Salvador, *Field Mus. Nat. Hist., Zool. Ser.,* 23, 1938: 321–328.

A. F. Skutch, Life History of the Allied Woodhewer, *Condor,* 47, 1945: 85–94.

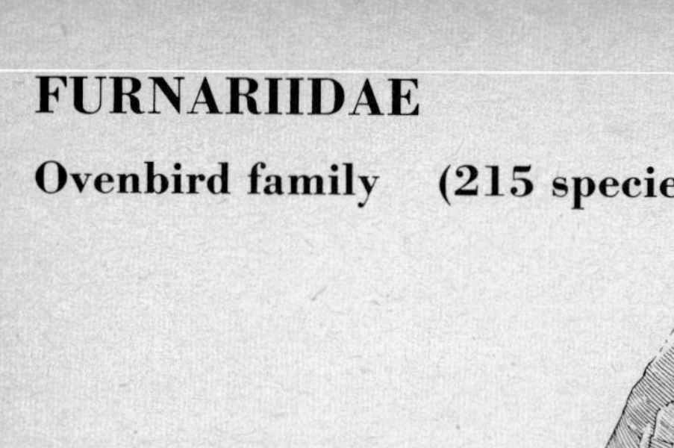

FURNARIIDAE

Ovenbird family (215 species)

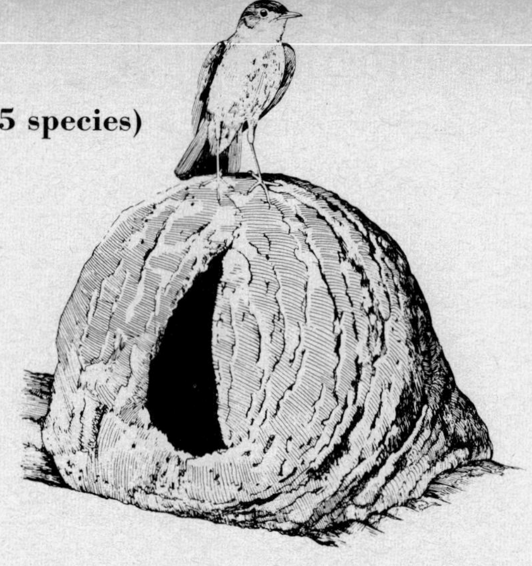

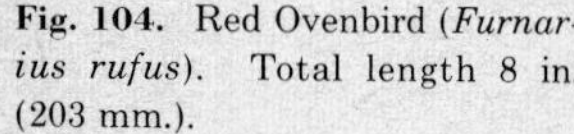

Fig. 104. Red Ovenbird (*Furnarius rufus*). Total length 8 in. (203 mm.).

Physical characteristics. Length—120 to 280 mm. ($4\frac{3}{4}$ to 11 in.). Plumage—very dark brown (sometimes with slate or black), olive-brown to cinnamon, buff, or gray. Most spp. show little pattern, but a few are streaked, spotted, or scaled; some have conspicuous light patch on spread wing; many have contrasting crown and/or throat. Under parts lighter in most spp. (largely white in some), marked with yellow in a few. Some spp. crested. Bill rather slender; very short to long; straight, curved, or (rarely) upturned. Wings short and rounded to rather long and pointed. Tail short to long (extremely long in *Sylviorthorhynchus*), rounded to acuminate, the feathers pointed in many spp. but tips soft in most. Legs short to medium. Anterior toes basally adherent. Sexes alike or nearly so.

Range. Southern Mexico, Central and S. America. Habitat—forest to semidesert; seashore, mountain cliffs, and rocky slopes. Most spp. nonmigratory.

Habits. Solitary or gregarious. Terrestrial or arboreal. Flight weak to strong, but not sustained. Many terrestrial forms walk. A few spp. climb tree trunks (some brace with tail). Voice (many spp. noisy)—harsh scolding notes; loud whistled calls; trilled songs.

Food. Insects and spiders; also (some spp.) seeds, crustacea.

Breeding. Well-lined nest in hole in ground, bank, or rocks; or in natural tree cavity; domed nest of mud on tree, post, or building; domed nest of grass or sticks in reeds, or bushes, or on ground.

Eggs. 2 to 5 (rarely 6); white to pale blue or bluish green; immaculate. Incubated by ♂ and ♀.

Young. Nidicolous. With down. Cared for by ♂ and ♀.

Technical diagnosis. Ridgway, pt. 5, 1911: 4, 157–158.

Classification. Peters, 7, 1951: 58–153.

References. W. H. Hudson, *Birds of La Plata,* London, vol. 1, 1920: 195–235, col. pl.

A. Wetmore, Observations on the Birds of Argentina, Paraguay, Uruguay, and Chile, *U. S. Natl. Mus. Bull.,* 133, 1926: 242–283.

J. D. Goodall *et al., Las Aves de Chile,* Buenos Aires, vol. 1, 1946: 199–266.

A. F. Skutch, Life History of the Chestnut-tailed Automolus, *Condor,* 54, 1952: 93–100.

FORMICARIIDAE

Antbird family

(222 species)

Fig. 105. Black-faced Ant-thrush (*Formicarius analis*). Total length 7½ in. (190 mm.).

Physical characteristics. Length—95 to 368 mm. (3¾ to 14½ in.). Plumage—loose-webbed; black, gray, browns (sometimes with white, rarely yellowish), in solid areas of color or (esp. below) streaked or strongly barred; ♀ commonly browner than ♂. Some spp. have bare red or blue orbital skin; some are crested; some have feathers of lower back long, dense, and with concealed white or rufous spotting. Bill strong, slightly to strongly hooked. Wings short and rounded; tail short to long. Legs short (arboreal spp.) to long (terrestrial spp.). Anterior toes somewhat adherent basally. Sexes unlike in most spp.

Range. Southern Mexico, Central America, and S. America to c. Argentina. Habitat —forests or brushland. Nonmigratory.

Habits. Usually solitary or in pairs. Arboreal or terrestrial. Flight weak. Some spp. accompany ant armies and prey on the insects flushed by them. Voice—sharp, often harsh, calls; low, rather melodious songs; or loud, mellow whistling notes.

Food. Insects.

Breeding. Open, cuplike nest, typically semipendent in horizontal fork of a bush or low tree; simple cup on or near ground; covered nest on ground; or lined cavity, usually in a tree.

Eggs. Usually 2; white or buffy, speckled or streaked with brown, red, or black. Incubated by ♂ and ♀.

Young. Nidicolous. With down (*Formicarius*) or naked. Cared for by ♂ and ♀.

Technical diagnosis. Ridgway, pt. 5, 1911: 8–9.

Classification. Peters, 7, 1951: 153–273.

References. A. F. Skutch, A Nesting of the Slaty Antshrike (*Thamnophilus punctatus*) on Barro Colorado Island. *Auk,* 51, 1934: 8–16, pl. 3.

J. Van Tyne, The Nest of the Antbird *Gymnopithys bicolor bicolor, Univ. Mich. Mus. Zool. Occ. Papers No. 491,* 1944: 1–5, pl. 1.

A. F. Skutch, On the Habits and Nest of the Ant-thrush *Formicarius analis, Wils. Bull.,* 57, 1945: 122–128.

A. F. Skutch, Life Histories of Two Panamanian Antbirds, *Condor,* 48, 1946: 16–28.

CONOPOPHAGIDAE

Antpipit family (11 species)

Fig. 106. D'Orbigny Antpipit (*Conopophaga ardesiaca*). Total length 5 in. (127 mm.).

Physical characteristics. Length—102 to 139 mm. (4 to 5½ in.). Plumage—soft and loose-textured; long and dense on lower back. Brown or olive-green above; brown, gray, or white below. Crown and/or throat demarked by contrasting color in several spp. Conspicuous white line behind eye in most spp. of *Conopophaga.* Bill rather broad, flattened, and slightly hooked. Head large; neck short; body stout. Wings short and rounded; tail short to medium. Legs short to rather long; feet large. Sexes rather similar.

Range. South America (exc. the extreme n.w., the w. coast, and the s. third of the continent). Habitat—forests. Nonmigratory.

Habits. Solitary. Flight weak. Timid and retiring. Feed on ground, scratching in the leaves. Voice—simple calls; whistling notes; a sharp *tsheep.*

Food. Insects.

Breeding. Nest of sticks and moss, on the ground or in low bushes.

Eggs. 2; cream-colored or buff, with pink or dark brown streaks and spots. Incubation not described.

Young. Not described.

Technical diagnosis. Ridgway, pt. 5, 1911: 4.

Classification. Peters, 7, 1951: 273–278.

References. W. A. Forbes, On some Points in the Anatomy of the Genus *Conopophaga,* and its Systematic Position, *Proc. Zool. Soc. London,* 1881: 435–438.

F. P. Penard and A. P. Penard, *De Vogels van Guyana,* Paramaribo, vol. 2, 1910: 339–342.

C. Chubb, On the Birds of Paraguay, *Ibis,* 1910: 517–519.

RHINOCRYPTIDAE

Tapaculo family (26 species)

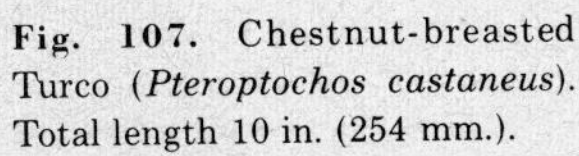

Fig. 107. Chestnut-breasted Turco (*Pteroptochos castaneus*). Total length 10 in. (254 mm.).

Physical characteristics. Length—114 to 254 mm. ($4\frac{1}{2}$ to 10 in.). Plumage—soft and loose-webbed; brown, gray, or black. Some spp. with areas of reddish brown and/or barring below; one sp. conspicuously spotted with white above and below. One sp. crested; one with loral plumes. Bill sharp-pointed; rather slender (in small spp.) to stout; culmen flat in *Acropternis.* Body compact. Wings rounded; tail short to rather long. Feet and claws large and strong. Sexes alike or nearly so.

Range. Mountains of Costa Rica, through Panama; w. S. America, and e. across s. Brazil to State of Baía. Habitat—dense forest undergrowth; grassland; semiarid brushy country. Nonmigratory.

Habits. Solitary or in small groups. Terrestrial; walk rather than hop (forest spp. "creep about like mice"); run with great speed (commonly holding tail erect); scratch like hens for food. Fly rarely. Very secretive. Voice—loud whistles; harsh barking calls; loud, deep *chirrup;* crowing songs; musical notes in descending scale.

Food. Insects, seeds.

Breeding. Nest of grass, moss, etc., in burrow in bank, in hole in cliff, or in abandoned mammal burrow; in hollow trunk or in crevice between bark and trunk; or domed nest in bush.

Eggs. 2 to 4; white. Incubation not described.

Young. Nidicolous. With down. Cared for by ♂ and ♀.

Technical diagnosis. Ridgway, pt. 5, 1911: 4–5.

Classification. Peters, 7, 1951: 278–289.

References. A. A. Lane, Field-Notes on the Birds of Chili, *Ibis,* 1897: 40–46.

A. Wetmore, Observations on the Birds of Argentina, Paraguay, Uruguay, and Chile, *U. S. Natl. Mus. Bull.,* 133, 1926: 289–293.

C. E. Hellmayr, The Birds of Chile, *Field Mus. Nat. Hist., Zool. Ser.,* 19, 1932: 214–230.

Francisco Behn K., Contribucion al estudio del *Pteroptochos castaneus* . . . , *Hornero,* 8, 1944: 464–470, col. pl.

J. D. Goodall *et al., Las Aves de Chile,* Buenos Aires, vol. 1, 1946: 267–287.

Synonyms: Pteroptochidae, Hylactidae.

COTINGIDAE

Cotinga family (90 species)

Fig. 108. Umbrellabird (*Cephalopterus ornatus*). Total length 20 in. (508 mm.).

Physical characteristics. Length—89 to 457 mm. ($3\frac{1}{2}$ to 18 in.). Plumage—in many spp. gray or brown, with little pattern; in others white, grayish white, black, or largely brilliant red, purple, blue, or green. Some spp. with bare skin or long erectile caruncles on head, or with bare gular pouch. *Cephalopterus* has great, umbrella-like crest; *Rupicola,* a strange, laterally compressed one. Bill moderately long and compressed to short and flattened. Wings short and rounded to rather long, with one or more primaries highly modified in many spp.; tail short to rather long (deeply forked in one sp.). Legs short; feet large. Sexes alike or unlike.

Range. Extreme s. edge of Arizona and Texas; Mexico, Central America, Jamaica, S. America (exc. s. third). Habitat—forests. Largely nonmigratory.

Habits. Usually solitary. Arboreal. Flight medium to strong. Voice—loud bell-like call; grunting sounds; some musical utterances, others with a "mechanical quality."

Food. Fruit; insects.

Breeding. Nest a lined tree cavity; shallow cup on branch; bulky covered nest on, or suspended from, branch tip; shallow mud nest plastered on steep rocky wall.

Eggs. 1 to 6; white to dark-colored, heavily marked. Incubated by ♀.

Young. Nidicolous. With down or naked. Cared for by ♂ and ♀.

Technical diagnosis. Ridgway, pt. 4, 1907: 769–771.

Classification. Hellmayr, pt. 6, 1929: 92–246 (include Rupicolidae).

References. Bent, No. 179: 1–11.

E. A. Goeldi, On the Nesting of *Phibalura flavirostris* . . . , *Ibis,* 1894: 484–494, illus.

A. F. Skutch, Life History of the Costa Rican Tityra, *Auk,* 63, 1946: 327–362.

A. F. Skutch, Life History of the White-winged Becard, *Auk,* 71, 1954: 113–129, pl. 9.

Helmut Sick, Zur Biologie des amazonischen Schirmvogels, *Cephalopterus ornatus, Jour. f. Ornith.,* 95, 1954: 233–244, pls. 5–6.

Synonymy: The Rupicolidae are included.

PIPRIDAE

Manakin family (59 species)

Fig. 109. Yellow-thighed Manakin (*Pipra mentalis*). Total length $4\frac{1}{2}$ in. (114 mm.).

Physical characteristics. Length (exc. for long central rectrices of *Chiroxiphia linearis*)—83 to 159 mm. ($3\frac{1}{4}$ to $6\frac{1}{4}$ in.). Plumage (♂) usually in a solid color (commonly black) with areas, esp. on crown or throat, of white or of bright, lustrous colors (scarlet, orange, yellow, blue); feathers of throat or crown elongated in some spp. Bill short and broad, slightly hooked. Wings short; tail typically short, with (in a few spp.) some elongated feathers. Legs short; 3rd toe fused at base with 2nd or 4th. Sexes usually different; ♀ typically olive-green.

Range. From s. Mexico to Paraguay. Habitat—humid tropical forests. Nonmigratory.

Habits. Solitary (occasionally form small flocks). Flight rapid and direct. ♂♂ have very striking and varied dance display (alone or in a group). Voice—short, rather low calls (louder, more spectacular sounds are made by remiges in many spp.).

Food. Fruit; some insects.

Breeding. Frail, semipensile nest in low bushes. Built by ♀.

Eggs. 2; spotted. Incubated by ♀.

Young. Nidicolous. Sparse down. Cared for by ♀.

Technical diagnosis. Ridgway, pt. 4, 1907: 723.

Classification. Hellmayr, pt. 6, 1929: 3–92.

References. C. E. Hellmayr, Fam. Pipridae, Wytsman's *Genera Avium*, pt. 9, 1910.

F. M. Chapman, The Courtship of Gould's Manakin (*Manacus vitellinus vitellinus*) on Barro Colorado Island, Canal Zone, *Amer. Mus. Nat. Hist. Bull.*, 68, 1935: 471–525.

Helmuth Wagner, Observaciones sobre el comportamiento de *Chiroxiphia linearis* durante su propagacion, *Anales Inst. Biol. Mex.*, 16, 1946: 539–546.

A. F. Skutch, Life History of the Yellow-thighed Manakin, *Auk*, 66, 1949: 1–24, pl. 1.

TYRANNIDAE

Tyrant-flycatcher family (365 species)

Fig. 110. Eastern Kingbird (*Tyrannus tyrannus*). Total length 8 in. (203 mm.).

Physical characteristics. Length—76 to 406 mm. (3 to 16 in.). Plumage—typically gray, brown, or olive-green, but some spp. are largely black, white, or yellow; a few spp. are streaked; many have a partly concealed crown patch of red, yellow, or white. Some spp. are crested. Bill extremely varied but usually rather broad, flattened, and slightly hooked; rictal bristles typically well developed. Wings short and rounded to long and pointed, the outer primaries of some spp. attenuate or much shortened; tail in most spp. medium in length and truncate (in a few spp. some tail feathers are greatly elongated). Legs and feet small and weak (exc. in terrestrial forms). Sexes alike in most spp.

Range. North America (exc. extreme n.) and S. America. Migratory (exc. most tropical forms).

Habits. Typically solitary and arboreal (in s. S. America are some long-legged spp. which are terrestrial and, in some cases, gregarious). Many spp. feed by watching from exposed perch, flying out to capture prey in air or on ground. Voice—many distinctive call notes, but song generally not well developed.

Food. Insects; fruit; small mammals, reptiles, amphibians, and fish.

Breeding. Cuplike nest in tree or on ground; domed nest in tree; pendent nest with entrance in side or bottom; nest in tree cavity or hole in ground; conical nest attached to reeds; covered nests captured from other spp.

Eggs. 2 to 6; white; spotted and/or streaked, or immaculate. Incubated by ♀, sometimes assisted by ♂.

Young. Nidicolous. With down on upper parts. Cared for by ♂ and ♀.

Technical diagnosis. Ridgway, pt. 4, 1907: 335–340.

Classification. Hellmayr, pt. 5, 1927.

References. Bent, No. 179: 11–314.

H. von. Ihering, The Biology of the Tyrannidae with Respect to Their Systematic Arrangement, *Auk*, 21, 1904: 313–322.

W. H. Hudson, *Birds of La Plata*, London, vol. 1, 1920: 135–192, 3 col. pls.

A. F. Skutch, Life History of the Boat-billed Flycatcher, *Auk*, 68, 1951: 30–49.

OXYRUNCIDAE

Sharpbill family (1 species)

Fig. 111. Crested Sharpbill (*Oxyruncus cristatus*). Total length 7 in. (177 mm.).

Physical characteristics. Length—165 to 177 mm. ($6\frac{1}{2}$ to 7 in.). Plumage—olive-green above; crown brownish black with light barring on forehead and sides of head; a partly concealed median crest of scarlet or orange-red feathers; wings and tail blackish brown, with green edging; under parts white or yellowish white, barred and spotted with brownish black. Bill rather long, straight, and acuminate; with short, fine, bristly feathers at the base. Wings rather long and rounded, the outer primary (at least usually) serrated in ♂; tail moderately long, truncate. Legs short; toes stout and strong; claws acute. Sexes similar, but ♀ may have paler crest.

Range. Costa Rica and Panama; British Guiana; s.e. Brazil and Paraguay. Habitat—humid forest. Nonmigratory?

Habits. Solitary. Flight strong.

Food. Fruit.

Breeding. Nest not described.

Eggs. Not described.

Young. Not described.

Technical diagnosis. Ridgway, pt. 4, 1907: 332.

Classification. Hellmayr, pt. 6, 1929: 1–3; F. M. Chapman, *Amer. Mus. Novitates, No. 1047,* 1939.

References. H. L. Clark, Anatomical Notes on Todus, Oxyruncus and Spindalis, *Auk,* 30, 1913: 402–406.

C. Chubb, *The Birds of British Guiana,* London, vol. 2, 1921: 239–240.

O. Bangs and T. Barbour, Birds from Darien, *Bull. Mus. Comp. Zoöl.,* 65, 1922: 220–221.

F. M. Chapman, The Riddle of *Oxyruncus, Amer. Mus. Novitates, No. 1047,* 1939.

Synonym: Oxyrhamphidae.

PHYTOTOMIDAE

Plantcutter family (3 species)

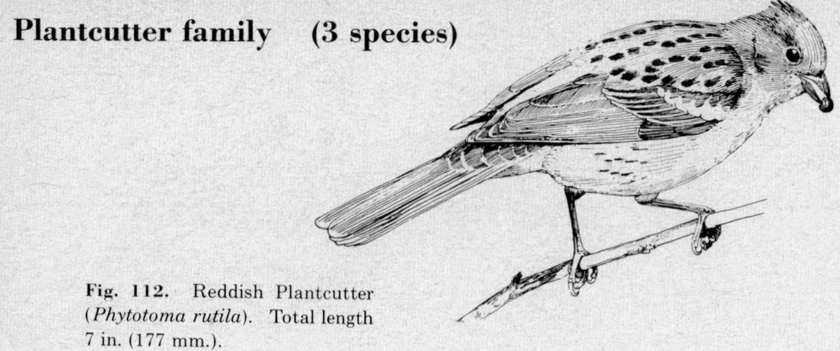

Fig. 112. Reddish Plantcutter (*Phytotoma rutila*). Total length 7 in. (177 mm.).

Physical characteristics. Length—165 to 177 mm. ($6\frac{1}{2}$ to 7 in.). Plumage—gray or brown above, streaked with black; crown and under parts rufous to brick-red; wings and tail black, marked with white. Crested. Bill short, heavy, and conical; finely serrated. Body stocky. Wings short, pointed; tail rather long. Legs short; feet large. Sexes unlike.

Range. Western Peru through Chile, Bolivia, and Argentina to about lat. 40°. Habitat—open brush country; cultivated fields and gardens. Migratory in part,

Habits. Usually solitary or in small flocks; sometimes gregarious in nonbreeding season. Flight weak and undulating; not sustained. Voice—loud harsh calls and metallic rasping cries; squeaking and croaking notes.

Food. Fruits, buds, shoots, leaves (also insects?).

Breeding. Round, open nest of twigs lined with fibers, placed in high bushes or in trees.

Eggs. 2 to 4; bluish green, flecked with black or dark brown. Incubated by ♀.

Young. Nidicolous. Not otherwise described. Fed by ♂ and ♀.

Technical diagnosis. Ridgway, pt. 4, 1907: 330–331.

Classification. Hellmayr, pt. 6, 1929: 247–250.

References. G. R. Gray, *The Genera of Birds,* London, vol. 2, 1849: [390], pl. 95.

A. A. Lane, Field-Notes on the Birds of Chili, *Ibis,* 1897: 35–36.

Rafael Barros V., La Rara (Phytotoma rara, Mol.), *An. Zool. Aplicada,* 6, 1919: 11–16, pl. 2.

W. H. Hudson, *Birds of La Plata,* London, vol. 1, 1920: 193–195.

W. Küchler, Anatomisch Untersuchungen an *Phytotoma rara* Mol., *Jour. f. Ornith.,* 84, 1936: 352–362.

J. D. Goodall *et al., Las Aves de Chile,* Buenos Aires, vol. 1, 1946: 197–198.

PITTIDAE

Pitta family (23 species)

Fig. 113. Hooded Pitta (*Pitta sordida*). Total length 7 in. (177 mm.).

Physical characteristics. Length—152 to 280 mm. (6 to 11 in.). Plumage—loose-webbed. Most spp. with bright, contrasted coloration; solid patches of scarlet, blue, green, purple, chestnut, tan, white, black. Some spp. heavily barred below, or with white wing patches; some largely dull-colored. Lustrous turquoise-blue on wing coverts and rump of several spp. Some forms with slight bushy crest or with "ear tufts." Bill strong, slightly curved. Neck short; body stout. Wings short and rounded; tail very short. Legs long and strong; feet large. Sexes alike or unlike.

Range. South-central Africa, India, Burma, Siam, Indo-China, s.e. China, East Indies, n. and e. Australia, and e. to Solomons. Habitat—forests or brushland. Some spp. migratory.

Habits. Solitary. Terrestrial, but roost in trees and perch to sing. Flight strong. Hop when on ground. Voice—loud whistling calls; grunting sounds; a whinny.

Food. Insects and other invertebrates; small vertebrates.

Breeding. Loosely constructed, domed nest on ground or in low branches.

Eggs. 2 to 7; white or buffy, speckled and blotched. Incubated by ♂ and ♀.

Young. Nidicolous. Naked. Cared for by ♂ and ♀.

Technical diagnosis. Baker, *Fauna,* 3, 1926: 441.

Classification. R. B. Sharpe, Hand-list of the Genera and Species of Birds, British Museum, 3, 1901: 179–185 [but omit *Mellopitta*].

References. Baker, *Fauna,* 3, 1926: 441–458; Baker, *Nidification,* 3, 1934: 250–260.

D. G. Elliot, A Monograph of the Pittidae, London, 1893–1895.

J. Delacour, The First Rearing of Pittas in Captivity, *Proc. 8th Internatl. Ornith. Congress, 1938:* 717–719.

ACANTHISITTIDAE

New Zealand Wren family (4 species)

Fig. 114. New Zealand Bushwren (*Xenicus longipes*). Total length 4 in. (102 mm.).

Physical characteristics. Length—76 to 102 mm. (3 to 4 in.). Plumage—soft; dull green or olive-brown above, darker on head, yellowish on rump; white, gray, or pale purplish brown below, yellowish on sides; wings black, olive-green, or brown, edged with green (barred with yellow in one sp.); tail black or olive-green; white superciliary stripe. Bill straight, very slender, and pointed. Wings rather short; tail extremely short, truncate. Legs and toes long and slender, the outer and middle toes joined basally; claws long (esp. on hallux), very acute. Sexes unlike.

Range. New Zealand. Habitat—forest, scrub. Migratory in part.

Habits. Solitary, or in small groups. Mainly arboreal. Flight weak; one sp. (now extinct ?) probably flightless. Very active, running about rocks, tree trunks, and branches in search of insects. Voice—sharp *cheep;* rasping note.

Food. Insects and their larvae; spiders.

Breeding. Nest a rounded structure of leaves, plant fragments, and feathers, with entrance in side, placed in crevice in tree, log, earth bank, or rocks.

Eggs. 2 to 5; white, immaculate. Incubated by ♂ and ♀.

Young. Nidicolous. Naked at hatching. Fed by ♂ and ♀.

Technical diagnosis. W. A. Forbes, *Proc. Zool. Soc. London,* 1882: 569–571.

Classification. W. R. B. Oliver, *New Zealand Birds,* Wellington, N. Z., 1930: 436–441.

References. W. P. Pycraft, Some Points in the Anatomy of *Acanthidositta chloris,* with some Remarks on the Systematic Position of the Genera *Acanthidositta* and *Xenicus, Ibis,* 1905: 603–621, pl. 13.

J. C. McLean, Field-Notes on some of the Bush-birds of New Zealand, *Ibis,* 1907: 536–540.

H. Guthrie-Smith, *Mutton Birds and Other Birds,* London, 1914: 123–126.

W. R. B. Oliver, *New Zealand Birds,* Wellington, N. Z., 1930: 436–441, col pl. 4.

Synonymy: Xenicidae, Xenicornithidae, and Traversiidae of Mathews.

PHILEPITTIDAE

Asity family (4 species)

Fig. 115. Velvet Asity (*Philepitta castanea*). Total length 5½ in. (139 mm.).

Physical characteristics. Length—102 to 165 mm. (4 to 6½ in.). Plumage—soft; the ♂ of one sp. sooty black, with yellow edge on bend of wing, the other spp. yellow, olive-green, blue above (crown and nape black in ♂ of one sp.), yellow or yellowish green below (immaculate or spotted and scaled with darker). Orbital skin bare in ♂, surmounted by bluish or greenish caruncle. Bill moderately long, slender, and slightly curved, to very long, attenuate, sharp-pointed, and strongly curved. Wing of medium length and rounded; tail short and somewhat rounded. Legs and feet large and strong; claws long and acute. Sexes unlike.

Range. Madagascar. Habitat—forest. Nonmigratory.

Habits. Usually solitary or in pairs; sometimes associated with flocks of other spp. Arboreal. Rather torpid. Flight strong but not sustained. Voice (rarely heard)—soft, thrushlike song; a soft hissing note.

Food. Fruit and buds; nectar; insects and spiders.

Breeding. Nest (*Philepitta*) a pear-shaped pendent structure of moss and palm fiber, placed in trees or high bushes.

Eggs. 3; white to bluish white, immaculate. Incubation not described.

Young. Not described.

Technical diagnosis. W. A. Forbes, *Proc. Zool. Soc. London,* 1880: 387–391; D. Amadon, *L'Ois. et Rev. Franç. d'Ornith.,* 21, 1951: 63.

Classification. D. Amadon, *L'Ois. et Rev. Franç. d'Ornith.,* 21, 1951: 59–63. (The spp. are *Philepitta castanea, P. schlegeli, Neodrepanis coruscans, N. hypoxantha.*)

References. A. Milne Edwards and A. Grandidier, Histoire naturelle des oiseaux, in *Histoire physique, naturelle et politique de Madagascar,* Paris, vol. 12; 1876–1885: 288–291, 295–303; vol. 14: pls. 106–112.

F. Salomonsen, Les Neodrepanis . . . , *L'Ois. et Rev. Franç. d'Ornith.,* 4, 1934: 1–9, pl. opp. p. 391.

A. L. Rand, The Distribution and Habits of Madagascar Birds, *Bull. Amer. Mus. Nat. Hist.,* 72, 1936: 425–427, 472 (*Neodrepanis*).

Synonym: Paictidae.

MENURIDAE

Lyrebird family (2 species)

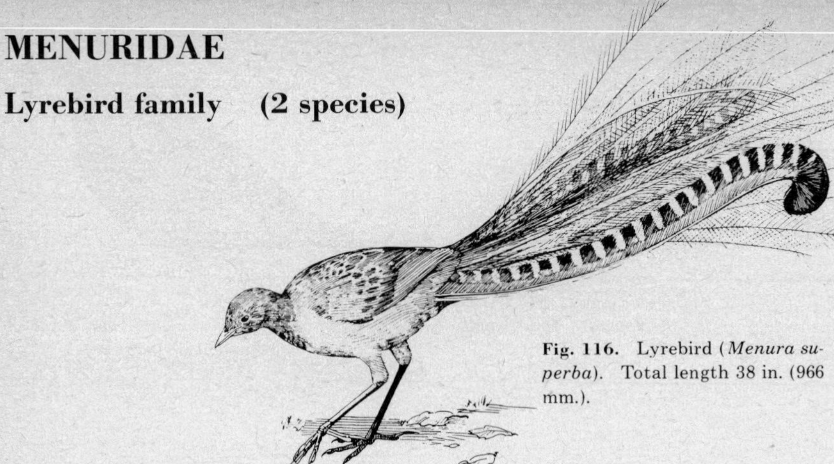

Fig. 116. Lyrebird (*Menura superba*). Total length 38 in. (966 mm.).

Physical characteristics. Length—762 to 1016 mm. (30 to 40 in.). Plumage—sooty brown above, brownish gray below, rufous brown on chin, throat, and wings. Bare space around eye bluish. Bill elongated, conical, sharp-pointed. Neck long. Wings short and rounded. Tail long (elaborate in ♂). Legs and feet large and strong; claws long. Sexes unlike.

Range. Southeastern Australia. Habitat—dense thickets of mountain forests. Nonmigratory.

Habits. Solitary. Terrestrial, but roost in trees. Run rapidly and leap with agility. Fly rarely, but volplane for considerable distances. Build mounds or make scrapes and perform elaborate display dance (♂). Voice—variety of notes and calls. Mimic mechanical sounds as well as voices of other animals.

Food. Mollusca, worms, spiders, insects.

Breeding. Apparently mate for life. Nest a large roofed structure of sticks and roots lined with bark, roots, and down, placed in hollow stump, under rock ledge, in roots of fallen tree, etc., or (more rarely) up to 60 ft. above the ground in a tree.

Eggs. 1; purplish gray, blotched with darker purple and brown. Incubated by ♀.

Young. Nidicolous. Almost naked at hatching; downy later. Cared for by ♀.

Technical diagnosis. Mathews, 7, 1919: 394.

Classification. G. M. Mathews, *Systema Avium Australasianarum,* London, pt. 1, 1927: 425–426.

References. Mathews, 7, 1919: 392–412, pls. 363–365.

A. E. Kitson, Notes on the Victoria Lyre-bird . . . , *Emu,* 5, 1905: 57–67, pls. 5–10.

S. Roberts, Prince Edward's Lyre-Bird at Home, *Emu,* 21, 1922: 242–252, pls. 51–53.

C. Barrett, Menura—Australia's Mockingbird, [*N. Y.*] *Zool. Soc. Bull.,* 30, 1927: 207–216.

T. Tregellas, The Truth About the Lyrebird, *Emu,* 30, 1931: 243–250, pls. 41–46.

L. H. Smith, *The Lyrebirds of Sherbrooke,* Melbourne, 1951.

ATRICHORNITHIDAE

Scrub-bird family (2 species)

Fig. 117. Noisy Scrub-bird (*Atrichornis clamosus*). Total length 9 in. (228 mm.).

Physical characteristics. Length—165 to 228 mm. ($6\frac{1}{2}$ to 9 in.). Plumage—rufous brown above, the feathers finely barred and vermiculated with blackish brown; lighter below (throat and breast white in *clamosus*). Bill rather large. Wings very small; tail long, broad, and slightly graduated. Legs strong; feet large. ♀ smaller than ♂ and somewhat different in coloration.

Range. New South Wales (*rufescens*); s.w. Australia (*clamosus*—possibly extinct). Habitat—dense thickets. Nonmigratory.

Habits. Solitary. Terrestrial. Very active; almost flightless, but run swiftly (holding tail erect). Scratch with feet for food. Very secretive and shy. Voice—notably loud; sharp, shrill, accelerated whistles. Mimic other birds.

Food. Snails' eggs, snails, worms, insects; seeds.

Breeding. Nest (*rufescens*) a dome with side entrance, built of grass and leaves, lined with a plaster of wood pulp; placed in a clump of grass.

Eggs. 2; white or reddish white, with reddish brown markings. Incubated by ♀.

Young. Nidicolous. Some down on upper parts. Cared for by ♀.

Technical diagnosis. R. B. Sharpe, Cat. of Birds in Brit. Mus., 13, 1890: 659.

Classification. G. M. Mathews, *Systema Avium Australasianarum,* London, pt. 2, 1930: 436.

References. Mathews, 8, pt. 1, 1920: 22–29, pl. 373.

H. L. White, The Rufous Scrub-Bird (Atrichornis rufescens) in Queensland. A new Sub-species, *Emu,* 19, 1920: 257–258, pl. 47 (col.).

S. W. Jackson, Second Trip to Macpherson Range, South-East Queensland, *Emu,* 20, 1921: 196–203, pls. 23, 25.

H. M. Whittell, The Noisy Scrub-bird (*Atrichornis clamosus*), *Emu,* 42, 1943: 217–234, pl. 20.

D. L. Serventy and H. M. Whittell, *A Handbook of the Birds of Western Australia,* Perth, 1948: 239–242.

A. H. Chisholm, The Story of the Scrub-birds, *Emu,* 51, pt. 2, 1951: 89–112, pls. 8–10; pt. 3, 1952: 285–297, pls. 15–16.

Synonym: Atrichiidae.

ALAUDIDAE

Lark family (75 species)

Fig. 118. Crested Lark (*Galerida cristata*). Total length 7 in. (177 mm.).

Physical characteristics. Length—120 to 228 mm. ($4\frac{3}{4}$ to 9 in.). Plumage—typically gray-brown and buff above, marked with dark brown and black in cryptic patterns; paler and less marked below. One sp. all black; others with black areas on head or under parts; many spp. with outer tail feathers white or edged with white; some with crest or "ear tufts." Bill rather long and curved to very short and stout. Wings rather long and, typically, pointed; tail short to medium. Legs short to fairly long; hind claw typically straight, long, and very sharp. Sexes in most spp. alike or nearly so in color, but ♀ smaller.

Range. North America to s. Mexico (Oaxaca); n.w. S. America (mts. of central Colombia); Africa (incl. Madagascar); Eurasia, Philippines, Borneo, Java, Timor, and Australia. Habitat—open, bare areas. Many spp. migratory.

Habits. Often gregarious. Terrestrial. Flight strong in many spp. Walk when on ground. Voice—many spp. have elaborate and beautiful songs, and many a soaring flight song.

Food. Seeds, insects, mollusca.

Breeding. Open or domed nest, almost always built on the ground.

Eggs. 2 to 6; speckled (a few unmarked). Incubated largely or entirely by ♀.

Young. Nidicolous. With thick down, esp. above. Cared for by ♂ and ♀.

Technical diagnosis. Ridgway, pt. 4, 1907: 289.

Classification. R. B. Sharpe, Hand-list of the Genera and Species of Birds, British Museum, 5, 1909: 154–187. New World: Hellmayr, pt. 8, 1935: 1–11.

References. Bent, No. 179: 314–371; Witherby, 1, 1938: 163–187; Baker, *Fauna,* 3, 1926: 302–356; Bannerman, 4, 1936: xx–xxi, 17–56; col. pl. 3.

G. B. Pickwell, The Prairie Horned Lark, *Trans. Acad. Sci. St. Louis,* 27, 1931: 1–153; 34 pls.

A. D. DuBois, Habits and Nest Life of the Desert Horned Lark, *Condor,* 38, 1936: 49–56.

R. Meinertzhagen, Review of the Alaudidae [*Mirafra, Eremopterix,* and *Eremophila* omitted], *Proc. Zool. Soc. London,* 121, 1951: 81–132.

HIRUNDINIDAE

Swallow family (75 species)

Fig. 119. Barn Swallow (*Hirundo rustica*). Total length 7 in. (177 mm.).

Physical characteristics. Length—95 to 228 mm. ($3\frac{3}{4}$ to 9 in.). Plumage—black, brown, dark green, or dark blue (with metallic luster in many spp.); a few spp. strongly streaked, esp. on under parts, and/or with white or buff rump; a number show white areas on spread tail; under parts of many spp. white, chestnut, or gray-brown. Bill short, broad-gaped, and flattened. Neck short; body slender. Wings very long and pointed; tail medium to very long, truncate to deeply forked. Legs very short, tarsi (and even toes) feathered in several spp.; feet very small and weak; front toes more or less united at base. Sexes alike or nearly so in most spp.

Range. World-wide, exc. extreme n. and some oceanic islands. Migratory.

Habits. Most spp. gregarious. Aerial. Flight very strong and agile. Feed on the wing. Perch, but are barely able to walk. Voice—twittering or squeaking notes; melodious notes or even song in some spp.

Food. Insects; rarely berries.

Breeding. Most spp. colonial or semicolonial. Nest in natural hollows in trees or rocks, or excavate burrows for nests in banks or level ground, or build mud nests (either cup- or retort-shaped).

Eggs. 3 to 7; white, immaculate or speckled. Incubated by ♂ and ♀, or by ♀ alone.

Young. Nidicolous. Some down on upper parts. Cared for by ♂ and ♀.

Technical diagnosis. Ridgway, pt. 3, 1904: 23–24.

Classification. R. B. Sharpe and C. W. Wyatt, Monograph of the Hirundinidae, London, 1885–1894.

References. Bent, No. 179: 371–516; Witherby, 2, 1938: 226–241; Baker, *Fauna,* 3, 1926: 225–253.

R. E. Moreau, Numerical Data on African Birds' Behaviour at the Nest—II. *Psalidoprocne holomelaena massaica* Neum., the Rough-wing Bank-Martin, *Ibis,* 1940: 234–248.

R. G. Kuerzi, Life History Studies of the Tree Swallow, *Proc. Linn. Soc. N. Y.,* Nos. 52–53, 1941: 1–52.

E. Mayr and J. Bond, Notes on the Generic Classification of the Swallows, *Ibis,* 1943: 334–341.

L. DeBraey, Auprès du Nid de l'Hirondelle de Cheminée, *Hirundo rustica rustica* Linné, *Gerfaut,* 36, 1946: 133–193.

R. W. Allen and M. M. Nice, A Study of the Breeding Biology of the Purple Martin (Progne subis), *Amer. Midl. Nat.,* 47, 1952: 606–665.

CAMPEPHAGIDAE

Cuckoo-shrike family (71 species)

Fig. 120. Great Cuckoo-shrike (*Coracina macei*). Total length 12 in. (305 mm.).

Physical characteristics. Length—127 to 311 mm. (5 to 12¼ in.). Plumage—soft, the feathers loosely attached. Bluish or brownish gray, black, blue, red, orange, or yellow, usually in solid areas but strongly barred below in some spp. Under parts white in several spp., chestnut in 2; some spp. have throat and breast gray or black. Tail plain; or tipped or edged with white, yellow, orange, or red. Rump barred or lighter than back in many spp. Bill of medium length, moderately to very heavy, slightly to strongly hooked. Two spp. (*Lobotos*) have orange wattles at gape. Wings medium to long. Tail typically graduated (forked in some); long in most spp. Legs short; feet weak to strong. Sexes alike or unlike.

Range. Africa, India to s. and e. China; Japan, Philippines, Malaysia, Papuan Region, Australia; e. to Samoa. Habitat—forests. Largely nonmigratory.

Habits. Often gregarious. Arboreal (one sp. terrestrial). Flight strong in some spp. but not sustained. Voice (many spp. noisy)—harsh or whistling notes.

Food. Insects; berries.

Breeding. Nest a shallow cup (covered with bark and lichens in many spp.), usually on a horizontal branch.

Eggs. 2 to 4; white, green, or blue, usually speckled and blotched. Incubated by ♂ and ♀.

Young. Nidicolous. Condition at hatching not described. Cared for by ♂ and ♀.

Technical diagnosis. F. J. Jackson, *The Birds of Kenya Colony and the Uganda Protectorate,* London, vol. 3, 1938: 1162–1163.

Classification. Genera: *Coracina* (incl. *Coquus, Pteropodocys, Volvocivora, Edolisoma*), *Cyanograucalus, Lalage, Campephaga, Chlamydochera, Campochera, Pericrocotus, Hemipus,* and *Tephrodornis.* (W. L. Sclater, *Systema Avium Aethiopicarum,* London, 2, 1930: 589–593; Baker, *Fauna,* 2, 1924: 305–314, 317–347; C. A. Gibson-Hill, An Annotated Checklist of the Birds of Malaya, *Bull. Raffles Mus. Singapore,* 20, 1949: 149–153; G. Mathews, *Systema Avium Australasianarum,* London, 2, 1930: 529–555.)

References. Baker, *Fauna,* 2, 1924: 305–314, 317–347; Bannerman, 5, 1939: xxxii–xxxiii, 303–321, col. pl. 7.

W. W. A. Phillips, Some Observations on the Nesting of *Hemipus picatus* . . . , *Ibis,* 1940: 450–454, pls. 5–6.

Synonym. Campophagidae. The Pericrocotidae are included.

DICRURIDAE

Drongo family (20 species)

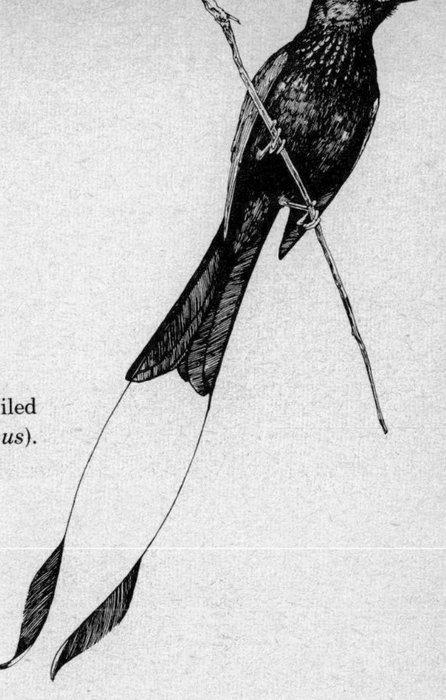

Fig. 121. Greater Racket-tailed Drongo (*Dicrurus paradiseus*). Total length 25 in. (635 mm.).

Physical characteristics. Length—177 to 635 mm. (7 to 25 in.). Plumage—black (typically with a high greenish, bluish, or purplish luster) or gray; in solid colors, but variously marked by ornamental specialization of feather structure; extremely elongate hairlike feathers in crest; "spangles" on head, chest, and throat feathers; glossy hackles; elaborated tail. White on face or belly in a few forms. Frontal crest in some spp. Eyes red in most spp. Bill stout, somewhat hooked and notched, the culmen arched. Wings long; tail medium to extremely long, truncate (rarely) to deeply forked (in many spp. with outer feathers curved, curled, and/or racquet-tipped). Legs short; toes and claws stout. Sexes alike but ♀ slightly smaller.

Range. Africa (s. of Sahara), including Madagascar; India, Burma, Siam, Indo-China, s. and e. China, Philippines, Malaysia, Papuan Region, n. and e. Australia, Solomon Ids. A few forms are migratory.

Habits. Solitary. Arboreal. Flight strong but not sustained. Feed chiefly on insects captured on the wing. Very pugnacious. Voice—variety of calls; melodious songs. Mimic other birds.

Food. Insects; nectar.

Breeding. Frail saucerlike nest, usually semipendent in horizontal fork of tree.

Eggs. 2 to 4; white or colored, immaculate or blotched and speckled. Incubated by ♀, sometimes assisted by ♂.

Young. Nidicolous. Naked. Cared for by ♂ and ♀.

Technical diagnosis. Baker, *Fauna,* 2, 1924: 352.

Classification. C. Vaurie, A Revision of the Bird Family Dicruridae, *Bull. Amer. Mus. Nat. Hist.,* 93, 1949: 217–332.

References. Baker, *Fauna,* 2, 1924: 352–381; Baker, *Nidification,* 2, 1933: 316–350; Bannerman, 5, 1939: xxxiv–xxxv, 321–336, col. pl. 8.

A. S. Thyagaraju, The King-Crow [*Dicrurus macrocercus peninsularis* (Ticehurst)], *Jour. Bombay Nat. Hist. Soc.,* 37, 1934: 727–728.

E. Mayr and C. Vaurie, Evolution in the Family Dicruridae (Birds), *Evolution,* 2, 1948: 238–265.

Synonym: Edoliidae.

ORIOLIDAE

Oriole family

(26 species)

Fig. 122. Golden Oriole (*Oriolus oriolus*). Total length $9\frac{1}{2}$ in. (241 mm.).

Physical characteristics. Length—177 to 305 mm. (7 to 12 in.). Plumage—largely yellow, olive-green, red, brown, or black; part or all of head black in most spp.; wings dark; tail partly black in most spp. Some spp. (or plumages) heavily streaked, chiefly below. Lores and orbital region feathered in *Oriolus,* bare in *Sphecotheres.* Bill red or blue in *Oriolus,* black in *Sphecotheres.* Bill strong, pointed, and slightly hooked; rather short to long. Wings long and pointed; tail medium to rather long. Legs strong but short. Sexes unlike in most spp.

Range. Africa, Eurasia (exc. n. part), East Indies, Philippines, n. and e. Australia. A few forms are migratory.

Habits. Solitary. Arboreal. Flight swift, undulating. Usually wary. Voice—loud, melodious, flutelike notes; harsh alarm notes.

Food. Insects; fruit.

Breeding. Semipendent, cup-shaped nest, usually high in tree; or (*Sphecotheres*) frail, saucer-shaped nest.

Eggs. 2 to 5; white or pinkish (greenish in *Sphecotheres*), strongly marked with brown and black. Incubated by ♀, assisted by ♂.

Young. Nidicolous. With some down. Cared for by ♂ and ♀.

Technical diagnosis. Witherby, 1, 1938: 47–48.

Classification. R. Meinertzhagen, *Ibis,* 1923: 52–96 (*Oriolus*); and G. M. Mathews, *Systema Avium Australasianarum,* London, pt. 2, 1930: 861–862 ("Sphecotheridae").

References. Witherby, 1, 1938: 47–50; Baker, *Fauna,* 3, 1926: 4–15; Mathews, 9, pt. 4, 1921: 158–170, col. pls. 419–420; 12, pt. 7, 1926: 264–280, col. pls. 578–579; Baker, *Nidification,* 2, 1933: 498–505; Bannerman, 5, 1939: xlii–xliii, 450–465, col. pl. 8.

Synonymy: The Sphecotheridae and Tylidae are tentatively included in this family.

CORVIDAE

Crow family (100 species)

Fig. 123. Collie Magpie-jay (*Callocitta formosa*). Total length 25 in. (635 mm.).

Physical characteristics. Length—177 to 699 mm. (7 to 27½ in.). The family includes the largest passerine birds. Plumage—black, black and white, or (jays) brightly colored: blue, green, yellow, purple, or brown; usually with large areas of solid color, but wings and tail barred in some. Some have crests and some have extremely long tails. Bill strong; nostrils usually round, nonoperculate, and shielded by forward-projecting feathers. Wings and tail strong, variable in shape. Tarsi large, strongly scutellated, booted behind. Sexes alike or nearly so.

Range. World-wide (exc. New Zealand and some oceanic islands). Family best developed in Northern Hemisphere. Most spp. are nonmigratory.

Habits. Typically gregarious. Flight strong. Bold, aggressive. "Mob" birds of prey. Some walk. Some bury or hide food. Voice—loud, usually harsh calls or croaks, sometimes melodious calls or even songs.

Food. Omnivorous. Often prey on eggs or young of other birds.

Breeding. Usually open nest in trees or on cliffs, but may be covered, or in holes in trees or in ground. Built by ♂ and ♀.

Eggs. 3 to 10; greenish or white, speckled in most species. Incubated by ♀.

Young. Nidicolous. Down sparse or absent. Fed by ♂ and ♀.

Technical diagnosis. Ridgway, pt. 3, 1904: 252–254.

Classification. D. Amadon, *Amer. Mus. Novitates, No. 1251,* 1944.

References. Bent, No. 191: 1–322; Witherby, 1, 1938: 7–39; Baker, *Fauna,* 1, 1922: 18–71.

G. K. Yeates, *The Life of the Rook,* London, 1934.

J. M. Linsdale, The Natural History of Magpies, *Pacif. Coast. Avif. No. 25,* 1937.

S. E. Aldous, The White-necked Raven in Relation to Agriculture, *U. S. Fish and Wildl. Serv. Res. Rept. 5,* 1942.

D. Amadon, A Preliminary Life History Study of the Florida Jay, *Cyanocitta c. coerulescens, Amer. Mus. Novitates, No. 1252,* 1944.

CRACTICIDAE

Bellmagpie family

(10 species)

Fig. 124. New Guinea Forest Butcherbird (*Cracticus cassicus*). Total length 14 in. (355 mm.).

Physical characteristics. Length—260 to 584 mm. ($10\frac{1}{4}$ to 23 in.). Plumage—black, or black (or gray) and white; some brown phases. Bill large, very stout, and slightly to strongly hooked in most spp. Head large; body compact. Wings rather short to long and pointed. Legs strong; medium to long. Sexes alike or unlike.

Range. Australia, including Tasmania; New Guinea and adjacent islands. Nonmigratory.

Habits. Usually gregarious. Arboreal but often feed on ground. Flight strong. Some impale food on thorns or wedge it in forked branches before tearing it apart, or store it in this way. Voice (most spp. vociferous)—loud metallic notes.

Food. Large insects and small vertebrates; fruit.

Breeding. Rather large, open cup of twigs, well lined with grass and rootlets, placed high in a tree.

Eggs. 3 to 4 (rarely 2 or 5); highly variable: pale blue or green to olive, or pink to reddish brown, usually heavily marked with dark colors. Incubated by ♀ (sometimes assisted by ♂?).

Young. Nidicolous. With down (?). Cared for by ♂ and ♀.

Technical diagnosis. J. A. Leach, *Emu,* 14, 1914: 2–38, pls. 1–3; see also Ridgway, pt. 3, 1904: 253.

Classification. G. M. Mathews, *Systema Avium Australasianarum,* London, pt. 2, 1930: 651–658. [*"Melloria"* and *"Bulestes"* to be included in the genus *Cracticus.*]

References. Mathews, 10, pts. 5–7, 1923: 334–434, col. pls. 483–490.

Hugh Wilson, The Life History of the Western Magpie (*Gymnorhina dorsalis*), *Emu,* 45, 1946: 233–244, 271–286.

D. L. Serventy and H. M. Whittell, *A Handbook of the Birds of Western Australia,* Perth, 1948: 340–345.

D. Amadon, Taxonomic Notes on the Australian Butcher-birds (Family Cracticidae), *Amer. Mus. Novitates, No. 1504,* 1951.

G. M. Storr, Remarks on the Streperidae, *S. Austral. Ornith.,* 20, 1952: 78–80.

D. Amadon, Further Notes on the Cracticidae, *S. Austral. Ornith.,* 21, 1953: 6–7.

Synonym: Streperidae.

GRALLINIDAE

Mudnest-builder family (4 species)

Fig. 125. Magpie-lark (*Grallina cyanoleuca*). Total length 11 in. (280 mm.).

Physical characteristics. Length—190 to 502 mm. ($7\frac{1}{2}$ to $19\frac{3}{4}$ in.). Plumage—black, boldly marked with white; or dark bluish and brownish gray, unmarked. Bill very short and stout to long, slender, and curved. Neck short. Wings short and rounded to long and pointed. Tail short and truncate to very long and rounded. Legs medium to rather long and stout. Sexes alike or unlike.

Range. Australia and n.w. New Guinea. Some spp. migratory.

Habits. Gregarious. Flight not strong. Jump from branch to branch in trees. Feed largely on the ground. Voice—melodious whistling notes; harsh cries; a plaintive *peewit.*

Food. Insects; seeds.

Breeding. Communal nesting habits. Nest a deep bowl made of mud and lined with grass and feathers. Usually placed on high, horizontal limbs of trees.

Eggs. 3 to 8; white to reddish white, marked with brown and black. Incubated by ♂ and ♀.

Young. Nidicolous. With some down. Cared for by ♂ and ♀.

Technical diagnosis. D. Amadon, Australian Mud Nest Builders, *Emu,* 50, 1950: 123–127.

Classification. D. Amadon, Australian Mud Nest Builders, *Emu,* 50, 1950: 124–127.

References. Mathews, 10, pt. 5, 1923: 320–333, pl. 482; 12, pt. 10, 1927: 413–425, pls. 598–599.

H. A. C. Leach, Notes on the White-Winged Chough, *Emu,* 29, 1929: 130–132, pls. 24–25.

Angus Robinson, Magpie-Larks—A Study in Behaviour, *Emu,* 46, 1947: 265–281, 382–391; 47, 1947: 11–28, 147–153.

D. L. Serventy and H. M. Whittell, *A Handbook of the Birds of Western Australia,* Perth, 1948: 258–260.

Synonymy: The Corcoraciididae and Struthiididae are included.

PTILONORHYNCHIDAE

Bowerbird family (18 species)

Fig. 126. Satin Bowerbird (*Ptilonorhynchus violaceus*). Total length 13 in. (330 mm.).

Physical characteristics. Length—228 to 368 mm. (9 to 14½ in.). Plumage—black, gray, brown, green, yellow, orange, lavender—plain or in bold combinations; some spp. spotted. Some spp. have brilliant crest (ranging from several long narrow crown feathers or a nuchal ruff to a "mane" or cape over most of the back). Bill stout, straight to rather curved, slightly hooked (notched in 3 spp.). Wings short to medium; rounded. Tail rather short to long; rounded, truncate, or emarginate. Legs rather short; legs and feet stout. Sexes unlike in most spp.

Range. New Guinea and adjacent islands; n. and e. Australia. Habitat—forests. Nonmigratory.

Habits. Largely solitary. Terrestrial, but nest and feed in trees. Flight swift. ♂♂ of most spp. build elaborate "bowers" or "playgrounds" of twigs, decorated with flowers, berries, bits of glass, etc. Voice—variety of ringing calls. Mimic other birds, other animals, and mechanical sounds.

Food. Fruit, berries, seeds, mollusca, insects.

Breeding. Nest a shallow or cup-shaped structure of twigs, sometimes lined with grass or leaves, placed in trees.

Eggs. 1 to 3 (usually 2); white to buff or greenish; spotted and scrawled or immaculate. Incubated by ♀.

Young. Nidicolous. With down. Cared for by ♀ (assisted by ♂ in some spp.).

Technical diagnosis. C. R. Stonor, *Proc. Zool. Soc. London,* 107B, 1937: 475–490.

Classification. A. J. Marshall, *Bower-birds,* London, 1954: vii (see also pp. 181–185).

References. R. B. Sharpe, Monograph of the Paradiseidae . . . and Ptilorhynchidae . . . , London, vol. 2, 1891–1898: 47–103, col. pls. 26–40.

T. Iredale, *Birds of Paradise and Bower Birds,* Melbourne, 1950: 173–226, col. pls. 25–33. (Reviewed by E. Mayr, *Emu,* 50, 1950: 214–216.)

A. J. Marshall, *Bower-birds,* London, 1954.

Synonymy: Sometimes included in Paradisaeidae.

PARADISAEIDAE

Bird-of-paradise family

(43 species)

Fig. 127. Red Bird-of-paradise (*Paradisaea rubra*). Total length 13 in. (330 mm.).

Physical characteristics. Length—139 to 1016 mm. ($5\frac{1}{2}$ to 40 in.). Plumage—black with brilliant metallic gloss, or bold combinations of velvet-textured black or brown, and red, yellow, orange, green, blue, purple, white; with spectacular erectile feathers of highly varied and extreme specialization: greatly elongated head or tail wires or plumes; enormous plumed "fans" arising from nape, breast, or flanks. Some spp. have wattles or bare spots on head. Bill medium (rather heavy in some spp.) to long, slender, and sickle-shaped; hooked in some spp. Wings medium, rather rounded; tail short and square to extremely long and graduated. Legs rather short; legs and feet stout. Sexes unlike.

Range. Moluccas; New Guinea and adjacent islands; n. and e. Australia. Also Fiji Ids., if *Lamprolia* is placed in this family. Habitat—forests. Nonmigratory.

Habits. Largely solitary. Arboreal. Flight slow (swift in a few spp.), not prolonged. ♂♂ of some spp. clear vegetation from forest areas for display grounds. ♂♂ have spectacular display of erectile plumes accompanied by elaborate acrobatics. Voice—loud, shrill calls, harsh shrieks, prolonged whistles.

Food. Fruit, berries, seeds, insects, frogs, lizards.

Breeding. Some spp. polygamous? Nest a cup, of plant fragments, placed in tree or in tree cavity.

Eggs. 2; pinkish white or brown, longitudinally streaked. Incubated by ♀.

Young. Nidicolous. With down or naked. Cared for by ♀; or by ♂ and ♀.

Technical diagnosis. C. R. Stonor, *Proc. Zool. Soc. London,* 107B, 1937: 475–490.

Classification. E. Mayr, List of New Guinea Birds, Amer. Mus. Nat. Hist., New York, 1941: 167–183; G. M. Mathews, *Systema Avium Australasianarum,* London, pt. 2, 1930: 866–882. See also T. Iredale, *Birds of Paradise and Bower Birds,* Melbourne, 1950: v–vii; E. Mayr, *Emu,* 50, 1950: 214–216; W. Rothschild, *Proc. VIIth Internatl. Ornith. Congress,* 1931: 288–289 (supposed hybrids).

References. R. B. Sharpe, Monograph of the Paradiseidae . . . , London, 1891–1898, vol. 1; vol 2 (through p. 46 and pl. 25).

A. L. Rand, On the Breeding Habits of Some Birds of Paradise in the Wild, *Amer. Mus. Novitates, No. 993,* 1938.

[S.] Dillon Ripley, Strange Courtship of Birds of Paradise, *Natl. Geogr. Mag.,* 97, 1950: 247–278, 16 col. pls.

Synonymy: The Epimachidae are included.

PARIDAE

Titmouse family (65 species)

Fig. 128. Green-backed Tit (*Parus monticolus*). Total length 5 in. (127 mm.).

Physical characteristics. Length—76 to 203 mm. (3 to 8 in.). Plumage—typically long, soft, and thick. In combinations (blended or bold) of gray, brown, yellow, orange, olive-green, gray-blue, vinous, black, white. A few spp. all black or largely white; none spotted, streaked, or barred; but many marked broadly with black on head and under parts. A few spp. crested. Bill rather small; stout in many spp., attenuate and sharp in some. Wings rounded, short to medium; tail very short and truncate to long and graduate. Legs short but strong. Sexes alike in most spp.

Range. North America (exc. extreme n.), s. to Guatemala; Old World (exc. Madagascar, extreme n. Asia, New Guinea, Australia, and Polynesia). Habitat—dense forest to desert brush. Most spp. nonmigratory.

Habits. Rather gregarious. Arboreal. Very restless and active. Flight weak. Voice—chattering or lisping notes, whistled calls.

Food. Insects and other invertebrates; nuts and seeds.

Breeding. Rather bulky nests of fur, moss, etc., in holes in trees, walls, earth- or rock-banks; or pendent, feltlike pouch with side entrance; or covered nest (with entrance near the top) of feathers, moss, etc., in bushes or in trees.

Eggs. 4 to 14; white or pinkish white; immaculate to heavily marked. Incubated in most spp. by ♀ alone.

Young. Nidicolous. Downy or naked at hatching. Cared for by ♂ and ♀.

Technical diagnosis. Ridgway, pt. 3, 1904: 375–378.

Classification. New World: Hellmayr, pt. 7, 1934: 70–92. Old World: C. E. Hellmayr, Wytsman's *Genera Avium,* pt. 18, 1911 [but omit Paradoxornithinae, Panurinae, and Certhiparinae].

References. Bent, No. 191: 322–460; Witherby, 1, 1938: 244–274; Baker, *Fauna,* 1, 1922: 72–102; Bannerman, 6, 1948: xx–xxi, 3–19, col. pl. 2.

E. P. Odum, Annual Cycle of the Black-capped Chickadee, *Auk,* 58, 1941: 314–333, 518–535; 59, 1942: 499–531.

K. L. Dixon, Behavior of the Plain Titmouse, *Condor,* 51, 1949: 110–136.

H. N. Kluijver, The Population Ecology of the Great Tit, *Parus m. major* L., *Ardea,* 39, 1951: 1–135.

Synonymy: The Remizinae and Psaltriparinae are tentatively included.

SITTIDAE

Common Nuthatch family (17 species)

Fig. 129. Red-breasted Nuthatch (*Sitta canadensis*). Total length $4\frac{1}{2}$ in. (114 mm.).

Physical characteristics. Length—95 to 190 mm. ($3\frac{3}{4}$ to $7\frac{1}{2}$ in.). Plumage—gray to blue-gray or blue above; top of head (or forehead) often black or brown; usually a dark eye line. Under parts unstreaked; light, usually with some brown (pale buff to rich chestnut), especially posteriorly. Tail usually marked with white. Slender, straight, unnotched bill. Nostrils nonoperculate, partly covered with forward-projecting feathers. Wings rather long, pointed; tail short, truncate. Tarsi short; toes (especially hind toe) long; claws laterally compressed. Sexes alike or nearly so; immatures like adults.

Range. North America and Eurasia exc. extreme n., Malaysia (exc. Celebes), Japan, Formosa, and Philippine Ids. Most spp. nonmigratory.

Habits. Typically solitary (some spp. flock). Arboreal (exc. 2 spp. of "rock nuthatches"). Climb with short, jerky hops—upward or head downward. Flight undulating. Voice—simple call notes; song usually a rhythmic repetition of similar notes.

Food. Insects, nuts, seeds.

Breeding. Nest in lined tree or rock cavity with entrance often reduced to small opening by plaster of pitch or clay (the rock nuthatches build a cone-shaped plaster projection extending 6 or 8 in. from rock face).

Eggs. 4 to 12; white, with rufous spots. Incubated by ♀ (sometimes also by ♂?).

Young. Nidicolous. With long, sparse down. Cared for by ♂ and ♀.

Technical diagnosis. Ridgway, pt. 3, 1904: 436–439.

Classification. New World: Hellmayr, pt. 7, 1934: 93–100. Old World: A. Dunajewski, *Acta Ornith. Mus. Zool. Polonici,* 1, 1934: 181–251, pls. 2–6.

References. Bent, No. 195: 1–55; Witherby, 1, 1938: 240–244; Baker, *Fauna,* 1, 1922: 120–133; Baker, *Nidification,* 1, 1932: 89–100.

H. C. Tracy, The Rock Nuthatch and Its Nest, *Wils. Bull.,* 14, 1902: 1–5, 1 pl.

C. E. Hellmayr, Fam. Sittidae, Wytsman's *Genera Avium,* pt. 16, 1911.

K. H. Voous and J. G. van Marle, The distributional history of the Nuthatch, *Sitta europaea* L., *Ardea,* 41, 1953: 1–68.

NEOSITTIDAE

Australian Nuthatch family

(5 species)

Fig. 130. Orange-winged Tree-runner (*Neositta chrysoptera*). Total length $4\frac{1}{4}$ in. (108 mm.).

Physical characteristics. Length—102 to 120 mm. (4 to $4\frac{3}{4}$ in.). Plumage—black, with pink lateral areas on tail (*Daphoenositta*); or gray above, streaked with brown, with crown white or black, rump and under parts white—the latter streaked in some spp.—and outer rectrices tipped with white. All spp. have a broad white or buffy band across the (spread) wing. Bill laterally compressed, slightly hooked, and notched; nostrils exposed, operculate. Bristles about base of bill, characteristic of other families of nuthatches, absent or only slightly developed. Wings long; tail medium. Sexes unlike in some spp.; immature spotted.

Range. New Guinea and Australia. Nonmigratory.

Habits. Gregarious (commonly found in small flocks). Arboreal. Very active, running upward or head downward along tree trunks. Flight undulating. Voice—soft, twittering notes, frequently uttered; "mournful, monotonous cries" also described.

Food. Insects and spiders.

Breeding. Nest (of *Neositta* [*"Sittella"*]), built by ♂ and ♀ of pair (often aided by several other adults), deep, well-constructed, cup-shaped (of spider webs and cocoons, or wool and hair, with outer covering of flakes of bark), placed in upright fork of tree—often 50 feet or more above the ground.

Eggs. 3 (rarely 4); grayish white, speckled and blotched with brown and black. Incubated by ♂ and ♀ of pair (assisted by other adults?).

Young. Nidicolous. Otherwise undescribed. Fed by both parents (and sometimes as many as 4 other adults).

Technical diagnosis. A. L. Rand, *Auk,* 53, 1936: 309.

Classification. New Guinea: E. Mayr, List of New Guinea Birds, Amer. Mus. Nat. Hist., New York, 1941: 187. Australia: Mathews, 11, pt. 2, 1923: 53–81, 2 col. pls.

References. T. Salvadori, Note on *Daphaenositta miranda* De Vis, *Ibis,* 1898: 208–209, col. pl. 4.

A. J. Campbell, *Nests and Eggs of Australian Birds,* Sheffield, England, pt. 1, 1901: 337–344, 1 pl.

A. L. Rand, The Rediscovery of the Nuthatch *Daphaenositta* with Notes on its Affinities, *Auk,* 53, 1936: 306–310.

Synonymy: Sometimes included in the Sittidae.

HYPOSITTIDAE

Coral-billed Nuthatch family (1 species)

Fig. 131. Coral-billed Nuthatch (*Hypositta corallirostris*). Total length 5 in. (127 mm.).

Physical characteristics. Length—about 127 mm. (5 in.). Plumage—greenish blue. Bill short, coral-red; slightly hooked. Nostrils not operculate (or only slightly so), partly concealed by forward-projecting feathers. Wing rather long and rounded; tail relatively long. Feet syndactyl; hind toe very long. Sexes unlike (♀ duller than ♂ above, brown and white below); immatures like adult ♀.

Range. Humid forest of e. Madagascar. Nonmigratory.

Habits. Behavior creeperlike (described as "climbing silently up one tree trunk, then flying down to climb another trunk"). Sometimes accompanies mixed flocks of other forest birds. Voice—undescribed.

Food. Insects.

Breeding. Nest unknown.

Eggs. Not described.

Young. Not described.

Technical diagnosis. Ridgway, pt. 3, 1904: 439.

Classification. A. L. Rand, *Auk,* 53, 1936: 310.

References. R. Ridgway, Relationships of the Madagascar genus Hypositta Newton, *Proc. Biol. Soc. Wash.,* 16, 1903: 125.

C. E. Hellmayr, Fam. Hypossittidae, Wytsman's *Genera Avium,* pt. 24, 1913 (with col. pl.).

A. L. Rand, The Distribution and Habits of Madagascar Birds, *Bull. Amer. Mus. Nat. Hist.,* 72, art. 5, 1936: 468–469.

Synonymy: Sometimes included in the Sittidae.

CERTHIIDAE

Creeper family (17 species)

Fig. 132. Brown Creeper (*Certhia familiaris*). Total length $5\frac{1}{4}$ in. (133 mm.).

Physical characteristics. Length—120 to 177 mm. ($4\frac{3}{4}$ to 7 in.). Plumage—brown to black above (streaked, barred, and spotted with white, buff, or darker brown) and white, gray, or buff below; olive-brown to blackish, streaked below with white; black, spotted with white (one sp.); or (one sp.) gray above and white below, with large crimson area on wing. Bill rather short to long; slender and laterally compressed; almost straight to strongly decurved. Wings long, rounded or pointed. Tail long and graduated, with stiff pointed tips; or short, rounded, and soft. Legs very slender to stout; toes long; claws curved and sharp, very long (esp. on hallux) in most spp. Sexes alike or nearly so.

Range. Europe and Africa through Asia and India to China and Japan; Australia, New Guinea, and the Philippines; N. and Central America. Some spp. migratory.

Habits. Solitary. Most spp. arboreal. Flight strong. Creep about trunks and branches of trees, over rocks, cliffs, and walls, hunting food in crevices. Voice—soft cheeping call; harsh piping notes; and (in most spp.) a clear sweet song.

Food. Mainly insects and spiders; seeds.

Breeding. Nest a pad of moss, grass, and bark, lined with hair, feathers, etc., placed in trees under overhanging bark, in rock crevices, etc.; or (*Salpornis*) a lichen-decorated cup of plant fragments placed on horizontal branch.

Eggs. 2 to 9 (usually 5 or 6); white or flesh, spotted with brown. Incubated by ♀ (sometimes assisted by ♂).

Young. Nidicolous. Downy. Fed by ♂ and ♀.

Technical diagnosis. Witherby, 1, 1938: 234.

Classification. C. E. Hellmayr, Fam. Certhiidae, Wytsman's *Genera Avium,* pt. 15, 1911.

References. Bent, No. 195: 56–79; Witherby, 1, 1938: 234–240; Baker, *Fauna,* 1, 1922: 428–443; Baker, *Nidification,* 1, 1932: 410–418.

F. E. Howe, The Genus Climacteris (Tree-creepers), *Emu,* 21, 1921: 32–41.

G. L. James, African Spotted Creeper (*Salpornis spilonota salvadori*), *Ostrich,* 19, 1948: 240–242, photo.

Synonymy: The Climacteridae are included.

TIMALIIDAE

Babbler family

(282 species)

Fig. 133. Variegated Laughing-thrush (*Garrulax variegatus*). Total length 9½ in. (241 mm.).

Physical characteristics. Length—89 to 406 mm. (3½ to 16 in.). Plumage—soft, lax, typically long and thick on lower back. Gray, buff, or chestnut (some spp. with much olive-green, black, white, or even yellow and red), usually in solid areas, but some spp. are streaked or scaled, esp. below, some with bold markings on head and neck. A few spp. crested. Bill very small and weak to long and sickle-shaped; or short, laterally compressed, and massive; or long and straight; or rather short and swollen; hooked in many spp. Wings short and rounded. Tail very short to long; truncate to graduated. Legs and feet strong. Sexes alike or unlike.

Range. Europe, Africa (incl. Madagascar), s. Asia, Malaysia, Papuan Region, Philippines, Australia; Oregon to Lower California. Largely nonmigratory.

Habits. Gregarious or solitary. Arboreal (some spp. largely terrestrial). Flight weak. Voice (many spp. very noisy)—harsh calls to rich musical songs.

Food. Insects and other small animals; fruit.

Breeding. Cuplike, or domed, nest, with side entrance; on ground (or in holes in ground or in bank), in grass, reeds, bushes, trees; or mud nests on rock ledges.

Eggs. 2 to 7; white, green, blue, or pink; immaculate in many spp. Incubated by ♂ and ♀, or by ♀ alone.

Young. Nidicolous. Naked or with down. Cared for by ♂ and ♀.

Technical diagnosis. Baker, *Fauna,* 2nd ed., vol. 1, 1922: 134–135.

Classification. J. Delacour, *L'Ois. et Rev. Franç. d'Ornith.,* 16, 1946: 14–31.

References. Bent, No. 195: 79–96; Witherby, 1, 1938: 274–277; Baker, *Fauna,* 1, 1922: 103–119, 134–337; Bannerman, 4, 1936: xxiv–xxv, 88–130, col. pl. 4; 6, 1948: xxiv–xxv, 113–120, col. pl. 1.

C. G. B. ten Kate, Zur Brutbiologie von Panurus biarmicus . . . , *Beitr. z. Fortpfl.-biol. d. Vögel,* 7, 1931: 1–7, 44–47, pls. 1–4.

M. M. Erickson, Territory, Annual Cycle, and Numbers in a Population of Wren-tits (Chamaea fasciata), *Univ. Calif. Publ. Zool.,* 42, 1938: 247–333, pls. 9–14.

Synonym: Timeliidae. The Chamaeidae, Cinclosomatidae, Eupetidae, Illadopsidae, Leiotrichidae, Liotrichidae, Orthonycidae, Panuridae, Paradoxornithidae, Picathartidae, and Turnoididae are included.

PYCNONOTIDAE

Bulbul family (109 species)

Fig. 134. Chinese Bulbul (*Pycnonotus sinensis*). Total length 7½ in. (190 mm.).

Physical characteristics. Length—139 to 286 mm. (5½ to 11¼ in.). Plumage—soft and long, esp. on lower back. Gray, brown, olive-green, sometimes with yellow, red, white, or black in bold contrast. Some spp. streaked or spotted (esp. below). Many have strong head pattern and/or brightly colored under tail coverts. Tail white-tipped in some spp. Some spp. crested. Hairlike feathers on nape and rictal bristles usually well developed. Bill short to medium in length; slightly curved; slender to stout; in some spp. hooked, or hooked and notched. Neck short. Wings rounded; short to medium. Tail medium to long; truncate to rounded (forked in *Microscelis*). Legs short. Sexes similar, but ♂ larger in a few spp.

Range. Africa (incl. Madagascar and Mascarene Ids.), s. Asia, Malaysia, Moluccas, and Philippines. Habitat—forests, brush, or gardens. Northern forms migratory.

Habits. Largely gregarious (often in mixed flocks). Mostly arboreal. Restless, agile. Flight not strong. Voice (most spp. garrulous)—a variety of short, loud notes and whistles, harsh or musical; some spp. have well-developed song. Some spp. mimic other birds.

Food. Berries, fruit, insects.

Breeding. Nest rather insubstantial; shallow, cup-shaped, or semipensile; its elevation varying from ground to high in tree.

Eggs. 2 to 4; pink, cream, or white; speckled and blotched. Incubated by ♂ and ♀.

Young. Nidicolous. Without down? Cared for by ♂ and ♀.

Technical diagnosis. J. Delacour, *Zoologica,* 28, pt. 1, 1943: 17–20.

Classification. J. Delacour, *Zoologica,* 28, pt. 1, 1943: 17–27.

References. Baker, *Fauna,* 1, 1922: 359–427; Baker, *Nidification,* 1, 1932: 333–409; Bannerman, 4, 1936: xxvi–xxvii, 130–198, col. pls. 5–6.

J. Delacour, *Birds of Malaysia,* New York, 1947: 216–227.

Synonym: Brachypodidae.

IRENIDAE

Leafbird family (15 species)

Fig. 135. Orange-bellied Leafbird (*Chloropsis hardwickii*). Total length $7\frac{1}{2}$ in. (190 mm.).

Physical characteristics. Length—120 to 241 mm. ($4\frac{3}{4}$ to $9\frac{1}{2}$ in.). Plumage—bright grass-green and black (or brown), with areas of blue and of yellow; or olive-green and black with yellow areas and white markings; or glossy blue and black. Elongated hairlike feathers on nape in some spp. Bill fairly long, somewhat curved, slightly hooked (notched in some spp.). Wings short to medium, rounded; tail short to fairly long, square or slightly rounded, the tail coverts much elongated in some spp. Feet rather small. Sexes unlike.

Range. India, Burma, Siam, Indo-China, s. China, Philippines, Malaysia. Habitat—forests and second growth. Nonmigratory except for local movements.

Habits. Most spp. gregarious. Arboreal. Flight swift. Active. Typically shy and retiring. *Aegithina tiphia* has acrobatic aerial courtship display. Voice—chattering and flutelike notes; shrill musical whistles; loud clear song. Some spp. mimic other birds.

Food. Mainly fruit; berries, seeds, and buds; insects.

Breeding. Nest a neat, lined cup or loosely constructed shallow saucer, placed in trees (often at great heights) or in scrub.

Eggs. 2 to 4; gray, cream, or pink, marked with brown. Incubated by ♂ and ♀ (at least in *Aegithina tiphia*).

Young. Not described? Cared for by ♂ and ♀.

Technical diagnosis. H. C. Oberholser, *Jour. Wash. Acad. Sci.,* 7, 1917: 538 (*Irena* only).

Classification. J. Delacour, *Birds of Malaysia,* New York, 1947: 211–216 [add *Chloropsis flavipennis* and *Irena cyanogaster* (J. Delacour and E. Mayr, *Birds of the Philippines,* New York, 1946: 172–173), *Ae. nigrolutea* and *C. jerdoni* (Baker, *Nidification,* 1, 1932: 321, 327)].

References. Baker, *Fauna,* 1, 1922: 337–344, 346–353; 3, 1926: 1–3; Baker, *Nidification,* 1, 1932: 315–329; 2, 1933: 496–498.

H. C. Robinson and F. N. Chasen, *The Birds of the Malay Peninsula,* London, vol. 1, 1927: 213–216, col. pl. 17; vol. 2, 1928: 171–176, col. pl. 14; vol. 4, 1939: 265–272, col. pl. 17.

A. Spennemann, Etwas über Aegithina tiphia scapularis (Horsf.) auf Java, *Beitr. z. Fortpfl.-biol. d. Vögel,* 10, 1934: 108–111.

Synonym: Aegithinidae. The Phyllornithidae are included.

CINCLIDAE

Dipper family

(5 species)

Fig. 136. White-breasted Dipper (*Cinclus cinclus*). Total length $7\frac{1}{4}$ in. (184 mm.).

Physical characteristics. Length—139 to 190 mm. ($5\frac{1}{2}$ to $7\frac{1}{2}$ in.). Plumage—firm and dense, with under coat of down; gray, brown (with chestnut shadings), or black; uniform, mottled with white, or with white areas (head, back, under parts, under side of wings). Bill straight, slender, and much compressed laterally, slightly hooked and notched. Body compact. Wings very short, somewhat pointed, very concave beneath; tail short, square or slightly rounded. Legs and toes long and stout; claws short but strong (the middle claw sometimes slightly pectinate). Sexes alike.

Range. Europe, c. Asia to China and Japan; w. America (from the Yukon) to Tucuman, Argentina. Habitat—chiefly swift mountain streams. Nonmigratory (but some altitudinal shift).

Habits. Solitary. Exclusively aquatic. Flight direct and rapid, usually close over water. Dive. Swim well, often under water. Walk on bottom. Restless; a frequent bobbing motion is responsible for the common name. Voice—rapid chatter, shrill whistle, prolonged deep *zurrrrr* (in display), elaborate song.

Food. Insects, esp. aquatic larvae; small crustacea, mollusca, and fishes; flatworms; some vegetable matter.

Breeding. Nest large, domed, with side entrance; built of moss and grass, lined with leaves; placed in hollow of wall, bridge, tree roots, etc., or on rock or fallen tree in midst of stream.

Eggs. 3 to 7 (usually 4 or 5); white, immaculate. Incubated by ♀.

Young. Nidicolous. Downy. Fed by ♂ and ♀.

Technical diagnosis. Ridgway, pt. 3, 1904: 675.

Classification. Hellmayr, pt. 7, 1934: 106–110; and E. Hartert, *Die Vögel der paläarktischen Fauna,* Berlin, 1, 1910: 788–799; *Ergänzungsb.,* Heft 4, 1935: 344–345 (genus *Cinclus*).

References. Bent, No. 195: 96–113; Baker, *Fauna,* 2, 1924: 1–6; Witherby, 2, 1938: 220–226.

E. Eggebrecht, Brutbiologie der Wasseramsel (*Cinclus cinclus aquaticus* (Bechst.)), *Jour. f. Ornith.,* 85, 1937: 636–676, illus.

G. C. S. Ingram, H. M. Salmon, and B. W. Tucker, The Movements of the Dipper under Water, *Brit. Birds,* 32, 1938: 58–63.

TROGLODYTIDAE

Wren family (63 species)

Fig. 137. Gray-breasted Wood-wren (*Henicorhina leucophrys*). Total length $4\frac{1}{2}$ in. (114 mm.).

Physical characteristics. Length—95 to 222 mm. ($3\frac{3}{4}$ to $8\frac{3}{4}$ in.). Plumage—reddish-, grayish-, olive-, or blackish-brown, often with white or chestnut areas, and typically barred, streaked, and/or spotted with white, buff, dark brown, or black, esp. on wings, tail, and sides. Bill rather slender, medium to long and curved. Wings short and rounded. Tail short to long. Legs and feet strong; anterior toes partly adherent; claws long. Sexes alike or nearly so.

Range. Northwest Africa (Tunis to Morocco), Europe (exc. extreme n.), Asia (exc. extreme n. and extreme s.), N. America (exc. extreme n.), and S. America. Northern forms migratory.

Habits. Typically solitary; certain tropical spp. somewhat gregarious when not breeding. Flight weak. Very active and inquisitive. Tail commonly carried erect. Voice—song highly developed; in many spp. the ♀ also sings, and antiphonal singing is recorded.

Food. Insects, spiders, etc.

Breeding. Polygamy frequent in at least some spp. Nest in cavities in trees, rocks, buildings, or banks; or build covered nest in grass, reeds, bushes, or trees; ♂♂ may make several unlined nests, not used for breeding ("cock nests").

Eggs. 2 to 10; white or brown, speckled or immaculate. Incubated by ♀ (or, in some spp., by ♂ and ♀?).

Young. Nidicolous. With some down on upper parts. Cared for by ♂ and ♀, or by ♀ alone.

Technical diagnosis. Ridgway, pt. 3, 1904: 473.

Classification. Hellmayr, pt. 7, 1934: 110–294; and E. Hartert, *Die Vögel der paläarktischen Fauna,* Berlin, 1, 1910: 776–784; *Ergänzungsb.,* Heft 4, 1935: 339–342 (genus *Troglodytes* only).

References. Bent, No. 195: 113–295; Witherby, 2, 1938: 213–219; Baker, *Fauna,* 1, 1922: 444–448 (genus *Troglodytes* only).

H. N. Kluijver *et al.,* De levenswijze van den winterkoning, *Troglodytes tr. troglodytes* (L.), *Limosa,* 13, 1940: 1–51 (with English summary).

A. F. Skutch, Social and Sleeping Habits of Central American Wrens, *Auk,* 57, 1940: 293–312, pl. 5.

S. C. Kendeigh, Territorial and Mating Behavior of the House Wren, *Illinois Biol. Monogr.,* 18, No. 3, 1941.

MIMIDAE

Mockingbird family (30 species)

Fig. 138. Brown Thrasher (*Toxostoma rufum*). Total length 11 in. (280 mm.).

Physical characteristics. Length—203 to 305 mm. (8 to 12 in.). Plumage—blue-gray, gray, gray-brown, or reddish brown above. Under parts from paler than back to white, slightly to boldly spotted in many spp. One sp. entirely iridescent black. Wings and tail blackish in some spp. Several spp. have white or white-tipped outer tail feathers and/or white areas or spotting on wings. Iris straw-colored, orange, or red in some spp. Bill strong, medium to long, nearly straight to sharply decurved. Rictal bristles reduced but always present. Wings short and rounded; tail long. Legs rather long. Base of middle toe adherent to outer toe. Sexes alike or nearly so.

Range. North America (from s. Canada), through Central America and the West Indies, to S. America (exc. s. third of Chile and Argentina). Migratory in higher latitudes.

Habits. Solitary or in pairs. Arboreal, but most spp. feed on ground, and some are largely terrestrial. Most spp. make only short flights. Voice—very highly developed song; harsh alarm notes. Some spp. mimic the songs and calls of other birds.

Food. Insects; fruit, seeds.

Breeding. Bulky, cup-shaped nest in bushes or on ground.

Eggs. 2 to 5; buffy, blue, or green; speckled in most spp. Incubated by ♂ and ♀, or by ♀ alone.

Young. Nidicolous. With some down on upper parts. Cared for by ♂ and ♀.

Technical diagnosis. Ridgway, pt. 4, 1907: 180–181 [but omit *Calyptophilus,* now considered a tanager].

Classification. Hellmayr, pt. 7, 1934: 295–350.

References. Bent, No. 195: 295–435.

W. H. Hudson, *Birds of La Plata,* London, vol. 1, 1920: 5–15.

L. S. V. Venables, Nesting Behaviour of the Galapagos Mockingbird, *Ibis,* 1940: 629–639.

W. L. Engels, Structural Adaptations in Thrashers (Mimidae: Genus Toxostoma) . . . , *Univ. Calif. Publ. Zool.,* 42, 1940: 341–400.

A. F. Skutch, Life History of the White-breasted Blue Mockingbird, *Condor,* 52, 1950: 220–227.

TURDIDAE

Thrush family (305 species)

Fig. 139. Song Thrush (*Turdus ericetorum*). Total length 9 in. (228 mm.).

Physical characteristics. Length—114 to 330 mm. (4½ to 13 in.). Plumage—highly glossy in a few spp.; browns, grays, olives, black, blue, usually in soft blended combinations, sometimes with bold contrast (e.g., black with white or bright chestnut), sometimes marked with red, rarely with green or yellow. Most juvenal plumages (and some adult) at least partly spotted or squamate. Bill of medium length, slender to fairly stout. Wings short and rounded to long and pointed; tail very short and truncate to long and graduate (deeply forked in a few spp.). Legs and feet typically stout; legs short in some spp. Most spp. with "booted" tarsus. Sexes alike or unlike.

Range. World-wide, exc. extreme n., New Zealand, and some oceanic islands. Most spp. migratory.

Habits. Solitary, but some flock in nonbreeding season. Arboreal or terrestrial. Flight weak to strong. Voice—extremely varied; some spp. have highly developed song.

Food. Varied (animal and vegetable).

Breeding. Nest an open cup (rarely domed) in bush or tree, or on ground; or nest in tree cavity or among rocks (rarely in hole in ground).

Eggs. 2 to 6; white, greenish or bluish white, olive-green; speckled or (uncommonly) immaculate. Incubated by ♀, or by ♂ and ♀.

Young. Nidicolous. Downy. Cared for by ♂ and ♀.

Technical diagnosis. Ridgway, pt. 4, 1907: 1–4.

Classification. S. D. Ripley, *Postilla* (Yale Peabody Museum), No. 13, 1952: 1–48 [but omit *Zeledonia* and *Prunella*].

References. Bent, No. 196: 1–330; Witherby, 2, 1938: 104–204; Baker, *Fauna,* 2, 1924: 7–187.

H. Seebohm and R. B. Sharpe, A Monograph of the Turdidae, London, 2 vols., 1898–1902.

G. J. Wallace, Bicknell's Thrush, Its Taxonomy, Distribution, and Life History, *Proc. Boston Soc. Nat. Hist.,* 41, No. 6, 1939.

D. Lack, *The Life of the Robin,* London, rev. ed. 1946; 2nd rev. ed., 1953 (Pelican Books).

J. Buxton, *The Redstart,* London, 1950.

Synonymy: The Enicuridae and Myiadestidae are included.

ZELEDONIIDAE

Wren-thrush family

(1 species)

Fig. 140. Wren-thrush (*Zeledonia coronata*). Total length 4½ in. (114 mm.).

Physical characteristics. Length—114 to 120 mm. (4½ to 4¾ in.). Plumage—soft and lax. Crown rufous orange, bordered laterally with dull black stripes. Nape, back, wings, tail, and flanks dark brownish olive; rest of plumage slate. Bill weak, somewhat flattened. Neck short. Wings and tail short, rounded, and soft. Legs rather long; feet large. Sexes alike.

Range. High mountain peaks (above 5000 ft.) of Costa Rica and Panama. Habitat—dense humid forest. Nonmigratory.

Habits. Solitary. "Continually creeping and hopping about under the masses of half decayed branches, searching for insects and larvae, and would be rarely seen or collected were it not for their song." Voice—"a clear, musical whistle . . . repeats the same note from six to eight times with the same interval between . . . the length of the note and the interval is about the same" (Carriker, 1910).

Food. "Insects and larvae."

Breeding. Nest not described.
Eggs. Not described.
Young. Not described.

Technical diagnosis. Ridgway, pt. 4, 1907: 69–70, 885, pl. 2.

Classification. Hellmayr, pt. 7, 1934: 484.

References. W. P. Pycraft, On the Systematic Position of *Zeledonia coronata,* with some Observations on the Position of the Turdidae, *Ibis,* 1905: 1–24; pls. 1 (col.), 2.

M. A. Carriker, Jr., An Annotated List of the Birds of Costa Rica including Cocos Island, *Ann. Carnegie Mus.,* 6, 1910: 332, 742–743.

SYLVIIDAE

Old-world Warbler family

(398 species)

Fig. 141. Blackcap (*Sylvia atricapilla*). Total length 6 in. (152 mm.).

Physical characteristics. Length—89 to 292 mm. (3½ to 11½ in). Plumage—typically pale, blending shades of brown, gray, or olive-green (some are white or yellow below); with little pattern, but a few spp. are streaked or barred below, or have contrasting head or throat. (The spp. in *Malurus* are glossy blue, chestnut, red, white, black in bold contrasts.) Young not spotted. Bill very small to rather long; slender to stout; straight or curved. Wings of medium length and rounded. Tail short to long, often graduated; broad and fan-shaped to vestigial. Legs short to medium; slender to rather stout. Sexes alike in most spp.

Range. North America (exc. extreme n.) s. to central Brazil and e. Peru; the Old World (exc. extreme n. and some oceanic islands). Many spp. migratory.

Habits. Solitary or gregarious. Arboreal, or frequent brush, reeds, etc. Flight weak. Voice—variety of notes and songs; some spp. have well-developed song.

Food. Insects and spiders; snails.

Breeding. Nest cup-shaped, domed, or placed in a curled leaf—in tree, bush, or marsh vegetation.

Eggs. 3 to 12; white, pink, or buff; speckled in most spp. Incubated by ♂ and ♀, or by ♀ alone.

Young. Nidicolous. With or without down. Cared for by ♂ and ♀.

Technical diagnosis. Ridgway, pt. 3, 1904: 691–693.

Classification. New World: Hellmayr, pt. 7, 1934: 484–514; pt. 3, 1924: 205–213 [*Ramphocaenus* and *Microbates*]. Old World: R. B. Sharpe, Hand-list of the Genera and Species of Birds, 4, 1903: 185–246 and 343–345.

References. Bent, No. 196: 330–418; Witherby, 1, 1938: 314–320, and 2, 1938: 1–104; Baker, *Fauna,* 2, 1924: 382–544.

H. E. Howard, *The British Warblers,* London, 1907–1915, 2 vols.

H. Lynes, Review of the Genus Cisticola, *Ibis,* 1930, Suppl. (673 + vii pp., 20 pls.).

C. B. Ticehurst, A Systematic Review of the Genus Phylloscopus, Brit. Mus. Nat. Hist., London, 1938 (193 pp., 2 col. pls.).

P. E. Brown and M. G. Davies, *Reed-warblers,* East Molesey, Surrey, 1949: 1–127, pls. 1–33.

Synonymy: The Regulidae, Acanthizidae, Polioptilidae, and Maluridae are included.

MUSCICAPIDAE

Old-world Flycatcher family

(328 species)

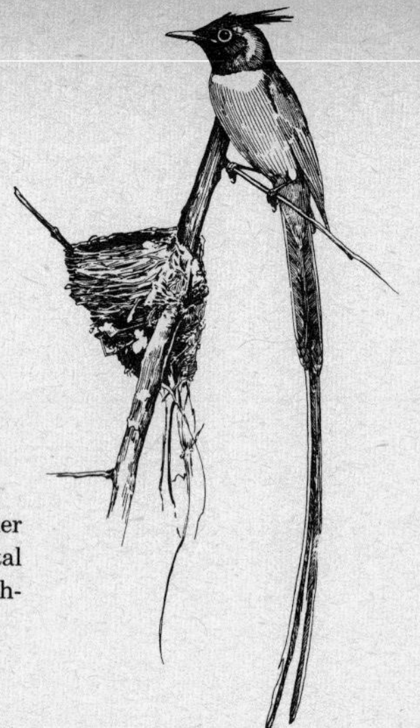

Fig. 142. Paradise Flycatcher (*Terpsiphone paradisi*). Total length (without central tail feathers) 8 in. (203 mm.).

Physical characteristics. Length—89 to 228 mm. ($3\frac{1}{2}$ to 9 in.). *Terpsiphone,* with streamerlike central tail feathers, may reach 533 mm. (21 in.). Plumage—extremely diverse in color: from dull gray or brown to brilliant blue, red, chestnut, yellow, black and white, etc.; usually in solid areas or broad bands. Young typically spotted. A few spp. crested; a few with face wattles. Bill from very narrow to very broad and flat, but typically broad. Wings short and rounded to long and rather pointed. Tail very short and narrow to extremely long and fanlike (or with very long central feathers). Legs rather short. Sexes alike or unlike.

Range. Old World (exc. extreme n. Asia) and e. in the Pacific to Hawaiian Ids. and Marquesas. Many spp. migratory.

Habits. Solitary. Largely arboreal, but some feed on the ground. Many spp. sally from exposed perch to capture prey in air or on ground. Voice—varied; some spp. have a well-developed (but not loud) song.

Food. Insects and spiders.

Breeding. Cup-shaped nest, placed on a branch of bush or tree, in tree cavity, on bank or ledge of rock.

Eggs. 2 to 6; spotted in most spp. Incubated by ♂ and ♀, or by ♀ alone.

Young. Nidicolous. With sparse down. Cared for by ♂ and ♀.

Technical diagnosis. Witherby, 1, 1938: 299.

Classification. R. B. Sharpe, Hand-list of the Genera and Species of Birds, 3, 1901: 204–286.

References. Witherby, 1, 1938: 299–314; Baker, *Fauna,* 2, 1924: 199–282.

V. MacCaughey, The Hawaiian Elepaio, *Auk,* 36, 1919: 22–35.

F. S. Parsons and J. N. McGilp, The Two Red-throated Whistlers, *Emu,* 35, 1935: 113–126, col. pls. 7, 8.

O. Steinfatt, Beobachtungen über das Brutleben des Grauschnäppers, *Muscicapa str. striata* in der Rominter Heide, *Jour. f. Ornith.,* 85, 1937: 624–635.

N. Jack, Territory and Nesting in the Rufous Whistler, *Emu,* 49, 1949: 26–34.

D. Summers-Smith, Breeding Biology of the Spotted Flycatcher, *Brit. Birds,* 45, 1952: 153–167.

Synonymy: The Falcunculidae, Pachycephalidae, and Turnagridae are included.

PRUNELLIDAE

Hedge-sparrow family (11 species)

Fig. 143. Altai Hedge-sparrow (*Prunella himalayana*). Total length 6 in. (152 mm.).

Physical characteristics. Length—127 to 177 mm. (5 to 7 in.). Plumage—brown (to black), gray, buffy, and chestnut; streaked above (exc. one sp.), plain or streaked below; chin and/or breast in contrasting color (sometimes spotted) in most spp.; light superciliary line in some. Bill medium in length, slender, finely pointed. Wings short and rounded to moderately long and pointed; tail short to moderately long, even or emarginate. Legs and feet strong. Sexes alike or nearly so.

Range. North Africa, Europe, Asia (exc. s. peninsulas). Habitat—brush or barrens. Migratory (only altitudinally in some spp.).

Habits. Most spp. gregarious. Largely terrestrial, feeding chiefly on or near ground, but some spp. perch in trees, esp. to sing. Flight strong and rapid in most spp., but brief, and usually low; straight or undulating. On ground walk or hop. Characteristically flick wings and jerk tail. Voice—loud metallic calls; twittering and chattering notes; warbling song.

Food. Insects and other small invertebrates; berries; seeds in winter.

Breeding. Nest a lined open cup of plant fragments, feathers, etc., placed on ground or in low shrubs (rarely at tip of tree branch), or among rocks or in a rock crevice.

Eggs. 2 to 7 (usually 3 or 4); blue, immaculate (rarely spotted). Incubated by ♂ and ♀, or by ♀ alone.

Young. Nidicolous. Downy. Fed by ♂ and ♀.

Technical diagnosis. Witherby, 2, 1938: 205.

Classification. S. D. Ripley, *Postilla* (Yale Peabody Museum), No. 13, 1952: 35–36.

References. Bent, No. 197: 1–3; Witherby, 2, 1938: 205–213; Baker, *Fauna,* 2, 1924: 187–198; Baker, *Nidification,* 2, 1933: 163–172.

H. E. Dresser, *A History of the Birds of Europe,* London, vol. 3, 1873–1880: 27–45, col. pls. 99–101.

O. Steinfatt, Das Brutleben der Heckenbraunelle, *Prunella m. modularis, Ornith. Monatsber.,* 46, 1938: 65–76.

Synonym: Accentoridae.

MOTACILLIDAE

Pipit family (48 species)

Fig. 144. White Wagtail (*Motacilla alba*). Total length $7\frac{1}{2}$ in. (190 mm.).

Physical characteristics. Length—127 to 222 mm. (5 to $8\frac{3}{4}$ in.). Plumage—black, gray, brown, to olive or yellow, plain or broadly streaked. Tail and often wings edged with white, buff, or yellow. Under parts in most spp. yellow, buff, or black and white, plain or streaked or spotted; with boldly contrasting chin, breast, and/or pectoral band in some spp. Bill medium to long; slender and pointed. Neck short; body slender. Wings medium to long and pointed; tail typically long. Legs medium to long; toes long; hind toe elongated in most spp. Sexes alike or unlike.

Range. World-wide, exc. extreme n. and some oceanic islands. Many spp. migratory.

Habits. Rather gregarious exc. in breeding season. Mainly terrestrial. Flight strong. Walk when on ground. "Tail-wagging" habit characteristic of most spp. Voice—many sharp call notes; a song, usually simple and repetitive, delivered in many cases on the wing while mounting or while hovering at considerable heights (several hundred feet).

Food. Insects, spiders, mollusca; some vegetable matter.

Breeding. Cuplike, or sometimes domed, nest on ground, or lined nest in cavities of rocks, walls, or trees.

Eggs. 2 to 7; white or colored, typically speckled. Incubated by ♀, or by ♂ and ♀.

Young. Nidicolous. With thick down on upper parts. Cared for by ♂ and ♀, or by ♀ alone.

Technical diagnosis. Ridgway, pt. 3, 1904: 1–2.

Classification. Old World: R. B. Sharpe, Hand-list of the Genera and Species of Birds, 5, 1909: 137–153. New World: Hellmayr, pt. 8, 1935: 82–103.

References. Bent, No. 197: 3–62; Witherby, 1, 1938: 187–233; Baker, *Fauna,* 3, 1926: 254–301.

G. Pickwell, The American Pipit in Its Arctic-Alpine Home, *Auk,* 64, 1947: 1–14, pls. 1–4.

Stuart Smith, *The Yellow Wagtail,* London, 1950.

R. E. Moreau, The African Mountain Wagtail *Motacilla clara* at the Nest, in *Ornith. als biologische Wissenschaft* [Festschrift v. Stresemann], Heidelberg, 1949, pp. 183–191.

BOMBYCILLIDAE

Waxwing family (3 species)[1]

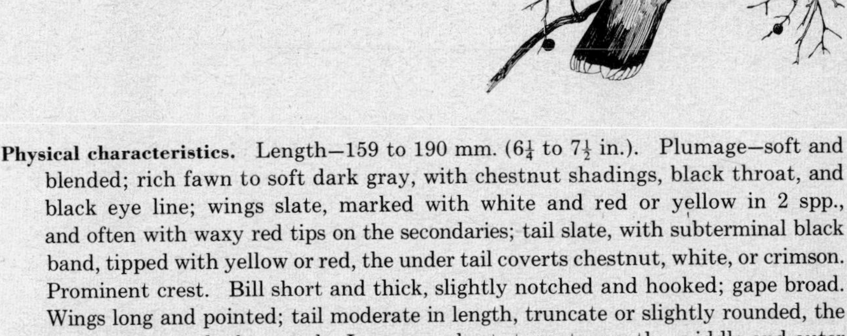

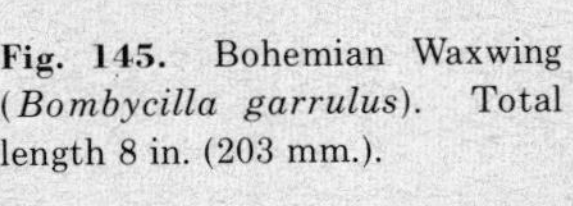

Fig. 145. Bohemian Waxwing (*Bombycilla garrulus*). Total length 8 in. (203 mm.).

Physical characteristics. Length—159 to 190 mm. ($6\frac{1}{4}$ to $7\frac{1}{2}$ in.). Plumage—soft and blended; rich fawn to soft dark gray, with chestnut shadings, black throat, and black eye line; wings slate, marked with white and red or yellow in 2 spp., and often with waxy red tips on the secondaries; tail slate, with subterminal black band, tipped with yellow or red, the under tail coverts chestnut, white, or crimson. Prominent crest. Bill short and thick, slightly notched and hooked; gape broad. Wings long and pointed; tail moderate in length, truncate or slightly rounded, the tail coverts much elongated. Legs very short; toes strong, the middle and outer toes united basally; claws long. Sexes nearly alike.

Range. Subarctic and temperate portions of N. Hemisphere (erratic in local distribution). Habitat—generally coniferous and birch forest. Migratory.

Habits. Gregarious, esp. in nonbreeding season. Arboreal (but often feed on ground). Flight rapid, light, and graceful. Catch insects on wing. Often tame and rather sluggish. Voice—soft, lisping call; high trill; short, loud chatter.

Food. Fruit, esp. berries; insects; flowers.

Breeding. Nest a bulky open cup of twigs, moss, and grass, lined with hair, down, and feathers; usually placed in trees.

Eggs. 3 to 7 (usually 4 or 5); ashy-gray or -blue, spotted and flecked with dark brown and black. Incubated by ♀ (at least chiefly).

Young. Nidicolous. Naked. Fed by ♂ and ♀.

Technical diagnosis. Ridgway, pt. 3, 1904: 103–104.

Classification. New World: Hellmayr, pt. 8, 1935: 103–105. Old World: E. Hartert, *Die Vögel der paläarktischen Fauna,* Berlin, 1, 1910: 455–458; *Ergänzungsb.,* Heft 3, 1934: 222–223.

References. Bent, No. 197: 62–102; Witherby, 1, 1938: 296–299; Baker, *Fauna,* 3, 1926: 223–224.

R. B. Lea, A Study of the Nesting Habits of the Cedar Waxwing, *Wils. Bull.,* 54, 1942: 225–237.

L. S. Putnam, The Life History of the Cedar Waxwing, *Wils. Bull.,* 61, 1949: 141–182.

M. D. Arvey, Phylogeny of the Waxwings and Allied Birds, *Univ. Kans. Publ., Mus. Zool.,* 3, 1951: 473–530.

Synonym: Ampelidae.

[1] *Hypocolius ampelinus* of Iraq (and southward and eastward) also seems to be related to this family (Delacour and Amadon, *Ibis,* 91, 1949: 427–429). It is sometimes considered a separate family, Hypocoliidae.

PTILOGONATIDAE

Silky-flycatcher family (4 species)

Fig. 146. Phainopepla (*Phainopepla nitens*). Total length $7\frac{1}{2}$ in. (190 mm.).

Physical characteristics. Length—184 to 248 mm. ($7\frac{1}{4}$ to $9\frac{3}{4}$ in.). Plumage—silky; never entirely unicolored, but never spotted or streaked, even in young; black, gray, brown, with (in 2 spp.) yellow and olive-yellow markings; large white central areas on wings or tail. Crested. Bill small, rather broad. Wings rather short; tail long. Legs short. Sexes unlike (*Phainoptila,* which does not conform to some of the above, should perhaps not be included in this family).

Range. Southwestern U. S. (s. Utah and c. California) through highlands of Mexico and Central America to w. Panama. Habitat—arid brushy country. Migratory in part.

Habits (based mainly on *Phainopepla*). Somewhat gregarious. Arboreal. Shy, active. Capture insects on wing. Voice—weak warbling song.

Food. Largely vegetable, especially mistletoe and other berries; also insects.

Breeding. Shallow nest in crotches or saddled on limbs of trees, 8 to 20 (sometimes 50) ft. up, built chiefly by ♂.

Eggs (*Phainopepla*). 2 to 3 (sometimes 4); grayish white, speckled profusely with brown and black. Incubated by ♂ and ♀.

Young. Nidicolous. With sparse down. Cared for by ♂ and ♀.

Technical diagnosis. Ridgway, pt. 3, 1904: 113–114.

Classification. Hellmayr, 13, pt. 8, 1935: 105–109.

References. Bent, No. 197: 102–114.

J. E. Crouch, Distribution and Habitat Relationships of the Phainopepla, *Auk,* 60, 1943: 319–333.

A. L. and R. M. Rand, Breeding Notes on the Phainopepla, *Auk,* 60, 1943: 333–341.

R. J. Newman, A Nest of the Mexican Ptilogonys, *Condor,* 52, 1950: 157–158.

DULIDAE

Palmchat family (1 species)

Fig. 147. Palmchat (*Dulus dominicus*). Total length 7 in. (177 mm.).

Physical characteristics. Length—about 177 mm. (7 in.). Plumage—olive to dark brown above, the feathers of head with dusky centers; the rump and upper tail coverts more greenish; wings and tail edged with yellowish olive; yellowish white below, with broad, dark brown shaft streaks. Bill rather long, heavy, laterally compressed, the upper mandible decurved. Wings medium in length, rounded; tail rather long. Legs and feet stout; toes and claws rather long. Sexes alike.

Range. Hispaniola and Gonave in the West Indies. Nonmigratory.

Habits. Gregarious. Arboreal. Noisy. Voice—a variety of chattering notes, some harsh and some "quite pleasing" (usually uttered in chorus).

Food. Berries, blossoms.

Breeding. Nest a large communal structure of twigs, usually placed in top of palm, with several compartments (lined with shreds of bark, grass, etc.), each having separate outside entrance; or smaller (sometimes single) nests in pines.

Eggs. 4; white, heavily spotted (in wreath at blunt end) with deep purplish gray. Incubated by ?

Young. Nidicolous. Naked at hatching? Cared for by ?

Technical diagnosis. Ridgway, pt. 3, 1904: 125.

Classification. J. Bond, *Check-list of Birds of the West Indies,* Philadelphia, 1950: 124.

References. A. Wetmore and B. H. Swales, The Birds of Haiti and the Dominican Republic, *U. S. Natl. Mus. Bull.,* 155, 1931: 345–352, pls. 23, 24.

J. Bond, *Birds of the West Indies,* Philadelphia, 1936: 298–299.

ARTAMIDAE

Wood-swallow family (10 species)

Fig. 148. White-browed Wood-swallow (*Artamus superciliosus*). Total length 7½ in. (190 mm.).

Physical characteristics. Length—146 to 203 mm. (5¾ to 8 in.). Plumage—soft and fine-textured. Head and upper parts plain black, slate-gray, brownish gray, or brown (the rump or whole back white in a few spp.). Under parts white, vinaceous ashy, gray-brown, brown, or chestnut. Tip of tail and/or margin of primaries white in some spp.; white superciliary line in one. Bill stout, rather long, slightly curved, rounded in cross section, pointed; gape wide. Neck short; body stout. Wings very long and pointed; tail medium in length, square or emarginate. Legs very short but stout; feet strong. Sexes alike or nearly so.

Range. India, Burma, Siam, Indo-China, s. and sw. China, East Indies, Philippines, Australia, and e. to Fiji Ids. Habitat—clearings or open country, esp. near water. Some spp. migratory.

Habits. Strongly gregarious. Rest on occasion in clustered masses. Arboreal. Flight gliding, very graceful. Usually feed on the wing. Sit quietly on exposed perch. Voice—twittering notes; harsh cries.

Food. Insects; rarely seeds.

Breeding. Sometimes colonial. Shallow cup-shaped nest in low tree or bush, or on a stump; or nest built in shallow cavity in tree.

Eggs. 2 to 4; whitish or buffy, speckled and blotched. Incubated by ♂ and ♀.

Young. Nidicolous. With some down on upper parts. Cared for by ♂ and ♀.

Technical diagnosis. Baker, *Fauna,* 2, 1924: 348.

Classification. Mathews, *Systema Avium Australasianarum,* London, pt. 2, 1930: 634–638; Baker, *Fauna,* 2, 1924: 348–350. [The spp. are: *Artamus fuscus, A. leucorhynchus, A. maximus, A. insignis, A. cinereus* (incl. *melanops*), *A. monachus, A. personatus, A. superciliosus, A. cyanopterus,* and *A. minor.*]

References. A. J. Campbell, *Nests and Eggs of Australian Birds,* Sheffield, England, vol. 1, 1901: 461–475.

A. F. D'Ombrain, The White-browed Wood-Swallow, *Emu,* 33, 1934: 292–297, pl. 51.

D. L. Serventy and H. M. Whittell, *A Handbook of the Birds of Western Australia,* Perth, 1948: 302–305.

VANGIDAE

Vanga-shrike family

(12 species)

Fig. 149. Hook-billed Vanga (*Vanga curvirostris*). Total length $9\frac{1}{2}$ in. (241 mm.).

Physical characteristics. Length—127 to 311 mm. (5 to $12\frac{1}{4}$ in.). Plumage—black (with green or purple metallic reflections) above and all or largely white below; chestnut and/or gray areas in some spp.; head white in 2 spp. *Oriolia* is all black with metallic reflections; *Cyanolanius* is brilliant blue above, white below; *Euryceros* is black and chestnut, with blue bill. Bill typically rather long and robust, hooked and toothed (long, slender, and sickle-shaped in *Falculea;* heavy and casqued in *Euryceros*). Wings short to rather long, rounded; tail moderately long and abruptly truncate in most spp. (rounded in 3 spp.). Legs and feet strong. Sexes alike or unlike.

Range. Madagascar. Habitat—forest and brushy areas. Nonmigratory.

Habits. Most spp. gregarious (often in mixed flocks of other birds). Arboreal. Flight strong in most spp. Fly or jump from branch to branch in search of insects. Voice—shrill whistle; chattering calls; harsh repetitive notes.

Food. Insects; small lizards, amphibians.

Breeding. Nest (*Falculea*) a large shallow structure of sticks, lined with grass, usually in fork, high in tree.

Eggs (described in 2 spp.; clutch size not recorded). White or green, spotted with pinkish brown. Incubation not recorded.

Young. Not described.

Technical diagnosis. A. Reichenow, *Die Vögel: Handbuch der Systematischen Ornithologie, Stuttgart,* vol. 2, 1914: 278, 291 ("Vanginae"). (For photograph of skins of 7 spp., see D. Amadon, *Bull. Amer. Mus. Nat. Hist.,* 95, 1950: pl. 13.)

Classification. W. L. Sclater, *Systema Avium Aethiopicarum,* London, pt. 2, 1930: 603–606 (and add *Falculea,* p. 671).

References. A. Milne Edwards and A. Grandidier, *Histoire physique, naturelle et politique de Madagascar,* vol. 12, *Histoire naturelle des oiseaux,* Paris, vol. 1, 1882: 303–311; 1885: 409–444; vol. 3, 1879: col. pls. 117 and (various) 156–172.

A. L. Rand, The Distribution and Habits of Madagascar Birds, *Amer. Mus. Nat. Hist. Bull.,* 72, 1936: 460–468.

Synonymy: The Eurycerotidae ["Aerocharidae"] and Falculidae are included.

LANIIDAE

Shrike family

(72 species)

Fig. 150. Loggerhead Shrike (*Lanius ludovicianus*). Total length 9 in. (228 mm.).

Physical characteristics. Length—159 to 368 mm. (6¼ to 14½ in.). Plumage—many spp. are gray or brown above and white below, with face and flight feathers boldly patterned in black and white; some African spp. are brightly colored (e.g., green and yellow, bright red) or entirely black; a very few spp. have streaked or barred areas. Bill strong, hooked, and in some spp. toothed; head large. Wings medium; tail long and narrow. Legs and feet strong; claws sharp. Sexes alike or unlike.

Range. Africa, Europe, Asia (s. to Timor and New Guinea), and N. America (s. to Tehuantepec). Habitat—open or semiopen country, rarely forest edge. Northern forms migratory.

Habits. Typically solitary. Watch for prey from exposed perches. Bold and aggressive. Flight strong. Most spp. impale their prey on thorns. Voice—great variety of notes; many spp. have well-developed song.

Food. Insects and small reptiles, birds and mammals.

Breeding. Deep bulky nest, usually placed in bushes or trees. Built—varying with the spp.—by ♂, by ♀, or by both.

Eggs. 2 to 8; spotted. Incubated chiefly by ♀, assisted by ♂ (in the few spp. studied).

Young. Nidicolous. With some down on upper parts. Fed by ♂ and ♀.

Technical diagnosis. Ridgway, pt. 3, 1904: 232–234.

Classification. Africa: W. L. Sclater, *Systema Avium Aethiopicarum,* London, 1930: 607–639. Eurasia: E. Hartert, *Die Vögel der paläarktischen Fauna,* Berlin, 1, 1907: 414–454; Suppl., 1934: 210–222. America: Hellmayr, pt. 8, 1935: 211–217.

References. Bent, No. 197: 114–182; Witherby, 1, 1938: 277–296.

Alden H. Miller, Systematic Revision and Natural History of the American Shrikes (Lanius), *Univ. Calif. Publ. Zool.,* 38, no. 2, 1931: 11–242, 65 figs.

T. Schreurs, *Lanius collurio* L. und *Lanius senator* L. Ein Beitrag zur Biologie zweier Würgerarten, *Jour. f. Ornith.,* 84, 1936: 442–470, illus.

Alden H. Miller, A Comparison of Behavior of Certain North American and European Shrikes, *Condor,* 39, 1937: 119–122.

G. Olivier, Monographie des Pies-Grièches du genre Lanius, Rouen, 1944.

Synonymy: The Laniariidae are included.

PRIONOPIDAE

Wood-shrike family

(13 species)

Fig. 151. Black-winged Helmet-shrike (*Prionops cristata*). Total length 8½ in. (216 mm.).

Physical characteristics. Length—190 to 254 mm. (7½ to 10 in.). Plumage—soft. Bold patterns of black (or brown) and white, or black and brown: some spp. with areas of gray, chestnut, or yellow. Tail conspicuously marked with white in most spp. Brightly colored fleshy orbital ring (exc. in *Eurocephalus*). Most spp. crested. Bill of medium length, rather stout, hooked. Wings medium to rather long. Tail medium to long; rounded. Legs short but strong. Sexes alike or nearly so.

Range. Africa s. of Sahara (exc. Madagascar). Nonmigratory exc. for local movements.

Habits. Gregarious. Largely arboreal but often descend to ground for food; also capture insects on the wing. Flight buoyant, but slow and of short duration. Voice—harsh, chattering notes; a nasal humming sound. Make snapping sound with bill.

Food. Insects.

Breeding. Some spp. colonial. Cup-shaped nest (of grass, leaves, and rootlets, bound with cobwebs) placed in trees.

Eggs. 2 to 6 (probably 2 or more ♀♀ lay in some nests); white or bluish green, spotted. Incubated by ♂ and ♀; also probably by several associated adults (*Prionops*).

Young. Nidicolous. Downy. Cared for by ♂ and ♀; also by several associated adults (*Prionops*).

Technical diagnosis. Bannerman, 5, 1939: 337; E. Mayr, *Ibis,* 1943: 216–218.

Classification. W. L. Sclater, *Systema Avium Aethiopicarum,* London, 1930: 597–601 (*Prionops, Sigmodus, Eurocephalus*).

References. Bannerman, 5, 1939: xxxvi–xxxvii, 337–348, col. pl. 10.

A. C. Stark and W. L. Sclater, *The Birds of South Africa,* London, vol. 2, 1901: 13–15, 47–52.

A. Roberts, *The Birds of South Africa,* London, 1940: 309–310 (Nos. 727–730), col. pl. 46.

F. M. Benson, Field-notes from Nyasaland, *Ostrich,* 17, 1946: 298, 308–314.

CALLAEIDAE

Wattlebird family
(3 species)

Fig. 152. Huia (*Neomorpha acutirostris*). Total length 21 in. (534 mm.). Upper, male; lower, female.

Physical characteristics. Length—254 to 534 mm. (10 to 21 in.). Plumage—plain blue-gray, brown, or black (back and crissum bright ferruginous in *Philesturnus,* tail broadly tipped with white in *Neomorpha*). Bill strong; from short and heavy to long and sickle-shaped. Large orange or blue wattles at corner of mouth. Wings weak. Legs and feet large and strong. Sexes alike in plumage but unlike in size, bill shape, or size of wattle. Extreme sexual dimorphism in bill of *Neomorpha.*

Range. New Zealand. Habitat—forests. Nonmigratory.

Habits. Usually found in pairs or small flocks. Very active, but nearly flightless. Progress by long hops from branch to branch or along the ground. Voice—great variety of musical whistling and flutelike sounds; rapid series of harsh notes; mewing.

Food. Insects, fruit, leaves, nectar.

Breeding. Nest of sticks lined with grass and feathers, in crotches or in cavities of trees.

Eggs. 2 to 3; gray, spotted and blotched with brown. Incubated by ♂ and ♀?

Young. Nidicolous. Some down on upper parts. Fed by ♂ and ♀.

Technical diagnosis. C. R. Stonor, *Ibis,* 1942: 1–18. (For photograph of skins of the 3 spp., see D. Amadon, *Bull. Amer. Mus. Nat. Hist.,* 95, 1950: pl. 14.)

Classification. W. R. B. Oliver, *New Zealand Birds,* Wellington, 1930: 494–503, pls. 5–6.

References. W. L. Buller, *A History of the Birds of New Zealand* (2nd ed.), London, vol. 1, 1888: 1–23, pls. 1–3; Suppl., vol. 2, 1905: 154–167.

J. C. M'Lean, Bush-Birds of New Zealand. Part IV, *Emu,* 11, 1912: 229–234.

H. Guthrie-Smith, *Bird Life on Island and Shore,* London, 1925: 156–174.

C. R. Stonor, Anatomical Notes on the New Zealand Wattled Crow (*Callaeas*), with especial Reference to its Powers of Flight, *Ibis,* 1942: 1–18, figs. 1–10.

H. R. McKenzie, Breeding of Kokako, *Notornis,* 4, 1951: 70–76, pls. 13–18.

Synonymy: The Creadiontidae of Oliver are here included. Also, *Callaeas wilsoni* is here considered a subspecies of *C. cinerea.*

STURNIDAE

Starling family (104 species)

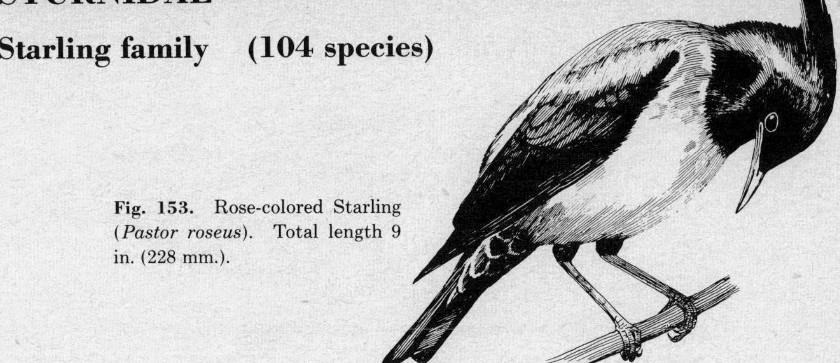

Fig. 153. Rose-colored Starling (*Pastor roseus*). Total length 9 in. (228 mm.).

Physical characteristics. Length—177 to 432 mm. (7 to 17 in.). Plumage—silky, the contour feathers, esp. on head and neck, often lanceolate. Dark metallic purples, greens, blues, and bronze (some spp. spotted, esp. in winter plumage, or with chestnut and/or white areas); black (usually glossy), with white, gray, or yellow (rarely crimson) markings; gray (or brown) and buff, streaked below in some spp. Some spp. with bare areas and/or wattles on head; some crested. Bill typically straight and rather long and slender (heavy and/or hooked in some spp.). Wings short and rounded to long and pointed. Tail usually short and square, but long and steeply graduated in some spp. Legs and feet strong. Sexes alike or unlike.

Range. Africa, Eurasia (exc. extreme n.), Malaysia, Papuan Region, n.e. Australia, and the islands of Oceania, e. to Tuamoto. Most spp. migratory, at least in part.

Habits. Most spp. highly gregarious. Arboreal or terrestrial. Flight swift and direct (spectacular mass evolutions in many spp.). Typically walk and run on ground. Voice (most spp. garrulous)—variety of harsh, grating notes, musical whistles and warbles. Many spp. mimic other birds.

Food. Omnivorous. Insects, fruit, grain, offal, birds' eggs, crustacea, lizards.

Breeding. Often colonial. Nest a pile of plant fragments in tree cavity, rock crevice, hole in bank, etc.; domed or cup-shaped nest in bush or on ground; one sp. builds hanging nests.

Eggs. 2 to 9 (usually 3 or 4); white or blue; spotted or immaculate. Incubated by ♂ and ♀, or by ♀ alone.

Young. Nidicolous. With down. Fed by ♂ and ♀.

Technical diagnosis. Witherby, 1, 1938: 39.

Classification. D. Amadon, *Amer. Mus. Novitates, No. 1247,* 1943: 1–16 [Add *Neocichla* (J. P. Chapin, *Auk,* 65, 1948: 289–291).]. (See also D. Amadon, *Amer. Mus. Novitates, No. 1803,* 1956.)

References. Bent, No. 197: 182–222; Witherby, 1, 1938: 39–47; Baker, *Fauna,* 3, 1926: 16–64; Baker, *Nidification,* 2, 1933: 506–536; Bannerman, 6, 1948: xxii–xxv, 41–112, col. pls. 4–7.

Synonymy: The Eulebetidae ["Graculidae"], Buphagidae, and Pityriasidae are included.

MELIPHAGIDAE

Honey-eater family (160 species)

Fig. 154. Regent Honey-eater (*Zanthomiza phrygia*). Total length 9 in. (228 mm.).

Physical characteristics. Length—102 to 355 mm. (4 to 14 in.). Plumage—green, gray, brown, red, or black, more or less solid or in combination. Some spp. streaked, barred, or "scaled"; many have small areas or stripes of yellow or white on head. Many spp. have bare skin on head (often brightly colored) and/or wattles or casque; some have white or yellow plumy tufts on chin, throat, or sides of head. Bill slender, curved, medium to long. Wings rather long and pointed; tail medium to long. Legs strong; short to medium. Sexes alike or unlike.

Range. Bali, Papuan Region, Australia; e. to New Zealand, Samoa, and Hawaii; n. to Marianas; also S. Africa (*Promerops*). Some spp. migratory.

Habits. Rather gregarious. Pugnacious. Largely arboreal. Flight typically undulating. Voice—loud, musical calls; harsh notes; well-developed song in some spp.

Food. Nectar, insects, fruit.

Breeding. A few spp. colonial. Nest in trees or bushes: cuplike, semipendent nest fastened to twigs; abandoned nests of other birds; domed nest with side entrance; or open nest of twigs.

Eggs. 1 to 4; buff, pink, or white, marked with red or black. Incubated by ♂ and ♀, or by ♀ alone.

Young. Nidicolous. With sparse down. Cared for by ♂ and ♀.

Technical diagnosis. H. Gadow, Cat. of Birds in Brit. Mus., 9, 1884: 127 (omit Zosteropinae).

Classification. G. M. Mathews, *Systema Avium Australasianarum,* London, pt. 2, 1930: 736–807 (add Bali to range of *Lichmera indistincta*); W. L. Sclater, *Systema Avium Aethiopicarum,* London, 1930: 713 (*Promerops*).

References. Mathews, 11, pts. 4–9, 1924: 237–568, col. pls. 511–541; 12, pts. 1–3, 1925: 1–123, col. pls. 542–556.

P. A. Gilbert, Notes on Honeyeaters, *Emu,* 23, 1923: 109–118, pls. 20–21.

N. W. Cayley, *What Bird Is That?,* Sidney, 1933 (esp. plates 12, 14, 15, 23, 24).

D. L. Serventy and H. M. Whittell, *A Handbook of the Birds of Western Australia,* Perth, 1948: 313–331, frontisp.

Synonym: Melithreptidae. The Promeropidae are tentatively included.

NECTARINIIDAE

Sunbird family
(104 species)

Fig. 155. Wedge-tailed Sunbird (*Nectarinia violacea*). Total length 6½ in. (165 mm.).

Physical characteristics. Length—95 to 254 mm. (3¾ to 10 in.). Plumage—typically marked by solid areas of red, orange, yellow, brown, black, and metallic green, blue, or purple. Some spp. plain olive-green (rarely streaked). Many spp. have tufts of yellow or orange feathers at sides of breast. Bill long, curved, and very finely serrate; very slender and pointed in most spp. Wings short and rounded; tail short or medium and truncate, to very long and pointed (the central feathers extremely long in some spp.). Legs short; legs and feet strong. Sexes unlike in most spp.

Range. Africa (s. of Sahara), incl. Madagascar; Palestine, s.e. Arabia, s. Persia, India, s.e. Asia (n. to c. China), Philippines, Malaysia, Papuan Region, extreme n.e. Australia (n. Queensland). Most spp. nonmigratory.

Habits. Sometimes gregarious. Arboreal. Flight strong. Very active. Males very pugnacious, esp. in breeding season. Habitually feed at flowers, usually while perched. Voice—sharp, metallic notes; some spp. have well-developed song.

Food. Nectar and small insects and spiders about flowers; fruit.

Breeding. Pouch nest with side entrance (often with porchlike projection), hung from leaf or twigs of tree, from grass clumps, or from roots projecting from bank; or sewn to under side of large leaf.

Eggs. 1 to 3; typically speckled or blotched. Incubated by ♀; rarely by ♂ and ♀.

Young. Nidicolous. With down on upper parts. Cared for by ♀, or by ♂ and ♀.

Technical diagnosis. J. Delacour, *Zoologica,* 29, pt. 1, 1944: 17–20.

Classification. J. Delacour, *Zoologica,* 29, pt. 1, 1944: 21–38 (but omit *Neodrepanis*).

References. Baker, *Fauna,* 3, 1926: 368–412; Bannerman, 6, 1948: xxvi–xxx, 137–264, pls. 8–13 (4 in color).

G. E. Shelley, A Monograph of the Nectariniidae . . . , London, 1876–1880 (121 col. pls.).

F. N. Chasen, *The Birds of the Malay Peninsula,* London, vol. 4, 1939: 379–402, col. pl. 24. (See also vols. 1 and 2, both by H. C. Robinson.)

N. S. Potter, III, Notes on the Yellow-breasted Sunbird, *Wils. Bull.,* 60, 1948: 159–163.

J. G. Williams, A Systematic Revision and Natural History of the Shining Sunbird of Africa, *Condor,* 57, 1955: 249–262, col. pl.

Synonymy: The Chalcopariidae are included.

DICAEIDAE

Flowerpecker family

(54 species)

Fig. 156. Fire-breasted Flowerpecker (*Dicaeum ignipectum*). Total length $3\frac{1}{4}$ in. (83 mm.).

Physical characteristics. Length—76 to 190 mm. (3 to $7\frac{1}{2}$ in.). Plumage—♂ typically dark and glossy above, light below, with (in many spp.) solid areas of bright red or yellow on breast (usually central), crown, back, or rump. ♀ typically dull-colored; ♂ also dull-colored in a few spp. Some spp. broadly streaked below. Bill thin, curved, and serrate to stout and not serrate. Neck short. Wings rather long; tail short. Legs short. Sexes alike or unlike.

Range. India, Burma, Siam, Malaysia, Papuan Region, Indo-China, s. China, Philippines, Australia, and e. to Solomon Ids. Nonmigratory.

Habits. Somewhat gregarious. Arboreal, typically frequenting treetops. Flight strong and swift. Voice—variety of sharp, metallic notes; some spp. have a warbling song.

Food. Insects, nectar, fruit (esp. mistletoe berries).

Breeding. Nest a cup or pendent pouch in trees or bushes (*Pardalotus* in holes in trees or in banks).

Eggs. 1 to 3; plain white or spotted. Incubated by ♀ or by both sexes.

Young. Nidicolous. No down? Cared for by ♂ and ♀.

Technical diagnosis. E. Mayr and D. Amadon, *Amer. Mus. Novitates, No. 1360,* 1947: 1.

Classification. E. Mayr and D. Amadon, *Amer. Mus. Novitates, No. 1360,* 1947: 1–32.

References. Baker, *Fauna,* 3, 1926: 420–440; Baker, *Nidification,* 3, 1934: 237–249.

L. G. Chandler, Notes on Pardalotes, *Emu,* 10, 1910: 113–118.

F. N. Chasen, *Birds of the Low-country Jungle and Scrub* (vol. 4 of H. C. Robinson and F. N. Chasen, *The Birds of the Malay Peninsula*), London, 1939: 403–416, pl. 25.

Cicely Lushington, Notes on the nesting of Legge's flowerpecker (*Acmonorhynchus vincens* [Sclater]), *Jour. Bombay Nat. Hist. Soc.,* 42, 1940: 186–187, 1 pl.

Synonymy: The Paramythiidae are included.

ZOSTEROPIDAE

White-eye family (80 species)

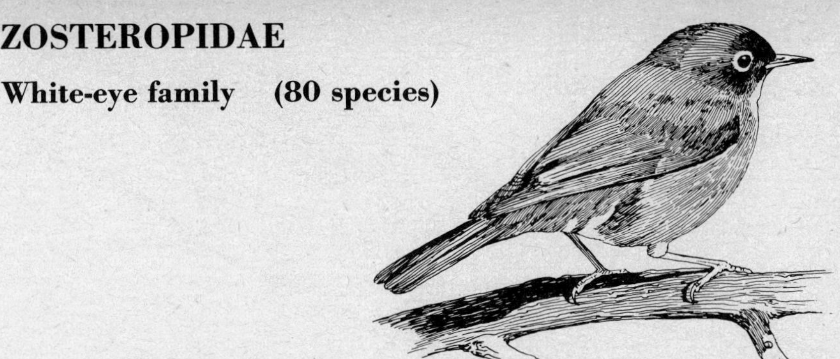

Fig. 157. Gray-breasted White-eye (*Zosterops lateralis*). Total length 5 in. (127 mm.).

Physical characteristics. Length—102 to 139 mm. (4 to $5\frac{1}{2}$ in.). Plumage—typically olive-green above, yellow (esp. throat) and white below; with (in most spp.) a conspicuous white eye ring. Some spp. have considerable gray or brown in the plumage (esp. below); one is uniformly bright cinnamon rufous; others have black crowns. Bill slender, pointed, and slightly curved. Wings rather pointed (with but 9 functional primaries); tail medium in length, truncate. Legs short but strong. Sexes alike.

Range. Africa (s. of Sahara), incl. Madagascar; India, Burma, Siam, Indo-China, e. China, Japan, Philippines, Malaysia, Papuan Region, Australia, e. to Fiji Ids., New Zealand, and the Chatham Ids. Largely nonmigratory.

Habits. Occur often in small flocks with other spp. Arboreal. Very active and restless. Voice—a twitter, a musical trill, a melodious warbling song.

Food. Insects, fruit.

Breeding. Semipendent cuplike nest, in forked twig.

Eggs. 2 to 4; white, pale blue or blue-green; immaculate. Incubated by ♂ and ♀.

Young. Nidicolous. With some down on head. Cared for by ♂ and ♀.

Technical diagnosis. Baker, *Fauna,* 3, 1926: 357.

Classification. R. B. Sharpe, Hand-list of the Genera and Species of Birds, vol. 5, 1909: 1-21, 632.

References. Baker, *Fauna,* 3, 1926: 357-367; Mathews, 11, pt. 3, 1923: 134-170, pls. 505-506; Bannerman, 6, 1948: xxvi-xxvii, 120-137, col. pl. 2.

E. Stresemann, Die Zosteropiden der indo-australischen Region, *Mitteil. Zool. Mus. Berlin,* 17, 1931: 201-238.

C. A. Fleming, Notes on the Life History of the Silver-eye based on Colour-banding, *Emu,* 42, 1943: 193-217, pls. 18-19.

CYCLARHIDAE

Pepper-shrike family

(2 species)

Fig. 158. Pale-billed Pepper-shrike (*Cyclarhis gujanensis*). Total length 6½ in. (165 mm.).

Physical characteristics. Length—139 to 177 mm. (5½ to 7 in.). Plumage—loose-webbed; olive-green above; crown gray or brown in some forms. Broad reddish brown stripe along side of head; cheeks gray. Under parts bright greenish yellow to buffy white. Bill heavy, laterally compressed, hooked. Head large, neck short, body heavy. Wings short and rounded; tail medium in length. Legs and feet strong. Sexes alike or nearly so.

Range. Southern Mexico (Veracruz and Puebla), through Central America and S. America to Uruguay. Habitat—brushland or thin forest. Probably nonmigratory.

Habits. Found singly or in pairs. Arboreal. Movements rather deliberate. Flight weak. Voice—harsh scolding notes; sweet warbling song (loud and frequently given).

Food. Insects; fruit.

Breeding. Fragile, loosely constructed, semipendent nest placed in horizontal fork of bush or low branch of tree.

Eggs. 2 to 3; pinkish white, blotched and speckled with brown. Incubated by ♂ and ♀?

Young. Nidicolous. Naked. Cared for by ♂ and ♀.

Technical diagnosis. W. P. Pycraft, *Proc. Zool. Soc. London,* 1907: 378.

Classification. Hellmayr, pt. 8, 1935: 193–211.

References. G. K. Cherrie, A Contribution to the Ornithology of the Orinoco Region, *Mus. Brooklyn Inst. Arts and Sci., Sci. Bull.,* 2, no. 2, 1916: 158.

A. Wetmore, Observations on the Birds of Argentina, Paraguay, Uruguay, and Chile, *U. S. Natl. Mus. Bull.,* 133, 1926: 366–367.

C. B. Worth, Nesting of the Pepper-shrike, *Auk,* 55, 1938: 539–540.

Synonym: Cyclorhidae.

VIREOLANIIDAE

Shrike-vireo family

(3 species)

Fig. 159. Chestnut-sided Shrike-vireo (*Vireolanius melitophrys*). Total length 7 in. (177 mm.).

Physical characteristics. Length—146 to 184 mm. ($5\frac{3}{4}$ to $7\frac{1}{4}$ in.). Plumage—loose-webbed, silky; parrot-green or olive-green above, with part or all of crown bright blue or gray. Two spp. have sides of head broadly banded with yellow, white, and black (gray in *Smaragdolanius leucotis*). Under parts greenish yellow (2 spp.) or white. *Vireolanius* has pectoral band and sides of chestnut. Bill rather stout, hooked. Head large, neck short, body heavy. Wings short and rounded; tail short or medium. Legs short but strong. Sexes alike (2 spp.) or very similar.

Range. Southern Mexico (Veracruz) through Central America and n. S. America to n. Bolivia and c. Brazil (n. Matto Grosso). Habitat—forests. Nonmigratory.

Habits. Solitary. Arboreal (*Smaragdolanius pulchellus* is said to be a bird of the treetops). Voice—loud, sweet whistling notes, persistently repeated.

Food. Fruit; probably insects.

Breeding. Nest not described.

Eggs. Not described.

Young. Not described.

Technical diagnosis. W. P. Pycraft, *Proc. Zool. Soc. London,* 1907: 378–379, 362 (fig. e).

Classification. Hellmayr, pt. 8, 1935: 186–193.

References. Osbert Salvin, Note on the Type of *Malaconotus leucotis,* Swainson, *Ibis,* 1878: 443–445, col. pl. 11.

Ludlow Griscom, Studies from the Dwight Collection of Guatemala Birds. III, *Amer. Mus. Novitates, No. 438,* 1930: 3.

Ludlow Griscom, The Distribution of Bird-life in Guatemala, *Bull. Amer. Mus. Nat. Hist.,* 64, 1932: 320–321.

VIREONIDAE

Vireo family

(37 species)

Fig. 160. Yellow-throated Vireo (*Vireo flavifrons*). Total length $5\frac{1}{2}$ in. (139 mm.).

Physical characteristics. Length—102 to 165 mm. (4 to $6\frac{1}{2}$ in.). Plumage—yellowish or greenish olive, olive-brown, or gray above. Crown in some spp. contrasting in color (olive-green, gray, reddish brown, or, in 1 sp., black); light superciliary line in some. Under parts white or buffy white to canary yellow; or gray. Some spp. have wing bars, but plumage never otherwise barred, streaked, or spotted, even in young. Irides of some spp. white or red. Bill medium to somewhat long, rather thick, slightly hooked. Neck short. Wings long and pointed to short and rounded (the 10th primary short to vestigial); tail medium. Legs rather short; anterior toes basally adherent. Sexes alike or nearly so.

Range. North America (exc. extreme n.), Central America, West Indies, and S. America (exc. s. third). Habitat—forests or brushland. Many spp. migratory.

Habits. Solitary. Arboreal. Typically feed among leaves and twigs, moving about rather deliberately. Often notably tame, esp. at nest. Voice—rather loud, frequently repeated, warbling songs; harsh scolding notes.

Food. Insects; some fruit.

Breeding. Cuplike, semipendent nest placed in horizontal fork of bush or tree.

Eggs. 2 to 5; white, very lightly speckled. Incubated by ♂ and ♀, or by ♀ alone.

Young. Nidicolous. With some down on upper parts; or naked. Cared for by ♂ and ♀.

Technical diagnosis. Ridgway, pt. 3, 1904: 128–130 (but omit *Vireolanius* and *Cyclarhis*).

Classification. Hellmayr, pt. 8, 1935: 111–186.

References. Bent, No. 197: 222–379.

A. Wetmore and B. H. Swales, The Birds of Haiti and the Dominican Republic, *U. S. Natl. Mus. Bull.,* 155, 1931: 352–363.

J. L. Peters, An Account of the Yellow-green Vireo (*Vireosylva flavoviridis* Cassin), *Auk,* 48, 1931: 575–587.

A. H. Miller and M. S. Ray, Discovery of a New Vireo of the Genus *Neochloe* in Southwestern Mexico, *Condor,* 46, 1944: 41–45, fig. 7, 1 col. pl.

G. M. Sutton, Studies of the Nesting Birds of the Edwin S. George Reserve, Part 1, The Vireos, *Univ. Mich. Mus. Zool. Misc. Publ. No. 74,* 1949.

L. de K. Lawrence, Nesting life and behaviour of the Red-eyed Vireo, *Canad. Field-Nat.,* 67, 1953: 47–77.

DREPANIIDAE

Hawaiian Honeycreeper family (22 species)

Fig. 161. Iiwi (*Vestiaria coccinea*). Total length 6 in. (152 mm.).

Physical characteristics. Length—114 to 222 mm. ($4\frac{1}{2}$ to $8\frac{3}{4}$ in.). Plumage—olive-green, yellow, orange, red, brown, gray, or black, with little pattern exc. for darker wings and tail; one sp. (*Palmeria*) has brightly spotted and streaked plumage and a crest. Bill extremely varied, ranging from very long, slender, and curved to very short, massive, and strongly hooked. Wings pointed (with but 9 functional primaries); tail of medium length and truncate or emarginate. Legs medium to rather short; feet strong. Sexes unlike, or alike (but the ♂ larger).

Range. Hawaiian Ids. Nonmigratory.

Habits. Solitary or in small loose flocks. Arboreal. Flight strong and, in some spp., noisy. Voice—loud clear notes and simple trills; some spp. have a "rather sweet" song.

Food. Nectar, insects, fruit, seeds.

Breeding. Loosely constructed, cup-shaped nest placed in trees, bushes, or grass tussocks.

Eggs. 2 to 4; white, spotted. Incubated by ♀.

Young. Nidicolous. With some down on upper parts. Cared for by ♂ and ♀.

Technical diagnosis. D. Amadon, *Bull. Amer. Mus. Nat. Hist.,* 95, art. 4, 1950: 163–164, pls. 9–12, 15.

Classification. D. Amadon, *Bull. Amer. Mus. Nat. Hist.,* 95, art. 4, 1950: 163–192.

References. S. B. Wilson and A. H. Evans, *Aves Hawaiienses,* London, 1890–1899: 3–98; 37 pls.

R. C. L. Perkins, An Introduction to the Study of the Drepanididae . . . , *Ibis,* 1901: 562–585.

G. C. Munro, *Birds of Hawaii,* Honolulu, 1944: 89–131, pls. 10–15.

D. Amadon, The Hawaiian Honeycreepers (Aves, Drepaniidae), *Bull. Amer. Mus. Nat. Hist.,* 95, art. 4, 1950: 151–262, pls. 9–15. (Reviewed by P. H. Baldwin, *Auk,* 69, 1952: 92–98.)

P. H. Baldwin, Annual Cycle, Environment and Evolution in the Hawaiian Honeycreepers . . . , *Univ. Calif. Publ. Zool.,* 52, 1953: 285–398.

Synonyms: Drepanididae, Drepanidae.

PARULIDAE

American Wood-warbler family (119 species)

Fig. 162. Black-throated Gray Warbler (*Dendroica nigrescens*). Total length 5 in. (127 mm.).

Physical characteristics. Length—108 to 184 mm. ($4\frac{1}{4}$ to $7\frac{1}{4}$ in.). Plumage—usually olive or gray, often brightly marked with yellow, orange, red, or gray-blue. Bill usually slender and pointed (a few spp. have a rather broad bill and pronounced rictal bristles; others have a rather heavy, tanagerlike bill). Primaries reduced to 9. Sexes alike or unlike.

Range. Alaska to Labrador s. through Central America and the West Indies to Uruguay and n. Argentina. North American spp. migratory.

Habits. Typically arboreal; some (*Seiurus*) are terrestrial (and walk rather than hop); others have creeperlike habits; others feed mainly by catching insects on the wing. Voice—a few have highly developed songs.

Food. Insects, fruits, nectar.

Breeding. Nest cup-shaped or domed. Placed on ground, in low plants, in shrubs, or in trees; in holes in trees or banks.

Eggs. 2 to 5 (rarely 6); usually white, marked with brown. Incubated by ♀.

Young. Nidicolous. With scant down, on upper surface; or naked. Cared for by ♂ and ♀.

Technical diagnosis. Ridgway, pt. 2, 1902: 425.

Classification. Hellmayr, pt. 8, 1935: 284–330 ("Coerebidae"), 331–526; W. J. Beecher, *Wils. Bull.,* 63, 1951: 274–287.

References. Bent, No. 197: 379–382 (*Coereba*); No. 203.

F. M. Chapman, *The Warblers of North America,* New York, 1907 (see also *Auk,* 42, 1925: 193–208).

H. W. Hann, Life History of the Oven-bird . . . , *Wils. Bull.,* 49, 1937: 145–237.

L. H. Walkinshaw, The Prothonotary Warbler . . . in Tennessee and Michigan, *Wils. Bull.,* 53, 1941: 3–21.

F. G. Schrantz, Nest Life of the Eastern Yellow Warbler, *Auk,* 60, 1943: 367–387.

S. C. Kendeigh, Nesting Behavior of Wood Warblers, *Wils. Bull.,* 57, 1945: 145–164.

A. F. Skutch, Life Histories of Central American Birds, *Pacif. Coast Avif. No. 31,* 1954: 339–386, 404–420.

Synonyms: Compsothlypidae, Mniotiltidae, Sylvicolidae. The Coerebidae (also "Caerebidae") are included in part (*Coereba, Conirostrum, Ateleodacnis*). Certain genera included in the Parulidae by Ridgway (and by Chapman, 1907) are now placed in the Thraupidae (*Rhodocichla, Hemispingus*) or Fringillidae (*Certhidea*).

ICTERIDAE

Troupial family (94 species)

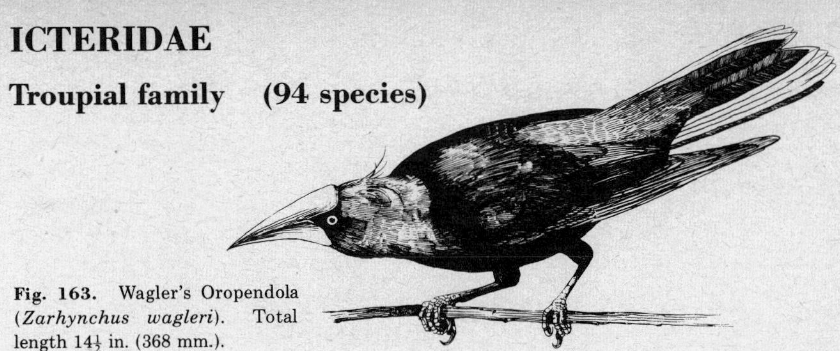

Fig. 163. Wagler's Oropendola (*Zarhynchus wagleri*). Total length 14½ in. (368 mm.).

Physical characteristics. Length—171 to 546 mm. (6¾ to 21½ in.). Plumage—uniform black (often with brilliant metallic gloss) or bold combinations of black with brown, chestnut, buff, orange, crimson, yellow; rarely streaked; often with white wing bars. A few spp. with neck ruff; a few with sparse crest. Bill conical; short and massive to moderately long and slender; in larger spp., rather heavy and casqued. Wings (9 primaries) typically long and pointed (short and rounded in some spp.). Tail short to long; truncate, rounded, or graduate (plicate in a few). Feet strong. Sexes unlike in most spp.

Range. South America, Central America, West Indies, and N. America (exc. extreme n.). Many spp. migratory.

Habits. Gregarious or solitary. Arboreal or terrestrial. Some spp. walk when on ground. Voice—a variety of calls, harsh and shrill to whistling or flutelike; some spp. have well-developed song.

Food. Insects, seeds, fruit, nectar, fish, amphibians, crustacea, other birds, small mammals.

Breeding. Some spp. colonial, some parasitic, some polygamous or promiscuous. Pensile or semipensile nest; cup-shaped nest in trees, on ground, in aquatic vegetation, in holes or crevices; nests of other birds.

Eggs. 2 to 7; pale blue or green, gray, buff, white; usually strongly marked. Incubated by ♀.

Young. Nidicolous. With sparse down or (*Amblycercus*) naked. Cared for by ♀, assisted by ♂ in some spp.

Technical diagnosis. Ridgway, pt. 2, 1902: 169–173.

Classification. Hellmayr, pt. 10, 1937: 1–221.

References. A. A. Allen, The Red-winged Blackbird . . . , *Proc. Linn. Soc. N. Y.,* Nos. 24/25, 1914: 43–128.

F. M. Chapman, The Nesting Habits of Wagler's Oropendola . . . , *Amer. Mus. Nat. Hist. Bull.,* 58, 1928: 123–166.

H. Friedmann, *The Cowbirds,* Springfield, Ill., 1929.

Laidlow Williams, Breeding Behavior of the Brewer Blackbird, *Condor,* 54, 1952: 3–47.

TERSINIDAE

Swallow-tanager family (1 species)

Fig. 164. Swallow-tanager (*Tersina viridis*). Total length 6½ in. (165 mm.).

Physical characteristics. Length—152 to 159 mm. (6 to 6¼ in.). Plumage of ♂—bright turquoise-blue, barred with black on flanks, the face and throat black, crissum and center of belly pure white; of ♀—green, barred with dark green and black on flanks, the crissum and center of belly pale yellow, lightly streaked with gray. Bill short, somewhat flattened, triangular (very broad at base), slightly hooked. Neck short. Wings long; tail medium. Legs very short. Sexes unlike, as described above.

Range. Eastern Panama and S. America (exc. the s. third). Migratory in part.

Habits. Gregarious. Arboreal. Flight strong. Feed in part on the wing. Voice—variety of call notes; song little developed.

Food. Fruit, green shoots; insects.

Breeding. Nest of roots and grass in a hole in the ground, in a bank, or in a tree. Use abandoned nesting holes of jacamars (Galbulidae) and swallow-winged puffbirds (Bucconidae).

Eggs. 2 to 4 (usually 3); glossy, white; immaculate. Incubated by ♀.

Young. Nidicolous. With sparse down. Cared for by ♀, assisted by ♂.

Technical diagnosis. R. Ridgway, *Proc. U. S. Natl. Mus.*, 18, 1896: 449–450; and F. A. Lucas, *Ibid.*, 505–507.

Classification. Hellmayr, pt. 9, 1936: 1–6.

References. F. P. Penard and A. P. Penard, *De Vogels van Guyana*, Paramaribo, vol. 2, 1910: 415.

W. E. C. Todd and M. A. Carriker, Jr., The Birds of the Santa Marta Region of Colombia, *Ann. Carnegie Mus.*, 14, 1922: 438–439.

K. Plath, The Swallow-Tanager (*Tersina viridis*), *Aviculture*, 5 (ser. 2), 1933: 37–38, col. pl.

E. Schaefer, Contribution to the Life History of the Swallow-tanager, *Auk*, 70, 1953: 403–460, pls. 11–18.

Synonym: Procniatidae.

THRAUPIDAE

Tanager family

(222 species)

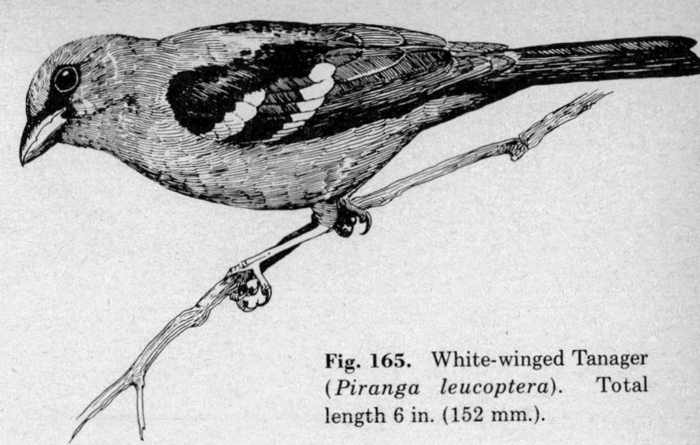

Fig. 165. White-winged Tanager (*Piranga leucoptera*). Total length 6 in. (152 mm.).

Physical characteristics. Length—76 to 305 mm. (3 to 12 in.). Plumage—brightly colored in many spp.; highly glossy in a few; green, yellow, orange, red, purple, blue, brown, black, white; color generally in solid patches with bold contrasting areas, but some spp. have spotted areas. A few spp. crested. Bill short to medium; typically rather conical; commonly hooked or notched; more or less "toothed" in large spp. Wings short to rather long. Tail short to medium in most spp.; emarginate, truncate, or rounded (long and graduate in *Cissopis*). Legs short. Sexes alike or unlike.

Range. North America (exc. extreme n.), Central America, West Indies, and S. America (exc. s. third). Habitat—forest or brushland. Some spp. migratory.

Habits. Solitary or (less commonly) gregarious. Arboreal. Flight strong but not sustained. Voice—varied; a few spp. have well-developed song.

Food. Fruit, flowers, insects.

Breeding. Shallow, often loosely constructed, cuplike nest, or domed nest with side entrance; placed in trees or bushes, or in shallow cavity in bank or tree.

Eggs. 1 to 5; white, greenish, or bluish; marked with brown or black (or, rarely, immaculate). Incubated by ♀.

Young. Nidicolous. With sparse down. Cared for by ♂ and ♀.

Technical diagnosis. Ridgway, pt. 2, 1902: 1.

Classification. Hellmayr, pt. 9, 1936: 6–447; pt. 8, 1935: 218–284; 330–331 (*Diglossa, Chlorophanes, Iridophanes, Cyanerpes, Dacnis, Hemidacnis, Xenodacnis, Oreomanes* and *Euneornis* of the "Coerebidae"; see Beecher, *Wils. Bull.*, 63, 1951: 274–287).

References. D. R. Dickey and A. J. van Rossem, The Birds of El Salvador, *Field Mus. Nat. Hist., Zool. Ser.*, 23, 1938: 541–562.

A. F. Skutch, Outline for an Ecological Life History of a Bird, Based upon the Song Tanager *Ramphocelus passerinii costaricensis, Ecology,* 31, 1950: 464–469.

A. F. Skutch, Life Histories of Central American Birds, *Pacif. Coast Avif. No. 31,* 1954.

G. C. Barnard, Notes on the nesting of the Thick-billed Euphonia in the Panama Canal Zone, *Condor,* 56, 1954: 98–101.

Synonyms: Tanagridae, Tangaridae. The Coerebidae (also "Caerebidae") are included in part.

CATAMBLYRHYNCHIDAE

Plush-capped Finch family (1 species)

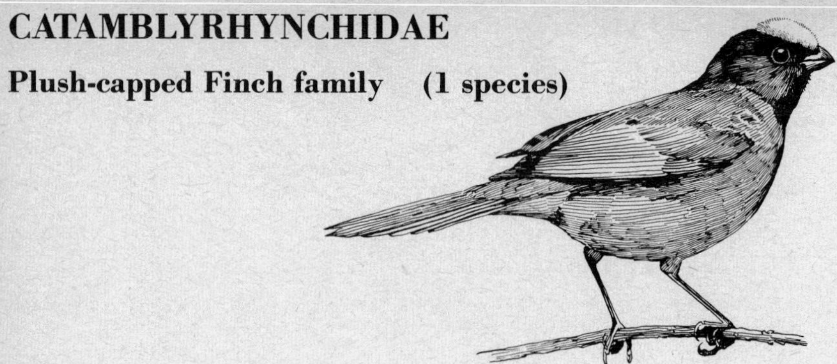

Fig. 166. Plush-capped Finch (*Catamblyrhynchus diadema*). Total length 6 in. (152 mm.).

Physical characteristics. Length—about 152 mm. (6 in.). Plumage—forepart of crown golden, "plushlike," the feathers erect and stiffened in the northern form, *Catamblyrhynchus d. diadema,* softer and recumbent, as well as lighter in color, in the southern form, *C. d. citrinifrons;* hind crown and nape black. Rest of upper parts bluish gray; under parts a uniform deep chestnut (paler in the immature). Bill short, massive, slightly hooked, higher than broad, flattened and grooved laterally; the lower mandible very thick. Wings short and rounded; tail medium in length, graduated. Legs stout, medium in length; feet strong, with large hind claw. Sexes similar, but ♀ duller.

Range. Andes of Colombia, Ecuador. and Peru, to central Bolivia. Nonmigratory?

Habits. The following two statements represent, apparently, the only data on the habits of this family (the first is here translated from the French): "They are met with in isolated pairs or mingled with flocks of other birds" (Jelski, quoted by Taczanowski, *Ornithologie du Pérou,* Rennes, vol. 3, 1886: 25). "We found them [3 ♂ ♂] singly in the higher trees" (W. Goodfellow, *Ibis,* 1901: 473).

Food. Not described.

Breeding. Nest not described.

Eggs. Not described.

Young. Not described.

Technical diagnosis. Ridgway, pt. 1, 1901: 19; G. R. Gray, *The Genera of Birds,* London, vol. 2, 1849: 385, col. pl. 93.

Classification. Hellmayr, pt. 11, 1938: 4–6.

References. J. T. Zimmer, Studies of Peruvian Birds. No. 54. The Families Catamblyrhynchidae and Parulidae, *Amer. Mus. Novitates, No. 1428,* 1949: 1–2.

E. Mayr and D. Amadon, A Classification of Recent Birds, *Amer. Mus. Novitates, No. 1496,* 1951: 27, 38.

PLOCEIDAE

Weaverbird family (313 species ±)

Fig. 167. Paradise Whydah (*Steganura paradisea*). Total length (without central tail feathers) 7½ in. (190 mm.).

Physical characteristics. Length—76 to 648 mm. (3 to 25½ in.). Plumage—from brown and gray in cryptic patterns to yellow, red, purple, blue, green, black in bold patterns; many spp. conspicuously spotted or barred with white or black. Bill very short (typically rather thick) and sharp-pointed to very massive, but never long (mandibles crossed in *Loxia*). Wings short and rounded to long and pointed. Tail very short to extremely long (with very broad, spatulate, or filiform feathers). Legs short. Sexes alike or unlike.

Range. World-wide, exc. some oceanic islands. A few spp. are migratory.

Habits. Many spp. gregarious. Arboreal or terrestrial. Flight strong in most spp. Voice—typically simple, chirping notes, often harsh; many spp. have well-developed song.

Food. Vegetable; animal (to a less extent).

Breeding. A number of spp. colonial. Monogamous, polygamous, polyandrous, or promiscuous. Nest types extremely diverse: elaborately woven and flask-shaped (often with tunnel entrance); or massive covered colonial nest in tree; lined tree cavity; old covered nests of other birds; bulky cup-shaped nest in tree; lined rock crevice. Some spp. (Viduinae) entirely parasitic.

Eggs. 2 to 8; white, green, pale blue, or reddish; speckled or immaculate. Incubated by ♀, or by ♂ and ♀.

Young. Nidicolous. With or without down. Cared for by ♂ and ♀.

Technical diagnosis. P. P. Sushkin, *Bull. Amer. Mus. Nat. Hist.*, 57, 1927: 1–32.

Classification. J. Delacour, *Zoologica,* 28, 1943: 69–86; J. P. Chapin, *Bull. Amer. Mus. Nat. Hist.*, 37, 1917: 243–280; J. Delacour and F. Edmond-Blanc, *L'Ois. et Rev. Franç. d'Ornith.* 3, 1933: 519–562, 687–726; 4, 1934: 52–110..

References. Witherby, 1, 1938: 51–102, 153–163; Baker, *Fauna,* 3, 1926: 65–97, 99–163, 166–188, 191–194; Bannerman, 7, 1949.

L. de K. Lawrence, The Red Crossbill at Pimisi Bay, Ontario, *Canad. Field-Nat.*, 63, 1949: 147–160.

H. Friedmann, The Breeding Habits of the Weaverbirds . . . , *Smiths. Rept. for 1949,* 1950: 293–315.

Synonyms: Malimbidae, Passeridae. The Carduelinae (hitherto placed in Fringillidae) and Bubalornithidae are included here.

FRINGILLIDAE

Finch family (375 species ±)

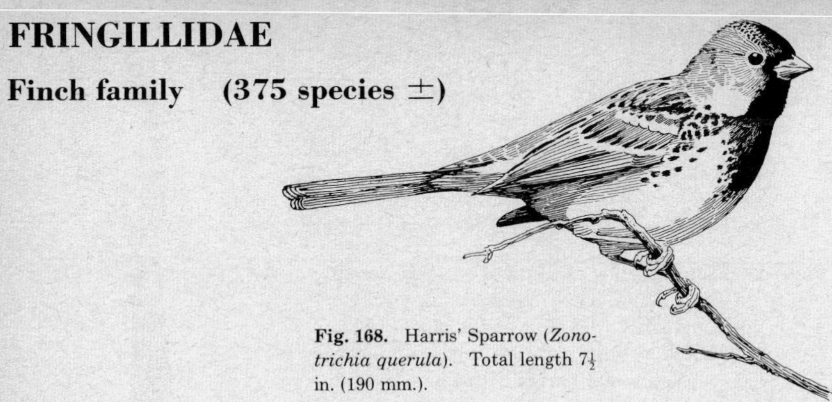

Fig. 168. Harris' Sparrow (*Zonotrichia querula*). Total length 7½ in. (190 mm.).

Physical characteristics. Length—95 to 273 mm. (3¾ to 10¾ in.). Plumage—from brown and gray in cryptic patterns to combinations of yellow, red, purple, blue, green, black, white, in bold patterns; many spp. with broad stripes on top or sides of head. Bill short and pointed; rather thick to very massive; sometimes hooked. Wings short and rounded to long and rather pointed; tail short to long. Legs typically of medium length. Sexes alike or unlike.

Range. World-wide (exc. Madagascar, the Papuan Region, Australia, and Oceania). Many spp. migratory.

Habits. Solitary or (esp. in nonbreeding season) gregarious. Terrestrial or arboreal. Flight weak to strong. Voice—extremely varied; many spp. have well-developed song.

Food. Typically seeds; other plant food and some insects.

Breeding. Cup-shaped nest in trees, shrubs, or herbage, or on ground; in rock crevice; in holes in trees or in covered nests of other birds (*Sicalis*).

Eggs. 2 to 6 (rarely 8); white, bluish or reddish white, or green; marked or immaculate. Incubated by ♀, or by ♂ and ♀.

Young. Nidicolous. With some down. Cared for by ♂ and ♀.

Technical diagnosis. Ridgway, pt. 1, 1901: 24.

Classification. New World: Hellmayr, pt. 11, 1938: 6–146, 158 (*Melanospiza*)–256, 306–644. Old World: R. B. Sharpe, Hand-list of the Genera and Species of Birds, 5, 1909: 188–196 ("*Ligurinus*" = *Chloris*), 200 (*Pheucticus*)–226, 261–262 (*Sicalis* only), 275 (*Urocynchramus*)–341.

References. Witherby, 1, 1938: 102–153; Baker, *Fauna,* 3, 1926: 163–166, 188–190, 195–222; Bannerman, 6, 1948: xxxiv, 299–320.

A. O. Gross, The Dickcissel (*Spiza americana*) of the Illinois Prairies, *Auk,* 38, 1921: 1–26, 163–184.

M. M. Nice, Studies in the Life History of the Song Sparrow, *Trans. Linn. Soc. N. Y.,* Nos. 4, 6, 1937 and 1943.

N. Tinbergen, The Behavior of the Snow Bunting in Spring, *Trans. Linn. Soc. N. Y.,* No. 5, 1939.

D. Lack, *Darwin's Finches,* Cambridge, England, 1947.

Synonymy: The Geospizinae, Fringillinae, Richmondeninae, Emberizinae, and *Certhidea* (formerly in Coerebidae) are included.

Ornithological sources

Encyclopedic Sources

In English

NEWTON, Alfred, and Hans GADOW. 1893–1896. *A Dictionary of Birds.* Adam and Charles Black, London. 1088 pp. One of the great reference books in ornithology. See also "Birds" (Gadow) and "Ornithology" (Newton) in the *Encyclopaedia Britannica,* 11th ed. (1910, 1911); and the articles by J. A. Thomson and A. A. Allen under "Birds" and by A. Wetmore under "Ornithology" in the 13th ed. (1949).

THOMSON, J. Arthur. 1923. *The Biology of Birds.* Macmillan Co., London and New York. 436 pp.

In German

STRESEMANN, Erwin. 1927–1934. Aves. Vol. 7, part 2, of W. Kükenthal and T. Krumbach's *Handbuch der Zoologie.* Walter de Gruyter and Co., Berlin. 899 pp. The classic scholarly summary (with extensive references) of scientific knowledge of birds.

In French

GRASSÉ, Pierre-P., *et al.* 1950. Oiseaux. Vol. 15 of Grassé's *Traité de Zoologie.* Masson and Co., Paris. 1164 pp. (About $24.00 in America.) This, the most recent encyclopedic treatment of birds, is an indispensable source book. The 33 sections, contributed by 12 specialists, are well illustrated and cover most major fields of ornithology from anatomy and physiology, through habits, to classification and distribution.

Selected Bibliographic Sources

In 1880 Elliott Coues was able to provide in less than 800 pages a nearly complete bibliography on the birds of the Western Hemisphere, but since that time the annual output of ornithological literature has been increasing year by year until the modern student needs every possible guide and index to assist him in his efforts to learn the boundaries of our knowledge.

Perhaps the best general directory of scientific libraries and catalog of published guides to their contents is Roger C. Smith's *Guide to the Literature of the Zoological Sciences.* 3rd ed., 1952. Burgess Publishing Co., Minneapolis 15, Minn. $2.50.

GENERAL ORNITHOLOGICAL INDICES, published periodically:

Aves section of the *Zoological Record.* 1864 to date.

This is the ornithologist's most important bibliographic source. Each number covers a calendar year. It is now organized as follows:

1. A numbered list (alphabetical by authors) of the exact titles and references for papers published during the year. *Caution:* A title overlooked by the compiler of the *Record* at time of publication and later called to his attention will be found in a subsequent volume.
2. A fairly detailed subject index (60 to 70 headings).
3. A geographical index.
4. A taxonomic index. *Note:* Major faunal books, though listed under author, are commonly *not* indexed under taxonomic headings.

[None of our bibliographic indices even approaches completeness. A recent survey (B. Glass, *A. I. B. S. Bull.,* 5, No. 1, 1955: 20–24) showed that in a sample year (1949) the *Zoological Record* omitted 35.8 per cent of the ornithological titles listed by *Biological Abstracts,* and that *Biological Abstracts* omitted 82 per cent of the titles listed by the *Zoological Record.*]

Address: Zoological Society of London, Regent's Park, London N.W. 1, England. Annual subscription about $1.00.

Biological Abstracts. 1926 to date.

This serial attempts to provide not only references but also abstracts. A several-hundred-page volume is published every month, and an index volume at the end of the year. The section devoted to "Aves" is very small, but additional titles on birds appear under "Ecology," etc.; all are indexed in one section at the end of the annual volume. *Biological Abstracts* is available in a great many libraries, but relatively few individuals attempt to buy it and provide shelf room for it. The ornithologist can subscribe for Section E, which includes "Aves" ($6.00 annually). Section A, which includes "Ecology," "Evolution," etc., requires another subscription ($5.00). *Biological Abstracts* has the very great virtue of providing English abstracts of foreign-language articles, but the coverage of the literature of ornithology is very far from complete. Address: University of Pennsylvania, Philadelphia 4, Pa.

Wildlife Review. 1935 to date.

A serially numbered, quarterly publication of the U. S. Fish and Wildlife Service. Titles are arranged by authors under various headings, mainly taxonomic, and there is an author index in each issue. Most titles are briefly annotated. The *Review* deals especially with game and predator species, but it includes many titles of general interest. Address: Patuxent Research Refuge, Laurel, Md. No subscription charge.

The "more than 10,000 titles" that appeared in Nos. 1 to 66 have been reorganized and combined in a single volume (435 pp.), *Wildlife Abstracts,* 1935–51, by Neil Hotchkiss. $2.00. Supt. of Documents, Government Printing Office, Washington, D. C.

JOURNALS WITH BIBLIOGRAPHY SECTIONS IMPORTANT TO ORNITHOLOGISTS:

Auk (quarterly). 1884 to date.

Contains reviews (usually critical appraisals) of books, and annotated listing of shorter papers, the latter arranged in each issue in a single alphabetical series. Book reviews are indexed in the *Auk's* 10-year indices and in some of the annual indices. Address: Intelligencer Printing Co., Lancaster, Pa.; or Care of Division of Birds, U. S. National Museum, Washington 25, D. C.

Bird-Banding (quarterly). 1930 to date.

Contains a very valuable section, "Recent literature," classified under subject headings since 1934. Address: E. Alexander Bergstrom, 37 Old Brook Road, West Hartford 7, Conn.

Ibis (quarterly). 1859 to date.

This is the oldest English-language ornithological journal in the world. Contains reviews and notices of new publications; with, since 1942, especially wide coverage and careful analysis. Book reviews have not been indexed in recent volumes. Address: Care of Bird Room, British Museum (Natural History), Cromwell Road, London S.W. 7, England.

Journal of Animal Ecology (semiannual). 1932 to date.

Published by the British Ecological Society. It contains not only reviews of major works but also an annotated list (about 25 pp.) of references to papers on the British fauna, classified under "Methods," "Food and Food Habits," etc.; these are of value to ornithologists everywhere. The section of abstracts (but not the reviews) can be purchased separately for the equivalent of about $0.75 per year. These separate copies are printed on only one side of the page to permit cutting and mounting the titles on cards, but the type page ($5\frac{1}{4}$ in., or 13.3 cm.) is too wide for library cards (12.5 cm.). Address: Cambridge University Press, 200 Euston Rd., London N.W. 1, England.

Quarterly Review of Biology. 1926 to date.

Contains classified brief notices and reviews, usually by well-qualified reviewers, of almost all new books (though not of journal articles) in the biology field. Address: Williams and Wilkins Co., Baltimore, Md.

Wilson Bulletin (quarterly). 1894 to date.

Reviews and lists of recent literature are found in some volumes; detailed, classified lists in the 1943–1948 volumes. Address: Wilson Ornithological Society Library, Museum of Zoology, Ann Arbor, Mich.

GENERAL BIBLIOGRAPHIES AND SPECIAL INDICES:

ANKER, Jean. 1938. *Bird Books and Bird Art:* An outline of the literary history and iconography of descriptive ornithology. 251 pp., 13 pls. (4 in col.). Munksgaard, Copenhagen. A most scholarly work, with valuable annotations on the history and significance of the books listed.

BAILEY, H. B. 1881. [Index to] "Forest and Stream" Bird Notes. Forest and Stream Publication Co., New York, N. Y. 195 pp. An annotated index, by species and author, of "all the ornithological matter" in the first 12 volumes (1873–1879) of the magazine *Forest and Stream,* an important place of publication in the years just preceding the era of specialized ornithological journals.

BRITISH MUSEUM. 1903–1940. Catalogue of the Books, Manuscripts, Maps and Drawings in the British Museum (Natural History). 8 vols. Vols. 1–5 (1903–1915) contain a single alphabetical listing of titles; vols. 6–8 (1922–1940) contain additions, in a second alphabetical series. A scholarly listing of perhaps the world's best library in this field.

COUES, Elliott. 1878–1880. [Bibliography of Ornithology]. 4 parts. This great work, the first part of a proposed general bibliography of ornithology, sets a scholarly standard rarely equaled by ornithologists in all the years that have followed. For a historical account and evaluation of Coues' work see Casey A. Wood's *An Introduction* to the *Literature of Vertebrate Zoology,* 1931, Oxford University Press, London, p. 302; also *Auk,* 45, 1928: 148–154.

Part 1. Faunal publications relating to North America (including Mexico and the Bahamas). 1878. *Misc. Publ. U. S. Geol. Surv. Terr.,* 11: 567–784. (Published as an appendix to "Birds of the Colorado Valley.")

Part 2. Faunal publications relating to the rest of America (i.e., West Indies except Bahamas; Central and South America). 1879. *Bull. U. S. Geol. and Geogr. Surv. Terr.,* 5: 239–330.

Part 3. Publications relating to species, genera, or families of American birds, arranged by families. 1879. *Bull. U. S. Geol. and Geogr. Surv. Terr.,* 5: 521–1072.

Part 4. Faunal publications relating to British birds. 1880. *Proc. U. S. Natl. Mus.,* 2: 359–477.

ENGELMANN, Wilhelm. 1846. *Bibliotheca Historico-Naturalis.* Engelmann, Leipzig. 786 pp. Scope: natural history of Europe (but many New World references are included), 1700–1846.

continued as:

CARUS, J. Victor, and Wilhelm ENGELMANN. 1861. *Bibliotheca Zoologica.* Engelmann, Leipzig. 2 vols. 2144 pp. Scope: a classified and cross-indexed listing of world natural history, 1846–1860.

continued as:

TASCHENBERG, O. 1887–1923. *Bibliotheca Zoologica.* II. Engelmann, Leipzig. 8 vols. 6620 pp. Scope: world natural history, 1861–1880.

GIEBEL, C. G. 1872–1877. *Thesaurus Ornithologiae.* Leipzig. 3 vols. First section (pp. 1–252) is a bibliography of ornithology (arranged in a rather curious manner under more than 30 headings); the balance (pp. 253–824) is a "Nomenclator Ornithologicus," alphabetical by generic names, and (pp. 825–861) an author index (with supplementary titles). Not a very dependable bibliography, but cannot be ignored.

NISSEN, Claus. 1936. *Schöne Vogelbücher.* Herbert Reichner, Leipzig. 95 pp., 41 pls. (2 in col.). A history of ornithological illustration and a bibliography of major illustrated works.

NISSEN, Claus. 1953. *Die illustrierten Vogelbücher.* Hiersemann, Stuttgart. 223 pp., 16 pls. A very useful work, with much detailed information and many references to other sources of bibliographic and biographic data.

SITWELL, Sacheverell, Handasyde BUCHANAN, and James FISHER. 1953. *Fine Bird Books: 1700–1900.* Collins and Van Nostrand, London. 120 pp., 36 pls. Folio. History and annotated bibliography. Only "fine" books are included, and these are not treated in much detail.

STRONG, Reuben Myron. 1939–1946. A Bibliography of Birds. *Field Mus. Nat. Hist., Zool. Ser.,* 26, pts. 1–2 (937 pp.), 3 (528 pp.). Contents: list of periodicals and their abbreviations, author catalog, and (part 3) subject index. Scope: titles through 1926 relating "especially to the field outside taxonomy," but some titles published as late as 1938 and many taxonomic papers are included.

WOOD, Casey A. 1931. *An Introduction to the Literature of Vertebrate Zoology.* Oxford University Press, London. 643 pp. Scope: an outline of the history of zoology; an annotated catalog (alphabetical by author) of the pertinent titles in the libraries of McGill University.

ZIMMER, John Todd. 1926. Catalogue of the Edward E. Ayer Ornithological Library. *Field Mus. Nat. Hist., Zool. Ser.,* 16. 706 pp., 12 pls. A scholarly description of the books in one of the world's great ornithological libraries. Book list is alphabetical by authors; the work closes with a list of more than 60 periodicals, mainly ornithological. The best single bibliography of ornithological books, with important collation data and details of various editions.

BIBLIOGRAPHIES OF BIRD GROUPS:

In "Birds of North and Middle America" (*U. S. Natl. Mus. Bull.*, 50, pts. 1–11, 1901–1950) by Robert Ridgway and (the more recent volumes) Herbert Friedmann, and in many other taxonomic works, may be found numerous references, arranged by bird group, to publications on habits and other matters not strictly taxonomic. Listed below are publications that are exclusively bibliographical.

WATERFOWL. Kuroda, Nagamichi. 1942. *A Bibliography of the Duck Tribe, Anatidae, mostly from 1926 to 1940, exclusive of that of Dr. Phillips' Work.* Herald Press, Tokyo. 852 pp. Titles on ducks, swans, geese, screamers for the period 1926–1940; also earlier titles not given by Phillips' bibliography in *The Natural History of the Ducks* (vol. 4, 1926: 321–447. Houghton Mifflin Co., Boston).

SHOREBIRDS. Low, G. Carmichael. 1931. *The Literature of the Charadriiformes from 1894 to 1928.* F. & G. Witherby, London. 2nd ed. 637 pp. Scope: Otididae, Burhinidae, Scolopacidae, Charadriidae, Jacanidae, Chionididae, Dromadidae, Glareolidae, and Thinocoridae; since the publication of R. B. Sharpe's volume on these groups in vol. 24 (1896) of the Catalogue of Birds in the British Museum.

GAME. Phillips, John C. 1930. *American Game Mammals and Birds . . . 1582 to 1925.* Houghton Mifflin Co., Boston. 639 pp. Contents: "General catalogue; conservation; periodical publications, pamphlets, etc."

BIBLIOGRAPHIES OF SPECIAL SUBJECTS:

HARTING, James Edmund. 1891. *Bibliotheca Accipitraria: A Catalogue of Books, Ancient and Modern, Relating to Falconry, with Notes, Glossary, and Vocabulary.* Quaritch, London. 289 pp.

MCATEE, W. L. 1913. Index to Papers Relating to the Food of Birds . . . in Publications of the United States Department of Agriculture. *U. S. Dept. Agric. Biol. Surv. Bull. No. 43.* 69 pp.

LINCOLN, Frederick C. 1928. A Bibliography of Bird Banding in America. *Auk,* 45, Supplement. 75 pp.

COCKRUM, E. Lendell. 1952. A Check-List and Bibliography of Hybrid Birds in North America North of Mexico. *Wils. Bull.,* 64: 140–159.

REGIONAL BIBLIOGRAPHIES:

NORTH AMERICA (including Mexico and the Bahamas). Coues, E. 1878. Part 1 of his bibliography. See "General Bibliographies."

SOUTH AND CENTRAL AMERICA (including West Indies except Bahamas). Coues, E. 1879. Part 2 of his bibliography. See "General Bibliographies."

ANTARCTIC. Roberts, Brian. 1941. A Bibliography of Antarctic Ornithology. *Brit. Graham Land Exped. 1934–37, Sci. Repts.* [British Museum (Natural History)], 1: 337–367. "Ornithological results of every antarctic expedition up to 1940" plus "Miscellaneous publications based on museum and literary research."

ARCTIC. Collins, Henry B. (Chairman, Directing Committee). 1953–1956. *Arctic Bibliography.* Government Printing Office, Washington, D. C. 6 vols.

AFRICA. Chapin, James P. 1954. The Birds of the Belgian Congo, Bibliography. *Bull. Amer. Mus. Nat. Hist.*, 75B: 739–809. See also: Anton Reichenow, Bibliographia Ornithologiae Aethiopicae, *Jour. f. Ornith.*, 42, 1894: 172–226.

AUSTRALIA. Whittell, Hubert Massey. 1954. *The Literature of Australian Birds: A History and Bibliography of Australian Ornithology.* Paterson Brokensha Pty., Ltd., Perth, Western Australia. 788 pp.

CALIFORNIA. Grinnell, Joseph. 1909, 1924, 1939. A Bibliography of California Ornithology [1797 through 1938]. *Pacific Coast Avifauna Nos. 5, 16, 26.* 592 pp. in all.

CHINA. Hachisuka, Masauji. 1952. Bibliography of Chinese Birds. *Quart. Jour. Taiwan Mus.*, 5, Nos. 2 and 3, Sept., 1952: 71–209.

FRANCE. Ronsil, René. 1948–1949. *Bibliographie Ornithologique Française . . . 1473 à 1944.* Lechevalier, Paris. 2 vols. 623 pp. French and Latin works published in France and its colonies.

GREAT BRITAIN. Mullens, W. H., and H. Kirke Swann. 1917. *A Bibliography of British Ornithology . . . to the end of 1912.* Macmillan, London. 691 pp. Scope: indicated by the title; emphasizes the major authors and gives biographical data on each. Irwin, Raymond. 1951. *British Bird Books: an Index to British Ornithology.* Grafton and Co., London. 398 pp. Arranged in part by subject. Despite title, the book deals extensively with periodical literature.

PACIFIC. Fisher, Harvey I. 1947. Utinomi's *Bibliographica Micronesica:* Chordate Sections. *Pacific Sci.*, 1: 129–150. Also: 1947. Bibliography of Hawaiian Birds since 1890. *Auk,* 64: 78–97.

COMPREHENSIVE LISTS OF PERIODICALS:

SMITH, William Allan, Francis L. KENT, and George B. STRATTON. 1952. *World List of Scientific Periodicals Published in the Years 1900–1950.* Butterworths Scientific Publications, London. 3rd ed. 1058 pp. More than 36,000 titles listed. Alphabetical arrangement.

GREGORY, Winifred. 1934. *Union List of Serials in Libraries of the United States and Canada.* H. W. Wilson Co., New York. 2nd ed. 3065 pp. See also: Second Supplement. 1953. 1365 pp.

UNDERWOOD, Margaret Hanselman. 1954. *Bibliography of North American Minor Natural History Serials in the University of Michigan Libraries.* University of Michigan Press, Ann Arbor, Mich. 197 pp. Alphabetical arrangement. Includes index of regions in which the journals were published.

LIBRARY OF CONGRESS. 1955. *Biological Sciences Serial Publications: A World List, 1950–1954.* Biological Abstracts, Philadelphia, Pa. An elaborately (and not always helpfully) classified list, with an index of titles by country of origin, subject index, etc. The principles used as basis for inclusion or exclusion of titles, for classification, and for indexing are not readily determinable.

Glossary

THE DEFINITIONS in this glossary are primarily in terms of ornithological usage.

Abductor. A muscle that moves a part away from the median plane or a specified axis. Cf. adductor.

Aberrant. Exceptional; divergent; having a marked difference (or differences) from other members of the group with which it is classified.

Abortive. Little developed; suppressed; remaining or becoming imperfect.

Acetabulum. The large socket in the pelvic girdle which receives the head of the femur.

Achilles' tendon (tendo Achillis). Tendon of the principal extensor muscle (M. gastrocnemius) of the tarsometatarsus.

Acicular. Needle-shaped; very slender and sharp-pointed.

Acromion. The anterior bony process (projection) of the scapula.

Acromyodian. With muscles of syrinx inserted on the extremities of the bronchial semirings; applied to passerine birds. Cf. mesomyodian.

Acropodium. The part of the podotheca (q.v.) that covers the dorsal surface of the toes.

Acrotarsium. The part of the podotheca that covers the front (anterior surface) of the tarsometatarsus (tarsus).

Aculeate. Slender-pointed.

Acuminate. Tapering gradually to a point. Cf. attenuate.

Acute. Sharp-pointed; sharp-angled.

Acutiplantar (of the oscine tarsus). Having the hinder (posterior) part of the tarsus sharp-angled. Cf. latiplantar.

Adductor. A muscle that moves a part toward the median plane or a specified axis. Cf. abductor.

Adult. Used properly of a bird only after it has assumed the final plumage. Even breeding birds are referred to as "immature" or subadult until this final plumage change (which may be at an age of from 3 months to 10 years). Cf. subadult, immature.

Aerial. Air-frequenting.

Affinity. A relationship between groups of birds indicating a common ancestor.

Aftershaft. A second, accessory feather (usually vestigial) arising from the inner surface of the shaft of the main feather.

"Age and area hypothesis." Proposal (by Willis) that the older a species is the wider will be its geographical distribution.

Aggressiveness. "The tendency to attack."

Air sacs. Extensions from the lungs in birds, occurring in the body cavity, under the skin, and in certain bones.

Ala spuria. See alula.

Alar. Pertaining to the wing (ala).

Albinism. The abnormal absence of color. Cf. melanism.

Alectoropodus. Pertaining to the Alectoropodes, a group in old classifications which included pheasants, grouse, etc.

Aliform. Winglike; wing-shaped.

Allele. "An alternative expression of a gene having the same locus in homologous chromosomes" (Mayr *et al.*). Cf. gene.

Allelomimetic behavior. "Any behavior in which two or more animals do the same thing, with some degree of mutual stimulation." Synonyms: contagious behavior, infectious behavior.

Allochronic species. Species which do not occur at the same time level. Cf. synchronic species.

Allopatric. Said of forms whose breeding ranges do not overlap. Cf. sympatric.

Allotype. A paratype (q.v.) of the opposite sex to the holotype.

Altricial. Said of birds whose young are helpless at hatching and require complete parental care for some time afterward. Cf. precocial, nidicolous.

Alula. The feathered "thumb" of the bird wing; also called "spurious wing" or "bastard wing."

Ambiens muscle. A long, slender muscle on the inner side of the thigh (in birds and reptiles only); much discussed by taxonomists since Garrod proposed its use in classification; absent in many groups of birds; "Am" in muscle formulae.

Amphicoelous. Having both the anterior and posterior articulating surfaces of the centrum (body) of a vertebra concave, i.e., biconcave.

Amphirhinal. With two bony nostrils on each side, a posterior and an anterior one (von Ihering, *Auk,* 1915: 150).

Anachromyodian. With the syringeal muscles inserted on the dorsal ends of the bronchial semirings (sometimes: "anachromyodous" or "anacromyodous").

Analogous. Superficially like, but not structurally (phylogenetically) related. Cf. homologous.

Anatine. Related to, or like, the Anatidae (Duck family); ducklike.

Ancipital. Two-edged.

Anconal (anconeal). Pertaining to the elbow. Also used to refer to the entire dorsal surface of the wing. Cf. palmar.

Angle of chin (the mental apex). "The anterior point of the space between the rhami [rami] of the lower jaw" (Ridgway).

Angle of mouth. Corner of mouth; commissural point.

Anisodactyl. With toes unevenly divided—3 directed forward and 1 backward. This is the common condition in birds.

Anisomyodian. With the syringeal muscles unequally inserted, either on the middle, or upon only one or the other (dorsal or ventral) ends of the bronchial semirings (sometimes: "anisomyodous").

Ankylosis. Stiffening or fixation of a joint. It may be a true (natural) union of two bones in an immovable joint, or it may be a pathological condition. (Incorrectly: anchylosis.)

Annular. Ringed; marked with rings; ringlike.

Anomalogonatae. A term (now obsolete) proposed by Garrod (1874) for a subclass of birds characterized by the absence of the ambiens muscle. Cf. Homalogonatae.

Anomalous. Deviating from the "normal," usual, or ordinary.

Anseres. Anseriformes.

Anserine. Gooselike.

Antaposematic. Pertaining to coloration or display used in threat or dominance against rivals, specifically of the same sex and species. Cf. aposematic.

Anterior. Forward, toward the head, in front.

Antiae. Projections of feathers on either side of the base of the culmen.

Anticoelous. Having the 2nd intestinal loop left-handed and lying dorsal to the 3rd loop, which is right-handed. A type of orthocoelous (q.v.) arrangement.

Antiopelmous. Having toes I, II, and IV connected with the tendon of M. flexor hallucis longus, and toe III with the flexor digitorum longus (type VI of Gadow); found in zygodactyl birds that lack the ambiens muscle (Piciformes).

Antipericoelous. Having the 2nd intestinal loop left-handed, open, and enclosing the 3rd loop, which is right-handed. Cf. isopericoelous, pericoelous.

Antrorse. Directed forward, as the nasal tufts or rictal bristles.

Anus. In mammals, the lower opening of the digestive tract (rectum and anal canal); in birds, often used for the opening of the cloaca to the exterior. Cf. vent.

Apodiformes. The order containing the swifts, crested-swifts, and hummingbirds. Also Micropodiformes, Macrochires.

Aponeurosis. A muscle attachment, differing from a tendon (q.v.) in being broad, membranous, and sheetlike.

Aposematic. Pertaining to coloration or behavior which functions as a warning or threat, against enemies, rivals, or in mimicry. Cf. antaposematic.

Apterium (pl. apteria). Bare (or downy) area between the tracts (pterylae, q.v.) of contour feathers (sometimes: apterion).

Aptosochromatism. Term applied to the supposed addition of color to feathers without the molt of old feathers and subsequent growth of new ones.

Aquatic. Water-frequenting.

Aquincubital (aquinto-cubital; aquintocubital). Wing with a gap between the 4th and 5th secondaries; diastataxic is preferred synonym. Cf. quincubital.

Arboreal. Tree-frequenting.

Archetype. The original form from which a given modern group of animals is presumed to be derived; "a hypothetical ancestral type arrived at by the elimination of specialized characters" (Mayr *et al.*).

Arcuate. Arched; bow-shaped.

Areola (pl. areolae [or areole, areoles]). Naked space between the scales on the feet; a small cavity in a bone, in areolar connective tissue, etc.

Areolar tissue. Loose connective tissue containing numerous interspaces or interstices.

Arm. Anatomically, the region between the shoulder and the elbow; loosely, the entire upper limb (arm, forearm, wrist, and hand).

Artenkreis (Rensch). Superspecies (q.v.).

Articulation. (1) A joint, i.e., the place where two or more bones meet or are joined together; such a joint may be freely movable, slightly movable, or immovable. (2) A movable joint; a joint in which one bone can move freely on another bone.

Asymmetrical. Not symmetrical.

Atavism. The recurrence in a descendent of characters of a remote, rather than an immediate, ancestor.

Atlas. The first cervical vertebra; it articulates with the skull (by a single occipital condyle) superiorly (anteriorly) and with the axis (epistropheus) inferiorly (posteriorly).

Atrophy. A gradual wasting of the tissues of a part or of the entire body; it may be pathological or it may be incidental to the normal development of an animal.

Attenuate. Tapering gradually. Cf. acuminate.

Auricular region. Area around the ear (external auditory meatus).

Auriculars. Feathers growing on the auricular region and covering the external ear opening.

Australasian region. One of six zoogeographical regions of the world, comprising Australia, Tasmania, New Zealand, New Guinea, and the South Pacific Islands. Cf. Oriental, Ethiopian, Neotropical, Nearctic, Palaearctic.

Autochthonous. Said of an animal belonging by origin to the area where it is now found. Cf. indigenous, endemic.

Avian. Pertaining to birds.

Axilla. Armpit or axillary space.

Axillars. Group of (usually elongate) feathers growing from the armpit region and closing the space between the spread wing and the body (sometimes: axillaries).

Axillary. Pertaining to the armpit or axilla.

Axis. Second cervical vertebra; epistropheus. The central line (usually longitudinal) of the body or any of its parts.

Azygos (azygous). Single; not paired.

Band. A broad transverse marking. Cf. bar, stripe.

Bar. A narrow transverse marking. Barred: marked with bars. Cf. band, stripe.

Barb. One of the branches from the shaft of a feather, which together form the vane; ramus (pl. rami).

Barbicel. One of the small projections on the barbules of feathers.

Barbule. One of the projections that fringe the barbs of a typical feather.

Basipterygoid. A projection from the base of the sphenoid bone and articulating with the pterygoid.

Basisphenoid. Basal part of sphenoid bone.

Bastard wing. See alula.

Belly. Part of lower (ventral) surface of the body between the breast and the vent.

Belly of muscle. The fleshy (composed of muscle fibers) part of a muscle as distinguished from the tendons or aponeuroses of its attachments (origin and insertion); or, the bulk of a muscle when its origin, insertion, or both, are "fleshy."

Belted. With a broad band across the breast or belly.

Bend of wing. The carpal or wrist joint; the anterior point in the folded wing.

Biceps. Literally, two-headed. The main flexor muscle of the forearm or the crus (tibiotarsus).

Bicolored. Two-colored.

Bill. The projecting jaws of a bird; the beak.

Binominal (binomial). Nomenclature, designation of the scientific name of an animal by both a generic and a specific (trivial) name.

Biome. A "climax" vegetational area, e.g., coniferous forest, deciduous forest, prairie grassland, and its animal inhabitants.

Blending inheritance. "Inheritance (generally due to multiple factors) in which clear segregation is not evident in the F_2 generation" (Mayr *et al.*). Cf. multiple factors.

Booted (of the tarsal sheath). Undivided in most or all of its extent. Ocreate.

Bristle. A feather with a stiff shaft and (usually) only a trace of web at the base.

Bronchidesmus. An elastic band extending between the right and left internal tympaniform membranes of the bronchi.

Brood patch. See incubation patch.

Brooding. Behavior of adults in keeping the young warm (to be distinguished from "incubating," or keeping the eggs warm).

Buccal. Pertaining to the cheeks.

Bullate. Resembling a bulla or blister; vesiculate.

Bursa Fabricii (of Fabricius). A dorsal diverticulum of the proctodeum (q.v.); generally atrophies after hatching (the rate varying in different groups of birds); used as a criterion of age, especially in gallinaceous birds; sometimes called a "cloacal thymus," because of the lymphoid tissue in its walls.

Caecum (pl. caeca). A diverticulum at the junction of the small and the large intestine; typically paired when present; also cecum.

Calamus. The hollow, vaneless base of a feather; quill.

Calcareous. Chalky.

Capitulum. A small head or rounded articular extremity of a bone.

Capitulum costae. The head of a rib which articulates with the body (centrum) of a vertebra. Cf. tuberculum costae.

Caprimulgi. Caprimulgiformes.

Carina. A longitudinal ridge or plate of bone on the ventral side of the sternum; called the keel.

Carinate. Having a keeled sternum. Cf. ratite.

Carnivorous. Flesh-eating.

Carotid artery. The main artery to the head; typically paired; many peculiar modifications in birds.

Carpal. Pertaining to the wrist or carpus. Cf. radiale, ulnare.

Carpal covert. The major upper covert of the carpal remex; it may be present when the carpal remex is absent.

Carpal remex. A feather on the dorsal surface of the wrist (carpus), in the gap between the primaries and secondaries, or at the base of the first primary.

Carpometacarpus. The bone formed by the fusion of carpal and metacarpal bones; or the part of the wing (feathers) supported by this bone.

Carpus. The wrist.

Caruncülate. Having caruncles, "naked, fleshy excrescence, usually about the head or neck, and ordinarily brightly colored, wrinkled, or warty" (Ridgway), as a comb or wattle (q.v.).

Casque. "The horn-like excrescence (*epithema*) developed on the bill of most" species of hornbills (Bucerotidae)—Gadow; a frontal shield, as in coots; also called "helmet." Casque usually refers to an enlargement in front of the head, on the dorsal surface of the bill; a shield lies at the base of the bill and extends backward over the forehead; a helmet is an "adornment" on top of the head, and sometimes refers to feathers, as in the "helmet-shrikes" (Prionopidae).

Catacromyodian. With the syringeal muscles inserted on the ventral ends of the bronchial semirings (sometimes: katacromyodian; "catacromyodous").

Caudad. Toward the tail; posteriorly. Cf. craniad.

Caudal. Pertaining to the tail (cauda).

Centrum. The body of a vertebra; the dorsal surface of the centrum forms the floor of the neural canal.

Cere. Name for basal covering of the upper mandible when this is soft (as in hawks, owls, parrots). In such bills the nostrils are placed within (or at the edge of) the cere. The cere is sometimes conspicuously swollen and/or distinctively colored; often feathered in parrots. The word is sometimes (incorrectly) used for caruncles on the forehead near the base of the bill. Formerly also called "cera," "ceroma."

Ceroma. Cere.

Cervical. Pertaining to the neck.

Cervix. "The hind neck, extending from the occiput to the commencement of the back. It has two subdivisions, namely, the nape and scruff (*nucha* and *auchenium*), which occupy respectively the upper and lower halves of the cervix" (Ridgway); of an organ, any necklike structure, or a constricted area.

Chin. The region between the branches (rami) of the lower mandible.

Choanae (sing. choana). The internal nares; openings of the nasal chambers into the roof of the pharynx.

Ciconine. Storklike.

Circum-. Around, about, as: circumanal, around the anus; circumorbital, around the orbit.

Cirrhous. Tufted.

Clavicle. One of three bones forming the pectoral girdle; in most birds the right and left clavicles fuse to form a furcula ("wishbone," "merrythought"). Cf. coracoid, scapula.

Claw. Horny sheath of the terminal phalanx of a digit, usually a toe.

Cloaca (a sewer). The common chamber which receives the rectum, ureters, and gonaducts (oviducts or ductus deferentia); subdivided into a coprodeum, urodeum, and proctodeum.

Clutch (of eggs). The total number of eggs laid by one female for a single nesting.

Cnemial. Pertaining to the crus or shin; crural.

Cnémidophore (of the tarsal sheath). Booted (French).

Coccygeal. Pertaining to the tail, caudal; but usually with special reference to the vertebrae, muscles, or blood vessels of the tail.

Coecum (pl. coeca). See caecum.

Coitus (coition). Copulation (q.v.).

Colii. Coliiformes.

Colymbiformes. Former name for the order containing the grebes. Now variously called Podicipediformes (A.O.U. Check-List), Podicipitiformes (British), Podicipedes (Stresemann; Mayr and Amadon). Also (formerly) by the British, the order name for the loons or divers.

Comb. Erect, fleshy lengthwise process, or caruncle, on top of the head, as in the domestic cock.

Commissural point. Angle or corner of the mouth.

Commissure. Line of closure of the two mandibles. Often improperly used to signify the *opening between* the mandibles; but this is the gape or rictus (q.v.) (Coues).

Compressed. Higher than wide. Opposite to depressed.

Concolored. Unicolored; of one uniform color.

Condyle. A rounded articular surface at the end of a bone.

Congeneric. A term applied to species of the same genus.

Conirostral. Having a conical bill, as in the finches.

Conspecific. A term applied to individuals or populations of the same species.

Continuous variation. Variation in which a series of individuals differ from each other by infinitely small steps. Cf. discontinuous variation.

Contour feathers. The outer feathers of the head, neck, body, and limbs (including the flight feathers).

Coprodeum (coprodaeum). That part of the cloaca which receives the rectum.

Copulation. Sexual union; transfer of sperm from male to female cloaca, accomplished in most birds by cloacal apposition; a cloacal penis (or clitoris) present in some birds (see p. 39). Coition.

Coraciae. Coraciiformes.

Coracoid. One of three bones forming the pectoral girdle; articulates with the sternum inferiorly, with the scapula and clavicle superiorly; takes part in the formation of the glenoid fossa, in which the head of the humerus articulates. Cf. clavicle, scapula.

Cordate. Heart-shaped; cordiform.

Coriaceous. Leathery.

Corneous. Horny.

Corniplume. Tuft of feathers on the head, erected like a horn.

Costal. Pertaining to the ribs.

Costiferous. Rib-bearing.

Cotype. Syntype (q.v.).

Coverts. The small feathers which overlie the bases of the flight feathers (remiges and rectrices) and several rows of smaller feathers between the bases of the flight feathers and the leading edge of the wing (especially on the dorsal surface); auricular feathers are called ear coverts. Cf. tectrix.

Craniad. Toward the head; anteriorly. Cf. caudad.

Crepuscular. Active at twilight.

Crest. A tuft of lengthened feathers on head, erect or capable of being erected.

Crissum. The under tail coverts, especially when unicolored; circumanal plumage; sometimes (formerly) an indefinite area between anal ring and under tail coverts.

Crown. Top of the head (between the forehead and occiput).

Crural. Pertaining to the crus or tibia (tibiotarsus).

Crus. The leg, tibia.

Cryptic. Adapted to conceal.

Cryptic plumage. That which aids in concealment.

Cryptic species. Sibling species (q.v.).

Cryptoptile. The theoretical simple filament which formed the coat of primitive birds of earlier geological ages (before birds developed protoptiles).

Crypturi. Tinamiformes.

Cubitals. Old term for secondary feathers.

Cucullate. Hooded (q.v.).

Culmen. Ridge or upper border of the maxilla.

Cultrate. Knifelike.

Cultrirostral. Having the bill shaped like a heron's.

Cuneate, cuneiform. Wedge-shaped.

Cuneiform. See ulnare.

Cursorial. Adapted to running or walking. Pertaining or belonging to the "Cursores" (an obsolete term).

Cuspidate. Pointed as a spearhead.

Cutaneous. Dermal; pertaining to the skin.

Cyanic (of eggs). Abnormally blue owing to the absence of reddish pigments.

Cyclocoelous. Having some of the intestinal loops arranged in a spiral. Cf. orthocoelous, telogyrous, mesogyrous.

Cypselidae. Former name for the swifts (Apodidae) and the crested-swifts (Hemiprocnidae).

Dasypaedic. Ptilopaedic (q.v.).

Deciduous. Temporary; shed periodically; falling early. The dorsal plumes of an egret are deciduous.

Decomposed. Used to describe a feather whose barbs hang loosely instead of being held, by means of barbules, in a compact web.

Decurved. Turned downward. Cf. recurved.

Deep plantar tendons. The tendons of Mm. flexor hallucis longus and flexor digitorum longus. Cf. vinculum, desmopelmous, antiopelmous.

Deltoid. Triangular; shaped like the Greek letter *delta.* Deltoid muscle; deltoid crest.

Dentate, denticulate. Toothed; notched as if toothed.

Dentirostral. Having a toothed bill, as in shrikes, vireos, and some wrens, thrushes, and wood-warblers.

Depressed. Broader than high; flattened dorsoventrally. Opposite to compressed.

Dermal. Pertaining to the skin.

Dertrotheca. Covering of tip of bill (rarely used).

Dertrum. Extremity of the upper mandible (maxilla); the hook of the bill.

Desmodactyli. With the deep plantar tendons (Mm. flexor hallucis longus and flexor digitorum longus) connected by a vinculum; but the term was applied by Forbes only to the broadbills (Eurylaimidae). Cf. Eleutherodactyli.

Desmopelmous. Having the tendons of Mm. flexor hallucis longus and flexor digitorum longus connected by a vinculum; a type of nomopelmous (q.v.) arrangement. These terms apparently proposed by D. G. Elliot in *The Riverside Natural History,* Vol. IV, 1885, pp. 368–369. Cf. schizopelmous, antiopelmous, heteropelmous, synpelmous.

Diacromyodi (suborder). Oscines (Pycraft).

Diacromyodian. With some syringeal muscles inserted on the dorsal and some on the ventral ends of the bronchial semirings.

Diagnosis. A statement of the characters that distinguish a population, species, genus, family, or higher group of birds.

Diastataxic. Wing with a gap between the 4th and 5th secondaries. Cf. aquincubital; eutaxic.

Dichotomous. Divided by pairs, as in a key.

Dichromatic. Having two color phases independent of age or sex.

Dichromatism. Condition of being dichromatic.

Didactyl (didactylous). Two-toed, as the ostrich.

Digital formula. A listing of the number of phalanges in each toe, beginning with the hallux (toe no. I).

Dimorphic. Having two forms.

Disc (or disk). Circlet of radiating feathers around the eye, as in the owls.

Discontinuous variation. Variation in which the individuals of a sample fall into definite classes which do not grade into each other. Cf. continuous variation.

Displacement reaction. "An irrelevant movement occurring when an animal is under the influence of a powerful urge but is in some way prevented from expressing the urge in the appropriate way." Synonyms: substitute activity; allochthonous activity.

Distal. Farthest from the trunk or mid-line; referring especially to the segments of the appendages; opposite of proximal (q.v.).

Diurnal. Active during the day.

Dorsal vertebrae. "Begin at the first that is connected with the sternum by a pair of complete ribs, and end at the last that is not fused" with the synsacrum (Newton, 1896: 849); many authors call these thoracic vertebrae (q.v.).

Dorsum. The back; the upper surface of the body, as opposed to the ventral or lower surface.

Down. Feathers of adults: plumules; small, soft feathers, without a vane and with a very short or vestigial rachis. Cf. powder-down feathers.

Downy. Applied to young of precocial species (usually) that are fully covered with a dense coat of down at hatching.

Ear coverts. Auriculars.

Eared. With tufts of feathers ("ear tufts") on the head that resemble the external ears of mammals.

Ecdysis. The shedding of plumage. Cf. endysis, molt.

Eclipse plumage. The dull plumage worn by the males of most Northern Hemisphere ducks (and some other birds) while growing new flight feathers.

Edge of wing. The anterior border of the wing as far as the bone extends; campterium (little used; Coues). Also, the coverts along the anterior margin of the manus (Sutton).

Egg-tooth. A horny tubercle near the tip of the upper mandible in the hatching bird; it is cast off shortly after hatching.

Elaeodochon. Oil gland.

Eleutherodactyli. With the deep plantar tendons (Mm. flexor hallucis longus and flexor digitorum longus) not connected by a vinculum; applied by Forbes to all passerine birds except the Eurylaimidae. Cf. Desmodactyli.

Eleutherodactylous. "Is sometimes said of any bird which has its toes free and not connected by a web, or otherwise bound together; equivalent to Fissipedal of some older authors" (Gadow).

Elevated. Said of hind toe (hallux) when above the level of the anterior toes. Cf. incumbent.

Emarginate. Of the tail: notched at the end; slightly forked. Of a remex: notched or abruptly narrowed or cut away along the edge. Cf. sinuate.

Emphysematous. Inflated by air or other gas; said of the skin in some diving birds.

Endaspidean (of the tarsal sheath). With anterior, scutellated segment of tarsal sheath extending across the inner side of the tarsus; the reverse of exaspidean (q.v.).

Endemic. Confined to, or indigenous to, a certain area or region. Cf. indigenous, autochthonous.

Endysis. Act of developing a new set of feathers; opposite to ecdysis (q.v.). Cf. molt.

Epigamic. Pertaining to coloration or behavior (display) which promotes sexual union.

Epignathous. Having a bill with the upper mandible longer than the lower mandible and its tip bent down over the lower mandible, as in hawks, parrots, gulls, etc.; hook-billed.

Epimeletic behavior. "The giving of care or attention, including parental care but also care by non-parents." Synonym: attentive behavior.

Episematic. Pertaining to coloration which aids in recognition and signalling, e.g., in parent-young recognition.

Epithema. A horny excrescence on the bill.

Erectile. Capable of being raised or dilated.

Erythrism. A state of plumage characterized by an abnormal amount of red coloration.

Etepimeletic behavior. "Calling or signalling for care and attention."

Ethiopian region. One of six zoogeographical regions of the world, comprising Africa south of the Palaearctic region and southern Arabia. Cf. Oriental, Neotropical, Nearctic, Palaearctic, Australasian.

Ethology. The objective study of behavior (Tinbergen).

Eurytopic. Ecologically very tolerant; can exist under a wide range of environmental conditions. Cf. stenotopic.

Eutaxic. Wing without a gap between the 4th and 5th secondaries; formerly "quincubital." Cf. diastataxic.

Even. "An *even* or *'square' tail* has, *when closed,* all the feathers terminating on the same transverse line; in other words, it is *truncated* at the tip. When spread, the tips of the feathers describe a semicircle, while an emarginate or slightly forked tail becomes even or truncated when spread" (Ridgway).

Exaspidean (of the tarsal sheath). With anterior, scutellated segment of tarsal sheath extending across the external side of the tarsus; the reverse of endaspidean (q.v.). Cf. ultraexaspidean.

Excrescence. An outgrowth, fleshy or cutaneous.

Excreta. Excrement; waste matter, especially feces and the nitrogenous products of metabolism.

Exotic. Foreign.

Extensor. Any muscle that extends or straightens a limb or other part.

Eyrie (eyry). Nest of a hawk or eagle.

Facet. A smooth, usually flattened, articulating surface.

Facial disc. See disc.

Faecal, faeces. See fecal.

Falcate, falciform. Sickle-shaped.

Falcones. Falconiformes.

Family. A taxonomic group, more comprehensive than the genus and more restrictive than the order; always ends in "idae."

Fasciae (sing. fascia). Discrete sheets of fibrous connective tissue that envelop the body under the skin, and that invest the organs of the body.

Fecal. Pertaining to excrement (feces).

Femoral. Pertaining to the femur.

Femur. The upper (proximal) bone of the posterior limb ("leg").

Feral. Wild, undomesticated; used especially of stocks that have escaped from domestication and become wild.

Fibula. An incomplete bone in the leg, rarely extending as far as the distal end of the tibiotarsus.

Filamentous. Threadlike.

Filiform. Threadlike.

Filoplume. A very specialized, hairlike or bristlelike feather.

Fimbriated. Fringed.

Fissipalmate. Lobe-footed; lobiped and semipalmate, as a grebe's foot.

Fissirostral. Having a short bill with a very wide gape, as in the Whip-poor-will, swifts, swallows.

Fledge. "To acquire the feathers necessary for flight"; "to rear or care for (a bird) until its plumage is developed so that it can fly" (Webster).

Fledgling. (1) A bird that has recently left the nest. (2) A young bird that is feathered. (3) A young bird that is still dependent on its parents for food.

Flexor. Any muscle that bends, i.e., reduces the angle between two bones.

Flight feathers. The remiges and rectrices taken collectively.

Foramen (pl. foramina). Opening, perforation; often, but not necessarily, in a bone.

Foramen triosseum. The space through which the tendon of M. supracoracoideus passes to its insertion on the humerus; bounded by clavicle, coracoid, and scapula.

Forearm. The region between the elbow and the wrist. See radius, ulna.

Forehead. Front; forepart of the top of the head, between the base of the bill and the crown.

Foreneck. ". . . indefinite . . . arbitrary . . . usually referring to the lower throat and jugulum, though not infrequently to the whole space included by the chin, throat, and jugulum. In long-necked birds only does the term become of definite application" (Ridgway).

Form. A neutral term for a single individual or taxonomic unit.

Formenkreis (Kleinschmidt). A collective category of allopatric species or subspecies.

Fossa. Cavity, depression.

Fossil. Any evidence of prehistoric life.

Fossorial. Digging, burrowing.

Foster parent. One that rears the young of another bird, especially of a nest parasite, such as certain cuckoos, honeyguides, cowbirds, and weaverbirds. (Synonym: host.) Foster young: the young of such parasitic species.

Frontal. Pertaining to the forehead.

Frugivorous. Fruit-eating.

Furcate. Forked.

Furcula. The "wishbone," formed by the fusion inferiorly (ventrally) of the two clavicles; also called the os furcatum.

Fusiform. Spindle-shaped; tapering at both ends.

Galli. Galliformes.

Gallinaceous. Pertaining to galliform birds, grouse, quail, pheasants, etc.

Gamosematic. Pertaining to coloration or behavior which assists the members of a pair to find each other.

Gape. The mouth opening; "the angle formed by the lower border of the upper jaw and the upper border of the lower jaw, when the bill is open." Cf. rictus, commissure.

Gause's rule. The theory that no two species with identical ecological requirements can coexist at the same place.

Gene. The unit of inheritance, located in a chromosome, transmitted from one generation to the next by the gametes (eggs and sperm), and controlling the development of the individual. Cf. allele.

Generic. Pertaining to the genus.

Genotype. In genetics, the sum total of the genes of an individual; cf. phenotype. In nomenclature (not recommended), the type species of a genus.

Genus (pl. genera). A taxonomic group more comprehensive than the species but less comprehensive than the family (or subfamily).

Gizzard. Ventriculus, the muscular portion of the stomach. Cf. proventriculus.

Gnathidium (pl. gnathidia). The ramus of the (lower) mandible (Coues).

Gnathotheca. The covering of the lower jaw or mandible.

Gonys. The ventral median ridge of the lower mandible, from its tip to its point of forking.

Gorget. Throat patch, when distinguished by the color or texture of the feathers.

Graduated (of tail). With the middle feathers the longest, the others successively and gradually shorter.

Grallatores. Obsolete name for an unnatural grouping of wading birds.

Grallatorial. Adapted for wading; of or pertaining to the "Grallatores" or waders.

Graminivorous. Grass-eating.

Granivorous. Seed-eating.

Gregarious. Habitually living or moving in flocks.

Gressores. Ciconiiformes except Phoenicopteridae.

Grues. Gruiformes.

Grypanium. A particular form of bill, in which the culmen is nearly straight, but bent downward at the tip (obsolete).

Gular. Pertaining to the throat (gula).

Guttate, guttiform. Drop-shaped, tear-shaped.

Gymnopaedic. Psilopaedic (q.v.).

Gymnorhinal. Having bare, unfeathered nostrils.

Hackles. The long, slender feathers on the neck of gallinaceous birds, especially *Gallus.*

Hallux. The first digit of the foot; usually directed backward, but in the woodpecker genus *Picoïdes* the hallux is lacking and toe IV is turned backward.

Hamulate. Having a small hook (hamulus).

Hamulus (pl. hamuli). A hooked barbicel.

Hand-quills. Primary quills, primaries.

Haploophone (ae). Applied to a division of rather primitive passerine birds (mesomyodian) characterized by a tracheobronchial syrinx: Pittidae, Philepittidae, Acanthisittidae, Tyrannidae, Pipridae, Cotingidae, Oxyruncidae, Phytotomidae. Cf. Tracheophone.

Hawking. Catching insects by flying about with open mouth. Falconry: the sport of hunting with hawks.

Helmet. See casque.

Hemiptile. Juvenal plumage; a term proposed by Bonhote (*Ibis,* 1921: 348) but not generally adopted.

Heterocoelous. Having the anterior and posterior articular surfaces of the centrum (body) of a vertebra saddle-shaped.

Heterodactyl. With toes I and II turned backwards, as in trogons. Cf. zygodactyl.

Heterogynism. The condition in which "taxonomic characters are more strongly pronounced in females than in males" (Mayr, *Amer. Mus. Novitates, No. 522:* 5).

Heteromeri. Term proposed by Garrod for those passerine birds (Pipridae and Cotingidae, except *Rupicola*) in which the femoral artery is presumed to be invariably larger than the ischiadic artery. Cf. Homoeomeri.

Heteromerous. Of or pertaining to, or resembling, the Heteromeri.

Heteropelmous. Having the tendon of M. flexor hallucis longus inserting on toes I and II, the tendon of M. flexor digitorum longus on toes III and IV; characteristic of the Trogonidae.

Hierarchy (behavior). "Any social rank-order established through direct combat, threat, passive submission, or some combination of these behavior patterns."

Hind-neck. See cervix.

Hirsute. Hairy.

Holarctic. The northern regions of the Old and New Worlds; includes Palaearctic and Nearctic regions (q.v.).

Holaspidean (of the tarsal sheath). With rear surface of tarsus covered by a single series of broad, rectangular scales.

Holorhinal. Having the nasal bones contiguous (Coues); "anterior margin of the nasal is concave" (Gadow); "condition in which the external nasal opening in the skull has its posterior border (formed by the margin of the nasal bone) rounded" (Witherby).

Holothecal (of tarsal sheath). A smooth, undivided sheath; a general term. Booted (obsolete). Cf. schizothecal.

Holotype. "The single specimen designated or indicated as 'the type' by the original author at the time of the publication of the original description."

Homalogonatae. A term (now obsolete) proposed by Garrod for a subclass of birds characterized by possession of the ambiens muscle. Cf. Anomalogonatae.

Homoeomeri. A term proposed by Garrod for those mesomyodian passerine birds in which the ischiadic artery is presumed to be invariably larger than the femoral artery. Cf. Heteromeri.

Homoeomerous (homeomerous). Of or pertaining to, or resembling, the Homoeomeri.

Homologous. Structurally similar (though perhaps superfically unlike). Cf. analogous.

Homonym. In nomenclature, one of two or more identical but independently proposed names for the same or different taxonomic categories.

Hooded. With the head feathers sharply contrasting with the rest of the plumage.

Host. Any bird that is parasitized by internal or external parasites, or by another bird for food or nests; any bird (fosterer) in whose nest a parasitic species lays eggs. Cf. foster parent.

Humeral. Flight feather attached to the skin overlying the humerus; usually called tertiaries or tertials. Pertaining to the humerus.

Humerus. The bone of the arm ("upper arm"), in contrast to the forearm.

Hybrid. Offspring of parents of two different species.

Hyoid (bone). Bony support for the tongue; it is composed of several elements.

Hypertrophy. Overgrowth or excessive development of a part or an organ; unusually well developed.

Hypodactylum. Soles of the toes.

Hypognathous. Having the lower mandible longer than the upper.

Hypophysis. Pituitary gland.

Hypopteron. The long under feathers of the wing next to the body; the axillars. Cf. parapteron.

Hypoptilum. The aftershaft of a feather; more commonly called hyporachis.

Hyporachis (hyporhachis; hyporrhachis). The aftershaft of a feather.

Hypotarsus. A bony structure on the posterior surface of the proximal end of the tarsometatarsus, which transmits the flexor tendons to the toes; it may take the form of two or more parallel ridges or of a process containing two or more bony canals.

Iliac. Relating to the ilium.

Ilium. One of the three paired bones that, with the synsacrum, form the pelvic girdle. Cf. ischium, pubis.

Imbricated. Overlapped. Imbrication: overlapping.

Immaculate (of plumage, eggs). Without markings of any kind.

Immature. Not adult, though full grown; usually based on plumage. Cf. adult, subadult.

Imperforate (of nostrils). Separated from each other by a nasal septum. (Not a synonym of impervious). Cf. perforate.

Impervious (of nostrils). Closed, as in adults of gannets, cormorants, etc. Cf. pervious.

Inconstant (anatomy). Said of a variable structure that is not always present.

Incubation. Keeping the eggs warm until they hatch (to be distinguished from brooding, or keeping the young warm).

Incubation patch. A modified (highly vascular) area of skin on the belly, applied to the surface of the eggs during incubation.

Incumbent. "Of a bird's hind toe, so placed that its whole length rests on the ground when the bird is standing" (Webster). Cf. elevated.

Indented. Notched.

Index. Used to refer to the principal digit of the wing, digit II; or, by some authors, to the pollex—according to the author's opinion of the homologies of the avian wing digits.

Indigenous. Native to a given country. Cf. autochthonous, endemic.

Inguinal. Pertaining to the groin; near the groin.

Inner toe. "In any position, the *inner toe,* properly speaking, is the second, that one with only three" phalanges (Coues).

Insectivorous. Insect-eating.

Insessorial. Perching.

Integument. Covering, envelope; the skin.

Interscapular region. The region on the back (dorsum) between the scapulae, or between the humeral feather tracts (scapulars).

Iris (pl. irides). Opaque, contractile diaphragm suspended in the aqueous humor in front of the lens of the eye.

Ischiadic. Ischiatic. Relating to the ischium.

Ischium. One of the three paired bones that, with the synsacrum, form the pelvic girdle. Cf. ilium, pubis.

Isocoelous. Having the 2nd, 3rd, and 4th (if present) loops of the small intestine closed and "left-handed" (i.e., with the descending branch lying to the left of the ascending branch). A type of orthocoelous (q.v.) arrangement.

Isopericoelous. Having the 2nd intestinal loop left-handed, open, and enclosing the 3rd loop, which also is left-handed. Cf. antipericoelous, orthocoelous.

Jugulum. "The lower throat or foreneck, immediately above the breast. It is a well-defined area in the Hawks, Vultures, Pigeons, Ducks, and some other groups" (Ridgway).

Juvenal (adj.). Applied to the plumage immediately succeeding the natal down (or succeeding the naked nestling stage of species which lack natal down); the first plumage composed of true contour feathers. Cf. juvenile.

Juvenile (adj.). Immature; young. Cf. juvenal.

Juvenile (n.). An immature bird.

Keel. See carina.

Knemidophorer (of the tarsal sheath). Booted (German).

Laciniate. Fringed (of the tongue).

Lacustrine. Lake-inhabiting.

Lamellate. Having numerous lamellae or thin plates, as along the sides of a duck's bill.

Lamellirostres. Cuvier's name for the Anatidae.

Lamina. A thin plate, scale, or layer.

Laminiplantar (of the tarsal sheath of passerine birds). With a smooth, undivided plantar (posterior) tarsal surface, but a scutellate acrotarsal (anterior) surface. Note: Ridgway's objection (*U. S. Natl. Mus. Bull.,* 50, pt. 1, 1901: 18, footnote 4) to Sundevall's taxonomic unit "Laminiplantares" is well founded, but that is no reason for refusing to use "laminiplantar" as a simple adjective to describe the tarsi of most oscine birds. Cf. scutelliplantar.

Lanceolate. Lance-shaped.

Lappet. A wattle, especially at the angle of the mouth.

Laro-Limicolae. Charadriiformes.

Lateral. Pertaining to the side, away from the mid-sagittal plane; laterally, toward the side; opposed to medial.

Latiplantar (of the oscine tarsus). Having the hinder part of the tarsus rounded. Cf. acutiplantar.

Lectotype. "One of a series of syntypes which, subsequent to the publication of the original description, is selected and designated through publication to serve as 'the type.' " Cf. syntype.

Leg. Anatomically, the region between the knee and ankle; the crus; in birds the region of the tibiotarsus; loosely, the entire lower limb.

Levator. Any muscle that lifts or raises.

Limicoline. Shore-inhabiting.

Lining of the wings. "The under wing-coverts taken collectively."

Littoral. Pertaining to the shore.

Lobed (of birds' feet). With "membranous flaps" (Webster, Ridgway).

Loral. Pertaining to the lores (the space between the eye and bill).

Lower parts. Under parts; the under surface, from chin to tail.

Lyrate. Lyre-shaped (as the tail of the Lyrebird).

Macrochires. Apodiformes (Micropodiformes).

Maculate. Spotted.

Malar region. The "cheek" (mala), the side of the jaw just behind the horny covering of the bill, between the throat and ear coverts.

Mandible. Lower half of the bill; used in the plural to describe the two halves of the bill. Cf. maxilla.

Mandibular. Pertaining to the mandible.

Mantle. Specifically, the feathers of the back and the folded wings; formerly called "pallium" and "stragulum."

Manubrium. Literally, handle; process at the anterior edge of the sternum at the root of the keel; the "manubrium sterni" of older works.

Manus. Hand; the carpometacarpus and digits; the part of the wing beyond the bend (wrist or carpus); bears the primary feathers.

Marbled. Marked irregularly with spots, speckles, streaks, etc.

Margined. With a narrow border.

Maxilla. Upper half of the bill. Cf. mandible.

Medial, median. Pertaining to the middle, or nearer the mid-sagittal plane; opposed to lateral.

Melanism. An unusual dark plumage due to increased amounts of black pigment. Cf. albinism.

Membranous. Formed of membrane; membranelike; skinlike.

Mental apex. The extreme anterior point of the chin, or mentum.

Mesentery. A double layer of peritoneum attached to the dorsal body wall and enclosing in its fold any part of the small intestine, conveying to it its vessels and nerves.

Mesocolon. The fold of peritoneum attaching the colon (large intestine; called "rectum" in birds) to the dorsal body wall. Cf. mesorectum.

Mesoduodenum. The mesentery (q.v.) of the duodenum.

Mesogyrous. A type of cyclocoelous (q.v.) pattern in which a spiral is formed by the the middle (or 2nd) intestinal loop, the caeca being located at the apex of the spiral; typical of passerine birds. Cf. telogyrous.

Mesomyodian. With the muscles of the syrinx inserted on the middle of the bronchial semirings; sometimes: "mesomyodous"; proposed by Garrod and restricted to passerine birds. Cf. acromyodian.

Mesoptile. One of the feathers in the 2nd of two successive coats of nestling down. Cf. protoptile.

Mesorectum. The fold of peritoneum attaching the large intestine ("rectum") to the dorsal body wall. Cf. mesocolon.

Mesorhinium. "Portion of bill between the nostrils. (Little used)" (Coues).

Metagnathous. Having a bill in which the tips of the mandibles cross each other, as in crossbills (*Loxia*).

Metapatagium. The double fold of skin extending from the body to the elbow, posterior to the humerus; also postpatagium. Cf. propatagium.

Metaptile. Obsolete term (used by Ewart, 1921) for plumose feathers of the adult plumage; ornithologists now use "teleoptile" to designate both plumose and pennaceous feathers of adult birds.

Middle toe. Toe III, that one having 4 phalanges in most birds; in zygodactyl birds it is the *outer* anterior toe; in heterodactyl birds it is the *inner* anterior toe; it is never versatile (= reversible).

Mimetic. Imitative; reproducing the voice, form, or color of another species.

Mirror. See speculum.

Molt (spelled moult by British). The renewal of plumage. Cf. ecdysis, endysis.

Monogamous. Copulating with but one of the opposite sex during one nesting cycle.

Mucronate. Spine-tipped.

Multiple factors. Two or more pairs of genes and their alleles with a complementary or cumulative effect. Cf. blending inheritance.

Muscle formula. See p. 56.

Myology. The study of muscles and their accessory parts.

Nail. A horny tip on upper mandible (maxilla) in ducks, geese, and swans.

Nape. That part of the hind-neck caudal to the occiput.

Naris (pl. nares). Nostril; the external opening of the nasal cavity.

Natatores. Swimming birds.

Navicular. Boat-shaped.

Nearctic region. One of six zoogeographical regions of the world, comprising North America and part of Mexico. Cf. Palaearctic, Neotropical, Ethiopian, Oriental, Australasian.

Neossoptile (or neoptile). Downy plumage of young birds (whether protoptile or mesoptile); nestling feathers, consisting of prepennae, prefiloplumae, and preplumulae (Hosker, 1936). Cf. teleoptiles.

Neotropical region. One of six zoogeographical regions of the world, comprising the lowlands of Mexico and Central and South America. Cf. Nearctic, Palaearctic, Ethiopian, Oriental, and Australasian.

Neotype. A specimen selected as the type subsequent to the original description in those cases where it is definitely known that the primary types have been destroyed.

Nestling. A young bird that has not yet left the nest.

Nictitating membrane. A "third eyelid"; a thin membrane at the inner corner of the eye that can be drawn across the eyeball.

Nidicolae. A term referring to all nidicolous (q.v.) birds; subdivided into four categories on p. 629 of Newton and Gadow's *A Dictionary of Birds*. Cf. nidifugae.

Nidicolous. Said of birds whose young remain in the nest for some time after hatching. A more restricted term than altricial, though sometimes used (incorrectly) as a synonym. Altricial (q.v.) birds may be either psilopaedic or ptilopaedic. Cf. nidifugous.

Nidification. Nest-building; manner of nesting.

Nidifugae. A term referring to all nidifugous (q.v.) birds. Cf. Nidicolae.

Nidifugous. Said of birds whose young leave the nest shortly after hatching. A more restricted term than precocial, which refers also to the condition of the young: i.e., densely covered with down and with eyes open at hatching. All nidifugous birds are ptilopaedic at hatching, but this fact is not included in the definition of nidifugous. Cf. nidicolous.

Nocturnal. Active at night.

Nomopelmous. Having the tendon of M. flexor hallucis longus inserting only on the hallux; the tendon of M. flexor digitorum longus inserting on toes II, III, and IV. Two types of nomopelmous arrangement are desmopelmous and schizopelmous (q.v.).

Nostril. Naris; external opening of nasal cavity.

Nuchal. Pertaining to the nape (nucha), or back of the neck.

Nuptial. Pertaining to the breeding season.

Obscure. Indistinct, ill-defined.

Obsolete. Indistinct; or wanting, absent; no longer used.

Occiput. The back part of the head, between the crown and nape.

Ocellate. Marked with eyespots (ocelli), as in the peacock's tail.

Ocreate (of the tarsal sheath). See booted.

Odontoid process. Cephalic projection of the axis (2nd cervical vertebra).

Oil gland. A gland, largest in aquatic birds, located dorsally at the base of the tail (on the rump); its secretion contains fatty acids and related substances, which are used in the care of epidermal structures, especially the feathers. Preen gland, uropygial gland.

Olecranon. A process on the proximal end of the ulna.

Oligomyodian. Having few syringeal muscles. Cf. polymyodian.

Omentum. A single or double fold of peritoneum extending from the stomach to some other abdominal organ.

Omnivorous. Eating plant and animal food.

Oölogy. The study of birds' eggs, and particularly just the chalky shell.

Operculum (of nostril). A scale or membrane usually above the nostril.

Opisthocoelous. Having the anterior articular surface of the centrum (body) of a vertebra convex, the posterior articular surface, concave; the opposite of procoelous.

Oral. Pertaining to the mouth.

Orbit. The cavity in the skull which houses the eye.

Orbital ring. A circular marking surrounding the eye.

Oriental region. One of six zoogeographical regions of the world, comprising India, Ceylon, South China, Malaysia, and the Malay Archipelago. Cf. Australasian, Ethiopian, Neotropical, Nearctic, Palaearctic.

Orthocoelous. Straight-gutted. Having the loops of the intestine parallel to each other and to the long axis of the body. An intestinal loop is "closed" when both the descending and ascending limbs of the loop are closely bound together by a part of the mesentery; a loop is "open" when its two limbs are not closely held together by mesentery and blood vessels, so that part of another loop may lie between the two limbs. A "right-handed" loop is one that has the same pattern as the duodenal (the 1st) loop, i.e., the descending limb lies to the right of the ascending limb; a "left-handed" loop is one in which the descending limb lies to the left of the ascending limb. Cf. antiocoelous, antipericoelous, isocoelous, isopericoelous, pericoelous, plagiocoelous, cyclocoelous.

Os. A bone. Also, mouth, especially applied to the opening of canals or tubes.

Os humeroscapulare. A sesamoid in the capsule of the shoulder joint and associated with the origin of M. deltoideus major; sometimes called scapula accessoria, os humerocapsulare.

Os opticus. A small cancellous bone, typically horseshoe-shaped, imbedded in the sclerotic coat of the eyeball and surrounding the optic nerve; "Gemminger's ossicle."

Oscines (suborder). Passeres, the true songbirds. Cf. Passeres.

Oscinine. Pertaining to the suborder Oscines.

Osseous. Bony.

Ossicle. A small bone.

Ossified. Changed to bone; hardened by the deposition of mineral salts.

Osteology. The study of bones; the bony framework of an animal.

Outer web (of wing or tail feather). The web on the side away from the mid-line of the body; pogonium externum.

Ovary. Female organ (gonad) which contains the ova or female germ cells, and which secretes sex hormones.

Overflow activity. Occurs "when an animal has one drive strongly activated and the releasing stimuli, indispensable for the performance of the executive motor patterns of the drive, are inadequate." Synonyms: vacuum activity, Leerlaufreaktionen.

Oviduct. Tubelike passage for the eggs leading from the vicinity of the ovary to the urodeum.

Oviparous. Egg-laying; in contrast to viviparous (q.v.).

Oviposition. The laying of eggs.

Ovulation. The release of an egg (ovum) from a Graafian follicle in the ovary into the abdominal cavity.

Ovum. Egg.

Palaearctic region. One of six zoogeographical regions of the world, comprising Europe, North Africa, Asia to the Indus and the Himalayas, and the Atlantic Islands. Cf. Australasian, Oriental, Ethiopian, Nearctic, Neotropical.

Palatal, palatine. Pertaining to the palate.

Palate. The roof of the mouth or oral cavity; a bony and a horny palate are distinguished in birds.

Palmar. Pertaining to the palm, to the under (ventral) surface of the manus. Also used to refer to the entire ventral surface of the wing. Cf. anconal.

Palmate, palmiped. Having the 3 front toes fully webbed. Cf. semipalmate, totipalmate.

Palpebral. Pertaining to the eyelid (palpebra).

Paludicole. Marsh-inhabiting.

Paludine, palustrine. Pertaining to a marsh or swamp; marsh- or swamp-frequenting.

Pamprodactyl. All 4 toes turned forward, as in colies and swifts.

Papilla (pl. papillae). A small, pimplelike protuberance.

Paradactylum. The sides of the toes, in any way distinguished from the dorsal or ventral (plantar) surfaces (Coues).

Paragnathous. Having the upper and lower mandibles equal in length and neither bent over the other.

Parapteron. The "tertial" and "humeral" feathers of the wing (a term proposed by Nitzsch; see Degen, *Bull. Brit. Ornith. Club,* 2: xxi.). Cf. hypopteron.

Paratype. A specimen other than the holotype which was before the author at the time of preparation of the original description and was so designated or indicated by the original author. Cf. allotype.

Parotic, parotid. Pertaining to the region near the ear.

Passeres. Suborder: Oscines, the true songbirds. Order: Passeriformes.

Passerine. Pertaining to the order Passeriformes.

Patagium. Patagial membrane. Cf. metapatagium, propatagium.

Patella. Kneecap; a sesamoid in the combined tendon of the extensor muscles of the crus (leg), i.e., the tibiotarsus.

Patronymic. In nomenclature, a dedicatory name based on that of one or more persons.

Pecten. A folded, pigmented, vascular organ projecting from the head of the optic nerve (cranial nerve II) into the vitreous body of the eye.

Pectinate. Having toothlike projections like the teeth of a comb, as the toes of grouse, or the middle claw of herons.

Pectoral. Pertaining to the breast (pectus).

Pectoral girdle. The part of the skeleton that supports the wings; includes the scapulae, coracoids, and furcula (clavicles).

Pelagic. Frequenting the high seas.

Pelvic girdle. The part of the skeleton that supports the lower limb; includes 3 paired bones (ilium, ischium, and pubis) and the synsacrum (q.v.).

Penna. "Generally a contour-feather (*pluma*), as distinguished from a down-feather (*plumula*); *particularly,* a large stiff feather of the wing or tail, one of the *remiges* or *rectrices*" (Coues).

Pennaceous. Applied to a normal contour feather (not downy).

Perforate (of nostrils). Pierced; communicating with each other owing to absence of, or a deficiency in, the nasal septum. Cf. imperforate.

Pericoelous. Having the 2nd intestinal loop left-handed, open, and enclosing the 3rd loop. A type of orthocoelous (q.v.) arrangement. Cf. antipericoelous, isopericoelous.

Peritoneal ligament. A fold of thickened peritoneum supporting any of the abdominal viscera.

Pervious (of nostrils). Open, as in most birds. Cf. impervious.

Phalanx (pl. phalanges). One of the long bones of the fingers or toes.

Phase (of plumage). A difference in color that is not related to sex, race, or age.

Phenotype. The group in which an individual falls on the basis of visible characters. Cf. genotype.

Phoenicopteri (order). Phoenicopteridae; the flamingos.

Pici. Piciformes.

Pigment. Coloring matter.

Pileated. With the whole pileum crested.

Pileum. The entire top of the head, including forehead, crown, and occiput; also "pileus."

Pinfeather. A new, growing feather still not unsheathed (erroneously used for filoplume).

Pinion. "Part of the wing beyond the wrist exclusive of the feathers; usually the metacarpus and phalanges; the hand bone. Not technically used synonymously with *quill* or *wing*" (Coues). Poetic: a wing; the flight feathers.

Pinnate, pinnated. "Having wing-like tufts of elongated feathers on the side of the neck" (Ridgway).

Pinniform. Finlike (as the wing of a penguin).

Pin-tailed. Having the central tail feathers elongated and narrowed.

Piscivorous. Fish-eating.

Pisiform process. A bony tubercle near the base of the palmar surface of the carpometacarpus; it serves as a pulley for the tendon of M. flexor digitorum profundus.

Plagiocoelous. Having secondary coils in (at least) the 2nd intestinal loop. Cf. orthocoelous, cyclocoelous.

Planta. Back of the tarsus (tarsometatarsus).

Plantar. Of or pertaining to the sole of the foot or the posterior side of the tarsus.

Plexus. A network, especially of anastomosing or interlacing nerves, blood vessels, or lymphatic vessels.

Plicate. Having parallel ridges on the surface; folded.

Plumose. Having feathers or plumes; feathered.

Plumula (pl. plumulae). A down feather.

Plumulaceous. Downy; bearing down.

Plumule (down feather). Small, downy feathers, more or less concealed, and with the shaft never highly developed; grow in either the pterylae or apteria.

Podicipedes. Podicipediformes; Podicipitiformes; Podicipiformes.

Podotheca. The modified integument covering the (unfeathered) tarsometatarsus (tarsus) and digits.

Point of the wing. "Is at the tip of the longest primary" (Coues).

Pollex. The thumb; the digit that bears the feathers of the alula (ala spuria, bastard wing).

Pollical. Of or pertaining to the pollex (thumb).

Polygamy. Mating of one male with several females (polygyny) or one female with several males (polyandry).

Polymyodian. Having many syringeal muscles. Cf. oligomyodian.

Post-. Behind, back of, as: postocular, behind the eye; postorbital, behind the orbit.

Powder-down feathers. Modified feathers which grow continuously and disintegrate at the tips, producing a powdery or scaly exfoliation. Cf. down.

Precocial. Said of birds whose young at hatching are well developed, covered with down, able to move about, and feed themselves; formerly, "praecocial." Cf. altricial.

Preen gland. See oil gland.

Premaxillary. The most anterior bone of the upper jaw (maxilla).

Prepennae. Nestling down feathers "preceding the contour feathers" (Pycraft).

Preplumulae. Nestling down feathers "preceding the future definitive down-feathers" (Pycraft).

Pressirostral. Having a bill like that of a plover (obsolete).

Prevomer. Median bone(s) of skull lying anterior and ventral to the parasphenoid rostrum and usually articulating with the palatine bones posteriorly; exhibits much variation in size and shape throughout the orders of birds and is absent in some; much used in technical diagnoses (see Chapter 2).

Primary feather. One of the flight feathers (remiges) attached to the hand (manus).

Procoelous. Having the anterior articular surface of the centrum (body) of a vertebra concave, the posterior articular surface, convex; the opposite of opisthocoelous.

Proctodeum (proctodaeum). The most caudal (and dorsal) part of the cloaca.

Pronator. A muscle that rotates the radius on the ulna so that the palm of the hand is turned downward. Cf. supinator.

Propatagium. The double fold of skin extending from shoulder to wrist, anterior to the wing bones; the fold encloses the tendon (sometimes the belly as well) of M. tensor patagii brevis and the biceps slip (when present); the tendon of M. tensor patagii longus passes distad in the leading edge of the fold; also, prepatagium. Cf. metapatagium.

Protoptile. One of the feathers in the 1st of two successive coats of nestling down. Cf. mesoptile.

Protractile. Capable of being thrust out; protrusile.

Proventriculus. The glandular portion of the stomach, which leads from the esophagus to the muscular portion (ventriculus, gizzard) of the stomach.

Proximal. Nearest the trunk or mid-line; opposite of distal (q.v.) or terminal.

Pseudoschizorhinal. A modification of the holorhinal type of nasal bones having a superficial resemblance to the schizorhinal type (see *Auk,* 1915: 153).

Psilopaedic. Naked at hatching, or having down growing only on the future pterylae; "gymnopaedic." Cf. ptilopaedic.

Psittaci. Psittaciformes.

Pterna. "Heel-pad" (Coues).

Pterygoid. A slender bone between the palatine and the quadrate.

Pteryla (pl. pterylae). One of the tracts or areas of skin to which contour feathers are limited. Cf. apterium.

Pterylography. The study of the feather tracts of birds; pterylosis.

Pterylology. The study of the arrangement of the feather tracts of birds (May, *Auk,* 1945: 308).

Pterylosis. Plumage, considered with reference to its distribution on the skin.

Ptilology. The general study of the plumage (ptilosis) of birds. (May, *Auk,* 1945: 308).

Ptilopaedic. Completely clothed with down at hatching (down growing from future apteria, as well as pterylae). Cf. psilopaedic.

Ptilopody. A highly recommended term, coined by Danforth (1919), for the condition of having feathers on the tarsus and toes. Unfortunately, feathered tarsi and toes are often referred to as "booted" or "booting" in poultry literature, in contrast to the ornithological use of the term booted (q.v.).

Ptilosis. The plumage of birds.

Pubis. One of the three paired bones that, with the synsacrum, form the pelvic girdle. Cf. ilium, ischium.

Pullus. A young bird, before its first complete plumage; a chick (obsolete term).

Pycnaspidean (of the tarsal sheath). With the rear (plantar) surface of the tarsus densely covered with small scales or granules.

Pygopodes. A group of birds distinguished "by the far backward position, and deep burial, in common integument of the legs" (Coues); an old term, proposed by Illiger in 1811, for several unrelated birds, including loons, grebes, and alcids.

Pygostyle. The terminal bone in the tail, formed by the fusion of several coccygeal vertebrae during development.

Quadrate bone. A 3-pronged bone which articulates with the skull above, the lower jaw (mandible) below, and the pterygoid bone anteromedially; in ratite birds there is a single condyle for articulation with the roof of the tympanic cavity; in other living birds, there is a double condyle. The quadrate bone of reptiles and birds becomes an ear ossicle (incus) in mammals.

Quill. Strictly, a primary feather.

Quincubital (quinto-cubital). Wing without a gap between the 4th and 5th secondaries; eutaxic is the preferred synonym. Cf. aquincubital.

Race. Subspecies (q.v.).

Rachis (or rhachis). The vane-bearing shaft of a feather.

Radiale. The anterior of the two carpal or wrist bones found in the adult; also called scapholunar. Cf. ulnare.

Radius (pl. radii). The anterior, more slender bone of the forearm.

Ramus (pl. rami). A branch or division of a nerve or blood vessel; "a part of an irregularly shaped bone (less slender than a 'process') which forms an angle with the main body"; barb (q.v.) of a feather.

Raphe. The seamlike union of the two halves of a part or organ, e.g., a connective tissue septum between parts of a muscle, or between bilaterally symmetrical muscles.

Raptorial. Pertaining to the birds of prey.

Rasores. Scratching birds.

Rassenkreis (Rensch). A polytypic species composed of several subspecies.

Ratite. With a flat, keelless sternum. Cf. carinate.

Recrudesce (recrudescence). To renew activity; applied to the gonads (see Chapter 7).

Rectrix (pl. rectrices). Tail feathers, exclusive of the coverts.

Recurved. Curved upward. Cf. decurved.

Releaser (social). A device (color, shape, sequence of movements, sound) specially differentiated to the function of eliciting a response in a fellow member of the species.

Remex (pl. remiges). One of the flight feathers attached to the ulna (secondaries) or manus (primaries).

Remicle. Reduced, outermost primary.

Reticulate. Marked in the form of a network, as the tarsus of some birds.

Retrorse. Directed backward.

Rhachis. See rachis.

Rhamphotheca. Covering of the whole bill.

Rhinal. Pertaining to the nostrils, or nose.

Rhinotheca. Covering of the upper mandible (maxilla).

Rhizonychium. Terminal bone of a toe bearing a claw (little used—Coues).

Rictal. Pertaining to the gape (rictus).

Rictal commissure. The soft tissue which spans the space between the two mandibles to form the rictus.

Rictus. Gape of the mouth (q.v.).

Rookery. Originally, the breeding place of a colony of rooks; now to include other gregarious birds, penguins, herons, etc.; heronry.

Rostral. Pertaining to the bill (rostrum).

Rostrum. The bill. A pointed projection on a bone.

Rounded. Of the tail—"Having the central feathers longest, the rest successively gradually and slightly shorter. A tail is *double-rounded* when, with central feathers shorter than the next, the rest are graduated as before" (Coues).

Rudimentary (rudiment). Little developed. An organ or part just beginning to develop, or one whose development has been arrested at an early stage; an anlage. Often used in contradistinction to vestigial (vestige), q.v.

Ruff. A "collar" of elongated (or otherwise modified) feathers around the neck.

Rugose (rugous). Wrinkled.

Rump. Area of upper parts, between the back and the upper tail coverts.

Rupicoline. Rock-frequenting.

Sacral. Pertaining to the sacrum or synsacrum, a region of the vertebral column lying between the back (dorsal) vertebrae and the free caudal vertebrae.

Saltatory. With the habit of progressing by leaps or hops.

Saxicoline. Inhabiting stony places.

Scansorial. With the habit of climbing; suited for climbing.

Scapholunar. See radiale.

Scapula. Shoulder blade; one of the three bones forming the pectoral girdle. Cf. clavicle, coracoid.

Scapula accessoria. The os humeroscapulare (q.v.).

Scapulars, scapularies. The feathers of the humeral feather tract (pteryla).

Scapus. "Entire stem of a feather; calamus plus rhachis" (Coues).

Schizopelmous. Deep plantar tendons not connected by a vinculum: M. flexor hallucis longus inserts on the hallux only; M. flexor digitorum longus inserts on digits II, III, and IV; Gadow's type VII; a type of nomopelmous arrangement. Cf. desmopelmous, antiopelmous, heteropelmous, synpelmous.

Schizorhinal. Having the posterior border of the external nares continued backward in a slit which extends beyond the frontal processes of the premaxilla.

Schizothecal (of tarsal sheath). Having the sheath divided, in any of several ways; a general term. Cf. holothecal.

Sciatic. See ischiadic.

Sclerotic ring. A series of 10 to 18 overlapping platelike bones found in the lateral (or anterior) part of the sclera of the eyeball; ringlike in most birds; conelike in a few birds (hawks, owls). The os opticus has been called the "posterior sclerotic ring" (Gadow).

Scute (pl. scutes). Any external horny plate; a thin lamina or plate of bone.

Scutellate. Covered with "scales" (scutella).

Scutelliplantar (of the tarsal sheath). Having at least one side of the plantar (posterior) surface of the tarsus divided by transverse sutures or broken up into small scutellae; for passerine birds only. Cf. laminiplantar.

Scutellum (pl. scutella). "Scales" of the tarsus and toes.

Secondary feather. One of the flight feathers (remiges) attached to the ulna; formerly called "cubitals."

Semi-nidicolous. Said of young birds that stay in the nest for a time after hatching but which leave long before they are able to fly; some (called "branchers") climb about the nest tree. Examples: some herons, the hoatzin, kagus, gulls, auks, Snowy Owls. Not precisely defined.

Semi-nidifugous. Said of young birds that *tend* to leave the nest fairly soon after hatching but which may remain in it for some days. Examples: some young sandpipers, plovers, skuas. Not precisely defined.

Semipalmate. Half-webbed; having the 3 front toes joined by a web along only the basal half (or less) of their length. Cf. palmate, totipalmate.

Semiplume. "Feather with pennaceous stem and plumulaceous web" (Coues).

Semitendinous. Partly tendinous and partly fleshy.

Septum. A partition.

Serrate. Toothed like a saw.

Sesamoid. A small bone (sometimes cartilage) in the tendon of a muscle (usually; rarely in a ligament); typically found where tendons cross joints.

Setae. Bristlelike feathers.

Seventy-five per cent rule. "The rule that population A can be considered subspecifically distinct from population B if 75 per cent of the individuals of A are different from 'all' the individuals of population B" (Mayr).

Shaft (of a feather). Calamus plus rachis.

Shank. Strictly, the shin (tibial section) of the leg; in birds, loosely, the tarsometatarsus (tarsus).

Sibling species. Pairs or groups of closely related species that are reproductively isolated but are morphologically nearly identical.

Sinuate (of a feather). With one edge gradually cut away. Cf. emarginate (abruptly cut away).

Soft parts. The nonbony and noncartilaginous parts of the body; viscera, muscles; used especially in reference to the color of rhamphotheca, iris, bare skin on head, and tarsi.

Spatulate. Spoon-shaped, narrowed and then abruptly expanded toward the end.

Speculum. A metallic or brightly colored area on the wing differing in color from adjacent feathers, especially as in certain ducks; mirror (formerly).

Spur. A horny modification of the skin surrounding a bony core; found on the tarsometatarsus (especially in some gallinaceous birds) or the carpometacarpus (Spur-winged Goose, screamers, jaçanas, some plovers, some pigeons).

Spurious primary. See remicle.

Spurious wing. The alula, bastard wing, ala spuria.

Squamose (squamous). Bearing scales; marked in the form of scales.

Steganopodes. Pelecaniformes.

Stenotopic. Ecologically very intolerant. Cf. eurytopic.

Sternal. Pertaining to the breastbone or sternum.

Stipula. A newly sprouted feather (Ridgway).

Stooping. Diving or swooping from a height in air in attack on prey, as by hawks.

Streak. A narrow longitudinal mark, as on a feather.

Striated. Marked with streaks (stria).

Striges. Strigiformes.

Stripe. A wide longitudinal marking. Cf. band, bar.

Sub-. Below, as: submalar, beneath the cheek; suborbital, beneath the eye. Not quite, as: subtypical, subspherical. Below the rank of, as: suborder, subfamily, subspecies.

Subadult. A term used chiefly with species of slow development and applied to an individual in which size, plumage, and coloration of soft parts indicate that full maturity is about to be reached. The term is not often applied to forms in which full maturity is reached within 1 year. It is regularly applied to individuals believed to be 2 or 3 years old and known to be molting into "full" breeding plumage or condition, e.g., *Larus argentatus* (Sutton). Cf. adult, immature.

Subspecies. "A geographically defined aggregate of local populations which differs taxonomically from other such subdivisions of the species" (Mayr).

Subulate. Awl-shaped.

Sulcate. With a groove (sulcus).

Super-, supra-. Above, as: supra-auricular, above the ear coverts or auriculars; supraloral, above the lores. Above the rank of, as: superorder, superfamily.

Superciliary. Pertaining to the eyebrow; supraorbital.

Superspecies. A monophyletic group of entirely or largely allopatric species. Cf. Artenkreis, allopatric.

Supinator. A muscle that rotates the radius on the ulna so that the palm of the hand is turned upward. Cf. pronator.

Suture. The seam or line of union between bones in an immovable articulation; an immovable joint.

Sympatric. Said of forms whose breeding ranges coincide or overlap. Cf. allopatric.

Symphysis. A type of (generally) fixed articulation in which the ends of the bones are covered by hyaline cartilage and the two bones are held together by fibrous tissue or fibrocartilage; e.g., the symphysis of the mandible, of the pubic bones.

Synchronic species. Species which occur at the same time level. Cf. allochronic species.

Syndactyl (e). Having two or more toes coalescent for a considerable part of their length.

Synonym. Any one of two or more different names that have been applied to the same taxonomic category.

Synoptic. A synopsis; a comprehensive review.

Synpelmous. A type of foot-tendon arrangement in which the tendons of Mm. flexor hallucis longus and flexor digitorum longus are blended into one before splitting to insert on the 4 toes; Gadow's type V^a; found in swifts, hummingbirds, nightjars, kingfishers, hornbills, etc. Incorrectly "sympelmous." Cf. nomopelmous, desmopelmous, schizopelmous, heteropelmous, antiopelmous.

Synsacral. Pertaining to the synsacrum.

Synsacrum. The region of the vertebral column that forms with the paired ilia, ischia, and pubes the pelvic girdle (q.v.); formed by the fusion of a variable number of so-called thoracic, lumbar, sacral, and urosacral vertebrae.

Syntype. "One of a number of specimens of equal nomenclatural rank which formed all or part of the material before the original author, in those cases where the author did not designate or indicate a holotype." Cotype. Cf. lectotype.

Syrinx (pl. syringes or syrinxes). Name proposed by T. H. Huxley for the "voice box" of birds; located at the inferior end of the trachea, at the fork of the bronchi; sometimes called "lower larynx." Adjective: syringeal.

Tameness. "The absence of conflict behavior toward people."

Tarsometatarsus. The "tarsus" or "shank"—the part of a bird's foot that bears the toes; usually covered, like the toes, with scalelike skin. A compound bone in birds, consisting of a small tarsal (ankle) bone, three metatarsal (instep) bones, and an accessory metatarsal bone (which bears the hind toe, or hallux).

Taxaspidean (of the tarsal sheath). With the rear surface of the tarsus covered by two (or, sometimes, three) series of small, rectangular (or hexagonal) scales.

Taxon (pl. taxa). Any taxonomic unit or category.

Taxonomy. Classification of animals and plants according to their natural relationships.

Tectrix (pl. tectrices). Wing coverts; those anterior and dorsal to the primaries are called primary coverts; those anterior and dorsal to the secondaries are called secondary coverts; except for the greater (major) under wing coverts, the feathers on the ventral surface of the wing are less fully developed; tail coverts.

Teleology. "Science of adaptation."

Teleoptiles. Adult-type feathers; the feathers or down which succeed the neossoptiles (q.v.). Some authors (e.g., Ingram, *Ibis,* 1920: 857) use "teleoptiles" for contour feathers only (not including down).

Telogyrous. A type of cyclocoelous (q.v.) intestinal arrangement in which the distal portion of any of the primary intestinal loops is coiled into a spiral. Cf. mesogyrous.

Temporal. Pertaining to the temples.

Tendon. A fibrous cord or band attaching a muscle to bone. Cf. aponeurosis.

Tenuirostral. Having a long, slender bill with a narrow gape, as in hummingbirds, creepers, and nuthatches.

Terrestrial. Ground-frequenting.

Tertials ("tertiaries"). Remiges growing from the skin overlying the humerus (not from the ulna). Sometimes several of the proximal secondaries (distinguished by size, shape, or color from the other secondaries) are incorrectly called tertials.

Tessellated. Checkered.

Testis (pl. testes). Male sex organs (gonads); secrete spermatozoa and sex hormones.

Theca. Sheath, covering: podotheca, covering of the foot; rhamphotheca, covering of the bill; rhinotheca, covering of the upper mandible; etc.

Thoracic. Pertaining to the chest (thorax).

Thoracic vertebrae. The anteriormost fused vertebrae in the synsacrum (Gadow); they may possess thoracic ribs which articulate with the sternum, but in most birds, thoracic ribs fuse with the dorsal segment of the preceding rib or end freely in the abdominal musculature. Cf. dorsal vertebrae.

Thumb. Pollex.

Tibiotarsus (pl. tibiotarsi). The main bone of the lower leg or crus (between the femur and the tarsometatarsus); also called simply the tibia (pl. tibiae or tibias), though it has tarsal elements fused to its lower end.

Tomium (pl. tomia). The cutting edge of the bill. There is a superior or maxillary tomium, and an inferior or mandibular tomium; each is double (i.e., right and left); together they are the tomia, mutually apposed when the bill is closed.

Topotype. A specimen collected at the type locality (q.v.)

Totipalmate. Having four toes united by webs. Cf. palmate, semipalmate.

Trachea. Windpipe.

Tracheophone (ae). Applied to a division of rather primitive passerine birds characterized by having the syrinx thin-walled and limited to the caudal end of the trachea: Dendrocolaptidae, Furnariidae, Formicariidae, Conopophagidae, and Rhinocryptidae. Cf. Haploophone.

Triceps. An extensor muscle, both in the wing and the thigh.

Trichoptile. Long, threadlike prolongations of the sheaths of developing feathers—especially of nestling cuckoos (Shelford, *Ibis,* 1900: 654).

Tridactyl (e). Three-toed.

Trinominal (trinomial). Designation of the scientific name by a generic, specific, and subspecific term.

Trivial name. The second and/or third word in a binominal or trinominal name of an animal; the specific and subspecific names.

Trochanter. Prominence at the top of the femur.

Trochlea. A pulley—part of a bone that acts as a pulley for a tendon.

Trogones. Trogoniformes.

Truncate, truncated. Cut off squarely, abruptly.

Tuberculum costae. That part of a rib which articulates with the transverse process of a vertebra. Cf. capitulum costae.

Tubinares. Procellariiformes.

Tylari. The wartlike pads on the under (ventral) surfaces of the toes, as in many hawks.

Tympanic. Relating to the tympanum (q.v.).

Tympanum. The eardrum; the middle ear cavity.

Type locality. The locality at which a holotype, lectotype, or neotype was collected. Cf. topotype.

Type species. The expression recommended by the International Commission on Zoological Nomenclature to refer to the concept of "a type species of a genus."

Ulna (pl. ulnae or ulnas). The posterior, stouter bone of the forearm, to which the secondaries are attached.

Ulnare. The posterior of the two carpal or wrist bones in the adult wing; also called cuneiform. Cf. radiale.

Ultraexaspidean. "The acrotarsium entirely inclosing the Tarsus, its two edges in close contact along posterior inner side" (Ridgway). Cf. exaspidean.

Umbilicus. Lower: hole at the basal end of the feather. Upper: small hole at the upper end of the calamus of the feather.

Unciform, uncinate. Hooked.

Uncinate process. A thin, bony plate either ankylosed to or articulating with a rib; it projects upward and backward to overlie the next succeeding rib, and thus strengthens the rib cage; it may occur on cervicodorsal (cervical) ribs, true (dorsal) ribs, or on thoracic ribs; found in all living birds except the screamers. Also called epipleural process.

Under parts. Lower parts; the under surface of the bird, from the chin to the tip of the tail.

Ungual (unguinal) phalanx. The terminal phalanx of the fingers or toes.

Upper parts. The entire upper surface, from the forehead to the tip of the tail.

Urodeum (urodaeum). That part of the cloaca that receives the ureters and the gonaducts (oviducts or ductus deferentia).

Urogenital (genitourinary). Referring to the excretory and reproductive systems.

Uropygial. Pertaining to the rump (uropygium).

Uropygial gland. See oil gland.

Vagina. A sheath; in birds, the terminal, constricted part of the oviduct.

Vane. The flat, expanded part of a feather bordering the rachis; vexillum; web.

Vent. Specifically, the opening of the cloaca to the surface of the body; also used as a synonym of anus (q.v.).

Ventral. Pertaining to the belly; opposite to dorsal. Below the vertebral column or the bony axis of a limb when in the primitive position.

Ventricle. A small cavity. Cerebral: a series of (usually) four interconnected cavities in the brain, which contain cerebrospinal fluid. Cardiac: the right ventricle receives venous blood from the right atrium and pumps the blood into the pulmonary trunk; the left ventricle receives arterial blood from the left atrium and pumps the blood into the right aortic arch.

Ventriculus. The muscular portion of the stomach; gizzard. Cf. proventriculus.

Vermiculate. Marked with fine wavy lines, like "worm tracks."

Vertebra (pl. vertebrae). One of the bones forming the vertebral column (the backbone).

Vestigial. Pertaining to a vestige; especially an organ or structure that is thought to have been more fully developed at some earlier stage in the evolutionary (or embryological) history. Cf. rudimentary.

Vexillum. See vane.

Vinculum. A uniting band of fibrous tissue; especially the band that unites the deep plantar tendons (q.v.), or the band between the tendons of Mm. flexor perforatus digiti III and flexor perforans et perforatus digiti III in some birds; also, any tendinous band given off the deep surface of a tendon and attaching to bone.

Vinculum elasticum secundariorum. A fibrous band extending along the posterior surface of the ulna and investing the bases of the calami of the secondary feathers.

Viviparous. Giving birth to living young; in contrast to oviparous (q.v.).

Vomer. See prevomer. Vomer has been used (inadvisedly) for pygostyle, the last bone in the vertebral column.

Wattle. An unfeathered, fleshy, usually wrinkled and brightly colored flap or area of skin on the head; found in some gallinaceous birds, plovers, jaçanas, cotingas, wattlebirds, starlings, honey-eaters, etc. Cf. caruncúlate.

Web. Of feather, see vane. Of toes, a fleshy membrane uniting (or attached to the sides of) the toes of aquatic birds.

Wildness. The tendency of an animal to escape people.

Xanthochroism. Abnormal yellow coloration.

Zoonerythrin (zooerythrin). An inexact term formerly used to designate red carotenoid pigments.

Zooxanthin. An inexact term formerly used to designate yellow carotenoid pigments.

Zygodactyl (e). Yoke-toed; with two toes in front (II, III) and two behind (I, IV), as in cuckoos, woodpeckers, etc. Cf. heterodactyl.

Index

Abmigration, 201, 203
Abyssinia, 175
Acanthisittidae, 164, 383, 498
Acanthizidae, 525
Accentoridae, 527
Accipiter, 38, 226
Accipiter cooperii, 80
Accipiter striatus, 364
Accipitridae, 22, 199, 381, 415, 416
Aceros undulatus, 54
Acid, uric, 38
Acrocephalus dumetorum, 63
Acrocephalus palustris, 63, 145
Acrocephalus scirpaceus, 63
Acromion, 52, 559
Acromyodian, *see* Syrinx
Acropodium, 559
Acropternis, 491
Acropternis orthonyx, 49
Acrotarsium, 48, 559
Acryllium vulturinum, 422
Act, consummatory, 118, 119, 120
Actitis, 198
Activity, displacement, 119, 566
  overflow, 119, 576
  vacuum, 119
Aechmophorus occidentalis, 393
Aegithina nigrolutea, 519
Aegithina tiphia, 519
Aegithinidae, 519
Aegotheles insignis, 463
Aegothelidae, 164, 382, 463
Aegypiidae, 415
Aepyornis, 15, 16, 42, 285
Aepyornithiformes, 15
Aepypodius, 418
Aerocharidae, 533
Aëronautes saxatalis, 465
Africa, African, 150, 169, 171, 173, 175, 184, 193, 252, 255, 278, 287, 288, 296, 306, 308, 310, 314, 315, 317, 385, 386, 399, 402, 406, 407, 408, 409, 410, 414, 416, 422, 426, 432, 436, 437, 438, 442, 445, 446, 451, 453, 456, 468, 469, 474, 476, 477, 478, 481, 482, 485, 486, 497, 502, 504, 505, 506, 516, 517, 518, 521, 527, 534, 535, 537, 538, 539, 540
Afrotis afra, 102
Aftershaft, 15, 76–78, 560
Agelaioides badius, 318
Agelaius phoeniceus, 144, 273
Agelaius phoeniceus littoralis, 302
Agelaius tricolor, 273, 291
Agelastes, 422
Agriocharis ocellata, 423
Aimophila cassinii, 142
Air cell, subcutaneous, 36
Air sac, 34, 35, 299, 560
  anterior abdominal, 35
  interclavicular, 35, 134
  posterior intermediate, 35
Aix sponsa, 194

Alaska, 192, 193, 205, 206, 207, 284, 361, 546
Alauda arvensis, 49, 142, 198
Alaudidae, 39, 48, 49, 79, 145, 165, 197, 383, 502
Albatross, 223, 224, 252, 282, 287, 301, 305, 380
  Black-footed, 394
  Royal, 246, 272, 274, 295, 297, 313, 315
  Wandering, 80, 85
Alberta, 186, 194
Albinism, 366, 560
Alcedinidae, 22, 46, 165, 382, 470
Alcedo, 80, 111
Alcidae, 52, 54, 94, 163, 199, 200, 232, 258, 381, 452
Alectoropodes, 560
Allele, 356, 357, 560
Allotype, 560
Aluconidae, 458
Alula, 82–83, 221, 560
Amadina fasciata, 298, 337
Amblycercus, 547
America, Central, 166, 197, 199, 205, 206, 287, 294, 314, 344, 354, 399, 408, 429, 432, 434, 437, 442, 451, 469, 487, 488, 489, 492, 516, 522, 530, 542, 543, 544, 546, 547, 549
  Middle, 402, 408, 467
  North, 156, 157, 158, 159, 160, 161, 164, 165, 166, 167, 173, 175, 177, 178, 183, 190, 197, 205, 206, 208, 211, 244, 366, 392, 399, 404, 413, 416, 420, 428, 443, 451, 454, 467, 494, 502, 512, 513, 521, 522, 525, 534, 544, 547, 549
  South, 86, 166, 168, 169, 173, 175, 178, 183, 186, 197, 199, 205, 206, 208, 316, 385, 397, 399, 402, 408, 409, 410, 411, 413, 416, 421, 424, 429, 430, 432, 437, 438, 442, 443, 448, 451, 454, 455, 467, 469, 481, 487, 488, 489, 490, 491, 492, 494, 502, 521, 522, 542, 543, 544, 547, 548, 549
American wood-warbler, *see* Wood-warbler, American
Ammomanes deserti hijazensis, 198
Ammospiza caudacuta, 92, 191
Ammospiza maritima, 191
Ampelidae, 529
Ampelion, 98
Anachromyodian, *see* Syrinx
Anas, 12
Anas platyrhynchos, 80, 194, 204
Anas strepera, 256
Anastomus, 408
Anatidae, 37, 39, 54, 79, 94, 199, 315, 316, 380, 412
Androgen, 141, 329
Anhima cornuta, 411
Anhimidae, 8, 35, 88, 163, 380, 411
Anhinga, 32, 54
Anhinga anhinga, 402
Anhinga, 7, 241, 280, 380, 402
Anhingidae, 380, 402
Ani, 285
  Groove-billed, 228, 253, 292
  Smooth-billed, 247, 291
Anisomyodian, *see* Syrinx
Anomalogonatae, 54, 561
Anomalopterygidae, 15
Anomalopteryx, 15
Anomalospiza, 319
Anseranas, 34
Anseriformes, 10, 43, 292, 380, 561
Ant, fire, 303
  red, 281
Antarctica, 385, 394
Antbird, 42, 58, 163, 165, 301, 383, 489
  Bicolored, 286
  Tyrannine, 289
Anthropoïdes virgo, 428
Anthus, 199
Anthus pratensis, 307
Anthus spragueii, 142
Antiae, 561
Antibodies, 36
Anting, 127
Antiopelmous, 58, 561
Antpipit, 42, 58, 163, 383, 490
  D'Orbigny, 490
Ant-thrush, Black-faced, 489
Apatornis, 10
Aphelocoma coerulescens, 243
Aphrizidae, 441
Apodidae, 33, 382, 465, 565
Apodiformes, 382, 561, 573
Aponeurosis, 561
Aptenodytes forsteri, 13, 246
Aptenodytes patagonica, 385
Aptenodytidae, 385
Apteria, 75, 88, 89, 91, 115, 293, 561
Apterygidae, 39, 164, 380, 390

Apterygiformes, 380
Apteryx, 23, 28, 40, 42, 79, 113, 114, 131, 285
Apteryx australis, 390
Aptosochromatism, 100, 561
Apus apus, 189, 246, 272, 289, 301
Apus caffer, 278
Apus caffer streubelii, 292
Apus melba, 289
Aquila, 226
Aquila chrysaëtos, 173
Aquilidae, 415
Aquincubital, 561
Ara macao, 46
Ara militaris, 86
Arabia, 198, 386, 407, 539
Arachnothera longirostris, 59
Aramidae, 46, 163, 165, 381, 429
Aramus guarauna, 46, 169, 429
Archaeopteryx, 3, 4, 6, 7, 8
Archaeopteryx lithographica, 5
Archaeopteryx siemensi, 6
Archaeornis siemensi, 6
Archaeornithes, 8, 233
Archetype, 561
Archilochus colubris, 37, 88, 199, 271
Ardea herodias, 56, 311, 404
Ardeidae, 22, 62, 79, 380, 404
Area centralis, 110
Arenaria interpres, 242
Arenariinae, 441
Argentina, 183, 207, 208, 391, 411, 429, 439, 447, 472, 483, 489, 496, 520, 522, 546
Arizona, 423, 469, 492
Arremon aurantiirostris, 139
Arremonops conirostris, 138
Artamella viridis, 50
Artamidae, 344, 384, 532
Artamus cinereus, 532
Artamus cyanopterus, 532
Artamus fuscus, 532
Artamus insignis, 532
Artamus leucorhynchus, 532
Artamus maximus, 532
Artamus minor, 532
Artamus monachus, 532
Artamus personatus, 532
Artamus superciliosus, 532
Artenkreis, 561
Artery, carotid, 59–60, 563
Artery, femoral, 60
  ischiadic, 60
Asia, 86, 156, 175, 179, 193, 399, 401, 402, 404, 410, 416, 420, 421, 436, 437, 438, 439, 442, 445, 453, 454, 455, 469, 476, 478, 516, 517, 518, 520, 521, 527, 534, 539
Asio flammeus, 247
Asio otus, 247
Asionidae, 459
Asity, 163, 383
  Velvet, 499
Aspatha, 472
Aspatha gularis, 278
Aspect ratio, 218, 222, 223, 224
Asyndesmus, 259
Asyndesmus lewis, 243
Ateleodacnis, 546
Atlantisia rogersi, 233
Atlapetes torquatus, 291
Atlas, 562
  notched, 45
  perforated, 45
Atrichiidae, 501
Atrichornis, 24
Atrichornis clamosus, 501
Atrichornis rufescens, 501
Atrichornithidae, 145, 164, 383, 501
Attagidae, 447
Attentiveness, 295, 305
Auk, 7, 51, 111, 163, 199, 277, 286, 287, 341, 381, 452
  Great, 13, 233, 452
Auriculars, 562
Australia, 86, 103, 139, 145, 146, 147, 148, 166, 174, 175, 252, 257, 272, 280, 281, 288, 306, 314, 362, 385, 388, 389, 398, 399, 402, 408, 409, 416, 418, 426, 427, 436, 437, 438, 442, 445, 446, 461, 463, 474, 497, 500, 501, 502, 504, 505, 506, 508, 509, 510, 511, 512, 514, 516, 517, 532, 537, 538, 539, 540, 541
Aves laevocarotidinae, 60
Avocet, 241, 287, 381, 442
Axillars, 562
Axis, 45, 562
Aythya, 12
Aythya innotata, 172

Babbler, 156, 165, 383, 517
Balaeniceps, 132

Balaeniceps rex, 406
Balaenicipitidae, 163, 380, 406
Balanosphyra, see Melanerpes formicivorus
Baldpate, 194, 256
Balearica, 428
Balearicidae, 428
Baptornis, 10
Barb, 70, 72, 562
Barbet, 24, 140, 167, 297, 301, 349, 383
  Black-spotted, 481
  Prong-billed, 344
Barbicel, 15, 72, 562
Barbule, 70, 72, 562
Barn-owl, 165, 173, 382, 458
Bartramia, 285
Baryphthengus, 472
Basileuterus fulvicauda, 140
Bathmocercus rufus, 133
Bathornis, 11
Bavaria, 5
Bee-eater, 80, 82, 92, 97, 145, 182, 184, 259, 297, 309, 317, 382
  Carmine, 255
  European, 473
Beeswax, 241, 255, 317, 482
Behavior, 108, 115–127
  aggressive, 329, 343
  allelomimetic, 560
  appetitive, 119, 120
  brooding, 294, 305
  contagious, 341, 560
  endogenous, 121
  epimeletic, 567
  etepimeletic, 567
  exploratory, 119
  hostile, 343
  incubation, 294–296
  infectious, 560
  innate, 118
  instinctive, 117, 119, 120, 126
  learned, 120
  pecking, 123
  self-differentiating, 121
  sexual, 329
Behavioral phenotype, 118, 126
Belgian Congo, 406
Bellmagpie, 164, 383, 508
Bering Straits, 156, 192, 193
Bermuda, 398
Biceps, muscle, 562
Biceps, propatagialis, 52
  slip, 52, 54
Bill, 30, 31, 114, 238, 239, 562
  conirostral, 31, 564
  cultrirostral, 565
  dentirostral, 566
  epignathous, 31, 567
  fissirostral, 31, 568
  grypanium, 570
  hypognathous, 31, 571
  metagnathous, 574
  paragnathous, 576
  pressirostral, 578
  tenuirostral, 583
Bill-clattering, 132, 140
Bill-pointing, 336
Binominal, 562
Biochromes, 97, 98–99
Biomes, 159–161, 162, 562
Biotic provinces, 161–162
Bird-of-paradise, 164, 241, 268, 271, 284, 337, 364, 367, 383
  Red, 511
  Twelve-wired, 93
Bishop-bird, Crimson-crowned, 276
Bittern, 111
  American, 76, 111, 133
  European, 273, 339
  Least, 99
Blackbird, 199, 300, 318
  Brewer's, 87, 336
  European, 145, 149, 256, 288, 331
  Gulf Coast Redwinged, 302
  Redwinged, 144, 268, 303, 333, 336, 340, 344, 359, 364
  Tricolored, 291
  Yellow-headed, 268
Blackcap, 525
Blackcock, 337
Bladder, gall, 33
  urinary, 38
Bluebird, Eastern, 198, 199, 289, 292, 307, 313
Bobolink, 87, 93, 142, 144, 207, 363
Bobwhite, 80, 114, 135, 139, 241, 249, 257, 258, 287, 291, 296, 359, 360
Bokmakierie, 140
Bolivia, 175, 177, 206, 207, 387, 434, 496, 543, 550
Bombycilla, 199
Bombycilla cedrorum, 252

Bombycilla garrulus, 529
Bombycillidae, 5, 163, 165, 377, 384, 529
Bonasa umbellus, 132, 167, 183, 271
Bone, adlacrimal, 7
basisphenoid, 43, 562
hyoid, 22, 31, 571
lacrimal, 7, 22
maxillopalatine, 42, 43, 44
nasal, 23, 40–42
palatine, 42, 43, 44
parasphenoid rostrum, 42, 43
ploughshare, 23
pneumatic, 7
prefrontal, 7
premaxilla, 41, 42, 43
prevomer, 42–44, 578
pterygoid, 42, 43, 44, 579
quadrate, 1, 10, 15, 23, 579
sesamoid, 22, 24, 581
vomer, 42
see also Os dorsale
Bone teeth, 13
Booby, 36, 256, 285, 287, 380, 403
Blue-faced, 400
Common, 167
Borneo, 418, 482, 486, 502
Botaurus lentiginosus, 76, 133
Botaurus stellaris, 273
Bowerbird, 145, 164, 271, 383
Satin, 510
Brachypodidae, 518
Brachypteraciidae, 474
Brachypteraciinae, 474
Brachyspiza capensis, 361
Bradypterus usambarae, 140
Brain, 21, 27–28, 126
case, 22
centers, co-ordination, 28
vestibular, 28
stem, 21, 126
Brant, 240, 250
Branta bernicla, 250
Branta canadensis, 44
Brazil, 207, 252, 387, 405, 434, 445, 462, 479, 480, 483, 491, 495, 525, 543
Bristle, 73, 74, 75, 115, 563
rictal, 75, 460, 461, 464, 480, 481, 518, 522, 546
Britain, 10, 175, 200, 287, 289
British Guiana, 207, 495
British Honduras, 416, 423
British Isles, 446
Broadbill, 56, 58, 383
Black and Yellow, 486
Bronchi, 34, 35, 58
Bronchidesmus, 59, 563
Brontornis, 11
Brooding, broodiness, 294–296, 563
Bubalornis, 39
Bubalornis albirostris, 309
Bubalornithidae, 551
Bubo, 12, 80, 94
Bubo virginianus, 170, 178
Bubonidae, 458, 459
Bubulcus ibis, 253
Bucconidae, 163, 165, 382, 480, 548
Bucephala clangula, 132
Buceros bicornis, 478
Bucerotidae, 35, 75, 95, 382, 478, 563
Bucorvus, 478
Budgerigar, 100
Buffalo-Weaver, 309
Bulbul, 300, 366, 383
Chinese, 518
Hairy-backed, 74
Yellowvented, 306
Bulestes, 508
Bulla ossea, 35, 141
Bunting, 274
Corn, 273
Indigo, 208, 364
Ortalan, 203
Snow, 137, 148, 149, 199, 334, 335, 336, 338
Buphagidae, 537
Buphagus, 255
Burhinidae, 39, 381, 445
Burhinus oedicnemus, 445
Burma, 426, 432, 444, 451, 461, 466, 481, 482, 497, 505, 519, 532, 540, 541
Bursa Fabricii, 33, 38, 563
Bush Chat, Kenya Red-tailed, 140
Bush-lark, 147
Bush-shrike, 140
Bushtit, Black-eared, 307
Bustard, 51, 62, 99, 102, 133, 255, 288, 381
Black-bellied, 436
Little, 132
Butcherbird, 140
New Guinea Forest, 508
Buteo, 226
Buteo albicaudatus, 241

Buteo jamaicensis, 80, 246
Buteo lineatus, 145, 175
Buteo platypterus, 199
Buteo swainsoni, 199
Buteonidae, 415
Buzzard, Jackal, 280
Bycanistes cristatus, 243

Cacatuidae, 455
Cacicus, 318
Cacomantis, 316
Caecum, 32, 38, 62, 563
Caerebidae, 546
Calamus, 54, 70, 72, 76, 563
Calandrella cinerea, 93
Calandrella cinerea dukhunensis, 93
Calandrella razae, 171
Calcarius lapponicus, 142
California, 5, 14, 15, 93, 156, 159, 162, 171, 177, 191, 192, 194, 195, 517, 530
Call notes, 135, 136, 300, 341
  distress, 135, 329, 330
  sequestration, 136, 143
Callaeas cinerea, 536
Callaeas wilsoni, 536
Callaeidae, 164, 384, 536
Callipepla, 86
Callipepla squamata, 46
Callocitta formosa, 507
Calyptophilus, 522
Camarhynchus pallidus, 243
Camaroptera superciliaris, 133
Campephagidae, 97, 383, 504
Campephilus imperialis, 484
Campophagidae, 504
Campylopterus curvipennis, 133
Campylorhamphus trochilirostris, 238
Canachites, 271
Canada, 10, 177, 191, 201, 208, 289, 401, 413, 421
Canary, 141, 144, 328
Cancromidae, 405
Cape Horn, 169, 439
Cape May, 200
Capella gallinago, 133, 336
Capella stenura, 86
Capito auratus, 167
Capito niger, 481
Capitonidae, 33, 383, 481
Capitulum, 23, 563
Caprimulgi, 563
Caprimulgidae, 40, 54, 102, 147, 382, 464
Caprimulgiformes, 382, 563
Cardinal, 139, 245, 249, 334
Carduelinae, 306, 551
Cardueline birds, 99, 199, 238, 258, 259, 339
Carduelis, 113
Carduelis cannabina, 144
Cariama, 163, 241, 381, 435
Cariama cristata, 435
Cariamidae, 163, 381, 435
Carina, 3, 7, 9, 15, 563
  sterni, 9, 34, 45, 47
Carinate bird, 39, 42, 45, 47, 563
Carpal, bone, 84
  covert, 80–81, 563
  remex, 80–81, 563
Carpodacus purpureus, 149
Carpometacarpus, 7, 8, 9, 52, 226, 563
Carpus, 52, 563
Cartilage, arytenoid, 34
  cricoid, 34
  procricoid, 34
  scleral, 109
Casmerodius albus egretta, 201
Casque, 388, 418, 419, 422, 478, 538, 547, 563
Cassidix mexicanus major, 302
Cassowary, 42, 51, 62, 76, 79, 164, 380
  One-wattled, 388
Castration, 141
Casuariidae, 39, 76, 164, 380, 388
Casuariiformes, 380
Casuarius, 37, 79
Casuarius unappendiculatus, 388
Catacromyodian, *see* Syrinx
Catamblyrhynchidae, 79, 163, 384, 550
Catamblyrhynchus diadema, 550
Catbird, 222, 223, 240, 307, 313
Catharactidae, 449
Cathartes, 226, 228
Cathartes aura, 56, 80, 170, 199
Cathartidae, 11, 163, 165, 380, 413, 415
Cauda equina, 28
Cavity, nasal, 30, 34
  oral, 30, 114
  peritoneal, 35
  thoraco-abdominal, 30, 36
Celebes, 173, 418, 513
Cell, bipolar, 110

Cell, ganglion, 110
interstitial, 149, 187
Centrocercus, 133, 271
Centropelma, 233, 393
Centropelma micropterum, 172
Centropus, 457
Centropus bengalensis javanicus, 140
Centropus phasianus, 60
Centrum, 7, 563
Centurus aurifrons, 361
Cephalopterus, 134
Cephalopterus ornatus, 492
Cepphus grylle, 452
Cercococcyx, 316
Cercomacra tyrannina, 290
Cere, 415, 417, 419, 449, 454, 458, 459, 563
Cerebellum, 8, 21, 28
Cerebral hemisphere, 8, 21, 27, 113, 126, 329
Certhia brachydactyla, 362
Certhia familiaris, 239, 272, 362, 516
Certhiaxis, 140
Certhidea, 546, 552
Certhiidae, 94, 165, 198, 239, 383, 516
Ceylon, 242, 444, 461, 466
Chachalaca, 134, 285
Chaetorhynchus, 87
Chaetura pelagica, 56, 199, 204, 289
Chaffinch, 144, 149
European, 196
Chalcites lucidus, 184, 185, 210
Chalcopariidae, 539
Chalk beds, Cretaceous, 8
Chamaea, 156
Chamaea fasciata, 272
Chamaeidae, 156, 517
Character gradient, 359
Charadriidae, 54, 199, 381, 440
Charadriiformes, 42, 82, 381, 572
Charadrius dominicus, 207
Charadrius hiaticula, 336
Charadrius melodus, 292
Charadrius semipalmatus, 103
Charmosyna papou, 366
Chat, Yellow-breasted, 147
Chauna, 32
Chauna chavaria, 61
Chelidoptera, 480
Chen caerulescens, 191, 412
Chen hyperborea, 191
Chen rossii, 191
Chiapas, 434
Chickadee, 287
Black-capped, 198, 270, 341
Chicken, Domestic, 328, 329, 330
Prairie, 86, 99, 271
Chile, 169, 173, 197, 361, 447, 496, 522
China, 51, 156, 175, 195, 416, 426, 486, 497, 504, 505, 516, 519, 520, 532, 539, 540, 541
Chionidae, 448
Chionididae, 381, 448
Chionis alba, 237, 448
Chiroxiphia linearis, 493
Chloris, 99, 552
Chloroceryle, 48
Chloroceryle amazona, 354
Chloroceryle americana, 354
Chlorophanes, 549
Chlorophonia, 31
Chloropsis flavipennis, 519
Chloropsis hardwickii, 519
Chloropsis jerdoni, 519
Chlorostilbon, 232
Choanae, *see* Nares
Chordae tendineae, 36
Chordeiles, 132
Chordeiles minor, 276, 336
Choriotis, 255
Choroid, 109
Chough, Yellow-billed, 203
Chrysococcyx, 32, 40, 316
Chunga, 435
Ciconia, 35
Ciconia ciconia, 140, 408
Ciconiidae, 37, 78, 380, 408
Ciconiiformes, 10, 39, 43, 380, 570
Ciliary body, 109, 111
Cinclidae, 383, 520
Cinclodes antarcticus, 41
Cinclosomatidae, 517
Cinclus, 52
Cinclus cinclus, 139, 143, 520
Circus, 38, 63
Circus cyaneus, 75, 247
Circus cyaneus hudsonius, 73
Cissopis, 549
Cisticola, 319
Clamator, 103, 316, 317
Clamatores, 58
Clavicle, 2, 24, 225, 226, 564
Claw, 564

Claw, pectinate, 403, 404, 405, 444, 446, 458, 464, 520
Climacteridae, 516
Cline, 359, 362
Cloaca, 33, 38, 39, 61, 114, 564
Cloacal, clitoris, 39
  penis, 39
  protuberance, 39
Clutch size, 287–291, 318, 564
Cnémidophore, 48, 564
Coccyzus, 332
Coccyzus americanus, 317
Coccyzus erythropthalmus, 228, 229, 317
Cochlea, 112
Cochleariidae, 162, 380, 405
Cochlearius, 132
Cochlearius cochlearius, 405
Cock nests, 276, 521
Cockatoo, Pink, 455
Coenocorypha, 441
Coereba, 314, 546
Coereba flaveola, 366
Coerebidae, 546, 549, 552
Coition, *see* Copulation
Colaptes, 99, 101
Colaptes auratus, 280, 291
Colaptes rupicola, 309, 484
Coliidae, 51, 163, 344, 382, 468
Coliiformes, 382, 564
Colinus, 80, 241
Colinus virginianus, 135, 257
Colius striatus, 468
Collared-hemipode, 381, 427
Collocalia, 33, 278
Colombia, 173, 175, 177, 178, 197, 460, 550
Colony, breeding, 341–343
  mixed, 280
Color, aposematic, 102
  countershading, 102
  cryptic, 102
  epigamic, 102
  episematic, 102
  functions of, 101–104
  gamosematic, 102
  pigment, 98
  structural, 99
Colubri coruscans, 467
Columba, 25, 29
Columba leuconota, 203
Columba livia, 211
Columba palumbus, 276, 454
Columbidae, 17, 22, 23, 31, 33, 54, 165, 199, 382, 454
Columbiformes, 382
Columella, 1, 112
Coly, 51, 94, 163, 258, 259, 300, 344, 382
  Bar-breasted, 468
Colymbidae, 392, 393
Colymbiformes, 564
Colymboides minutus, 5
Commissure, 564
  rictal, 580
Community singing, 140
Compsothlypidae, 351, 546
Conditioning, 113, 124
Condor, 221
  Andean, 80, 84, 85
  California, 80, 228
Condyle, 15, 564
  occipital, 1, 562
Cone, 109, 110
Conirostrum, 546
Conjugate point, 211
Conopophaga ardesiaca, 490
Conopophaga aurita, 59
Conopophagidae, 42, 163, 383, 490
Continental drift, 186
Contopus virens, 147
Convergence, 366, 370
Coot, 102, 125, 221, 226, 232, 256, 279, 316, 563
  American, 291, 297, 331, 335, 338
  European, 331
Coprodeum, 33, 38, 565
Copulation, 125, 135, 272, 329, 333, 334, 337, 338, 339, 340, 565
Copulatory organ, 33, 39
Coraciae, 565
Coracias, 80
Coracias benghalensis, 474
Coraciidae, 382, 474, 475
Coraciiformes, 382, 565
Coraciinae, 474
Coracoid, 24, 45, 54, 225, 226, 565
Coragyps, 80, 226, 228
Coral-billed nuthatch, 163, 383, 515
Corcoraciididae, 509
Coriolis force, 210, 211
Cormorant, 7, 40, 51, 74, 109, 110, 233, 241, 258, 260, 340, 380
  Double-crested, 232, 252, 254

Cormorant, Flightless, 233, 272
  Great, 401
  Olivaceous, 169
Cornea, 109, 110, 111
Corniplume, 565
Corpuscles, of Grandry, 114
  of Herbst, 114, 115
  of Key-Retzius, 114
  red blood, 2
Cortex, vicarious, 27
Corvidae, corvid, 41, 80, 165, 199, 241, 243, 251, 309, 339, 370, 383, 507
Corvus, 25, 353, 368
Corvus brachyrhynchos, 41, 187, 246
Corvus corax, 44
Corvus frugilegus, 203
Corythaeola, 456
Cossypha heuglini, 145
Costa Rica, 205, 206, 291, 314, 481, 491, 495, 524
Cotinga, 35, 98, 134, 163, 165, 289, 383, 492
Cotingidae, 60, 163, 165, 383, 492, 570
Cotype, 565
Coua caerulea, 80, 90
Coua, Blue, 80
Courser, 446
Courtship, 329
  feeding, 338, 339
Covert, 565
  carpal, 80–81
  primary, 85
  secondary, 85
  tail, 87
  wing, 85–86
Cowbird, 136, 304, 332, 336, 344
  Bay-winged, 279, 318
  Brown-headed, 136, 249, 253, 273, 291, 295, 318
  Giant, 318
  Glossy, 168
  Screaming, 318
  Shiny, 318
Crabplover, 287, 381, 444
Cracidae, 14, 23, 39, 78, 163, 165, 381, 419
Cracticidae, 140, 145, 164, 383, 508
Cracticus cassicus, 508
Crane, 34, 40, 41, 51, 99, 165, 203, 381
  Demoiselle, 428
  Sandhill, 290, 359
Crax rubra, 419
Creadiontidae, 536
Crèche, 332
Creeper, 94, 165, 198, 362, 366, 383
  Brown, 272, 516
Crested-Swift, 33, 287, 344, 382, 561, 565
  Indian, 466
Cretaceous, 1, 2
Crinifer, 456
Crissum, 424, 548, 565
Crocethia alba, 207, 242
Crocodilia, 2, 61
Crop, 31, 238, 239, 249
Crossbill, 238, 299
  Scottish, 274
  White-winged, 177
Crotophaga, 86, 87, 308, 457
Crotophaga ani, 247, 291
Crotophaga major, 285
Crotophaga sulcirostris, 228, 229, 253, 292
Crow, 40, 102, 113, 145, 150, 165, 199, 204, 259, 294, 344, 353, 383, 507
  American, 41, 187, 246
Cryptic plumage, 565
Cryptoptiles, 71, 565
Crypturi, 565
Crypturidae, 391
Crypturus, 273
Crypturus variegatus, 140
Cuba, 205, 207, 247, 428
Cuckoo, 45, 51, 58, 75, 82, 83, 86, 90, 103, 104, 140, 145, 147, 165, 198, 253, 285, 300, 305, 315, 316–317, 332, 382, 457
  Black-billed, 228, 229, 317
  Bronze, 184, 185, 210
  European, 291, 316, 317
  Long-tailed, 184
  Roadrunner, 51
  Yellow-billed, 317, 339
Cuckoo-roller, 76, 163, 382, 475
Cuckoo-shrike, 97, 383
  Great, 504
Cuculidae, 33, 75, 87, 165, 198, 315, 382, 457
Cuculiformes, 12, 382
Cuculus, 33
Cuculus canorus, 291, 316
Culmen, 565
Curassow, 34, 73, 78, 163, 165, 381
  Great, 419
Curlew, Bristle-thighed, 74
  Hudsonian, 175, 176

Cursoriidae, 446
Cyanerpes, 549
Cyanerpes cyaneus, 147
Cyanocitta cristata, 96, 145, 259
Cyanolanius, 533
Cyanopica cyanus, 175
Cyclarhidae, 163, 165, 384, 542
Cyclarhis gujanensis, 542
Cyclopsittacidae, 455
Cyclorhidae, 542
Cypselidae, 465, 565
Cypsiurus parvus, 278

Dacelo, 60
Dacelo gigas, 140
Dacelo novaeguinae, 470
Dacelonidae, 470
Dacnis, 549
Daphoenositta, 514
Day-length, 186–189, 314
  summation of, 188
Dendragapus, 86, 247, 271
Dendragapus obscurus, 195
Dendrite, 27
Dendrochelidonidae, 466
Dendrocolaptes platyrostris, 49
Dendrocolaptidae, 49, 78, 163, 165, 238, 383, 487
Dendrocopos, 259
Dendrocopos major, 247
Dendrocygna, 309
Dendrocygna bicolor, 175
Dendroica coronata, 240
Dendroica discolor, 282
Dendroica kirtlandii, 172, 209, 277, 352
Dendroica nigrescens, 546
Dendroica palmarum, 312
Dendroica striata, 205
Desert, Colorado, 93, 242
  Sahara, 173, 402, 422, 438
Desmodactyli, 56, 566
Desmognathae, 45
Desmopelmous, 58, 566
Determinate laying, 291
Diacromyodian, *see* Syrinx
Diaphragm, thoraco-abdominal, 35
Diastataxy, 81–82, 566
Diatryma giganteum, 11
Diatryma steini, 10
Diatrymiformes, 10
Dicaeidae, 32, 367, 384, 540
Dicaeum, 240
Dicaeum ignipectum, 540
Dicholophidae, 435
Dichromatism, 364, 566
Dicruridae, 87, 363, 383, 505
Dicrurus adsimilis, 171
Dicrurus hottentottus, 74, 363
Dicrurus ludwigii, 171
Dicrurus megarhynchus, 363
Dicrurus paradiseus, 505
Dididae, 454
Didunculidae, 454
Diglossa, 314, 549
Diglossa carbonaria brunneiventris, 175, 177
Dimorphism, sexual, 31, 141, 333, 364, 365
Dinornis, 15
Dinornithidae, 15
Dinornithiformes, 15
Dinosaur, birdlike, 2
  predentate, 2
Diomedea, 80
Diomedea epomophora, 246, 274
Diomedea exulans, 85, 394
Diomedea nigripes, 394
Diomedeidae, 380, 394
Dipper, 52, 241, 383
  European, 139
  White-breasted, 520
Directive marks, 297, 298
Directiveness, 116, 117
Disc, facial, 458, 566
Display, 334–340
  antaposematic, 335, 561
  aposematic, 335, 561
  dance, 408, 433, 434, 493
  epigamic, 337, 340, 567
  gamosematic, 336, 569
Dissemurus, *see Dicrurus*
Diver, 564
Divergence, 366, 370
Diving-petrel, 232, 380
  Peruvian, 397
Dodo, 17, 454
Dolichonyx oryzivorus, 87, 93, 142, 207
Dominance, 328, 329
Donacobius, 140
Donacobius atricapillus, 133
Dormitory, 344
Dotterel, 440
Dove, 125, 268, 274, 332

Dove, Mourning, 37, 99, 124, 132, 139, 222, 228, 232, 258, 275, 276, 278, 296, 310, 319
Ringed Turtle, 296
Rock, 339
Turtle, 203
Dovekie, 99, 179
Down, 73, 75, 95, 96, 293, 567
mesoptile, 95, 573
natal (or nestling), 71, 331
neossoptile, 75, 574
powder, 75, 76, 578
protoptile, 95, 579
Drepanidae, 545
Drepanididae, 545
Drepaniidae, 31, 79, 166, 238, 366, 384, 545
Drive, 117, 118, 124
instinctive, 118
Dromadidae, 381, 444
Dromaeidae, 389
Dromaeognathae, 42
Dromaeus, 42
Dromaiidae, 389
Dromas ardeola, 444
Dromiceiidae, 39, 76, 164, 380, 389
Dromiceius, 79
Dromiceius novae-hollandiae, 134, 389
Dromococcyx, 316
Drongo, 104, 171, 255, 359, 363, 383
Greater Racket-tailed, 505
Malayan Racket-tailed, 304
Spangled, 74
Dryocopus, 366
Dryocopus pileatus, 280
Duck, 15, 35, 51, 62, 71, 78, 79, 95, 97, 99, 111, 113, 114, 125, 134, 141, 172, 199, 203, 204, 221, 231, 271, 273, 285, 287, 291, 315, 333, 335, 380, 412
Baldpate, 194, 256
Black, 232
Black-headed, 316
Blue-winged Teal, 97
Brant, 240
diving, 111, 239
Gadwall, 256
Goldeneye, 132
Harlequin, 171
Mallard, 80, 194, 204, 239, 273, 295, 330
Muscovy, 125, 330
Pochard, 175
Ruddy, 97
Duck, Scaup, 194
Shelduck, 332
Shoveller, 97
Steamer, 233, 234
stiff-tailed, 316
Tree, 175
Tufted, 280
Wood, 194, 239
Duct, ampullary, 39
bile, 32
deferent, 39
ejaculatory, 39
pancreatic, 32, 33
thoracic, 37
Ductus deferentia, 38, 39
Dulidae, 163, 165, 377, 384, 531
Dulus dominicus, 531
Dumetella, 222
Dumetella carolinensis, 240
Duodenum, 32, 33, 61

Eagle, 224
Bald, 93, 201, 202, 256, 359
Golden, 82, 173
Harpy, 240
Philippine Monkey-eating, 240
Ear, 111–112
drum, 112
stones, 112
Ecdysis, 92, 567
Ectopistes, 80
Ecuador, 175, 177, 447, 460, 550
Edoliidae, 505
Egg, 2, 16, 17, 39, 282–286
infertile, 272, 273
Egg-tooth, 2, 297, 567
Egret, 366
American (Common), 201, 220
Cattle, 253
Snowy, 201
Eider, 239
Common, 246
Elaeis, 169
Elephantbirds, 15, 17
Eleutherodactyli, 56, 567
Emberiza, 274
Emberiza calandra, 273
Emberiza citrinella, 288
Emberiza hortulana, 203
Emberizinae, 552

Emeus, 15
Empidonax, 332
Empidonax flaviventris, 288
Empidonax minimus, 270, 362
Empidonax trailii, 142, 362
Empidonax virescens, 362
Emu, 42, 51, 62, 76, 77, 79, 134, 164, 285, 380
Common, 389
Endings, sensory, 114, 115
Endysis, 92, 567
England, 167, 194, 196, 212, 249, 298
Enicuridae, 523
Enlargement, cervical, 28
lumbosacral, 28
Ensifera ensifera, 239
Enzyme, diastatic, 33
Epicardium, 36
Epiglottis, 114
Epimachidae, 511
Epipleural appendage, *see* Process, uncinate
Epoch, Eocene, 4, 6, 10, 11, 12, 13
Miocene, 5, 6, 13, 14
Oligocene, 4, 5, 6, 10, 12, 14
Pleistocene, 6, 14, 15
Pliocene, 6, 14
Recent, 6, 10, 15
Equilibration, 30, 113
Era, Cenozoic, 6, 10
Mesozoic, 5, 6
Palaeozoic, 5, 6
Eremialectoridae, 453
Eremophila alpestris, 93, 142, 173, 199, 332
Eremophila alpestris peregrina, 178
Erolia bairdii, 178
Erolia fuscicollis, 178
Erolia melanotos, 133, 178
Erythrism, 99
Erythrocyte, 36
Esophagus, 31, 32, 34, 133
Estrildinae, 306, 319
Estrogen, 141, 329
Ethology, 567
Eudocimus albus, 409
Eudromias morinellus, 440
Eudynamis, 103, 316
Eudynamis taitensis, 184
Eulebetidae, 537
Eumomota superciliosa, 277
Euneornis, 549
Euparkeria, 1, 2, 7
Eupetidae, 517
Euphagus cyanocephalus, 87
Euphonia, 32
Euplectes hordeacea, 273, 276
Euplectes nigroventris, 273
Eupodotis rüppelli, 102
Eurasia, 173, 175, 192, 244, 392, 408, 409, 474, 485, 502, 506, 513, 537
Eurocephalus, 535
Europe, 10, 11, 145, 156, 167, 179, 193, 194, 203, 287, 399, 410, 420, 436, 439, 442, 445, 476, 516, 517, 520, 521, 527, 534
Eurostopodus guttatus, 103
Euryapteryx, 15, 16
Euryceros, 533
Eurycerotidae, 533
Eurylaimi, 383
Eurylaimidae, 56, 58, 383, 486
Eurylaimus ochromalus, 486
Eurypyga helias, 434
Eurypygidae, 163, 165, 381, 434
Eutaxy, 81–82, 568
Eutoxeres aquila, 239
Eye, eyeball, 22, 109, 114, 188
Eyelash, 73, 75, 457, 478

Falco, 25, 38, 40, 226
Falco albigularis, 240
Falco columbarius, 255
Falco mexicanus, 80
Falco peregrinus, 173, 417
Falcon, 40, 164, 204, 223, 381
Peregrine, 173, 240, 417
Prairie, 80, 240, 280
Pygmy, 280
White-throated, 240
Falconidae, 22, 23, 199, 381, 417
Falconiformes, 11, 43, 250, 380, 568
Falculea, 533
Falculidae, 533
Falcunculidae, 526
Falsterbo, 189, 200
Family, 351, 352, 368, 376–552, 568
Fat deposition, 188
Feather tracts, 88–91
alar, 3
femoral, 4
Feathers, 70–90, 221
chin-growth, 327

Feathers, contour, 4, 8, 72–73, 87–88, 115, 564
down, 71, 73, 75, 76, 95, 96, 293
ferric-oxide stain on, 99
flank-plumes, 327
origin of, 71
ruff, 327
throat-plumes, 327
white, 98
Fecal sac, 299, 306, 307
artificial, 307
Feeding, courtship, 338–339
social, 251–257
Feet, anisodactyl, 560
didactyl, 566
heterodactyl, 51, 570
pamprodactyl, 51, 576
semizygodactyl, 456, 475
syndactyl, 51, 470, 471, 472, 473, 478, 486, 515, 583
totipalmate, 51, 584
tridactyl, 57, 584
zygodactyl, 51, 455, 457, 479, 480, 481, 482, 483, 484, 485, 586
Femur, 35, 568
Fenestra, ischiadic, 60
Fibula, 7, 568
Fieldfare, 167
Filoplume, 73, 74, 568
Filum terminale, 28
Finch, 79, 166, 199, 291, 300, 309, 332, 384, 552
Bramble, 239
Cutthroat, 298, 337
Darwin's, 166
Galápagos, 238, 240, 247, 339, 366
Plush-capped, 79, 163, 384, 550
Purple, 149, 240, 364
Rosy, 239
Zebra, 338
Finfoot, 381
African, 432
Finland, 194, 247, 249
Flamingo, 78, 79, 102, 114, 299, 332, 380
American, 242, 410
Lesser, 242
Fledgling, 300, 332, 568
Flicker, 101
Yellow-shafted, 280, 290, 334
Flight, courtship, 441
flapping, 3, 225
origin of, 2
Flight, soaring, 3, 224, 225
speed, 204, 231
Flightless birds, 13, 47, 79, 172, 225, 233–234, 385, 386, 387, 388, 389, 390, 393, 401, 412, 425, 431, 433, 452, 498
Florida, 15, 201, 202, 205, 253, 429
Florida caerulea, 201
Flowerpecker, 32, 240, 384
Fire-breasted, 540
Flycatcher, Alder, 150, 275
Boat-billed, 366
Crested, 295
Derby, 366
Least, 270, 362
Old-world, 384, 526
Olive-sided, 150, 171
Paradise, 295, 296, 366, 526
Sulphur-bellied, 205, 207
Traill's, 142, 150, 275, 362
Yellow-bellied, 288
See also Tyrant-flycatcher
Flyway, 194
Foramen magnum, 29
triosseum, 24, 568
Formenkreis, 569
Formicariidae, 41, 42, 78, 163, 165, 383, 489
Formicarius analis, 489
Formula, digital, 566
muscle, 56
Fossa, 569
glenoid, 24
Fossil, 4, 5, 6, 10, 13, 14, 15, 569
Fossil Lake, 15
Foster parent, 569
Fovea, 110
central, 111
temporal, 111
Fowl, Mallee, 418
France, 10, 196, 204, 453
Fregata, 24, 256
Fregata magnificens, 167, 403
Fregatidae, 380, 403
Fregilupus varius, 53, 55
French Guiana, 460
Frigatebird, 221, 224, 256, 276, 380
Magnificent, 167, 403
Fringilla coelebs, 144, 196
Fringillidae, fringillid, 31, 33, 39, 49, 79, 85, 166, 199, 285, 287, 301, 340, 367, 370, 384, 546, 551, 552
Fringillinae, 552

Frogmouth, 62, 102, 382
  Tawny, 461
Front, cold, 190
  species, 204
  warm, 190
Frontal shield, 431, 563
Fruit-pigeon, 239
Fulica, 37, 431
Fulica americana, 256, 331
Fulica atra, 331
Fulmar, 343, 395
Fulmaridae, 395
Fulmarus glacialis, 343, 395
Furcula, 7, [illegible], 24, 52, 225, 226, 569
Furnariidae, 41, 42, 139, 163, 165, 318, 383, 488
Furnarius rufus, 140, 488

Gadwall, 256
Galbula melanogenia, 479
Galbulidae, 163, 165, 382, 479, 548
Galerida cristata, 272, 502
Gall bladder, 33
Galliformes, 31, 39, 40, 42, 54, 381, 569
Gallinaceous birds, 80, 95, 125, 222, 249, 258, 259, 273, 287, 291, 305, 332, 367, 563, 569
Gallinago, see Capella
Gallinula, 52
Gallinula chloropus, 95, 173
Gallinule, 52, 279, 307
  Common, 173
  Purple, 287
Ganglion, 27, 29, 30
Gannet, 40, 196, 287, 334, 340
Gape, 569
Gaping, 297, 299, 331
  spontaneous, 331
Garrulax erythrocephalus, 140
Garrulax variegatus, 517
Garrulus glandarius, 169, 170
Gastralia, 7
Gavia, 57
Gavia arctica, 392
Gavia immer, 13
Gavia stellata, 392
Gaviidae, 52, 94, 163, 199, 380, 392
Gaviiformes, 380
Gene, 354, 356, 358, 569
Genital tubercle, 141
Gennaeus, see Lophura
Genotype, 353, 569
Genus, 350, 351, 352, 353, 368, 569
Geococcyx, 51, 132, 366
Geococcyx californianus, 228, 229, 230, 457
Georgia, 175, 191, 208, 257
Geospiza, 166
Geospizinae, 367, 552
Germany, 149, 211, 247, 250, 446
Gerygone palpebrosa, 281
Girdle, pectoral, 4, 22, 24, 54, 225, 226, 577
  pelvic, 7, 8, 22, 24, 225, 577
Gizzard, 31, 32, 239, 569
Gland, adrenal, 39
  endocrine, 33, 314
  exocrine, 33
  Harder's, 30
  oil, 62, 115, 575
  pituitary, 17, 187, 188
    refractory phase of, 187
  salivary, 30, 33, 278
  sweat, 34
  thymus, 38
  uropygial, 62, 585
Glandula picorum, 33
Glareola pratincola, 446
Glareolidae, 381, 446
Glottis, 31, 34, 133
Glycogenic body, 28
Gnatcatcher, Blue-gray, 135
Gnathotheca, 31, 569
Goldeneye, Common, 132
Goldfinch, American, 135, 138, 238, 272, 275, 277, 285, 291, 295, 300, 303, 304, 312, 313, 319, 342, 363
Gonads, 146, 149, 186, 187, 188, 313, 314
Gonys, 569
Goose, geese, 15, 71, 99, 125, 199, 203, 204, 240, 274, 315, 335
  Blue, 191, 192, 412
  Canada, 125
  Ross', 191, 192
  Snow, 191, 192
  Spur-winged, 582
Gouridae, 454
Grackle, 238, 240, 241, 280, 336, 344
  Boat-tailed, 302
Graculidae, 401, 537
Grallina cyanoleuca, 135, 509

Grallina picata, 509
Grallinidae, 140, 147, 164, 383, 509
Grassquit, Yellow-faced, 138, 291
Graucalus macei, 504
Grebe, 15, 52, 78, 79, 86, 172, 232, 233, 285, 339, 340, 377, 380
Pied-billed, 393
Greenland, 167, 193, 206
Gregariousness, 345
Grit, 239
Grosbeak, Evening, 191, 193
Pine, 199, 364
Rose-breasted, 93, 144, 363
Ground roller, 366, 474
Ground-tyrant, Rufous-backed, 207
Grouse, 40, 41, 47, 78, 163, 165, 268, 274, 367, 381
Black, 420
Blue, 86, 195, 247, 271
Ruffed, 132, 167, 183, 271, 334, 360
Sage, 133, 240, 271, 337
Sharp-tailed, 271
Spruce, 240, 271
Gruidae, 23, 41, 54, 165, 381, 428, 430
Gruiformes, 10, 42, 381, 570
Grus, 33, 73
Grus canadensis, 41, 54, 290
Guatemala, 166, 208, 314, 423, 512
Guillemot, 339
Black, 452
Guineafowl, 34, 86, 163, 381
Vulturine, 422
Guira, 308
Gular pouch, 239, 399, 405, 492
Gull, 7, 41, 51, 62, 79, 80, 82, 109, 199, 241, 243, 258, 259, 268, 274, 316, 341, 381
Black-backed, 212, 230, 450
Black-headed, 272, 280
Glaucous, 240
Herring, 93, 115, 196, 232, 253, 291, 330, 339
Laughing, 285, 339
Ring-billed, 101
Guttera plumifera, 34
Gygis, 51
Gymnogyps, 80, 228
Gymnopithys leucaspis, 41, 286
Gymnorhina, 83
Gymnostinops, 318
Gypogeranidae, 414
Gypohierax angolensis, 169

Habia rubica, 147
Habituation, 123–124
Haematopodidae, 381, 439
Haematopus ostralegus, 336
Haematopus palliatus, 439
Halcyon chloris humii, 281
Halcyonidae, 470
Haliaeetus, 226, 256
Haliaeetus leucocephalus, 93, 201
Hallux, 3, 8, 10, 26, 51, 52, 57, 570
elevated, 15, 51, 391, 433, 448, 567
incumbent, 51, 571
Hammerhead, 163, 380, 407
Hamulus, 70, 72, 570
Hand, *see* Manus
Haploophonae, 570
Harpia harpyja, 240
Harrier, 63, 224
Hatching, asynchronous, 303
sequence, 293
Hawaiian honeycreeper, 79, 166, 238, 366, 384, 545
Hawk, 22, 47, 77, 110, 111, 164, 189, 199, 224, 226, 238, 241, 249, 259, 260, 271, 274, 294, 299, 332, 381, 415
Broad-winged, 199, 228
Cooper's, 80, 240
Duck, 231
Marsh, 75, 247
Pigeon, 240, 255
Red-shouldered, 145, 175
Red-tailed, 80, 246, 359, 360, 363
Sharp-shinned, 240, 364
Sparrow, 232, 359
Swainson's, 199, 363
White-tailed, 241
Hawk-eagle, Crowned, 415
Hearing, 30, 111–112
Heart, 36
four-chambered, 2
lymph, 37
Hedge-sparrow, 163, 384
Altai, 527
Heel-pad, 297, 478, 479, 483, 485, 579
Heligoland, 200
Heliopais, 432
Heliornithidae, 381, 432
Helmet-shrike, 563
Black-winged, 535

Helpers at the nest, 307
Hemidacnis, 549
Hemignathus procerus, 238
Hemipode-quail, 140, 271, 273, 381
  Spotted, 426
Hemiprocne coronata, 466
Hemiprocnidae, 33, 344, 382, 466, 565
Hemisphere, Northern, 97, 148, 173, 183, 184, 186
  Southern, 97, 183, 185, 252
  Western, 156
Hemispingus, 546
Henicorhina leucophrys, 521
Heron, 32, 51, 62, 76, 77, 79, 241, 259, 260, 268, 280, 299, 309, 332, 339, 366, 380
  Black-crowned Night, 201, 336, 341
  Boat-billed, 132, 162, 380, 405
  Great Blue, 56, 231, 311, 404
  Little Blue, 201
Heronry, 280, 580
Hesperiphona vespertina, 191
Hesperornis, 9, 10, 13
Hesperornis regalis, 1
Hesperornithiformes, 9
Heterogynism, 570
Heteromeri, 60, 570
Heteronetta, 412
Heteronetta atricapilla, 316
Heteropelmous, 570
Heterotrogon vittatum, 140
Hierarchy, 570
  nervous, 119
  social, 328
  taxonomic, 351–353
High Plains, 14
Himantopus mexicanus, 442
Hippoboscidae, 281
Hirundinidae, 79, 199, 383, 503
Hirundo abyssinica, 279
Hirundo daurica, 242
Hirundo rustica, 503
Hispaniola, 177, 445, 462, 531
Histrionicus histrionicus, 171
Hoatzin, 75, 78, 80, 163, 381, 424
Holland, 288
Holotype, 353, 571
Homalogonatae, 54, 571
Homing, 209
Homoeomeri, 60, 571
Homoiothermism (homoiothermic), 2, 3, 71, 299
Homonym, 571
Honey-buzzard, 189
Honeycreeper, 240, 291, 366
  Blue, 147
Honey-eater, 32, 240, 369, 384
  Regent, 538
Honeyguide, 79, 241, 255, 297, 317, 383
  Greater, 482
Hoopoe, 305, 306, 317, 382, 476
Hoplopterus indicus, 283
Hormone, 36, 115, 141, 329, 345
  gonadotropic, 188
  imbalance, 141
Hornbill, 35, 38, 51, 75, 78, 95, 109, 239, 255, 294, 295, 297, 382, 563
  Great, 478
  Ground, 478
  Silvery-cheeked, 243
Hornet-nest bird, 281
Host, 315, 318, 319, 569, 571
Hudson Bay, 191
Huia, 536
Humero-ulnar pulley, 54
Humerus, 9, 24, 35, 54, 83, 84, 226, 230, 571
Hummingbird, 17, 32, 37, 62, 80, 82, 86, 163, 165, 223, 229, 230, 238, 239, 240, 245, 247, 255, 276, 285, 287, 289, 291, 299, 314, 367, 376, 382, 467, 561
  Hermit, 271
  Ruby-throated, 37, 88, 199, 271
  Singing, 133
  White-eared, 309
Hybridization, 367
Hydrobatidae, 380, 396
Hydrophasianus, 57, 437
Hydroprogne caspia, 175
Hylactidae, 491
Hylocharis leucotis, 309
Hylocichla minima, 139, 205, 362
Hylocichla mustelina, 134
Hylocichla ustulata, 362
Hylomanes, 472
Hyperpituitarism, 17
Hyperstriatum, 27
Hyphantornis capensis, 273
Hypochera, 319
Hypocleidium, 24

Hypocoliidae, 529
Hypocolius ampelinus, 529
Hypodactylum, 571
Hypoptilum, 76, 571
Hyporachis, 76, 571
Hypositta corallirostris, 515
Hyposittidae, 163, 383, 515
Hypotarsus, 571
Hypothalamus, 188

Ibidae, 409
Ibididae, 409
Ibidorhyncha, 442
Ibidorhyncha struthersii, 195, 237
Ibis ibis, 34
Ibis, 280, 316, 380
  White, 409
  Wood, 220
Ibis-bill, 195
Iceland, 156, 175, 439
Ichthyornis, 9, 10
Ichthyornithiformes, 9
Icteria virens, 147
Icteridae, icterid, 31, 39, 46, 79, 85, 163, 165, 199, 241, 284, 289, 309, 315, 318, 384, 547
Icterus, 199
Idaho, 195
Iiwi, 545
Ileum, 32
Ilium, 7, 15, 24, 571
Illadopsidae, 517
Illinois, 194, 195
Imprinting, 125–126, 330
Inattentiveness, 295, 305
Incubation, 271, 292–296, 571
  behavior, 294–296
  patch, 292, 293, 571
  period, 135, 148, 266, 277, 293–296, 309, 339
Indeterminate laying, 290
India, 175, 426, 432, 446, 451, 461, 466, 469, 481, 486, 497, 504, 505, 516, 519, 532, 540, 541
Indiana, 195
Indicator, 317, 318
Indicator indicator, 482
Indicatoridae, 33, 79, 241, 255, 315, 317, 383, 482
Indies, East, 173, 399, 402, 408, 416, 474, 497, 506, 532
  West, 167, 173, 177, 197, 204, 205, 410, 429, 442, 469, 531, 544, 546, 547, 549
Indo-China, 426, 446, 451, 466, 481, 486, 497, 505, 519, 532, 540, 541
Infertility, 272, 273
Infundibulum, 38
Innate releasing mechanism, 108, 119, 126
Instinct, 117, 118
Intelligence, 122, 123
Intestinal convolutions, 60–62
  anticoelous, 60, 61, 561
  antipericoelous, 61, 561
  cyclocoelous, 60, 565
  isocoelous, 60, 61, 572
  isopericoelous, 61, 572
  mesogyrous, 573
  orthocoelous, 60, 575
  pericoelous, 577
  plagiocoelous, 61, 578
  telogyrous, 61, 583
Intestine, large, 32, 33, 62
  small, 32, 33, 60–62
  See also Caecum, Duodenum
Iraq, 529
Ireland, 196
Irena, 255
Irena cyanogaster, 519
Irenidae, 164, 383, 519
Iridophanes, 549
Iridoprocne bicolor, 292, 344
Iris, 109, 522, 544, 572
Irrisoridae, 477
Ischium, 7, 15, 24, 572
Islands, Aleutian, 439
  Antilles, 168, 193
  Aru, 463
  Ascension, 313
  Baffin, 191, 192
  Bahama, 209, 416
  Barro Colorado, 286
  Cape Verde, 171
  Chatham, 541
  Comores, 475
  Drummond, 167
  Falkland, 173, 207
  Faroes, 175
  Fergusson, 463
  Fiji, 511, 541

Islands, Galápagos, 166, 173, 385, 399, 401, 442
Goodenough, 463
Gough, 171
Hawaiian, 173, 442, 526, 538, 545
Henderson, 171
Inaccessible, 171, 233
Laysan, 171
Magellanic, 207
Marianas, 418, 454, 538
Mascarene, 17, 518
Moluccan, 463, 511, 518
Nicobars, 418
Philippines, 193, 402, 408, 418, 426, 437, 438, 442, 461, 466, 469, 474, 478, 481, 486, 502, 504, 505, 506, 513, 516, 517, 518, 519, 532, 539, 540, 541
Razo, 171
Sable, 171, 191
Singapore, 306
Solomon, 184, 185, 210, 418, 426, 461, 466, 474, 478, 497, 505, 540
Southampton, 191, 192
St. Lucia, 168
Tobago, 472
Tristan de Cunha, 171
Wake, 171
Isolating mechanisms, 137, 357, 358, 367
Isolation, ecological, 367
geographical, 357
reproductive, 354, 358
"Ixobrychus neoxenus," 99

Jacamar, 163, 165, 297, 382, 548
Rufous-tailed, 479
Jacamaralcyon, 479
Jacana spinosa, 437
Jaçana, 381, 582
American, 437
Jacanidae, 381, 437
Jackdaw, 125
Jaeger, 223, 257
Long-tailed, 449
Jamaica, 462, 492
Jan Mayan, 167, 315
Japan, 175, 438, 476, 504, 513, 516, 520, 541
Java, 486, 502
Jay, 199, 240
Blue, 96, 145, 333
Brown, 134, 307
Jay, California, 243
Canada, 244
Common, 169, 170
Junco hyemalis, 186, 195
Junco oreganus, 187
Junco, 187, 188
Slate-colored, 186, 189, 195
Jurassic, 2, 5, 6, 9, 186
Jyngidae, 33, 40, 383, 485
Jynx ruficollis, 31
Jynx torquilla, 485

Kagu, 164, 233, 381, 433
Kakatoe leadbeateri, 455
Kansas, 1, 8, 14
Keel, *see* Carina
Kidney, 37, 38, 39
Killdeer, 232
Kingbird, Eastern, 198, 494
Gray, 205, 207
Kingfisher, 51, 80, 95, 111, 165, 241, 249, 276, 280, 282, 297, 317, 339, 354, 382, 470
American green, 48
Belted, 232, 246
Whitecollared, 281
Kinglet, 198, 240, 255
Ruby-crowned, 136, 150
Kite, Everglade, 169
Kiwi, 79, 164, 285, 380
South Island, 390
Knemidophorer, 48, 572
Kookaburra, 140
Laughing, 470

Labrador, 193, 546
Lagena, 112
Lagopus, 86, 92
Laiscopus himalayanus, 527
Lake, Alaotra, 172
Huron, 167
Junín, 170
Superior, 205
Titicaca, 170, 172
Lamprolia, 511
Landrail, Banded, 288
Laniariidae, 534
Laniarius, 98
Laniarius ferrugineus, 140
Laniarius funebris, 140
Laniidae, 80, 165, 258, 384, 534

Lanius, 12, 81, 199, 244
Lanius excubitor borealis, 178
Lanius ludovicianus, 89, 91, 534
Lapland, 249
Lapwing, 203, 336, 340
  Redwattled, 283
Laridae, 37, 52, 54, 79, 381, 450
Lark, 48, 79, 165, 171, 197, 199, 238, 300, 383
  Bogotá Horned, 178
  Crested, 272, 502
  Horned, 93, 142, 173, 332, 359, 360
  Short-toed, 93
Laro-Limicolae, 572
Larosterna, 450
Larus, 25, 37, 57
Larus argentatus, 93, 115, 196, 253, 582
Larus atricilla, 44, 285
Larus delawarensis, 101
Larus fuscus graellsii, 212
Larus hyperboreus, 240
Larus marinus, 450
Larynx, 30, 34, 35
Laughing-thrush, Variegated, 517
Law, biogenetic, 352
  of Priority, 351
  temperature, 157
Leafbird, 164, 255, 383
  Orange-bellied, 519
Learning, 118, 122–126
Lectotype, 573
Legatus albicollis, 279
Legatus leucophaius, 279
Leiotrichidae, 517
Leipoa ocellata, 418
Leks, 132, 271
Leptocoma jugularis microleuca, 223
Leptosomatidae, 76, 163, 382, 475
Leptosomus discolor, 475
Lerwa lerwa, 203
Lessonia rufa, 207
Leucophoyx thula, 201
Leucosticte tephrocotis, 239
Leucotreron cincta, 103
Lichmera indistincta, 538
Life zones, 157–159
Lift, 219, 220
Ligaments, peritoneal, 33, 577
"Ligurinus," 552
Limpkin, 163, 165, 169, 316, 381, 429
Linnet, 144
Liotrichidae, 517
Lissotis, 99
Lissotis melanogaster, 436
Liver, 33, 37, 38
Lobipes lobatus, 140, 271, 443
Lobophasis bulweri, 86
Lobotos, 504
Longspur, Lapland, 142
Loon, 94, 110, 163, 199, 221, 232, 287, 380
  Arctic, 392
  Common, 13
Lophortyx californicus, 99, 257, 341
Lophortyx gambelii, 258
Lophotis, 99
Lophura edwardsi, 73
Lophura nycthemera, 421
Loriidae, 455
Lorius roratus, 364
Lory, 38
  Long-tailed New Guinea, 366
Louisiana, 191
Loxia, 238, 551
Loxia curvirostra scotica, 274
Loxia leucoptera leucoptera, 177
Loxia leucoptera megaplaga, 177
Lungs, 34, 35, 36, 560
Luscinia megarhyncha, 134
Lymph, heart, 37
  nodes, 37
Lymphatic tissue, 37–38
Lyrebird, 58, 83, 164, 272, 287, 383, 500
Lyrurus tetrix, 420

Macaw, Military, 86
Macrocephalon, 418
Macrochires, 561, 573
Macronus gularis, 140
Macronus ptilosis, 140
Macronyx, 366
Macropterygidae, 466
Madagascar, 15, 163, 172, 173, 184, 366, 407, 409, 422, 425, 442, 444, 454, 474, 475, 476, 499, 515, 518, 533, 539
Magnetism, terrestrial, 210–211
Magpie, 145, 247, 255
  Azure-winged, 175
  Black-billed, 248, 259
Magpie-jay, Collie, 507
Magpie-lark, 135, 140, 147, 148, 509
Maine, 207, 244, 253
Malay peninsula, 432, 486

Malaysia, 74, 103, 426, 437, 438, 442, 461, 466, 469, 478, 481, 482, 504, 505, 513, 517, 518, 519, 537, 539, 540, 541
Malimbidae, 551
Mallard, 80, 194, 204, 239, 273, 295, 330
Mallee Fowl, 418
Mallophaga, 281
Maluridae, 525
Malurus, 525
Manacus vitellinus, 271
Manakin, 132, 163, 165, 268, 276, 289, 337, 364, 367, 383
  Gould's, 132, 271, 333
  Yellow-thighed, 493
Manchuria, 175
Mandible, 22, 573
  lower, 31
  upper, 31
Mandibular hook, 318
Manitoba, 361
Manucodia, 34
Manus, 8, 52, 226, 229, 573
Mareca americana, 256
Martin, Brown-chested, 207
  Purple, 272, 291, 301
  Rough-wing Bank, 295
Massachusetts, 191, 201, 204, 209
Maturity, age at sexual, 273, 274
Maxilla, 22, 573
Meadowlark, 143, 170, 199, 285, 333, 366
Meadow-Pipit, 307
Medulla oblongata, 21, 28
Megaceryle alcyon, 46, 246
Megalaemidae, 481
Megalaima chrysopogon, 349
Megalapteryx, 15
Megalornithidae, 428
Megapode, 278, 294, 301, 381, 418
Megapodiidae, 381, 418
Megapodius, 126, 418
Megarhynchus pitangua, 366
Melanerpes formicivorus, 244, 308
Melanism, 366, 573
Melanitta deglandi, 191, 232
Melanospiza, 552
Meleagrididae, 163, 165, 381, 423
Meleagris, 80
Melichneutes, 317, 482
Meliphagidae, 32, 365, 367, 384, 538
Melithreptidae, 538
Mellivora capensis, 317
Mellopitta, 497
Melloria, 508
Melopsittacus undulatus, 100
Melospiza georgiana, 361
Melospiza lincolnii, 361
Melospiza melodia, 190, 196
Membrane, nictitating, 30, 109
  tympanic, 112
Menura, 83
Menura superba, 500
Menurae, 383
Menuridae, 145, 164, 272, 383, 500
Mergus, 33
Meropidae, 92, 97, 382, 473
Meropogon, 473
Merops, 80, 182, 184
Merops apiaster, 473
Merops nubicoides, 182, 184
Merops nubicus, 182, 184, 255
Mesentery, 573
Mesite, 24, 62, 76, 163, 233, 381
  Brown, 425
Mesitidae, 425
Mesitornithidae, 425
Mesoduodenum, 33, 573
Mesoenas, 62
Mesoenas unicolor, 425
Mesoenatidae, 76, 163, 381, 425
Mesoenidae, 425
Mesomyodi, 5
Mesomyodian, *see* Syrinx
Mesoptiles, 71, 573
Mesotubarium, 38
Metabolic rate, 34
Metacarpal, 7, 84, 225
Metapatagium, 574
Metasternum, 47
Mexico, 156, 173, 175, 178, 205, 207, 391, 405, 408, 423, 428, 429, 437, 445, 469, 472, 479, 480, 487, 488, 489, 492, 493, 502, 530, 542, 543
Michigan, 150, 172, 192, 193, 199, 209, 265, 275, 276, 288, 290, 292, 303, 310, 311, 344, 361, 367
Microbates, 525
Microparra, 437
Micropodidae, 465
Micropodiformes, 561, 573
Micropsitta, 240, 455
Micropus, *see Apus*
Microscelis, 518

Microscelis criniger, 74
Microscelis leucocephalus, 366
Migrant, instinct, 190
  weather, 190
Migration, diurnal, 198, 200
  individual, 196
  nocturnal, 198, 200
  northward, 201
  partial, 196
  restlessness, 212
Mimicry, 103
  vocal, 145, 146
Mimidae, 163, 165, 384, 522
Mirafra javanica, 147
Mistle-Thrush, 275
Mniotilta varia, 205
Mniotiltidae, 351, 546
Moa, 15, 16, 42
Mockingbird, 137, 139, 145, 147, 163, 165, 268, 340, 383, 522
Mocking-thrush, 133
Molothrus ater, 249, 253, 273, 318
Molothrus bonariensis, 168, 318
Molothrus rufo-axillaris, 318
Molt, 92–97, 574
  annual, 92, 97
  centrifugal, 94
  centripetal, 94
  order of, 94
  postjuvenal, 96
  postnuptial, 92, 93, 97
Momotidae, 163, 165, 382, 472
Momotus momota, 472
Monias, 233, 425
Moorhen, 173
Mortality, 302–304
  nest, 273, 303
Morus bassanus, 196, 257
Mosasaur, 9
Motacilla, 12, 98
Motacilla alba, 528
Motacilla flava, 192
Motacillidae, 79, 165, 384, 528
Motmot, 82, 86, 163, 165, 241, 282, 306, 382
  Blue-crowned, 472
  Blue-throated Green, 278
  Turquoise-browed, 277
Mountains, Andes, 167, 172, 175, 447
  Chisos, 150
  Everest, 203
Mountains, Great Smoky, 195
  Himalayan, 203, 482
  Rocky, 195
  Shanhaikuan, 195
Mudnest-builder, 164, 383, 509
Mullerornis, 15
Murre, 199, 232, 268, 286, 341
  Thick-billed, 258
Muscadivores, 239
Muscicapidae, 366, 377, 384, 526
Muscivora forficata, 49
Muscle, ambiens, 2, 24, 54, 56, 57, 560
  biceps brachii, 52, 53, 55, 230, 232, 233
  biceps slip, 52–54
  brachialis, 25
  Brücke's, 110, 111
  coracobrachialis, 25
  costopulmonary, 35
  Crampton's, 110, 111
  cucullaris, 30
  deltoideus major, 52, 53, 230, 233
  depressor mandibulae, 30
  depressor palpebrae, 30
  dorsalis scapulae, 54
  expansor secundariorum, 54, 55
  extensor metacarpi radialis, 24, 52, 53, 55, 230
  femorotibialis, 24
  flexor carpi ulnaris, 24, 133
  flexor digitorum longus, 56, 566
  flexor hallucis longus, 25, 56, 566
  flexor perforans et perforatus digiti III, 56, 57, 585
  flexor perforatus digiti III, 56, 57, 585
  formula, 56–57
  geniohyoideus, 30
  gluteus medius et minimus, 56
  iliotrochantericus anterior, 57
  iliotrochantericus medius, 56
  intraocular, 110
  keratomandibularis, 30
  Müller's, 110
  mylohyoideus posterior, 30
  papillary, 36
  pectoralis, 25, 52, 54, 55, 226, 227, 228, 230, 232, 234
  piriformis, 56
  postaxial, 26
  preaxial, 26
  red, 25
  rhomboideus, 25

Muscle, sartorius, 25
semimembranosus, 25
semitendinosus, 56
smooth, 25, 35
sphincter colli, 30
sternocleidomastoideus, 28
sternocoracoideus, 54
striated, 24, 35
subcoracoideus, 54
supracoracoideus, 24, 225, 227, 228, 230, 233, 234
syringeal, 59, 370
tensor patagii brevis, 52, 53, 55, 230
tensor patagii longus, 52, 53, 55, 232
tensor periorbita, 30
thigh, 54, 56
triceps brachii, 24, 230
white, 25
Musophaga, 456
Musophagidae, 99, 163, 382, 456
Musophagiformes, 382
Mutation, 356, 357, 358
Myelinization, 126
Myiadestidae, 523
Myioborus, 291
Myioborus miniatus aurantiacus, 277
Myiodynastes luteiventris, 205, 207
Myiopsitta, 455
Myiopsitta monachus, 309
Myiozetes, 270
Myocardium, 36
Myoglobin, 25
Myzomela cardinalis, 369
Myzomela melanocephala, 369
Myzomela nigrita, 365, 369
Myzomela obscura, 369

Nannopterum, 233, 401
Nannopterum harrisi, 272
Nares, amphirhinal, 41, 42, 560
external, 23, 34, 40
gymnorhinal, 570
holorhinal, 10, 40, 41, 570
imperforate, 40, 571
impervious, 40, 571
internal, 31
obsolete, 399, 400, 401, 402, 403
perforate, 40, 577
pervious, 40, 577
pseudoschizorhinal, 41, 42, 579
schizorhinal, 41, 581
Nasopharynx, 34
Natal, 444
Natural selection, 357-359
Nebraska, 14, 211
Nectarinia violacea, 539
Nectariniidae, 32, 97, 384, 539
Neocathartes grallator, 11, 12
Neocerebellum, 28
Neocichla, 537
Neodrepanis coruscans, 59, 499
Neodrepanis hypoxantha, 499
Neognathae, 352
Neomorpha, 31
Neomorpha acutirostris, 536
Neornithes, 8, 233, 352
Neositta chrysoptera, 514
Neosittidae, 164, 383, 514
Neossiosynoeca scatophaga, 282
Neossoptiles, 71, 574
Neotis cafra, 133
Neotype, 574
Nerve, cochlear, 112
cranial, 27-30
of Von Lenhossék, 29
optic, 21, 22, 110, 126
recurrent laryngeal, 30
sciatic, 60
spinal, 27, 29
spinal accessory, 28, 29, 30
Nervous system, 27-30
Nest, 274-280
brood, 279
cock, 276
parasitism, 315-319
sanitation, 306-307
Nest-building, 124, 135, 275-278
symbolic, 340
Nesting, associates, 280-282
colonial, 309, 341-343
communal, 308
co-operative, 308
threshold theory, 343
young-pioneer theory, 343
Nestling, 297-302, 331, 332, 574
period, 266, 300-302, 305, 309
Nestoridae, 455
Nest-site selection, 274-275
Netta erythrophthalma, 175
Neurobiotaxis, 28
Neuroglia, 27
Neuron, 27

Neuron, postganglionic, 29
preganglionic, 29
New Caledonia, 433, 463
New Guinea, 185, 193, 240, 352, 359, 360, 388, 418, 463, 508, 509, 510, 511, 512, 514, 516, 534
New Hebrides, 418
New Jersey, 10
New Mexico, 10, 11
New South Wales, 501
New Zealand, 13, 15, 16, 131, 164, 175, 184, 185, 186, 210, 315, 390, 402, 442, 464, 498, 536, 538, 541
New Zealand Bushwren, 498
New Zealand wren, 164, 233, 383, 498
Newfoundland, 175, 207, 361
Nighthawk, Common, 132, 276, 336
Nightingale, 134, 141, 147
Nightjar, 40, 51, 58, 102, 145, 147, 164, 277, 287, 382
Pennant-winged, 464
Spotted, 103
Nodes, lymph, 37
Nomopelmous, 575
Norway, 167
Nostrils, *see* Nares
Notarium, 23
Notharcus macrorhynchos, 480
Nothocrax urumutum, 419
Notiochelidon pileatus, 278
Notornis, 47
Nova Scotia, 171, 191
Nucifraga, 244
Nucifraga caryocatactes, 272
Numenius phaeopus, 176, 441
Numenius tahitiensis, 74
Numida, 86
Numididae, 163, 381, 422
Nutcracker, 244
Thick-billed, 272
Nuthatch, 165, 198, 244, 245, 287
Australian, 164, 305, 307, 383, 514
British, 339
Common, 190, 383, 513
Coral-billed, 163, 383, 515
European, 272
Red-breasted, 513
White-breasted, 150, 259, 272
Nuttallornis borealis, 171
Nyctea scandiaca, 178, 179
Nyctibiidae, 163, 165, 382, 462
Nyctibius griseus, 462
Nycticorax nycticorax, 201
Nyctidromus albicollis, 291
Nyctiornis, 473

Oaxaca, 178, 480, 502
Ocean, Atlantic, 171, 206, 448
Indian, 444, 448
Pacific, 171, 206
Oceania, 537, 552
Oceanites oceanicus, 207, 396
Ocreatus underwoodii, 467
Odontognathae, 8, 9
Odontolcae, 9
Odontophoridae, 421
Odontophorus gujanensis, 140
Odontopterygiformes, 14
Odontornithes, 8
Odontotormae, 9
Oecophylla smaragdina, 281
Oedicnemidae, 445
Oenanthe oenanthe, 193, 204
Oenanthe oenanthe leucorhoa, 193
Ohio, 159, 190, 201
Oidemia nigra, 233
Oilbird, 7, 163, 278, 309, 382, 460
Oilpalm, 169
Olfaction, 113–114
Olfactory bulb, 21, 113
Oligomyodian, *see* Syrinx
Olor columbianus, 34, 88
Ontario, Point Pelee, 200
Operculum, 40, 447, 514, 575
Opisthocomidae, 75, 78, 163, 381, 424
Opisthocomus, 24, 31, 32, 80
Opisthocomus hoazin, 424
Optic, lobe, 8, 21, 28
nerve, 21, 110, 126
Orbit, 7, 22, 33, 109, 575
Oregon, 15, 156, 517
Oreomanes, 549
Oreortyx pictus, 195
Organ, copulatory, 33, 39
excretory, 38
phalloid, 39
reproductive, 38
sense, 109–115
Oriole, 199, 240, 284, 383
Bullock's, 139
Golden, 506

Oriole, Old-world, 98
  Orchard, 364
Oriolia, 533
Oriolidae, 80, 145, 383, 506
Oriolus, 98
Oriolus oriolus, 506
Ornithischia, 2
Ornithosuchus, 2
Oropendola, 240
  Wagler's, 132, 135, 271, 276, 277, 302, 547
Ortalis, 34
Ortalis vetula, 134
Orthonycidae, 517
Orthotomus, 278
Orthotomus sutorius maculicollis, 279
Ortyxelos, 426
Os dorsale, 23
  humeroscapulare, 24, 576
  opticus, 22, 109, 576
  radiale, 84, 579
  ulnare, 84, 584
Oscines, 4, 48, 58, 78, 352, 370, 383, 576
  acutiplantar, 5, 48, 559
  latiplantar, 48, 573
Osprey, 80, 173, 174, 224, 231, 256, 280, 381, 416
Osseus bulla, 35, 141
Ossicle, 576
  Gemminger's, 109
Osteodontornis, 5, 14
Osteodontornis orri, 13
Ostinops, 318
Ostinops alfredi, 46
Ostrich, 7, 17, 42, 51, 62, 75, 78, 79, 87, 88, 285, 377, 379, 386, 566
Otidae, 436
Otididae, 62, 99, 381, 436
Otis tetrax, 132
Otolith, 112
Otus asio, 167, 366
Ovary, 38, 141, 318, 319, 576
Ovenbird, 42, 58, 142, 148, 163, 165, 276, 297, 301, 318, 383
  Red, 140, 488
Overlap, conforming, 85
  contrary, 85
Oviduct, 38, 39, 576
Owl, 22, 47, 51, 58, 71, 78, 94, 95, 102, 109, 111, 112, 224, 238, 243, 244, 249, 271, 273, 274, 282, 294, 305
Owl, Barn, 165, 170, 173, 382, 458
  Great Horned, 80, 170, 178, 359
  Long-eared, 247
  Screech, 167, 359, 360, 366
  Short-eared, 247
  Snowy, 178, 179, 315
  Spectacled, 459
Owlet-frogmouth, 164, 382, 463
Oxpecker, 255
Oxyrhamphidae, 495
Oxyruncidae, 163, 165, 383, 495
Oxyruncus cristatus, 495
Oystercatcher, 336, 381
  American, 439

Pachycephala pectoralis, 364
Pachycephalidae, 526
Pachycoccyx, 316
Pachyornis, 15
Paictidae, 499
Painted-snipe, 81, 140, 273, 381, 438
Pair formation, 328, 333
Palaeoscinidae, 5
Palaeoscinis turdirostris, 5
Palaeospiza bella, 5
Palaeospizidae, 5
Palamedeae, 411
Palamedeidae, 411
Palatal keel, 238
Palate, 30, 114, 576
  aegithognathous, 43, 44
  apterygiform, 42
  casuariiform, 42
  desmognathous, 43, 44
  dromaeognathous, 42, 43, 44
  horny, 31
  saurognathous, 44
  schizognathous, 7, 42, 44
  struthioniform, 42
  tinamiform, 42
Palmchat, 163, 165, 309, 377, 384, 531
Palmeria, 545
Palm-Swift, 278
Panama, 170, 199, 206, 481, 491, 495, 524, 530, 548
  Isthmus of, 166
Pancreas, 32, 33, 34
Pandion, 51, 80, 226, 256
Pandion haliaetus, 173, 174, 416
Pandionidae, 381, 415, 416
Panuridae, 517

Paradisaea, 271
Paradisaea rubra, 511
Paradisaeidae, 80, 164, 383, 510, 511
Paradoxornis paradoxa, 51
Paradoxornithidae, 517
Paraguay, 419, 462, 472, 480, 483, 493, 495
Parakeet, 113, 309
Paramythiidae, 540
Paratype, 576
Pardalotus, 540
Paridae, 165, 198, 251, 258, 383, 512
Parridae, 437
Parrot, 7, 24, 34, 38, 47, 51, 62, 76, 77, 100, 111, 114, 145, 257, 280, 282, 309, 376, 382, 455
  Golden-shouldered, 282
  King, 364
  Pygmy, 240
Partridge, 190
Parula americana, 265
Parulidae, 39, 79, 163, 165, 199, 351, 352, 384, 546
Parus, 209, 249
Parus atricapillus, 198
Parus major, 288
Parus monticolus, 512
Passer, 12, 25
Passer domesticus, 274, 367
Passer hispaniolensis, 367
Passer montanus, 209
Passerculus princeps, 171, 191
Passerella iliaca, 148
Passeres, 58, 204, 352, 370, 377, 383, 577
Passerherbulus henslowii, 147
Passeridae, 551
Passeriformes, 22, 28, 37, 58, 352, 370, 383
Passerina cyanea, 208
Passerines, 35, 40, 43, 45, 48, 52, 54, 56, 58, 60, 62, 78, 79, 80, 82, 83, 85, 87, 88, 93, 95, 96, 113, 114, 139, 141, 146, 222, 231, 245, 251, 258, 273, 287, 296, 299, 305, 315, 332, 370, 577
Pastor roseus, 537
Patagonia, 205
Patronym, 351, 577
Pattern, disruptive, 103, 104
  fixed-action, 118
Pauraque, 291
Pavo, 82, 86, 87
Peafowl, 82, 86, 87
Peck, dominance, 141
  order, 328
Pecten, 110, 577
Pedioecetes, 271
Pedionomidae, 381, 427
Pedionomus torquatus, 427
Pelecanidae, 23, 380, 399
Pelecaniformes, 10, 14, 33, 43, 292, 380, 582
Pelecanoidae, 397
Pelecanoides garnotii, 397
Pelecanoididae, 380, 397
Pelecanus, 12
Pelecanus erythrorhynchos, 86
Pelecanus occidentalis, 166, 399
Pelican, 36, 52, 95, 109, 224, 229, 230, 239, 380
  Brown, 166, 399
  White, 86
Pellet, food, 243, 247, 249, 259, 404, 458, 459
Pelvic wing, 3
Pelvis, 2, 10, 38
Penelope, 419
Penelopina, 419
Penguin, 7, 12, 13, 71, 75, 88, 94, 95, 109, 111, 241, 287, 332, 379, 385
  Adélie, 258, 287
  Emperor, 13, 246, 278, 315
  King, 71, 232, 278, 385
  Peruvian, 258
  Yellow-eyed, 274, 289
Peninsula, Gaspé, 200
  Iberian, 196
  Melville, 207
Penis, 141
  cloacal, 39
Pennsylvania, 211, 231, 275
Pepper-shrike, 163, 165, 384
  Pale-billed, 542
Perception, 117, 124
Perdicidae, 421
Perdix, 25
Perdix perdix, 190
Pericardium, 36
Pericrocotidae, 504
Period, Cretaceous, 6, 8, 9
  egg-laying, 291–292
  incubation, 148, 293–296
  Jurassic, 2, 5, 6, 9, 186
  nestling, 148, 266, 300–302, 305, 309

Period, Permian, 5
Quaternary, 6
Tertiary, 4, 6, 14
Triassic, 5, 6
Perisoreus canadensis, 244
Perissocephalus, 134
Peristeridae, 454
Pernis apivorus, 189
Persia, 539
Peru, 169, 175, 178, 387, 397, 405, 434, 445, 460, 496, 525, 550
Petrel, 252, 258, 282, 287, 315
diving, 51, 397
Wilson's, 207, 396
Petrochelidon pyrrhonota, 272
Pewee, Eastern Wood, 147
Pezophaps, 17
Phaeomyias, 240
Phaeoprogne tapera fusca, 207
Phaëthon, 54
Phaëthon lepturus, 398
Phaëthon rubricauda, 398
Phaëthontidae, 380, 398
Phaethornis, 232, 271
Phaethornis superciliosus, 239
Phaethornithinae, 82
Phaëtontidae, 398
Phainopepla, 359
Phainopepla nitens, 240, 276, 530
Phainopepla nitens lepida, 93
Phainopepla, 93, 530
Phainoptila, 530
Phalacrocoracidae, 380, 401
Phalacrocorax, 12
Phalacrocorax auritus, 252, 254
Phalacrocorax carbo, 401
Phalacrocorax nigrogularis, 401
Phalacrocorax olivaceus, 169
Phalanges, 35, 50, 84, 577
Phalarope, 52, 163, 273, 287, 364, 381
Northern, 140, 271, 334, 443
Phalaropodidae, 163, 381, 443
Phalaropus, 443
Pharynx, 30, 31, 112, 114
Phasianidae, 22, 46, 77, 165, 381, 421
Phasianus, 77, 86
Phasidus, 422
Pheasant, 41, 47, 77, 82, 94, 165, 274, 381
Ring-necked, 86, 273, 318
Silver, 86, 421
White-tailed Wattled, 86
Phenotype, 577
Pheucticus, 552
Pheucticus ludovicianus, 93, 144
Philepitta castanea, 499
Philepitta schlegeli, 499
Philepittidae, 163, 383, 499
Philesturnus, 536
Philetairus socius, 308
Philohela, 82, 198
Philohela minor, 111, 132, 237
Philomachus pugnax, 271
Phloeoceastes, 366
Phoebe, Black, 170
Eastern, 275, 285
Phoebetria, 394
Phoenicircus, 98
Phoeniconaias minor, 242
Phoenicopteri, 577
Phoenicopteridae, 78, 380, 410, 570, 577
Phoenicopterus, 54
Phoenicopterus ruber, 242, 410
Phoeniculidae, 163, 382, 477
Phoenicurus, 289
Phoenicurus gibraltariensis, 272
Phonygammus, 34
Phororhacos, 11
Phyllornithidae, 519
Phytotoma rara, 49
Phytotoma rutila, 496
Phytotomidae, 49, 163, 383, 496
Pica pica, 247, 248, 255, 259
Picathartidae, 517
Picidae, 22, 33, 94, 166, 198, 383, 484
Piciformes, 42, 382, 577
Picoïdes, 570
Picoïdes arcticus, 178
Piculus, 98
Picumninae, 484
Picus, 98
Pigeon, 24, 62, 78, 109, 113, 114, 133, 165, 199, 204, 211, 238, 257, 273, 278, 287, 309, 329, 339, 382, 582
Band-tailed, 240
Passenger, 80, 240
Snow, 203
White-headed Fruit, 103
Wood, 454
Pigments, of eggs, 284
of feathers, 98–99
Pinfeather, 577
Pinguinus impennis, 13, 233

Pipilo, 241
Pipilo fuscus, 137
Pipit, 79, 165, 199, 203, 366, 384, 528
  Sprague's, 142
Pipra mentalis, 364, 493
Pipridae, 60, 132, 163, 165, 383, 493, 570
Pipromorpha, 270
Piranga leucoptera, 549
Pitangus sulphuratus, 366
Pithecophaga jefferyi, 240
Pitta, 383
  Hooded, 497
Pitta sordida, 497
Pittidae, 383, 497
Pitylus grossus, 237
Pityriasidae, 537
Plantain-eater, *see* Touraco
Plantcutter, 163, 383
  Reddish, 496
Plasticity, 361
Plataleidae, 409
Plautus alle, 99, 179
Plectrophenax nivalis, 137, 199
Plegadidae, 409
Pleistocene, epoch, 6
  glaciation, 166, 185
  glacier, 177
  ice front, 184
Plexus, 578
  brachial, 26, 29
  lumbosacral, 26, 29
Ploceidae, 39, 97, 258, 306, 315, 319, 384, 551
Ploceinae, 319
Ploceus, 98
Ploceus nigerrimus, 310
Ploceus philippinus, 271, 273, 276
Plotidae, 402
Plover, 223, 287, 381, 440, 582
  Eastern (American) Golden, 193, 284
  Golden, 51, 207
  Piping, 292
  Ring, 336
  Semipalmated, 103, 104
  Upland, 139, 285
Plumage, adult winter, 96
  disruptive, 103, 104
  eclipse, 97, 567
  first nuptial, 96
  first winter, 96
  internuptial, 96
Plumage, juvenal, 96
  second winter, 96
  succession, 92
Plumule, 75, 578
Plush-capped finch, 79, 163, 384, 550
Pluvialis dominica, 193, 284
Pnoepyga, 86
Pochard, Southern, 175
Podargidae, 62, 102, 382, 461
Podargus strigoides, 461
Podica senegalensis, 432
Podicepidae, 393
Podiceps, 57
Podiceps rufolavatus, 172
Podicipedes, 564, 578
Podicipedidae, 52, 78, 380, 393
Podicipediformes, 380, 564, 578
Podicipidae, 393
Podicipiformes, 578
Podicipitidae, 393
Podicipitiformes, 564, 578
Podilymbus podiceps, 393
Podotheca, 47, 578
  booted, 47, 48, 49, 523, 563
  cnémidophore, 48, 564
  endaspidean, 48, 49, 567
  exaspidean, 48, 49, 568
  holaspidean, 48, 49, 570
  holothecal, 570
  knemidophorer, 48
  laminiplantar, 48, 49, 572
  ocreate, 47, 48
  pycnaspidean, 48, 49, 579
  reticulate, 47
  scaleless, 48
  schizothecal, 581
  scutellate, 47, 581
  scutellate-reticulate, 47
  taxaspidean, 48, 49, 583
  ultraexaspidean, 584
Poephila guttata, 338
Poikilothermism, 299
Polihiërax, 40
Polihiërax semitorquatus, 280
Polioptila caerulea, 135
Polioptilidae, 525
Pollex, 82, 578
Polyboridae, 417
Polymorphism, 364
Polymyodian, *see* Syrinx
Polynesia, 512

Pomacea (Ampullaria), 169, 429
Pomatorhinus erythrogenys, 140
Pons, 28
Porphyrula martinica, 287
Portugal, 175, 426, 453
Porzanula, 78, 79
Potoo, 163, 165, 278, 287, 382
  Common, 462
Pouch, buccal food, 239
Powder down, 75, 76, 578
Pratincole, 277, 381, 446
Preening, 300
Primary feather, 8, 78–79, 84, 85, 132, 578
  digital, 79
  metacarpal, 79
  outermost, 78
Prinia, 278, 319
Prioniturus, 455
Prionopidae, 163, 258, 384, 535, 563
Prionops, 307
Prionops cristata, 535
Priotelus, 80
Proavian, 2
Procellariidae, 380, 395, 396
Procellariiformes, 13, 14, 52, 252, 380, 584
Process, epipleural, 1, 585
  extensor, 52
  iliopectineal, 24
  oblique, 47
  odontoid, 45
  pectineal, 24
  pisiform, 577
  posterolateral, 47
  retroarticular, 7
  sternocoracoidal, 47
  sternocostal, 23
  uncinate, 1, 7, 8, 10, 585
  xiphoid, 47
Processus, intermedius, 47
  lateralis, 47
  obliquus, 47
Procniatidae, 548
Proctodeum, 33, 39, 578
Prodotiscus, 317, 318
Progne subis, 272
Promeropidae, 538
Promerops, 538
Propatagium, 52, 578
Protocalliphora metallica, 281
Protonotaria citrea, 270
Protoptiles, 71, 579
Proventriculus, 31, 32, 579
Prunella, 523
Prunellidae, 39, 163, 165, 384, 527
Psalidoprocne holomelaena, 295
Psaltriparinae, 512
Psaltriparus melanotis, 307
Psephotus chrysopterygius, 282
Pseudodontornithidae, 14
Pseudosuchia, 2, 7
Psilorhinus, 134
Psittacidae, 22, 31, 33, 46, 382, 455
Psittaciformes, 382, 579
Psomocolax oryzivorus, 318
Psophia, 82
Psophia leucoptera, 430
Psophiidae, 163, 381, 428, 430
Ptarmigan, 86, 92, 240
Pteroclidae, 23, 31, 382, 453
Pterolestes rufofuscus, 280
Pteroptochidae, 491
Pteroptochos, 87
Pteroptochos castaneus, 491
Pterosaurs, 3, 7
Pterylae, 72, 75, 88, 96, 115, 579
Pterylography, 89, 91, 579
Pterylosis, 83, 88–91, 579
Ptilogonatidae, 163, 165, 377, 384, 530
Ptilogonys cinereus, 240
Ptilonorhynchidae, 145, 164, 271, 383, 510
Ptilonorhynchus violaceus, 146, 510
Ptilopody, 48, 579
Ptilosis, 83, 579
Pubis, 2, 7, 24, 57, 579
Puffbird, 163, 165, 382
  Swallow-winged, 548
  White-necked, 480
Puffin, 232, 339, 341
Puffinidae, 395
Puffinus, 92, 232
Puffinus griseus, 206, 207
Puffinus puffinus, 209
Pulmonary aponeurosis, 35
Pulsatrix perspicillata, 459
Purposiveness, 116, 117, 119
Pycnonotidae, 5, 74, 383, 518
Pycnonotus goiavier personatus, 306
Pycnonotus sinensis, 518
Pygoscelis adeliae, 258
Pygostyle, 7, 8, 15, 23, 35, 57, 579
Pyrrhocorax graculus, 203

Quail, California, 99, 257, 341
Gambel's, 258
Mountain, 195
Scaled, 86
Queensland, 388, 539
Quelea quelea, 280
Quetzal, 297, 469
Quiscalus, 238

Rachis, 70, 72, 579
Rackettail, White-booted, 467
Radius, 7, 84, 226, 579
Rail, 40, 41, 47, 51, 78, 79, 85, 86, 94, 102, 133, 171, 198, 233, 241, 279, 307, 316, 381
King, 354, 431
Virginia, 354
Rain call, 149
Rallidae, 54, 62, 198, 381, 431
Rallus aquaticus, 233
Rallus elegans, 431
Ramphastidae, 22, 33, 52, 163, 165, 383, 483
Ramphastos, 40
Ramphastos cuvieri, 483
Ramphocaenus, 525
Ramphocelus, 270
Ramphocelus icteronotus, 354
Ramphocelus passerinii, 289, 354
Ramphomicron microrhynchum, 239
Ramus, 580
Rancho la Brea, 14
Raphidae, 454
Raphus, 17
Rassenkreis, 580
Ratitae, 42
Ratite birds, 8, 15, 17, 23, 24, 39, 45, 47, 58, 76, 85, 292, 580
Raven, 125, 145, 243, 276
Razorbill, 232
Rectrices, 8, 72, 86–87, 115, 580
Rectum, 32, 33
Recurvirostra americana, 237
Recurvirostridae, 381, 442
Redshank, 268, 336
Redstart, 289, 291
Black, 272
Costa Rican Orange-bellied, 277
Reflex, eye movements, 109
grasping, 299
neck movements, 109
Regulidae, 525
Regulus, 198
Regulus calendula, 136, 150
Releaser, 119, 330, 580
Remex, remiges, 72, 78–85, 115, 580
carpal, 80–81
Remicle, 78, 580
Remiz pendulinus, 271
Remizinae, 512
Renal depression, 38
Retina, 109, 110
Rexroad fauna, 14
Rhachis, *see* Rachis
Rhamphastidae, 483
Rhamphotheca, 31, 580
Rhea, 24, 33, 79, 377
Rhea americana, 43, 387
Rhea, 42, 51, 62, 78, 79, 162, 380
Common, 387
Rheidae, 39, 162, 380, 387
Rheiformes, 380
Rhinencephalon, 188
Rhinochetidae, 433
Rhinochetos jubatus, 433
Rhinocryptidae, 49, 87, 163, 165, 383, 491
Rhinopomastus cyanomelas, 477
Rhinotheca, 31, 580
Rhipidura leucophrys, 147
Rhodocichla, 546
Rhynchopidae, 451
Rhynchotus rufescens, 391
Rhynochetidae, 164, 381, 433
Ribs, 22, 23, 35
cervical, 7, 45
cervicodorsal, 45
dermal, 7
sternal, 23, 47
thoracic, 23
true, 23
Richmondena cardinalis, 49, 139
Richmondeninae, 552
Riparia, 276
Roadrunner, 51, 132, 228, 229, 230, 240, 242, 339, 366
Greater, 457
Robin, American, 74, 198, 199, 205, 256, 269, 270, 311, 344
British, 139, 334
English, 102, 329
European, 137, 139, 144, 148, 288
Rods, 109, 110

Roller, 80, 282, 366, 382
Ground, 366, 474
Indian, 474
Rook, 203, 276, 344
Roosting, 344
Rostratula, 34, 81, 273
Rostratula benghalensis, 438
Rostratulidae, 381, 438
Rostrhamus sociabilis, 169
Ruff, 271, 337
Rule, Allen's, 359
Bergmann's, 359, 362
Gause's, 569
Gloger's, 360, 362
Kelso's, 360
Rupicola, 60, 98, 492, 570
Rupicolidae, 492
Ruwenzorornis, 456
Rynchopidae, 381, 451
Rynchops nigra, 237, 451

Sabre-wing, Wedge-tailed, 133
Sac, fecal, 299, 306, 307
pericardial, 36
pleural, 35
Sagittariidae, 163, 381, 414
Sagittarius, 243, 414
Sagittarius serpentarius, 11, 414
Salpinctes obsoletus, 259
Salpornis, 516
Saltator albicollis, 142, 284
Saltator maximus, 140
Saltator, Buff-throated, 140, 291
Streaked, 142
Salt-eating, 258–259
Samoa, 504, 538
Sanderling, 51, 207, 242, 441
Sandgrouse, 47, 257, 382
Pallas, 179
Tibetan, 453
Sandlark, 198
Sandpiper, 223, 231, 242, 287, 381, 441
Baird's, 178
Green, 135
Pectoral, 133, 178
Spotted, 198
White-rumped, 178
Sanitation, nest, 306–307
Sapsucker, 240
Sarcoramphidae, 413
Sarcoramphus, 80
Sarcoramphus papa, 413
Sarothrura elegans, 133
Saurolophus, 7
Sauropsida, 1
Saxicola torquata, 272
Sayornis nigricans, 170
Sayornis phoebe, 275
Scapula, 24, 54, 581
accessoria, 24, 581
Scaup, 194
Schemochromes, 97, 99–100
Schizochroism, 99
Schizognathae, 45
Schizopelmous, 58, 581
Scimitarbill, 477
Sclera, 22, 109
Sclerotic ring, 7, 22, 109, 581
Scolopacidae, 199, 381, 441
Scopidae, 163, 380, 407
Scopus umbretta, 407
Scoter, Common, 233
White-winged, 191, 232
Screamer, 35, 36, 61, 88, 163, 380, 582
Horned, 411
Scrub-bird, 58, 164, 383
Noisy, 501
Scrub-warbler, 140
Scrub-wren, 139
Sea, Bering, 394
Mediterranean, 203, 446
North, 200
Red, 444
Secondary feather, 8, 54, 80–82, 84, 133, 581
aquincubital, 81, 561
diastataxic, 81, 566
eutaxic, 81, 568
quincubital, 81
Secretarybird, 11, 163, 243, 381, 414
Seedeater, Variable, 291
Seedsnipe, 163, 381
D'Orbigny, 447
Seiurus, 546
Seiurus aurocapillus, 142, 297
Selenidera maculirostris, 349
Seleucides melanoleucus, 93
Semeïphorus vexillarius, 464
Seminal glomera, 39
Seminal vesicles, 39
Semiplume, 72, 73, 581
Semnornis frantzii, 344

Senses, special, 109–115
Septum, interatrial, 36
internasal, 40
interventricular, 36
oblique, 35
Seriema, Crested, 435
Serinus, 99
Serpentariidae, 414
Sesamoid bone, 22, 24, 581
Sex, differentiation, 38
ratio, 302
recognition, 333, 334
Sharpbill, 163, 165, 383
Crested, 495
Shearwater, 92, 142, 232, 252, 258, 287, 380, 395
Manx, 209, 212
Sooty, 206, 207
Sheathbill, 381, 448
Shelduck, 332
Shorebird, 51, 62, 82, 164, 199, 204, 286, 315
Shoveller, 97
Shrike, 81, 89, 91, 98, 165, 199, 241, 244, 384
Loggerhead, 139, 534
Northern, 178
Red-backed, 339
Shrike-vireo, 163, 165, 384
Chestnut-sided, 543
Sialia sialis, 198, 199, 289
Siam, 426, 432, 461, 466, 481, 482, 497, 505, 519, 532, 540, 541
Siberia, 175
Sicalis, 552
Sigmodus, 535
Sign stimuli, 119
Silky-flycatcher, 163, 165, 240, 377, 384, 530
Sinaloa, 405, 462
Singapore, 223, 279, 281
Sinus, rhomboid, 28
Siphonaptera, 281
Siskin, 113
Sitta canadensis, 513
Sitta carolinensis, 150, 259, 272
Sitta europaea, 190, 272
Sittasomus griseicapillus, 239
Sittella, 514
Sittidae, 165, 198, 383, 513, 514, 515
Skeleton, appendicular, 22
Skeleton, axial, 22
Skimmer, 381
Black, 451
Skua, 257, 381, 449
Great, 257
Long-tailed, 315
Skull, 22, 42–45
Skylark, 142, 144
Smaragdolanius leucotis, 543
Smaragdolanius pulchellus, 543
Snipe, Common, 112, 133, 336
Pintail, 86
Snow-partridge, 203
Social, hierarchy, 328
intolerance, 345
Solitaire, 17, 454
Somateria mollissima, 246
Song, 136–142
advertising, 137, 149
antiphonal, 140, 521
cycles, 146–149
dawn, 147
dialect, 149
emotional, 138
female, 139, 141
flight, 142, 336
geographical variation of, 150
ontogeny of, 143
phylogeny of, 142
postbreeding, 138, 148, 149
primary, 137
race, 149
secondary, 138, 139
signal, 137
subsong, 138, 139
territorial, 137, 149
twilight, 138, 147
ways of recording, 150–152
whispering, 139, 147
winter, 138, 148
Songbird, 4, 139, 146, 245, 377
Song-Thrush, 256, 289
European, 243
Sonora, 255, 419, 472
South Dakota, 14
Spain, 175, 416, 426, 453
Sparking over, 119
Sparrow, 96
Black-striped, 138, 291
Cassin's, 142
Chipping, 299

Sparrow, Crowned, 197
European Tree, 209
Field, 147, 149, 275, 299
Fox, 148, 360, 361
Gambel White-crowned, 194
Harris', 552
Henslow's, 147
House, 113, 222, 245, 256, 259, 268, 272, 277, 291, 311, 313
Ipswich, 171, 191
Lincoln's, 361
Orange-billed, 139, 148
Seaside, 191
Sharp-tailed, 92, 191
Song, 134, 135, 137, 138, 141, 142, 143, 146, 148, 149, 190, 196, 268, 269, 270, 275, 289, 291, 307, 311, 312, 313, 329, 332, 333, 334, 335, 340, 359, 360, 361
Swamp, 361
Tree, 196, 228, 245
White-crowned, 139, 149
White-throated, 189, 208
Willow, 367
Speciation, 356–358
Species, 350, 351, 352, 353–358, 376
allochronic, 560
allopatric, 357, 560
altricial, 126, 285, 297, 299, 329, 331, 332, 560
colonial, 342
congeneric, 250, 280
cyclic, 251
dimorphic, 364
mimetic, 146
monogamous, 273
multiple-brooded, 272, 310
nidicolous, 96, 574
nidifugous, 290, 575
parasitic, 294, 304, 315–319, 482, 547, 551
plastic, 361
polyandrous, 273
polygynous, 273
precocial, 126, 266, 285, 297, 301, 329, 578
psilopaedic, 96, 579
ptilopaedic, 96, 579
semi-nidicolous, 581
semi-nidifugous, 581
sibling, 362, 581
single-brooded, 310, 312
Species, stable, 361
sympatric, 357, 358, 362, 582
synchronic, 582
Specific action potential, 118–119
Speculum, 582
Sperm, 272, 273
life, 273
Spermatogenesis, 146
Spermestes cucullatus, 281
Sphecotheres, 506
Sphecotheridae, 506
Sphenisci, 385
Spheniscidae, 379, 385
Sphenisciformes, 12, 379
Spheniscus, 111
Spheniscus humboldti, 258
Sphenodon, 1
Sphincter, muscles of iris, 109
pyloric, 32
Spina, communis, 47
externa, 47
interna, 45
pubica, 24
Spinal cord, 28
cervical enlargement, 28
lumbosacral enlargement, 28
Spinetail, 139
Spinus, 99
Spinus tristis, 135, 238
Spizella arborea, 196
Spizella passerina, 299
Spizella pusilla, 147, 299
Spleen, 38
Sporophila aurita, 315
Spur, 421, 422, 423, 582
Squatarola squatarola, 237
Stalling angle, 219
Starling, 96, 126, 145, 204, 211, 212, 256, 275, 288, 292, 309, 344, 384
Rose-colored, 537
Steatornis, 278
Steatornis caripensis, 59, 460
Steatornithidae, 163, 382, 460
Steganopus, 443
Steganura, 319
Steganura paradisea, 551
Stelgidopteryx ruficollis, 170
Stephanoaëtus coronatus, 415
Stercorariidae, 257, 381, 449
Stercorarius longicaudus, 449
Sterna fuscata, 313

Sterna hirundo, 285
Sternidae, 450
Sternum, 15, 22, 23, 45–47, 54, 225, 226, 233
entire, 47
fenestrate, 47
notched, 47
Stilt, Black-necked, 442
Stipiturus, 86
Stomach, 31, 32
Stonechat, 272
Stonecurlew, 445
Stork, 58, 78, 79, 241, 274, 285, 294, 340, 380
Whale-billed, 132, 163, 380, 406
White, 140, 408
Storm-petrel, 380, 396
Streperidae, 508
Streptopelia risoria, 296
Streptopelia turtur, 203
Strigidae, 62, 165, 250, 382, 458, 459
Strigiformes, 382, 582
Strigops, 47, 111
Stringopidae, 455
Strix, 12, 94
Struthidea, 83
Struthiididae, 509
Struthio, 23, 24, 29, 37
Struthio camelus, 386
Struthiones, 12
Struthionidae, 39, 75, 379, 386
Struthioniformes, 379
Sturnella, 143, 199, 285, 366
Sturnella magna, 170
Sturnidae, 384, 401, 537
Sturnus vulgaris, 31, 96, 145, 211, 256, 274
Subfamily, 351, 368
Subsong, 136, 138, 139
Subspecies, 353–358, 582
Sudan, 406, 414
Sula, 256
Sula dactylatra, 400
Sula leucogaster, 167, 400
Sula nebouxii, 400
Sulidae, 380, 400
Sumatra, 432, 482, 486
Sun-arc, 213
Sunbird, 32, 59, 97, 240, 278, 287, 384
Wedge-tailed, 539
Yellowbreasted, 223
Sunbittern, 163, 165, 381, 434
Superspecies, 582
Surniculus, 316, 457
Surniculus lugubris, 104
Swallow, 35, 79, 92, 164, 199, 223, 276, 279, 286, 296, 301, 309, 383
Barn, 307, 503
Cliff, 272, 280, 345
Cobán, 278
European Barn, 307
Red-rumped, 242
Rough-winged, 170
Tree, 292, 303, 344
Swallow-tanager, 79, 163, 272, 291, 294, 384, 548
Swan, 15, 34, 45, 221, 240
Whistling, 88
Sweden, 189, 200, 244
Swift, 33, 35, 43, 51, 86, 164, 223, 260, 272, 274, 278, 286, 292, 301, 309, 312, 382, 561, 565
Chimney, 56, 199, 204, 289, 344
Common, 189, 246, 260, 287, 289, 298, 303
White-rumped, 278
White-throated, 465
Sylvia atricapilla, 143, 525
Sylvia communis, 144
Sylvicolidae, 546
Sylviidae, sylviid, 63, 86, 133, 139, 140, 141, 148, 165, 278, 319, 366, 377, 384, 525
Sylviorthorhynchus, 86, 488
Symphysis, 582
ischiadic, 24
pubic, 7, 24
Synapse, 29
Synpelmous, 58, 583
Synsacrum, 7, 23, 24, 583
Syntype, 583
Syria, 386
Syrinx, 28, 30, 58–59, 134, 141, 583
acromyodian, 58, 559
anachromyodian, 59, 560
anisomyodian, 59, 560
bronchial, 58, 59
catacromyodian, 59, 563
diacromyodian, 59, 566
mesomyodian, 58, 573
oligomyodian, 59, 575
polymyodian, 59, 578

Syrinx, tracheal, 58, 59
tracheobronchial, 58, 59
Syrrhaptes paradoxus, 179
Syrrhaptes tibetanus, 453
System, circulatory, 36–37
digestive, 30–34
lymphatic, 36
muscular, 24–27
nervous, 27–30, 36, 117, 126
neuromuscular, 123
reproductive, 38–39, 188
respiratory, 34–35
self-differentiating, 121
skeletal, 22–24
urogenital, 38–39

Tabasco, 434
Tachyeres brachypterus, 233, 234
Tachyeres patachonicus, 234
Tachyeres pteneres, 233
Tachypetidae, 403
Tailor-bird, 278
Long-tailed, 279
Tamaulipas, 405, 462, 472
Tanager, 31, 79, 163, 165, 167, 199, 240, 287, 291, 354, 384, 549
Black, 175, 177
Red Ant, 147
Scarlet, 307, 363
Song, 289
White-winged, 549
Tanagra, 31, 240
Tanagridae, 549
Tangaridae, 549
Tangavius, 318
Tantalidae, 409
Tapaculo, 58, 163, 165, 383, 491
Tapera, 83, 316
Tarsal sheath, *see* Podotheca
Tarsometatarsus, 8, 10, 47, 50, 56, 297, 583
acutiplantar, 48, 559
latiplantar, 48, 573
See also Podotheca
Tarsus, 47, 559
Tasmania, 389, 439, 461, 463, 508
Taste buds, 114
Tauraco, 83
Tauraco macrorhynchus verreauxi, 456
Tchitrea perspicillata, 295
Teal, Blue-winged, 97
Tectrices, 85–86, 583
Tectum, 28
Teeth, "bone," 13
thecodont, 2
Tehuantepec, 534
Teleoptiles, 71, 583
Telophorus zeylonus, 140
Temperature, body, 34, 36
control, 299
laws, 157
Tendon, Achilles', 559
deep plantar, 56, 566
Tennessee, 195, 303
Tephrodornis, 504
Teratornis, 14
Termitaria, 280, 282
Tern, 51, 223, 280, 403, 450
Caspian, 175
Common, 272, 285, 334
Fairy, 51
Sandwich, 332
Sooty, 313
Terpsiphone, 366
Terpsiphone paradisi, 526
Territory, territoriality, 137, 267–270, 335, 343
Tersina viridis, 272, 548
Tersinidae, 79, 163, 384, 548
Tertial, tertiary, 54, 83–84, 583
Testis, 38, 39, 149, 186, 583
recrudescence of, 186–188
refractory phase of, 189
Testosterone, phenylacetate, 141
proprionate, 141, 146
Tetrao, 34
Tetraonidae, 77, 78, 163, 165, 381, 420
Tetrapteryx, 3
Texas, 150, 191, 241, 419, 469, 492
Thalassidromidae, 396
Thamnophilus, 140
Thecodont, reptiles, 2
teeth, 2
Thick-knee, 241, 381, 445
Thinocoridae, 31, 163, 381, 447
Thinocorus orbignyianus, 447
Thinocorythidae, 447
Thrasher, Brown, 256, 275, 522
California, 140
Thraupidae, 32, 79, 163, 165, 199, 384, 546, 549
Threskiornithidae, 380, 409

Thrombocyte, 36
Thrush, 126, 134, 141, 145, 147, 165, 198, 240, 300, 309, 312, 339, 384, 523
Gray-cheeked, 139, 205, 362
Olive-backed, 362
Song, 139, 523
Swainson's, 362
Wood, 333
Tiaris olivacea, 138, 315
Tibiotarsus, 26, 297, 584
Tierra del Fuego, 169, 207
Timaliidae, timaliid, 86, 140, 156, 165, 258, 308, 309, 383, 517
Timor, 502, 534
Tinamidae, 23, 39, 42, 45, 46, 76, 162, 165, 380, 391
Tinamiformes, 380, 565
Tinamou, 37, 42, 45, 62, 75, 76, 162, 165, 273, 284, 285, 377, 380
Rufous-winged, 391
Variegated, 140
Tinamus major, 46
Tit, Blue, 298
Great, 288, 289, 292, 298, 312
Green-backed, 502
Long-tailed, 307
Penduline, 271
Titmouse, 165, 198, 244, 245, 249, 250, 274, 287, 295, 298, 383, 512
Tockus, 478
Todidae, 163, 165, 382, 471
Todus multicolor, 471
Todus subulatus, 471
Tody, 163, 165, 382
Cuban, 471
Toes, 50–52
inner, 572
middle, 574
Tomium, 584
Tongue, 30, 31, 114, 297
Toothed birds, Cretaceous, 8, 10
Topotype, 584
Totanus flavipes, 204
Totanus totanus, 268, 336
Toucan, 24, 40, 51, 78, 86, 94, 163, 165, 240, 241, 285, 297, 299, 301, 349, 376, 383
Cuvier, 483
Touraco, 51, 60, 83, 99, 163, 300, 382
Red-tipped Crested, 456
Towhee, Brown, 137
Towhee, Rufous-sided, 275
Toxostoma redivivum, 140
Toxostoma rufum, 256, 275, 522
Trachea, 31, 34, 35, 58, 134, 419, 428, 584
Tracheal bulla, 35
Tracheal loops, 34
Tracheophonae, 58, 584
Trachyphonus, 481
Trachyphonus d'arnaudii, 140
Tragopan, 421
Traversiidae, 498
Tree-duck, 309
Fulvous, 175
Tree-finch, Darwin's, 243
Tree-runner, Orange-winged, 514
Treronidae, 454
Tringa ochropus, 135
Trinidad, 460, 472
Triopidae, 465
Trochilidae, 22, 32, 33, 163, 165, 382, 467
Troglodytes aedon, 173, 299
Troglodytes musculus, 173
Troglodytes troglodytes, 156, 175
Troglodytidae, 156, 165, 198, 384, 521
Trogon collaris, 237
Trogon mexicanus, 469
Trogon, 51, 82, 240, 241, 382
Bar-tailed, 140
Cuban, 80
Mexican, 469
Trogonidae, 297, 382, 469
Trogoniformes, 12, 382, 584
Tropicbird, 36, 224, 277, 287, 380
White-tailed, 398
Troupial, 79, 163, 165, 287, 318, 384, 547
Trumpeter, 82, 163, 381
White-winged, 430
Tuamoto, 537
Tube, eustachian, 31
pharyngotympanic, 31, 112
Tuberculum, 23, 584
Tubinares, 40, 584
Turco, Chestnut-breasted, 491
Turdidae, 39, 49, 140, 147, 165, 198, 377, 384, 523
Turdus ericetorum, 143, 243, 256, 523
Turdus merula, 126, 145, 256
Turdus migratorius, 49, 74, 198, 199, 205, 256
Turdus pilaris, 167
Turdus viscivorus, 275

Turkey, 125, 163, 165, 330, 381
Ocellated, 423
Wild, 80
Turnagridae, 526
Turnicidae, 381, 426
Turnix, 271, 273, 339
Turnix ocellata, 426
Turnoididae, 517
Turnstone, 242, 280
Turturidae, 454
Tylidae, 506
Tympanuchus, 86, 271
Tympanuchus cupido, 99
Type species, 594
Typical-owl, 165, 382, 459
Tyranni, 383
Tyrannidae, 49, 63, 163, 165, 198, 383, 494
Tyrannus dominicensis, 205, 207
Tyrannus tyrannus, 198, 494
Tyrant-flycatcher, 63, 92, 140, 145, 147, 163, 165, 198, 240, 241, 279, 280, 287, 289, 291, 296, 300, 332, 362, 366, 383, 494
Tyto, 94
Tyto alba, 170, 173, 458
Tytonidae, 165, 382, 458

Uganda, 406
Ulna, 7, 80, 84, 226, 584
Umbilicus, 70, 72, 585
Umbrellabird, 492
United States, 10, 15, 145, 149, 150, 169, 177, 178, 179, 183, 191, 195, 199, 201, 209, 252, 253, 255, 259, 275, 289, 366, 402, 408, 409, 423, 530
Upupa epops, 476
Upupidae, 382, 476
Uratelornis, 366, 474
Ureter, 38
Uria lomvia, 99, 258
Uriidae, 452
Urinatoridae, 392
Urocynchramus, 552
Urodeum, 38, 39, 585
Urostyle, 23
Uruguay, 411, 542, 546
Utah, 530
Uterus, 38

Vagina, 38, 585
Valve, atrioventricular, 36
ileocecal, 32
semilunar, 36
Vane, 70, 72, 73, 74, 75, 585
Vanellinae, 440
Vanellus, 12, 203
Vanellus vanellus, 336
Vanga curvirostris, 533
Vanga, Hook-billed, 533
Vanga-shrike, 163, 241, 384, 533
Vangidae, 50, 80, 163, 384, 533
Vanginae, 533
Variation, age, 364
continuous, 564
discontinuous, 566
geographical, 150, 355, 361
individual, 354, 363
seasonal, 363
sexual, 364
Vein, caval, 37
coccygeal, 37
hepatic, 37
hypogastric, 37
jugular, 37
renal portal, 37
Venezuela, 175, 178, 207, 430, 460
Vent, 33, 585
Ventricle, 585
cerebellar, 28
lateral, 27
of heart, 36
Ventriculus, 31, 32, 585
Vera Cruz, 483
Veracruz, 178, 479, 542, 543
Vermivora chrysoptera, 142, 367
Vermivora lawrencei, 367
Vermivora leucobronchialis, 367
Vermivora pinus, 142, 367
Vertebra, 35, 585
amphicoelous, 7, 9, 560
caudal, 23
cervical, 7, 23, 45
dorsal, 7, 23, 45, 566
free caudal, 7, 8, 23
heterocoelous, 7, 9, 570
lumbar, 7, 23
opisthocoelous, 7, 575
procoelous, 7, 578
sacral, 7, 23
synsacral, 23, 38

Vertebra, thoracic, 23, 584
urosacral, 23
Vestiaria coccinea, 545
Vexillum, *see* Vane
Vidua, 319
Viduinae, 319, 551
Vinculum, 56, 57, 585
Vireo altiloquus, 205
Vireo flavifrons, 237, 544
Vireo gilvus, 96, 148
Vireo olivaceus chivi, 208
Vireo olivaceus olivaceus, 147, 207, 208
Vireo, 63, 79, 148, 163, 165, 198, 208, 384
Black-whiskered, 205
Red-eyed, 147, 207, 270, 276, 291
Solitary, 361
Warbling, 96, 148
Yellow-throated, 544
Vireolaniidae, 163, 165, 384, 543
Vireolanius melitophrys, 543
Vireonidae, 63, 79, 163, 165, 198, 384, 544
Vision, 30, 109–111, 211
Volvocivora, 504
Vultur, 80, 84
Vultur gryphus, 85
Vulture, 14, 113, 169
American, 40, 58, 78, 163, 165, 227, 228, 241, 380, 413
Black, 80
King, 80, 413
Turkey, 56, 80, 170, 199, 228
Vulturidae, 413, 415

Wagtail, 98, 274
White, 528
Yellow, 192
Warbler, Audubon's, 354
Bay-breasted, 364
Black-and-White, 205
Blackpoll, 205, 206, 364
Black-throated, 281
Black-throated Gray, 546
Blue-winged, 142, 148, 367
Blyth's Reed, 63
Brewster's, 367
Buff-rumped, 140, 291
Golden-winged, 142, 148, 367
Kirtland's 134, 172, 209, 277, 342, 352
Lawrence's, 367
Marsh, 63, 145
Warbler, Myrtle, 240, 354
Old-world, 63, 148, 165, 268, 319, 384, 525
Ovenbird, 142, 148
Palm, 312
Parula, 265
Prairie, 282
Prothonotary, 134, 270, 277, 303, 312, 313
Reed, 63
Yellow, 270, 275
Yellowthroat, 333
Wattlebird, 164, 233, 384, 536
Waxbill, Violet-eared, 139
Waxwing, 163, 165, 199, 276
Bohemian, 529
Cedar, 240, 245, 252, 272, 277, 291, 304, 312, 339, 377, 384
Weaver, Black, 310
Sociable, 280, 308
Weaverbird, 97, 98, 273, 279, 280, 281, 288, 306, 309, 319, 339, 384, 551
Philippine, 271, 276
Red-billed, 280
Wheatear, 193, 204, 307
Whimbrel, 441
Whip-poor-will, 568
Whistler, 364
White-eye, 384
Gray-breasted, 541
Whitethroat, 144
Whydah, Paradise, 551
Willet, 268
Willie Wagtail, 147
Wing, diastataxic, 8, 566
elliptical, 222
eutaxic, 8, 569
formula, 63
high-aspect-ratio, 223
high-lift, 224
high-speed, 223
slots, 221, 222, 223
slotted soaring, 224
Wing-tip vortex, 220
Wisconsin, 194
Wishbone, 24
Woodcock, American, 82, 111, 112, 132, 198, 222
Woodcreeper, 58, 163, 165, 238, 241, 366, 383, 487

Woodcreeper, Ivory-billed, 487
Woodhewer, *see* Woodcreeper
Woodhoopoe, 163, 305, 382, 477
Woodpecker, 51, 62, 78, 80, 81, 85, 94, 95, 98, 99, 114, 132, 164, 166, 198, 222, 239, 255, 259, 276, 282, 285, 296, 297, 301, 306, 339, 366, 383
  Acorn, 240, 244, 308
  Arctic, 178
  Black-backed Three-toed, 178
  Downy, 354
  Flint-billed, 366
  Golden-fronted, 361
  Great Spotted, 247, 249
  Hairy, 354, 359, 360
  Imperial, 484
  Lewis', 243
  Pileated, 280, 366
Wood-Pigeon, 276
Wood-quail, Marbled, 140
Wood-shrike, 163, 307, 309, 384, 535
Wood-swallow, 309, 344, 384, 532
  White-browed, 532
Wood-warbler, American, 79, 148, 149, 163, 165, 199, 222, 240, 266, 268, 291, 300, 301, 309, 332, 351, 384, 546
Woodwren Gray-breasted, 521
Wren, 140, 156, 165, 198, 276, 287, 291, 300, 309, 384, 521
  Cactus, 344
  House, 173, 291, 296, 299, 303, 313
  Lawrence's Musician, 344
  Neotropic House, 291
  New Zealand, 164, 233, 383, 498
  Rock, 259
Wren-thrush, 163, 384, 524
Wrentit, 139, 156, 272
Wren-warbler, 278
Wrist, *see* Carpus
Wryneck, 40, 287, 291, 297, 383
  Eurasian, 485
Wyoming, 10, 11, 12

Xanthocephalus xanthocephalus, 273
Xanthocroism, 100, 586
Xenicidae, 498
Xenicornithidae, 498
Xenicus longipes, 498
Xenodacnis, 549
Xiphorhynchus flavigaster, 238, 487

Yellowhammer, 288
Yellowlegs, Greater, 354
  Lesser, 204, 354
Yellowthroat, 333
Young, 297–300, 329
  dasypaedic, 565
  gymnopaedic, 570
  nidicolous, 96, 574
  nidifugous, 290, 575
  psilopaedic, 96, 579
  ptilopaedic, 96, 579
  semi-nidicolous, 581
  semi-nidifuguous, 581
Yucatán, 410, 416, 423
Yuhina brunneiceps, 308
Yungidae, 485

Zanthomiza phrygia, 538
Zarhynchus, 318
Zarhynchus wagleri, 132, 271, 273, 547
Zeledonia coronata, 524
Zeledoniidae, 163, 384, 524
Zelornis, 15
Zenaidura macroura, 37, 99, 132
Zone, North Temperate, 184, 252, 287, 303
  Temperate, 313, 314
Zonotrichia, 92
Zonotrichia albicollis, 189, 208
Zonotrichia capensis, 197
Zonotrichia leucophrys, 149
Zonotrichia leucophrys gambelii, 194
Zonotrichia querula, 552
Zoological regions, 156–157
  Australian, 155, 156, 157, 164, 562
  Ethiopian, 155, 156, 163, 567
  Holarctic, 155, 156, 163
  Indo-African, 157
  Lemurian, 157
  Madagascan, 157
  Nearctic, 155, 156, 163, 574
  Neotropical, 155, 156, 162, 163, 391, 419, 434, 472, 574
  Oriental, 155, 156, 164, 575
  Palaearctic, 155, 156, 163, 576
Zosteropidae, 31, 145, 258, 384, 541
Zosterops lateralis, 541